Rick Adams
915 Sunset
539-5273

D1030955

Andersen and Wenzel *Introduction to Chemical Engineering*
Aries and Newton *Chemical Engineering Cost Estimation*
Badger and Banchero *Introduction to Chemical Engineering*
Bennett and Myers *Momentum, Heat, and Mass Transfer*
Clarke and Davidson *Manual for Process Engineering Calculations*
Comings *High Pressure Technology*
Coughanowr and Koppel *Process Systems Analysis and Control*
Dodge *Chemical Engineering Thermodynamics*
Griswold *Fuels, Combustion, and Furnaces*
Groggins *Unit Processes in Organic Synthesis*
Harriott *Process Control*
Henley and Bieber *Chemical Engineering Calculations*
Huntington *Natural Gas and Natural Gasoline*
Johnson *Automatic Process Control*
Johnstone and Thring *Pilot Plants, Models, and Scale-up Methods in Chemical Engineering*
Katz, Cornell, Kobayashi, Poettmann, Vary, Elenbaas, and Weinaug *Handbook of Natural Gas Engineering*
Kirkbride *Chemical Engineering Fundamentals*
Knudsen and Katz *Fluid Dynamics and Heat Transfer*
Kohl and Riesenfeld *Gas Purification*
Lapidus *Digital Computation for Chemical Engineers*
Leva *Fluidization*
Lewis, Radasch, and Lewis *Industrial Stoichiometry*
Mantell *Adsorption*
Mantell *Electrochemical Engineering*
McAdams *Heat Transmission*

McCabe and Smith, J. C. *Unit Operations of Chemical Engineering*
Mickley, Sherwood, and Reed *Applied Mathematics in Chemical Engineering*
Nelson *Petroleum Refinery Engineering*
Perry (Editor) *Chemical Business Handbook*
Perry (Editor) *Chemical Engineers' Handbook*
Peters *Elementary Chemical Engineering*
Peters *Plant Design and Economics for Chemical Engineers*
Reid and Sherwood *The Properties of Gases and Liquids*
Robinson and Gilliland *Elements of Fractional Distillation*
Schechter *The Variational Method in Engineering*
Schmidt and Marlies *Principles of High-polymer Theory and Practice*
Schweyer *Process Engineering Economics*
Sherwood and Pigford *Absorption and Extraction*
Shreve *Chemical Process Industries*
Smith, B. D. *Design of Equilibrium Stage Processes*
Smith, J. M. *Chemical Engineering Kinetics*
Smith, J. M., and Van Ness *Introduction to Chemical Engineering Thermodynamics*
Treybal *Liquid Extraction*
Treybal *Mass-transfer Operations*
Van Winkle *Distillation*
Vilbrandt and Dryden *Chemical Engineering Plant Design*
Volk *Applied Statistics for Engineers*
Walas *Reaction Kinetics for Chemical Engineers*
Walker, Lewis, McAdams, and Gilliland *Principles of Chemical Engineering*
Williams and Johnson *Stoichiometry for Chemical Engineers*
Wilson and Ries *Principles of Chemical Engineering Thermodynamics*

MASS-TRANSFER OPERATIONS

Second Edition

ROBERT E. TREYBAL
Professor of Chemical Engineering
New York University

McGRAW-HILL BOOK COMPANY New York
St. Louis San Francisco Toronto London Sydney

*Library of Congress Catalog Card
Number* 67-22972

ISBN 07-065189-2

13 14 15 16   K P K P   81 82 80 79 8

PREFACE

In presenting a revised edition of this book, my purpose has remained unchanged: to provide a vehicle for teaching, either through a formal course or through self-study, the techniques of and the principles of equipment design for the mass-transfer operations of chemical engineering. These operations largely remain, as they were when the book was first offered, the responsibility solely of the chemical engineer, who alone is expected to be thoroughly familiar with their engineering applications.

There have been profound changes in the training of chemical engineers since the appearance of the first edition. Most universities now include more extensive training in mathematics and also in the fundamentals of the rate or transport processes upon which the subjects of this book are based. Students consequently approach the problems of design with a greater degree of sophistication in these areas than ever before. At the same time these changes have not altered, in my experience, their degree of judgment regarding the suitability and limitations of methods and results nor of self-confidence in dealing with engineering problems where detailed information may be lacking. In some cases the time devoted to practical design matters has been greatly curtailed, so that self-study is necessary.

In preparing this revision, I have tried to bear all these developments in mind yet at the same time keep the subject accessible to those who have not previously studied the transport processes. As a result, there are many things which have been changed, and the others which have not. The basic approach, which treats the major subjects in categories of gas-liquid, liquid-liquid, and fluid-solid contact, was somewhat of an innovation when first presented, and is retained. The development of the design methods progressively, rather than as completely generalized procedures later to be particularized, is also largely retained. These I have found in my own teaching to be most effective. Subject-matter changes, for purposes of both modernization and improved presentation, have been made throughout. The greatest of these is in the introductory material of the first five chapters, which reflects to some extent the matters referred to above, and in the gas-liquid operations, which reflects the greater attention which has been given the development of these most important subjects. Enthalpy-concentration methods for distillation have been added, as well as a quantitative treatment for absorption and distillation of multicomponent systems. There are many new problems for student practice, all thoroughly student tested, and many problem answers are given. The problems require some such collection of physical property data as "The Chemical Engineers' Handbook," to be at hand, since extensive tables of these are not included.

I remain, as before, greatly indebted to many firms and publications for permission to use their material, and these are acknowledged throughout the text. I am also beholden to an anonymous group of chemical engineers who, at my request and with the cooperation of the publishers, generously provided many excellent suggestions as to what would be appropriate for this revision. Keeping the book to a reasonable length was the only reason for not including more of them.

Robert E. Treybal

CONTENTS

MASS-TRANSFER OPERATIONS

CHAPTER ONE
THE MASS-TRANSFER
OPERATIONS

A substantial number of the unit operations of chemical engineering are concerned with the problem of changing the compositions of solutions and mixtures through methods not necessarily involving chemical reactions. Usually these operations are directed toward separating a substance into its component parts. In the case of mixtures, such separations may be entirely mechanical, such as the filtration of a solid from a suspension in a liquid, the classification of a solid into fractions of different particle size by screening, or the separation of particles of a ground solid according to their density. On the other hand, if the operations involve changes in composition of solutions, they are known as the mass-transfer operations and it is these which concern us here.

The importance of these operations is profound. There is scarcely any chemical process which does not require a preliminary purification of raw materials or final separation of products from by-products, and for these the mass-transfer operations are usually used. One can perhaps most readily develop an immediate appreciation of the part these separations play in a processing plant by observing the large number of towers which bristle from a modern petroleum refinery, in each of which a mass-transfer separation operation takes place. Frequently the major part of the cost of a process is that for the separations. These separation or purification costs depend directly upon the ratio of final to initial concentration of the separated substances, and if this ratio is large, the product costs are large. Thus, sulfuric acid is a relatively low-priced product in part because sulfur is found naturally in a relatively pure state, whereas pure uranium is expensive because of the low concentration in which it is found in nature.

The mass-transfer operations are characterized by transfer of a substance through another on a molecular scale. For example, when water evaporates from a pool into an air stream flowing over the water surface, molecules of water vapor diffuse through those of the air at the surface into the main portion of the air stream, whence they are carried away. It is not bulk movement as a result of a pressure difference, as in the case of pumping a liquid through a pipe, with which we are primarily concerned. In the problems at hand, the mass transfer is a result of a concentration difference, or gradient, the diffusing substance moving from a place of high to one of low concentration.

CLASSIFICATION OF THE MASS-TRANSFER OPERATIONS

It is useful to classify the operations and to cite examples of each, in order to indicate the scope of the subject matter of this book, and to provide a vehicle for some definitions of terms which are commonly used.

1. Direct contact of two immiscible phases

This category is by far the most important of all and includes the bulk of the mass-transfer operations. Here we take advantage of the fact that in a two-phase system of several components at equilibrium, with few exceptions the compositions of the phases are different. The various components, in other words, are differently distributed between the phases.

In some instances, the separation thus afforded leads immediately to a pure substance because one of the phases at equilibrium contains only one constituent. For example, the equilibrium vapor in contact with a liquid aqueous salt solution contains no salt regardless of the concentration of the liquid. Similarly the equilibrium solid in contact with such a liquid salt solution is either pure water or pure salt, depending upon which side of the eutectic composition the liquid happens to be. Starting with the liquid solution, one may then obtain a complete separation by boiling off the water. Alternatively, pure salt or pure water may be produced by partly freezing the solution; or, in principle at least, both may be obtained pure by complete solidification followed by mechanical separation of the eutectic mixture of crystals. In cases like these, when the two phases are first formed, they are immediately at their final equilibrium compositions, and the establishment of equilibrium is not a time-dependent process. Such separations, with one exception, are not normally considered to be among the mass-transfer operations.

In the mass-transfer operations, neither equilibrium phase consists of only one component. Consequently when the two phases are initially contacted, they will not (except fortuitously) be of equilibrium compositions. The system then attempts to reach equilibrium by a relatively slow diffusive movement of the constituents, which transfer in part between the phases in the process. Separations are therefore never complete, although, as will be shown, they can be brought to as near completion as desired (but not totally) by appropriate manipulations.

The three states of aggregation, gas, liquid, and solid, permit six possibilities of phase contact.

Gas-gas. Since with very few exceptions all gases are completely soluble in each other, this category is not practically realized.

Gas-liquid. If all components of the system distribute between the phases at equilibrium, the operation is known as *fractional distillation* (or frequently just *distillation*). In this instance the gas phase is created from the liquid by application of heat; or conversely, the liquid is created from the gas by removal of heat. For example, if a liquid solution of acetic acid and water is partially vaporized by heating, it is found that the newly created vapor phase and the residual liquid both contain acetic acid and water but in proportions at equilibrium which are different for the two phases and different from those in the original solution. If the vapor and liquid are separated mechanically from each other and the vapor condensed, two solutions, one richer in acetic acid and the other richer in water, are obtained. In this way a certain degree of separation of the original components has been accomplished.

Both phases may be solutions, each containing, however, only one common component (or group of components) which distributes between the phases. For example, if a mixture of ammonia and air is contacted with liquid water, a large portion of the ammonia, but essentially no air, will dissolve in the liquid, and in this way the air-ammonia mixture may be separated. The operation is known as *gas absorption*. On the other hand, if air is brought into contact with an ammonia-water solution, some of the ammonia leaves the liquid and enters the gas phase, an operation known as *desorption* or *stripping*. The difference is purely in the direction of solute transfer.

If the liquid phase is a pure liquid containing but one component while the gas contains two or more, the operation is *humidification* or *dehumidification*, depending upon the direction of transfer (this is the exception mentioned earlier). For example, contact of dry air with liquid water results in evaporation of some water into the air (humidification of the air). Conversely, contact of very moist air with pure liquid water may result in condensation of part of the moisture in the air (dehumidification). In both cases, diffusion of water vapor through air is involved, and we include these among the mass-transfer operations.

Gas-solid. Classification of the operations in this category according to the number of components which appear in the two phases is again convenient.

If a solid solution were to be partially vaporized without the appearance of a liquid phase, the newly formed vapor phase and the residual solid would each contain all the original components, but in different proportions, and the operation is *fractional sublimation.*   As in distillation, the final compositions are established by interdiffusion of the components between the phases.   While such an operation is theoretically possible, practically it is not generally done because of the inconvenience of dealing with solid phases in this manner.

All components may not be present in both phases, however.   If a solid which is moistened with a volatile liquid is exposed to a relatively dry gas, the liquid leaves the solid and diffuses into the gas, an operation generally known as *drying,* sometimes as *desorption.*   A homely example is the drying of laundry by exposure to air, and there are many industrial counterparts such as the drying of lumber or the removal of moisture from a wet filter cake by exposure to dry gas.   In this case, the diffusion is, of course, from the solid to the gas phase.   If the diffusion takes place in the opposite direction, the operation is known as *adsorption.*   For example, if a mixture of water vapor and air is brought into contact with activated silica gel, the water vapor diffuses to the solid, which retains it strongly, and the air is thus dried.   In other instances, a gas mixture may contain several components each of which is adsorbed on a solid but to different extents (*fractional adsorption*).   For example, if a mixture of propane and propylene gases is brought into contact with activated carbon, the two hydro-carbons are both adsorbed, but to different extents, thus leading to a separation of the gas mixture.

The case where the gas phase is a pure vapor, such as in the sublimation of a volatile solid from a mixture with one which is nonvolatile, is an operation dependent more on the rate of application of heat than on concentration difference and is essentially nondiffusional.   The same is true of the condensation of a vapor to the condition of a pure solid, where the rate depends on the rate of heat removal.

Liquid-liquid. Separations involving the contact of two insoluble liquid phases are known as *liquid-extraction* operations.   A simple example is the familiar laboratory procedure: if an acetone-water solution is shaken in a separatory funnel with carbon tetrachloride and the liquids allowed to settle, a large portion of the acetone will be found in the carbon tetrachloride-rich phase and will thus have been separated from the water.   A small amount of the water will also have been dissolved by the carbon tetrachloride, and a small amount of the latter will have entered the water layer, but these effects are relatively minor.   As another possibility, a solution of acetic acid and acetone may be separated by adding it to the insoluble mixture of water and carbon tetrachloride.   After shaking and settling, both acetone and acetic acid will be found in both liquid phases, but in different proportions.   Such an operation is known as *fractional extraction.*   Another form of fractional extraction may be effected by producing two liquid phases from a single-phase solution by cooling the latter below its critical solution temperature.   The two phases which form will be of different composition.

Liquid-solid. When all the constituents are present in both phases at equilibrium, we have the operation of *fractional crystallization.*   Perhaps the most interesting examples of this are the special techniques of *zone refining*, used to obtain ultrapure metals and semiconductors, and *adductive crystallization*, where a substance, such as urea, has a crystal lattice which will selectively entrap long straight-chain molecules like the paraffin hydrocarbons but which will exclude branched molecules.

Cases where the phases are solutions (or mixtures) containing but one common component occur more frequently. Selective solution of a component from a solid mixture by a liquid solvent is known as *leaching* (sometimes also as solvent extraction), and as examples we cite the leaching of gold from its ores by cyanide solutions and of cottonseed oil from the seeds by hexane. The diffusion is, of course, from the solid to the liquid phase. If the diffusion is in the opposite direction, the operation is known as *adsorption*. Thus, the colored material which contaminates impure cane sugar solutions may be removed by contacting the liquid solutions with activated carbon, whereupon the colored substances are retained on the surface of the solid carbon.

Solid-solid. Because of the extraordinarily slow rates of diffusion within solid phases, there is no industrial separation operation in this category.

2. Phases separated by a membrane

These operations are used relatively infrequently, although they are rapidly increasing in importance. The membranes operate in different ways, depending upon the nature of the separation to be made. In general, however, they serve to prevent intermingling of two miscible phases. They also prevent ordinary hydrodynamic flow, and movement of substances through them is by diffusion. And they permit a component separation by selectively controlling passage of the components from one side to the other.

Gas-gas. In *gaseous diffusion* or *effusion*, the membrane is microporous. If a gas mixture whose components are of different molecular weights is brought into contact with such a diaphragm, the various components of the gas pass through the pores at rates dependent upon the molecular weights. This leads to different compositions on opposite sides of the membrane and consequent separation of the mixture. In this manner large-scale separation of the isotopes of uranium, in the form of gaseous uranium hexafluoride, is carried out. In *permeation*, the membrane is not porous, and the gas which is transmitted through the membrane first dissolves in it and then diffuses through. Separation in this case is brought about principally by difference in solubility of the components. Thus, helium may be separated from natural gas by selective permeation through fluorocarbon-polymer membranes.

Gas-liquid. These are *permeation* separations where, for example, a liquid solution of alcohol and water is brought into contact with a suitable nonporous membrane, in which the alcohol preferentially dissolves. After passage through the membrane the alcohol is vaporized on the far side.

Liquid-liquid. The separation of a crystalline substance from a colloid, by contact of their solution with a liquid solvent with an intervening membrane permeable only to the solvent and the dissolved crystalline substance, is known as *dialysis*. For example, aqueous beet-sugar solutions containing undesired colloidal material are freed of the latter by contact with water with an intervening semipermeable membrane. Sugar and water diffuse through the membrane, but the larger colloidal particles cannot. *Fractional dialysis* for separating two crystalline substances in solution makes use of the difference in membrane permeability for the substances. If an electromotive force is applied across the membrane to assist in the diffusion of charged particles, the operation is *electrodialysis*. If a solution is separated from the pure solvent by a membrane which is permeable only to the solvent, the solvent diffuses into the solution, an operation known as *osmosis*. This is not a separation operation, of course, but by superimposing a pressure to oppose the osmotic pressure the flow of solvent is reversed, and the solvent and solute of a solution may be separated by *reverse osmosis*. This is one of the processes which may be important in the desalination of sea water.

3. Direct contact of miscible phases

The operations in this category, because of the difficulty in maintaining concentration gradients without mixing of the fluid, are not generally considered practical industrially except in unusual circumstances.

Thermal diffusion involves the formation of a concentration difference within a single liquid or gaseous phase by imposition of a temperature gradient upon the fluid, thus making a separation of the components of the solution possible. In this way, He^3 is separated from its mixture with He^4.

If a condensable vapor, such as steam, is allowed to diffuse through a gas mixture, it will preferentially carry one of the components along with it, thus making a separation by the operation known as *sweep diffusion*. If the two zones within the gas phase where the concentrations are different are separated by a screen containing relatively large-size openings, the operation is called *atmolysis*.

If a gas mixture is subjected to a very rapid *centrifugation*, the components will be separated because of the slightly different forces acting on the various molecules owing to their different masses. The heavier molecules thus tend to accumulate at the periphery of the centrifuge.

4. Use of surface phenomena

Substances which when dissolved in a liquid produce a solution of lowered surface tension (in contact with a gas) are known to concentrate in solution at the liquid surface. By forming a foam of large surface, as by bubbling air through the solution, and collecting the foam, the solute may be concentrated. In this manner, detergents have been separated from water, for example. The operation is known as *foam separation*. It is not to be confused with the flotation processes of the ore-dressing industries, where insoluble solid particles are removed from slurries by collection into froths.

Direct and indirect operations. The operations depending upon contact of two immiscible phases particularly may be further subclassified into two types. The *direct* operations produce the two phases from a single-phase solution by addition or removal of heat. Fractional distillation, fractional crystallization, and one form of fractional extraction are of this type. The *indirect* operations involve addition of a foreign substance and include gas absorption and stripping, adsorption, drying, leaching, liquid extraction, and certain types of fractional crystallization.

It is characteristic of the direct operations that the products are obtained directly, free of added substance, and they are therefore sometimes favored over the indirect if they can be used.

If the separated products are required relatively pure, the disadvantages of the indirect operations which are incurred by addition of a foreign substance are several. The removed substance is obtained as a solution, which in this case must in turn be separated, either to obtain the pure substance or the added substance for reuse, and this represents an expense. The separation of added substance and product can rarely be complete, and this may lead to difficulty in meeting product specifications. In any case, addition of a foreign substance may add to the problems of building corrosion-resistant equipment, and the cost of inevitable losses must be borne. Obviously the indirect methods are used only because they are, in the net, less costly than the direct methods if there is a choice. Frequently there is no choice.

When the separated substance need not be obtained pure, many of these disadvantages may disappear. For example, in ordinary drying, the water vapor–air mixture is discarded since neither constituent need be recovered. In the production of hydrochloric acid by washing a hydrogen chloride–containing gas with water, the acid-water solution is sold directly without separation.

CHOICES AMONG SEPARATION METHODS

The chemical engineer faced with the problem of separating the components of a solution must ordinarily choose among several possible methods. While the choice is usually limited owing to peculiar physical characteristics of the materials to be handled, the necessity for making a decision nevertheless almost always exists. Until the fundamentals of the various operations have been clearly understood, of course, no basis for such a decision is available, but it is well at least to establish the nature of the alternatives at the beginning.

One may sometimes choose between using a mass-transfer operation of the sort discussed in this book and a purely mechanical separation method. For example, in the separation of a desired mineral from its ore, it may be possible to use either the mass-transfer operation of leaching with a solvent or the purely mechanical methods of flotation. Vegetable oils may be separated from the seeds in which they occur by expression or by leaching with a solvent. A vapor may be removed from a mixture with a permanent gas by the mechanical operation of compression or by the mass-transfer operations of gas absorption or adsorption. Sometimes both mechanical and mass-transfer operations are used, especially where the former are incomplete, as in processes for recovering vegetable oils wherein expression is followed by leaching. A more commonplace example is the wringing of water from wet laundry followed by air drying.   It is characteristic that at the end of the operation the substance removed by mechanical methods is pure, while if removed by diffusional methods it is associated with another substance.

One may also frequently choose between a purely mass-transfer operation and a chemical reaction, or a combination of both.   Water may be removed from an ethanol-water solution either by causing it to react with unslaked lime or by special methods of distillation, for example.   Hydrogen sulfide may be separated from other gases either by absorption in a liquid solvent with or without simultaneous chemical reaction or by chemical reaction with ferric oxide.   Chemical methods ordinarily destroy the substance removed, while mass-transfer methods usually permit its eventual recovery in unaltered form without great difficulty.

There are also choices to be made within the mass-transfer operations.   For example, a gaseous mixture of oxygen and nitrogen may be separated by preferential adsorption of the oxygen on activated carbon, by adsorption, by distillation, or by gaseous effusion.   A liquid solution of acetic acid may be separated by distillation, by liquid extraction with a suitable solvent, or by adsorption with a suitable adsorbent.

The principal basis for choice in any case is cost: that method which costs the least is usually the one to be used.   Occasionally other factors also influence the decision, however.   The simplest operation, while it may not be the least costly, is sometimes desired because it will be trouble-free.   Sometimes a method will be discarded because of imperfect knowledge of design methods or unavailability of data for design, so that results cannot be guaranteed.   Favorable previous experience with one method may be given strong consideration.

METHODS OF CONDUCTING THE MASS-TRANSFER OPERATIONS

Several characteristics of these operations influence our method of dealing with them and are described in terms which require definition at the start.

Solute recovery and fractionation

If the components of a solution fall into two distinct groups of quite different properties, so that one can imagine that one group of components comprises the solvent and the other group the solute, then separation according to these groups is usually relatively easy, and amounts to a *solute-recovery* or *solute-removal* operation.   For example, a gas consisting of methane, pentane, and hexane may be imagined to consist of methane as solvent with pentane plus hexane as solute, the solvent and solute in this case differing considerably in at least one property, vapor pressure. A simple gas-absorption operation, washing the mixture with a nonvolatile hydrocarbon oil, will easily provide a new solution of pentane plus hexane in the oil, essentially methane-free; and the residual methane will be essentially free of pentane and hexane.   On the other hand, a solution consisting of pentane and hexane alone cannot be classified so readily.   While the component properties differ, the differences are small, and to separate them into relatively pure components requires a different technique. Such separations are termed *fractionations*, and in this case we might use fractional distillation as a method.

Whether a solute-recovery or fractionation procedure is used may depend upon the property chosen to be exploited. For example, to separate a mixture of propanol and butanol from water by a gas-liquid contacting method, which depends on vapor pressures, requires fractionation (fractional distillation) because the vapor pressures of the components are not greatly different. But nearly complete separation of the combined alcohols from water can be obtained by liquid extraction of the solution with a hydrocarbon, using solute-recovery methods because the solubility of the alcohols as a group and water in hydrocarbons is greatly different. The separation of propanol from butanol, however, requires a fractionation technique (fractional extraction or fractional distillation, for example), because all their properties are very similar.

Unsteady-state operation

It is characteristic of unsteady-state operation that concentrations at any point in the apparatus change with time. This may result from changes in concentrations of feed materials, flow rates, or conditions of temperature or pressure. In any case, *batch* operations are always of the unsteady-state type. In purely batch operations, all the phases are stationary from a point of view outside the apparatus, i.e., no flow in or out, even though there may be relative motion within. The familiar laboratory extraction procedure of shaking a solution with an immiscible solvent is an example. In *semibatch* operations, one phase is stationary while the other flows continuously in and out of the apparatus. As an example, we may cite the case of a drier where a quantity of wet solid is contacted continuously with fresh air, which carries away the vaporized moisture until the solid is dry.

Steady-state operation

It is characteristic of steady-state operation that concentrations at any position in the apparatus remain constant with passage of time. This requires continuous, invariable flow of all phases into and out of the apparatus, a persistence of the flow regime within the apparatus, constant concentrations of the feed streams, and unchanging conditions of temperature and pressure.

Stagewise operation

If two insoluble phases are first allowed to come into contact so that the various diffusing substances may distribute themselves between the phases, and if the phases are then mechanically separated, the entire operation, and the equipment required to carry it out, are said to constitute one *stage*, e.g., laboratory batch extraction in a separatory funnel. The operation may be carried on in continuous fashion (steady-state) or batchwise fashion, however. For separations requiring greater concentration changes, a series of stages may be arranged so that the phases flow through the assembled stages from one to the other, for example, in countercurrent flow. Such an assemblage is called a *cascade*.   In order to establish a standard for the measurement of performance, the *ideal*, or *theoretical*, stage is defined as one where the effluent phases are in equilibrium, so that a longer time of contact will bring about no additional change of composition.   The approach to equilibrium realized in any stage is then defined as the *stage efficiency*.

Continuous-contact (differential-contact) operation

In this case the phases flow through the equipment in continuous, intimate contact throughout, without repeated physical separation and recontacting.   The nature of the method requires the operation to be either semibatch or steady-state, and the resulting change in compositions may be equivalent to that given by a fraction of an ideal stage or by many stages.   Equilibrium between two phases at any position in the equipment is never established; indeed, should equilibrium occur anywhere in the system, the result would be equivalent to the effect of an infinite number of stages.

The essential difference between stagewise and continuous-contact operation may then be summarized.   In the case of the stagewise operation the diffusional flow of matter between the phases is allowed to reduce the concentration difference which causes the flow.   If allowed to continue long enough, an equilibrium is established, after which no further diffusional flow occurs.   The rate of diffusion and the time then determine the stage efficiency realized in any particular situation.   On the other hand, in the case of the continuous-contact operation the departure from equilibrium is deliberately maintained, and the diffusional flow between the phases may continue without interruption.   Which method will be used depends to some extent on the stage efficiency that can be practically realized.   A high stage efficiency can mean a relatively inexpensive plant and one whose performance can be reliably predicted.   A low stage efficiency, on the other hand, may make the continuous-contact methods more desirable for reasons of cost and certainty.

DESIGN PRINCIPLES

There are four major factors to be established in the design of any plant involving the diffusional operations: the number of ideal stages or their equivalent, the time of phase contact required, the permissible rate of flow, and the energy requirements.

Number of ideal stages

In order to determine the number of ideal stages required in a cascade to bring about a specified degree of separation, or the equivalent quantity for a continuous-contact device, the equilibrium characteristics of the system and material-balance calculations are required.

Time requirement

In stagewise operations the time of contact is intimately connected with stage efficiency, whereas for continuous-contact equipment the time leads ultimately to the volume or length of the required device.   The factors which help establish the time are several.

Material balances permit calculation of the relative quantities required of the various phases. The equilibrium characteristics of the system establish the ultimate concentrations possible, and the rate of transfer of material between phases depends upon the departure from equilibrium which is maintained. The rate of transfer additionally depends upon the physical properties of the phases as well as the flow regime within the equipment.

It is important to recognize that, for a given degree of intimacy of contact of the phases, the time of contact required is independent of the total quantity of the phases to be processed.

Permissible flow rate

This factor enters into consideration of semibatch and steady-state operations, where it leads to the determination of the cross-sectional area of the equipment. Considerations of fluid dynamics establish the permissible flow rate, and material balances determine the absolute quantity of each of the streams required.

Energy requirements

Heat and mechanical energies are ordinarily required to carry out the diffusional operations. Heat is necessary for the production of any temperature changes, for the creation of new phases (such as vaporization of a liquid), and for overcoming heat-of-solution effects. Mechanical energy is required for fluid and solid transport, for dispersing liquids and gases, and for operating moving parts of machinery.

The ultimate design, consequently, requires us to deal with the equilibrium characteristics of the system, material balances, diffusional rates, fluid dynamics, and energy requirements. In what follows, basic considerations of diffusion rates are discussed first (Part 1) and these are later applied to specific operations. The principal operations, in turn, are subdivided into three categories, depending upon the nature of the insoluble phases contacted, gas-liquid (Part 2), liquid-liquid (Part 3), and solid-fluid (Part 4), since the equilibrium and fluid dynamics of the systems are most readily studied in such a grouping. Part 5 considers briefly some of the less frequently used operations.

PART ONE
DIFFUSION AND
MASS TRANSFER

We have seen that most of the mass-transfer operations which are used for separating the components of a solution achieve this result by bringing the solution to be separated into contact with another insoluble phase. As will be developed, the rate at which a component is then transferred from one phase to the other depends upon a so-called mass-transfer, or rate, coefficient and upon the degree of departure of the system from equilibrium. The transfer stops when equilibrium is attained.

Now the rate coefficients for the various components in a given phase will differ from each other to the greatest extent under conditions where molecular diffusion prevails, but even then the difference is not really large. For example, gases and vapors diffusing through air will show transfer coefficients whose ratio at most may be 3 or 4 to 1. The same is true when various substances diffuse through a liquid such as water. Under conditions of turbulence, where molecular diffusion is relatively unimportant, the transfer coefficients become much more nearly alike for all components. Consequently, while in principle some separation of the components could be achieved by taking advantage of their different transfer coefficients, the degree of separation attainable in this manner is small. This is especially significant when it is considered that we frequently wish to obtain products which are nearly pure substances, where the ratio of components may be of the order of 1,000 or 10,000 to 1, or even larger.

Therefore we depend almost entirely upon the differences in concentration which exist at equilibrium, and not upon the difference in transfer coefficients, for making separations. Nevertheless, the mass-transfer coefficients are of great importance, since, as they regulate the rate at which equilibrium is approached, they control the time required for separation and therefore the size and cost of the equipment used. The transfer coefficients are also important in governing the size of equipment used for entirely different purposes, such as carrying out chemical reactions.   For example, the rate at which a reaction between two gases occurs on a solid catalyst is frequently governed by the rate of transfer of the gases to the catalyst surface and the rate of transfer of the product away from the catalyst.

The mass-transfer coefficients, their relationship to the phenomenon of diffusion, fluid motion, and to related rate coefficients, such as those describing heat transfer, are treated in Part 1.

CHAPTER TWO
MOLECULAR DIFFUSION
IN FLUIDS

Molecular diffusion is concerned with the movement of individual molecules through a substance by virtue of their thermal energy. The kinetic theory of gases provides a means of visualizing what occurs, and indeed it was the success of this theory in quantitatively describing the diffusional phenomena which led to its rapid acceptance. In the case of a simplified kinetic theory, a molecule is imagined to travel in a straight line at a uniform velocity until it collides with another molecule, whereupon its velocity changes both in magnitude and direction. The average distance the molecule travels between collisions is its mean free path, and the average velocity is dependent upon the temperature. The molecule thus travels a highly zigzag path, and the net distance in one direction which it moves in a given time, the rate of diffusion, is only a small fraction of the length of its actual path. For this reason the diffusion rate is very slow, although we can expect it to increase with decreasing pressure, which reduces the number of collisions, and with increased temperature, which increases the molecular velocity.

The importance of the barrier which molecular collision presents to diffusive movement is profound. Thus, for example, it can be computed through the kinetic theory that the rate of evaporation of water at 25°C into a complete vacuum is roughly ⅓ g/(sec)(sq cm) of water surface.   But placing a layer of stagnant air at 1 atm pressure and only 0.1 mm thick above the water surface reduces the rate by a factor of about 600.   The same general mechanism prevails also for the liquid state, but because of the considerably higher molecular concentration, we find even slower diffusion rates than in gases.

The phenomenon of molecular diffusion ultimately leads to a completely uniform concentration of substances throughout a solution which may initially have been nonuniform.   Thus, for example, if a drop of blue copper sulfate solution is placed in a beaker of water, the copper sulfate eventually permeates the entire liquid.   The blue color in time becomes everywhere uniform, and no subsequent change occurs.

We must distinguish at the start, however, between molecular diffusion, which is a slow process, and the more rapid mixing which can be brought about by mechanical stirring and convective movement of the fluid.   Visualize a tank 5 ft in diameter into which has been placed a salt solution to a depth of 2.5 ft.   Imagine that a 2.5-ft-deep layer of pure water has been carefully placed over the brine, in such a manner as not to disturb the brine in any way.   If the contents of the tank are left completely undisturbed, the salt will, by molecular diffusion, completely permeate the liquid, ultimately coming everywhere to one-half its concentration in the original brine. But the process is very slow, and it can be calculated that the salt concentration at the top surface will still be only 87.5 percent of its final value after 10 years and will reach 99 percent of its final value only after 28 years.   On the other hand, it has been demonstrated that a simple paddle agitator rotating in the tank at 60 rpm will bring about complete uniformity in about 30 sec.   The mechanical agitation has produced rapid movement of relatively large chunks, or eddies, of fluid characteristic of turbulent motion, and these have carried the salt with them.   This method of solute transfer is known as eddy or turbulent diffusion, as opposed to molecular diffusion. Of course, within each eddy, no matter how small, uniformity is achieved only by molecular diffusion, which is the ultimate process.   We see then that molecular diffusion is the mechanism of mass transfer in stagnant fluids or in fluids which are moving only in laminar flow, although it is nevertheless always present even in highly developed turbulent flow.

In a two-phase system not at equilibrium, such as a layer of ammonia and air as a gas solution in contact with a layer of liquid water, spontaneous alteration through molecular diffusion also occurs, ultimately bringing the entire system to a state of equilibrium, whereupon alteration stops.   At the end, we observe that the concentration of any constituent is the same throughout a phase, but it will not necessarily be the same in both phases.   Thus the ammonia concentration will be uniform throughout the liquid and uniform at a different value throughout the gas.   On the other hand, the chemical potential of the ammonia (or its activity if the same reference state is used), which is differently dependent upon concentration in the two phases, will be uniform everywhere throughout the system at equilibrium, and it is this uniformity which has brought the diffusive process to a halt.   Evidently, then, the true driving force for diffusion is activity or chemical potential, and not concentration. In multiphase systems, however, we customarily deal with diffusional processes in each phase separately, and within one phase it is usually described in terms of that which is most readily observed, namely, concentration changes.

Molecular diffusion

We have noted that if a solution is everywhere uniform in concentration of its constituents, no alteration occurs, but that as long as it is not uniform, the solution is spontaneously brought to uniformity by diffusion, the substances moving from a place of high concentration to one of low.   The rate at which a solute moves at any point in any direction must therefore depend on the concentration gradient at that point and in that direction.   In describing this quantitatively, we need an appropriate measure of rate.

Rates will be most conveniently described in terms of a molar flux, or moles/ (time)(area), the area being measured in a direction normal to the diffusion.   In a nonuniform solution even containing only two constituents, however, both constituents must diffuse if uniformity is the ultimate result, and this leads to the use of two fluxes to describe the motion of one constituent: N, the flux relative to a fixed location in space; and J, the flux of a constituent relative to the average molar velocity of all constituents.   The first of these is of importance in the applications to design of equipment, but the second is more characteristic of the nature of the constituent. For example, a fisherman is most interested in the rate at which a fish swims upstream against the flowing current to reach his baited hook (analogous to N), but the velocity of the fish relative to the stream (analogous to J) is more characteristic of the swimming ability of the fish.

The *diffusivity*, or *diffusion coefficient*, D_{AB} of a constituent A in solution in B, which is a measure of its diffusive mobility, is then defined as the ratio of its flux J_A to its concentration gradient

$$J_A = -D_{AB}\frac{\partial c_A}{\partial z} \tag{2.1}$$

which is Fick's first law written for the z direction.   The negative sign emphasizes that diffusion occurs in the direction of a drop in concentration.   The diffusivity is a characteristic of a constituent and its environment (temperature, pressure, concentration, whether in liquid, gas, or solid solution, and the nature of the other constituents).

Consider the element of fluid of Fig. 2.1, of unit cross-sectional area.   To the left of the section at P, the concentration of substance A is higher than on the right, while that of B is higher on the right than on the left.   Diffusion of the substances then

Fig. 2.1   *Diffusion in a binary solution.*

occurs in the directions shown. The volume rate (or velocity for unit cross section) of movement of A is u_A, that of B is $u_B = -u_A$, and the volume on either side of the section at P remains constant. The rate at which moles of A pass an observer at P is $N_A = u_A \rho_A / M_A = u_A c_A$, and for B, $N_B = u_B \rho_B / M_B = u_B c_B$, where c_A and c_B are the molar concentrations of the constituents. The net rate of movement of moles past the observer at P is $N_A + N_B$, and the molar average of the velocities is

$$u_M = \frac{u_A c_A + u_B c_B}{c} = \frac{N_A + N_B}{c} \tag{2.2}$$

where $c = $ total molar concentration or density $= c_A + c_B$. If the observer wished to see no molar flux, he would have to move at a velocity u_M, whereupon the number of moles to his left and right would always be the same. The flux N_A with respect to the fixed position P must be larger than J_A by the amount of A in the volume rate u_M, or

$$N_A = u_M c_A + J_A \tag{2.3}$$

$$N_A = (N_A + N_B)\frac{c_A}{c} - D_{AB}\frac{\partial c_A}{\partial z} \tag{2.4}$$

The counterpart of Eq. (2.4) for B is

$$N_B = (N_A + N_B)\frac{c_B}{c} - D_{BA}\frac{\partial c_B}{\partial z} \tag{2.5}$$

Adding these, there results

$$-D_{AB}\frac{\partial c_A}{\partial z} = D_{BA}\frac{\partial c_B}{\partial z} \tag{2.6}$$

or $J_A = -J_B$. If $c_A + c_B = $ const, it follows that $D_{AB} = D_{BA}$ at the prevailing concentration and temperature.

All the above has considered diffusion in only one direction, but in general concentration gradients, velocities, and diffusional fluxes exist in all directions, so that counterparts of Eqs. (2.1) to (2.6) for all three directions in the cartesian coordinate system exist. In certain solids, the diffusivity D_{AB} may also be direction-sensitive, although in fluids it is not.

The equation of continuity

Consider the volume element of fluid of Fig. 2.2, where a fluid is flowing through the element. We shall need a material balance for a component of the fluid applicable to a differential fluid volume of this type.

The mass rate of flow of component A into the three faces with a common corner at E is

$$M_A[(N_{Ax})_x \, \Delta y \, \Delta z + (N_{Ay})_y \, \Delta x \, \Delta z + (N_{Az})_z \, \Delta x \, \Delta y]$$

where N_{Ax} signifies the x-directed flux and $(N_{Ax})_x$ its value at location x. Similarly the mass rate of flow out of the three faces with a common corner at G is

$$M_A[(N_{Ax})_{x+\Delta x} \, \Delta y \, \Delta z + (N_{Ay})_{y+\Delta y} \, \Delta x \, \Delta z + (N_{Az})_{z+\Delta z} \, \Delta x \, \Delta y]$$

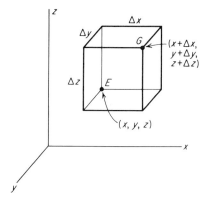

Fig. 2.2   *An elemental fluid volume.*

The total component A in the element is $\Delta x\,\Delta y\,\Delta z\,\rho_A$, and its rate of accumulation is there-fore $\Delta x\,\Delta y\,\Delta z\,\partial\rho_A/\partial\theta$.   If, in addition, A is generated by chemical reaction at the rate R_A moles/(time)(volume), its production rate is $M_A R_A\,\Delta x\,\Delta y\,\Delta z$, mass/time.   Since, in general,

$$\text{Rate out} - \text{rate in} + \text{rate of accumulation} = \text{rate of generation}$$

then

$$M_A\{[(N_{Ax})_{x+\Delta x} - (N_{Ax})_x]\,\Delta y\,\Delta z + [(N_{Ay})_{y+\Delta y} - (N_{Ay})_y]\,\Delta x\,\Delta z$$

$$+ [(N_{Az})_{z+\Delta z} - (N_{Az})_z]\,\Delta x\,\Delta y\} + \Delta x\,\Delta y\,\Delta z\,\frac{\partial \rho_A}{\partial \theta} = M_A R_A\,\Delta x\,\Delta y\,\Delta z \qquad (2.7)$$

Dividing by $\Delta x\,\Delta y\,\Delta z$ and taking the limit as the three distances become zero,

$$M_A\left(\frac{\partial N_{Ax}}{\partial x} + \frac{\partial N_{Ay}}{\partial y} + \frac{\partial N_{Az}}{\partial z}\right) + \frac{\partial \rho_A}{\partial \theta} = M_A R_A \qquad (2.8)$$

Similarly, for component B,

$$M_B\left(\frac{\partial N_{Bx}}{\partial x} + \frac{\partial N_{By}}{\partial y} + \frac{\partial N_{Bz}}{\partial z}\right) + \frac{\partial \rho_B}{\partial \theta} = M_B R_B \qquad (2.9)$$

The total material balance is obtained by adding those for A and B

$$\frac{\partial(M_A N_A + M_B N_B)_x}{\partial x} + \frac{\partial(M_A N_A + M_B N_B)_y}{\partial y} + \frac{\partial(M_A N_A + M_B N_B)_z}{\partial z} + \frac{\partial \rho}{\partial \theta} = 0 \qquad (2.10)$$

where $\rho = \rho_A + \rho_B =$ the solution density, since the mass rate of generation of A and B must equal zero.

Now the counterpart of Eq. (2.3) in terms of masses and in the x direction is

$$M_A N_{Ax} = u_x \rho_A + M_A J_{Ax} \qquad (2.11)$$

where u_x is the mass-average velocity such that

$$\rho u_x = u_{Ax}\rho_A + u_{Bx}\rho_B = M_A N_{Ax} + M_B N_{Bx} \qquad (2.12)$$

Therefore,

$$\frac{\partial(M_A N_A + M_B N_B)_x}{\partial x} = \rho\frac{\partial u_x}{\partial x} + u_x\frac{\partial \rho}{\partial x}$$

Equation (2.10) therefore becomes

$$\rho\left(\frac{\partial u_x}{\partial x} + \frac{\partial u_y}{\partial y} + \frac{\partial u_z}{\partial z}\right) + u_x\frac{\partial \rho}{\partial x} + u_y\frac{\partial \rho}{\partial y} + u_z\frac{\partial \rho}{\partial z} + \frac{\partial \rho}{\partial \theta} = 0 \qquad (2.13)$$

which is the "equation of continuity," or a mass balance, for total substance. If the solution density is constant, it becomes

$$\frac{\partial u_x}{\partial x} + \frac{\partial u_y}{\partial y} + \frac{\partial u_z}{\partial z} = 0 \qquad (2.14)$$

Returning to the balance for component A, we see from Eq. (2.11) that

$$M_A\frac{\partial N_{Ax}}{\partial x} = u_x\frac{\partial \rho_A}{\partial x} + \rho_A\frac{\partial u_x}{\partial x} + M_A\frac{\partial J_{Ax}}{\partial x} = u_x\frac{\partial \rho_A}{\partial x} + \rho_A\frac{\partial u_x}{\partial x} - M_A D_{AB}\frac{\partial^2 c_A}{\partial x^2} \qquad (2.15)$$

Equation (2.8) then becomes

$$u_x\frac{\partial \rho_A}{\partial x} + u_y\frac{\partial \rho_A}{\partial y} + u_z\frac{\partial \rho_A}{\partial z} + \rho_A\left(\frac{\partial u_x}{\partial x} + \frac{\partial u_y}{\partial y} + \frac{\partial u_z}{\partial z}\right)$$

$$- M_A D_{AB}\left(\frac{\partial^2 c_A}{\partial x^2} + \frac{\partial^2 c_A}{\partial y^2} + \frac{\partial^2 c_A}{\partial z^2}\right) + \frac{\partial \rho_A}{\partial \theta} = M_A R_A \qquad (2.16)$$

which is the equation of continuity for substance A. For a solution of constant density, we can apply Eq. (2.14) to the terms multiplying ρ_A. Dividing by M_A, we then have

$$u_x\frac{\partial c_A}{\partial x} + u_y\frac{\partial c_A}{\partial y} + u_z\frac{\partial c_A}{\partial z} + \frac{\partial c_A}{\partial \theta} = D_{AB}\left(\frac{\partial^2 c_A}{\partial x^2} + \frac{\partial^2 c_A}{\partial y^2} + \frac{\partial^2 c_A}{\partial z^2}\right) + R_A \qquad (2.17)$$

In the special case where the velocity equals zero and there is no chemical reaction, it reduces to Fick's second law

$$\frac{\partial c_A}{\partial \theta} = D_{AB}\left(\frac{\partial^2 c_A}{\partial x^2} + \frac{\partial^2 c_A}{\partial y^2} + \frac{\partial^2 c_A}{\partial z^2}\right) \qquad (2.18)$$

This is frequently applicable to diffusion in solids and to limited situations in fluids.

In similar fashion, it is possible to derive the equations for a differential energy balance. For a fluid of constant density, the result is

$$u_x\frac{\partial t}{\partial x} + u_y\frac{\partial t}{\partial y} + u_z\frac{\partial t}{\partial z} + \frac{\partial t}{\partial \theta} = \alpha\left(\frac{\partial^2 t}{\partial x^2} + \frac{\partial^2 t}{\partial y^2} + \frac{\partial^2 t}{\partial z^2}\right) + \frac{Q}{\rho C_p} \qquad (2.19)$$

where $\alpha = k/\rho C_p$ and Q is the rate of heat generation within the fluid per unit volume from a chemical reaction. The significance of the similarities between Eqs. (2.17) and (2.19) will be developed in Chap. 3.

STEADY-STATE UNIDIRECTIONAL MOLECULAR DIFFUSION IN FLUIDS AT REST AND IN LAMINAR FLOW

Applying Eq. (2.4) to the case of diffusion only in the z direction, with N_A and N_B both constant (steady state), the variables are readily separated, and if D_{AB} is constant, it may be integrated

$$\int_{c_{A1}}^{c_{A2}} \frac{-dc_A}{N_A c - c_A(N_A + N_B)} = \frac{1}{c D_{AB}}\int_{z_1}^{z_2} dz \qquad (2.20)$$

where 1 indicates the beginning of the diffusion path (c_A high), and 2 the end of the diffusion path (c_A low).   Letting $z_2 - z_1 = z$,

$$\frac{1}{N_A + N_B} \ln \frac{N_A c - c_{A2}(N_A + N_B)}{N_A c - c_{A1}(N_A + N_B)} = \frac{z}{c D_{AB}} \qquad (2.21)$$

or
$$N_A = \frac{N_A}{N_A + N_B} \frac{D_{AB} c}{z} \ln \frac{N_A/(N_A + N_B) - c_{A2}/c}{N_A/(N_A + N_B) - c_{A1}/c} \qquad (2.22)$$

Integration under steady-state conditions where the flux N_A is not constant is also possible. Consider radial diffusion from the surface of a solid sphere into a fluid, for example. Equation (2.20) may be applied, but the flux is a function of distance owing to the geometry.   Most practical problems which deal with such matters, however, are concerned with diffusion under turbulent conditions, and the transfer coefficients which are then used are based upon a flux expressed in terms of some arbitrarily chosen area, such as the surface of the sphere.   These matters are considered in Chap. 3.

Molecular diffusion in gases

When the ideal-gas law can be applied, Eq. (2.21) can be written in a form more convenient for use with gases.   Thus,

$$\frac{c_A}{c} = \frac{p_A}{P_t} = y_A \qquad (2.23)$$

where p_A = partial pressure of component A
P_t = total pressure
y_A = mole fraction concentration†

Further,
$$c = \frac{n}{V} = \frac{P_t}{RT} \qquad (2.24)$$

so that Eq. (2.22) becomes

$$N_A = \frac{N_A}{N_A + N_B} \frac{D_{AB} P_t}{RTz} \ln \frac{[N_A/(N_A + N_B)]P_t - p_{A2}}{[N_A/(N_A + N_B)]P_t - p_{A1}} \qquad (2.25)$$

or
$$N_A = \frac{N_A}{N_A + N_B} \frac{D_{AB} P_t}{RTz} \ln \frac{N_A/(N_A + N_B) - y_{A2}}{N_A/(N_A + N_B) - y_{A1}} \qquad (2.26)$$

In order to use these, the relation between N_A and N_B must be known.   This is usually fixed by other considerations.   For example, if methane were being cracked on a catalyst,

$$CH_4 \rightarrow C + 2H_2$$

under circumstances such that CH_4 (A) diffuses to the cracking surface and H_2 (B) diffuses back, then the reaction stoichiometry fixes the relationship $N_B = -2N_A$, and

$$\frac{N_A}{N_A + N_B} = \frac{N_A}{N_A - 2N_A} = -1$$

† The component subscript A on y_A will differentiate mole fraction from the y meaning distance n the y direction.

On other occasions, in the absence of chemical reaction, the ratio may be fixed by enthalpy considerations.   In the case of the purely separational operations, there are two situations which frequently arise.

1. Steady-state diffusion of A through nondiffusing B. This might occur, for example, if ammonia (A) were being absorbed from air (B) into water.   In the gas phase, since air does not dissolve appreciably in water, and if we neglect the evaporation of water, only the ammonia diffuses.   Thus, $N_B = 0$, $N_A = $ const,

$$N_A/(N_A + N_B) = 1,$$

and Eq. (2.25) becomes

$$N_A = \frac{D_{AB}P_t}{RTz} \ln \frac{P_t - p_{A2}}{P_t - p_{A1}} \tag{2.27}$$

Since $P_t - p_{A2} = p_{B2}$, $P_t - p_{A1} = p_{B1}$, $p_{B2} - p_{B1} = p_{A1} - p_{A2}$, then

$$N_A = \frac{D_{AB}P_t}{RTz} \frac{p_{A1} - p_{A2}}{p_{B2} - p_{B1}} \ln \frac{p_{B2}}{p_{B1}} \tag{2.28}$$

Letting

$$\frac{p_{B2} - p_{B1}}{\ln (p_{B2}/p_{B1})} = p_{BM} \tag{2.29}$$

then

$$N_A = \frac{D_{AB}P_t}{RTzp_{BM}} (p_{A1} - p_{A2}) \tag{2.30}$$

This equation is shown graphically in Fig. 2.3.   Substance A diffuses by virtue of its concentration gradient, $-dp_A/dz$.   Substance B is also diffusing relative to the average molar velocity at a flux J_B which depends upon $-dp_B/dz$, but like a fish which swims

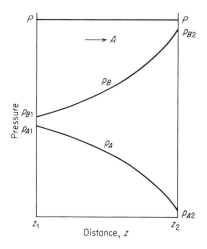

Fig. 2.3   *Diffusion of A through stagnant B.*

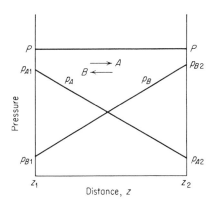

Fig. 2.4 *Equimolal counterdiffusion.*

upstream at the same velocity as the water flows downstream, $N_B = 0$ relative to a fixed place in space.

2. **Steady-state equimolal counterdiffusion.** This is a situation which frequently pertains in distillation operations. $N_A = -N_B = $ const. Equation (2.25) becomes indeterminate, but we can go back to Eq. (2.4), which, for gases, becomes

$$N_A = (N_A + N_B)\frac{p_A}{P_t} - \frac{D_{AB}}{RT}\frac{dp_A}{dz} \tag{2.31}$$

or, for this case,

$$N_A = -\frac{D_{AB}}{RT}\frac{dp_A}{dz} \tag{2.32}$$

$$\int_{z_1}^{z_2} dz = -\frac{D_{AB}}{RTN_A}\int_{p_{A1}}^{p_{A2}} dp_A \tag{2.33}$$

$$N_A = \frac{D_{AB}}{RTz}(p_{A1} - p_{A2}) \tag{2.34}$$

This is shown graphically in Fig. 2.4.

Steady-state diffusion in multicomponent mixtures. These can frequently be handled by the use of an "effective" diffusivity in Eq. (2.25), where the effective diffusivity of a component can be synthesized from its binary diffusivities with each of the other constituents.[2] Thus, in Eq. (2.25), $N_A + N_B$ is replaced by $\sum_{i=A}^{n} N_i$, where N_i is positive if diffusion is in the same direction as that of A and negative if in the opposite direction, and D_{AB} is replaced by the effective D_{Am}

$$\frac{1}{D_{Am}} = \frac{\sum_{i=A}^{n}\dfrac{1}{D_{Ai}}(y_i N_A - y_A N_i)}{N_A - y_A\sum_{i=A}^{n} N_i} \tag{2.35}$$

The D_{Ai} are the binary diffusivities. This indicates that D_{Am} may vary considerably from one end of the diffusion path to the other, but a linear variation with distance may usually be assumed for practical calculations.[2] A commonly arising situation is when all the N's except N_A are zero; i.e., all but one component is stagnant. Equation (2.35) then becomes[14]

$$D_{Am} = \frac{1 - y_A}{\displaystyle\sum_{i=B}^{n} \frac{y_i}{D_{Ai}}} = \frac{1}{\displaystyle\sum_{i=B}^{n} \frac{y_i'}{D_{Ai}}} \tag{2.36}$$

where y_i' is the mole fraction of component i on an A-free basis.

Illustration 2.1. Oxygen (A) is diffusing through carbon monoxide (B) under steady-state conditions, with the carbon monoxide nondiffusing. The total pressure is 1 atm, and the temperature 0°C. The partial pressure of oxygen at two planes 0.2 cm apart is, respectively, 100 and 50 mm Hg. The diffusivity for the mixture is 0.185 sq cm/sec. Calculate the rate of diffusion of oxygen in g moles/sec through each square centimeter of the two planes.

Solution. Equation (2.30) applies. $D_{AB} = 0.185$ sq cm/sec, $P_t = 1.0$ atm, $z = 0.2$ cm, $R = 82.06$ (cu cm)(atm)/(g mole)(°K), $T = 273°K$, $p_{A1} = 100/760 = 0.1317$ atm, $p_{A2} = 50/760 = 0.0658$ atm, $p_{B1} = 1 - 0.1317 = 0.8683$ atm, $p_{B2} = 1 - 0.0658 = 0.9342$ atm.

$$p_{BM} = \frac{p_{B1} - p_{B2}}{\ln (p_{B1}/p_{B2})} = \frac{0.8683 - 0.9342}{\ln (0.8683/0.9342)} = 0.901 \text{ atm}$$

$$N_A = \frac{D_{AB}P_t}{RTzp_{BM}}(p_{A1} - p_{A2}) = \frac{0.185(1.0)(0.1317 - 0.0658)}{82.06(273)(0.2)(0.901)}$$

$$= 3.01(10^{-6}) \text{ g mole/(sec)(sq cm)} \quad \textbf{Ans.}$$

Illustration 2.2. Recalculate the rate of diffusion of oxygen (A) in Illustration 2.1, assuming that the nondiffusing gas is a mixture of methane (B) and hydrogen (C) in the volume ratio 2:1. The diffusivities are estimated to be $D_{O_2-H_2} = 0.690$, $D_{O_2-CH_4} = 0.184$ sq cm/sec.

Solution. Equation (2.25) will become Eq. (2.30) for this case. $P_t = 1.0$ atm, $T = 273°K$, $p_{A1} = 0.1317$ atm, $p_{A2} = 0.0658$ atm, $p_{iM} = 0.901$ atm, $z = 0.2$ cm, $R = 82.06$ (cu cm)(atm)/(g mole)(°K), as in Illustration 2.1. In Eq. (2.36), $y_B' = 2/(2 + 1) = 0.667$, $y_C' = 1 - 0.667 = 0.333$, whence

$$D_{AM} = \frac{1}{y_B'/D_{AB} + y_C'/D_{AC}} = \frac{1}{0.667/0.184 + 0.333/0.690} = 0.244 \text{ sq cm/sec}$$

Therefore, Eq. (2.30) becomes

$$N_A = \frac{0.244(1.0)(0.1317 - 0.0658)}{82.06(273)(0.2)(0.901)} = 3.97(10^{-6}) \text{ g mole/(sec)(sq cm)} \quad \textbf{Ans.}$$

Diffusivity of gases

The diffusivity, or diffusion coefficient, D is a property of the system dependent upon the temperature, pressure, and nature of the components. An advanced kinetic theory[7] predicts that in binary mixtures there would be only a small effect of composition. Its dimensions may be established from its definition, Eq. (2.1), and are length²/time. In the cgs system, sq cm/sec are ordinarily used. The corresponding English-system units are sq ft/hr.

$$D \text{ sq cm/sec } (3.87) = D \text{ sq ft/hr}$$

A few typical data are listed in Table 2.1; a longer list is available in "The Chemical Engineers' Handbook."[10]

Table 2.1. Diffusivities of gases at atmospheric pressure

System	Temp, °C	Diffusivity, sq cm/sec	Ref.
H_2–CH_4	0	0.625	3
O_2–N_2	0	0.181	3
CO–O_2	0	0.185	3
CO_2–O_2	0	0.139	3
Air–NH_3	0	0.198	17
Air–H_2O	25.9	0.258	4
	59.0	0.305	4
Air–ethanol	0	0.102	8
Air–n-butanol	25.9	0.087	4
	59.0	0.104	4
Air–ethyl acetate	25.9	0.087	4
	59.0	0.106	4
Air–aniline	25.9	0.074	4
	59.0	0.090	4
Air–chlorobenzene	25.9	0.074	4
	59.0	0.090	4
Air–toluene	25.9	0.086	4
	59.0	0.092	4

Expressions for estimating D in the absence of experimental data are based on considerations of the kinetic theory of gases. The Wilke-Lee modification[16] of the Hirschfelder-Bird-Spotz method[6] is recommended for mixtures of nonpolar gases or of a polar with a nonpolar gas†

$$D_{AB} = \frac{(0.00107 - 0.000246\sqrt{1/M_A + 1/M_B})T^{3/2}\sqrt{1/M_A + 1/M_B}}{P_t(r_{AB})^2[f(kT/\epsilon_{AB})]} \quad (2.37)$$

where D_{AB} = diffusivity, sq cm/sec

T = abs temperature, °K

M_A, M_B = mol wt of A and B, respectively

P_t = abs pressure, atm

r_{AB} = molecular separation at collision, Å

= $(r_A + r_B)/2$

ϵ_{AB} = energy of molecular interaction, ergs

= $\sqrt{\epsilon_A \epsilon_B}$

k = Boltzmann's constant

$f(kT/\epsilon_{AB})$ = collision function given by Fig. 2.5

† The listed units must be used in Eq. (2.37). For mixtures of polar gases, see Ref. 13.

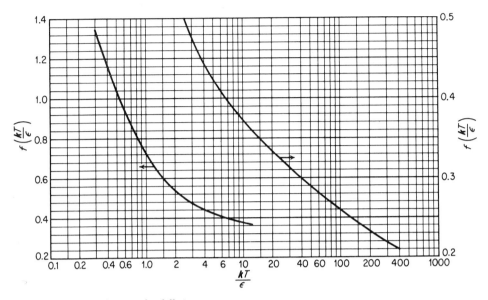

Fig. 2.5   *Collision function for diffusion.*

**Table 2.2. Force constants of gases as deter-
mined from viscosity data**†

Gas	ϵ/k, °K	r, Å
Air	97.0	3.617
H_2	33.3	2.968
N_2	91.46	3.681
CO_2	190	3.996
N_2O	220	3.879
NO	119	3.470
CH_4	136.5	3.882
O_2	113.2	3.433
CO	110.3	3.590
A	124.0	3.418
Ne	35.7	2.80
He	6.03	2.70

† By permission from Hirschfelder,
Bird, and Spotz, *Trans. ASME*, **71,** 921 (1949).
See also "The Chemical Engineers' Hand-
book," 4th ed., p. 14-20.

The values of r and ϵ, such as those listed in Table 2.2, can be calculated from other properties of gases, such as viscosity. If necessary, they can be estimated for each component empirically[16]†

$$r = 1.18v^{\frac{1}{3}} \tag{2.38}$$

$$\frac{\epsilon}{k} = 1.21T_b \tag{2.39}$$

where v = molal volume of liquid at normal boiling point, cu cm/g mole (estimate from Table 2.3)

T_b = normal boiling point, °K

In using Table 2.3, the contributions for the constituent atoms are added together. Thus, for toluene, C_7H_8, $v = 7(14.8) + 8(3.7) - 15 = 118.2$. Diffusion through air, when the constituents of the air remain in fixed proportions, is handled as if the air were a single substance.

Table 2.3. **Atomic and molecular volumes**

Atomic volume		Molecular volume	
Carbon	14.8	H_2	14.3
Hydrogen	3.7	O_2	25.6
Chlorine	24.6	N_2	31.2
Bromine	27.0	Air	29.9
Iodine	37.0	CO	30.7
Sulfur	25.6	CO_2	34.0
Nitrogen	15.6	SO_2	44.8
Nitrogen in primary amines	10.5	NO	23.6
Nitrogen in secondary amines	12.0	N_2O	36.4
Oxygen	7.4	NH_3	25.8
Oxygen in methyl esters	9.1	H_2O	18.9
Oxygen in higher esters	11.0	H_2S	32.9
Oxygen in acids	12.0	COS	51.5
Oxygen in methyl ethers	9.9	Cl_2	48.4
Oxygen in higher ethers	11.0	Br_2	53.2
Benzene ring: subtract	15	I_2	71.5
Naphthalene ring: subtract	30		

Illustration 2.3. Estimate the diffusivity of ethanol vapor (A), C_2H_5OH, through air (B) at 1 atm pressure, 0°C.

Solution. $T = 273$°K, $P_t = 1$ atm, $M_A = 46.07$, $M_B = 29$. From Table 2.2 for air, $\epsilon_B/k = 97.0$, $r_B = 3.617$. Values for ethanol will be estimated through Eqs. (2.38) and (2.39). From Table

———

† The listed units must be used in Eqs. (2.38) and (2.39).

2.3, $v_A = 2(14.8) + 6(3.7) + 7.4 = 59.2$, whence $r_A = 1.18(59.2)^{1/3} = 4.60$. The normal boiling point is $T_{bA} = 351.4°K$, and $\epsilon_A/k = 1.21(351.4) = 425$.

$$r_{AB} = \frac{r_A + r_B}{2} = \frac{4.60 + 3.617}{2} = 4.11$$

$$\frac{\epsilon_{AB}}{k} = \sqrt{\frac{\epsilon_A}{k}\frac{\epsilon_B}{k}} = \sqrt{425(97.0)} = 203$$

$$\frac{kT}{\epsilon_{AB}} = \frac{273}{203} = 1.345$$

Fig. 2.5: $f(kT/\epsilon_{AB}) = 0.62$. $\sqrt{1/M_A + 1/M_B} = 0.237$. Eq. (2.37):

$$D_{AB} = \frac{[0.00107 - 0.000246(0.237)](273)^{3/2}(0.237)}{1(4.11)^2(0.62)} = 0.103 \text{ sq cm/sec}$$

The observed value (Table 2.1) is 0.102 sq cm/sec.

Equation (2.37) shows D varying almost as $T^{3/2}$ (although a more correct temperature variation is given by considering also the collision function of Fig. 2.5) and inversely as the pressure, which will serve for pressures up to about 15 atm.[11] The coefficient of self-diffusion, or D for a gas diffusing through itself, can be determined experimentally only by very special techniques involving, for example, the use of radioactive tracers. It can be estimated from Eq. (2.37) by setting $A = B$.

Molecular diffusion in liquids

The integration of Eq. (2.4) to put it in the form of Eq. (2.22) requires the assumption that D_{AB} and c are constant. This is satisfactory for binary gas mixtures but not in the case of liquids, where both may vary considerably with concentration. Nevertheless, in view of our very meager knowledge of the D's, it is customary to use Eq. (2.22), together with an average c and the best average D_{AB} available. Equation (2.22) is also conveniently written†

$$N_A = \frac{N_A}{N_A + N_B} \frac{D_{AB}}{z}\left(\frac{\rho}{M}\right)_{av} \ln \frac{N_A/(N_A + N_B) - x_{A2}}{N_A/(N_A + N_B) - x_{A1}} \tag{2.40}$$

where ρ and M are the solution density and molecular weight, respectively. As in the case of gases, the value of $N_A/(N_A + N_B)$ must be established by the circumstances prevailing. For the most commonly occurring cases, we have, as for gases:

† The component subscript on x_A indicates mole fraction A, to distinguish it from x meaning distance in the x direction.

1. Steady-state diffusion of A through nondiffusing B. $N_A = $ const, $N_B = 0$,

whence
$$N_A = \frac{D_{AB}}{z x_{BM}} \left(\frac{\rho}{M}\right)_{av} (x_{A1} - x_{A2}) \qquad (2.41)$$

where
$$x_{BM} = \frac{x_{B2} - x_{B1}}{\ln (x_{B2}/x_{B1})} \qquad (2.42)$$

2. Steady-state equimolal counterdiffusion. $N_A = -N_B = $ const.

$$N_A = \frac{D_{AB}}{z} (c_{A1} - c_{A2}) = \frac{D_{AB}}{z}\left(\frac{\rho}{M}\right)_{av} (x_{A1} - x_{A2}) \qquad (2.43)$$

Illustration 2.4. Calculate the rate of diffusion of acetic acid (A) across a film of nondiffusing water (B) solution 0.1 cm thick at 17°C when the concentrations on opposite sides of the film are, respectively, 9 and 3 wt % acid. The diffusivity of acetic acid in the solution is $0.95(10^{-5})$ sq cm/sec.

Solution. Equation (2.41) applies. $z = 0.1$ cm, $M_A = 60.03$, $M_B = 18.02$. At 17°C, the density of the 9% solution is 1.0120 g/cu cm. Therefore

$$x_{A1} = \frac{0.09/60.03}{0.09/60.03 + 0.91/18.02} = \frac{0.0015}{0.0520} = 0.0288 \text{ mole fraction acetic acid}$$

$$x_{B1} = 1 - 0.0288 = 0.9712 \text{ mole fraction water}$$

$$M = \frac{1}{0.0520} = 19.21 \text{ g/g mole}$$

$$\frac{\rho}{M} = \frac{1.0121}{19.21} = 0.0527 \text{ g mole/cu cm}$$

Similarly the density of the 3% solution is 1.0032 g/cu cm, $x_{A2} = 0.0092$, $x_{B2} = 0.9908$, $M = 18.40$, and $\rho/M = 0.0545$.

$$\left(\frac{\rho}{M}\right)_{av} = \frac{0.0527 + 0.0545}{2} = 0.0536 \text{ g mole/cu cm}$$

$$x_{BM} = \frac{0.9908 - 0.9712}{\ln (0.9908/0.9712)} = 0.980$$

Eq. (2.41):
$$N_A = \frac{0.95(10^{-5})}{0.1(0.980)} 0.0536(0.0288 - 0.0092)$$

$$= 1.018(10^{-7}) \text{ g mole/(sq cm)(sec)} \quad \textbf{Ans.}$$

Diffusivity of liquids

The dimensions for diffusivity in liquids are the same as those for gases, length²/time. Unlike the case for gases, however, the diffusivity varies appreciably with concentration. A few typical data are listed in Table 2.4, and larger lists are available.[5,9,10]

Estimates of the diffusivity in the absence of data cannot be made with anything like the accuracy with which they can be made for gases, owing to the inadequate development of any sound theory of the structure of liquids. For dilute solutions of

Table 2.4. Liquid diffusivities[8]

Solute	Solvent	Temp, °C	Solute concn, g moles/liter	Diffusivity,† sq cm/sec (10^5)
Cl_2	Water	16	0.12	1.26
HCl	Water	0	9	2.7
			2	1.8
		10	9	3.3
			2.5	2.5
		16	0.5	2.44
NH_3	Water	5	3.5	1.24
		15	1.0	1.77
CO_2	Water	10	0	1.46
		20	0	1.77
NaCl	Water	18	0.05	1.26
			0.2	1.21
			1.0	1.24
			3.0	1.36
			5.4	1.54
Methanol	Water	15	0	1.28
Acetic acid	Water	12.5	1.0	0.82
			0.01	0.91
		18.0	1.0	0.96
Ethanol	Water	10	3.75	0.50
			0.05	0.83
		16	2.0	0.90
n-Butanol	Water	15	0	0.77
CO_2	Ethanol	17	0	3.2
Chloroform	Ethanol	20	2.0	1.25

† For example, D for Cl_2 in water 0.0000126 sq cm/sec.

nonelectrolytes, the empirical correlation of Wilke and Chang[14,15] is recommended†

$$D_{AB} = \frac{7.4(10^{-8})(\phi M_B)^{0.5} T}{\mu' v_A^{0.6}} \qquad (2.44)$$

where D_{AB} = diffusivity of A in dilute soln in solvent B, sq cm/sec
   M_B = mol wt of solvent
   T = temp, °K
   μ' = soln viscosity, centipoises
   v_A = solute molal vol at the nbp, cu cm/g mole
    = 75.6 for water as solute
   ϕ = association factor for solvent
    = 2.6 for water as solvent
    = 1.9 for methanol as solvent
    = 1.5 for ethanol as solvent
    = 1.0 for unassociated solvents such as benzene and ethyl ether

† The listed units must be used in Eq. (2.44).

The value of v_A may be estimated from the data of Table 2.3, except when water is the diffusing solute, as noted above. The association factor for a solvent can be estimated only when diffusivities in that solvent have been experimentally measured. If a value of ϕ is in doubt, the empirical correlation of Scheibel[12] may be used to estimate D. There is also some doubt about the ability of Eq. (2.44) to handle solvents of very high viscosity, say 100 centipoises or more.

The diffusivity in concentrated solutions differs from that in dilute solutions because of changes in viscosity with concentration and also because of changes in the degree of ideality of the solution. In the case of strong electrolytes dissolved in water, the diffusion rates are those of the individual ions, which move more rapidly than the large, undissociated molecules, although the positively and negatively charged ions must move at the same rate in order to maintain electrical neutrality of the solution. Estimations of these effects have been thoroughly reviewed[5,11] but are beyond the scope of this book.

Illustration 2.5. Estimate the diffusivity of mannitol, $CH_2OH(CHOH)_4CH_2OH$, $C_6H_{14}O_6$, in dilute solution in water at 20°C. Compare with the observed value, $0.56(10^{-5})$ sq cm/sec.
    Solution. From the data of Table 2.3,

$$v_A = 14.8(6) + 3.7(14) + 7.4(6) = 185.0$$

For water as solvent, $\phi = 2.6$. $M_B = 18.02$, $T = 293°K$. For dilute solutions, the viscosity μ' may be taken as that for water, 1.005 centipoises.

Eq. (2.44):
$$D_{AB} = \frac{7.4(10^{-8})[2.6(18.02)]^{0.5}(293)}{1.005(185)^{0.6}}$$

$$= 0.644(10^{-5}) \text{ sq cm/sec} \quad \textbf{Ans.}$$

Illustration 2.6. Estimate the diffusivity of mannitol in dilute water solution at 70°C, and compare with the observed value, $1.56(10^{-5})$ sq cm/sec.
    Solution. At 20°C, the observed $D_{AB} = 0.56(10^{-5})$ sq cm/sec, and $\mu' = 1.005$ centipoises (Illustration 2.5). At 70°C, the viscosity of water is 0.4061 centipoise. Equation (2.44) indicates that $D_{AB}\mu'/T$ should be constant

$$\frac{D_{AB}(0.4061)}{70 + 273} = \frac{0.56(10^{-5})(1.005)}{20 + 273}$$

$$D_{AB} = 1.62(10^{-5}) \text{ sq cm/sec at 70°C} \quad \textbf{Ans.}$$

Applications of molecular diffusion

The expressions developed for the rate of mass transfer under conditions where molecular diffusion defines the mechanism of mass transfer (fluids which are stagnant or in laminar flow) are of course directly applicable to the experimental measurement of the diffusivities, and they are extensively used for this.

In the practical applications of the mass-transfer operations, the fluids are always in motion, even in batch processes, so that we do not have stagnant fluids. While occasionally the moving fluids are entirely in laminar flow, more frequently the motion is turbulent. If the fluid is in contact with a solid surface, where the fluid velocity is zero, there will be a region in laminar flow adjacent to the surface. Mass transfer must then usually take place through the laminar region, and molecular diffusion governs the rate there. When two immiscible fluids in motion are in contact and mass transfer occurs between them, there may be no laminar region, even at the interface between the fluids.

In practical situations such as these, it has become customary to describe the mass-transfer flux in terms of mass-transfer coefficients. The relationships of this chapter are then rarely used directly to determine mass-transfer rates, but they are particularly useful in establishing the form of the mass-transfer coefficient-rate equations and in computing the mass-transfer coefficients for laminar flow.

MOMENTUM AND HEAT TRANSFER IN LAMINAR FLOW

In the flow of a fluid past a phase boundary, such as that through which mass transfer occurs, there will be a velocity gradient within the fluid, which results in a transfer of momentum through the fluid. In some cases there is also a transfer of heat by virtue of a temperature gradient. The processes of mass, momentum, and heat transfer under these conditions are intimately related, and it is useful briefly to consider this.

Momentum transfer

Consider the velocity profile for the case of a gas flowing past a flat plate, as in Fig. 2.6. Since the velocity at the solid surface is zero, there must necessarily be a laminar layer (the laminar sublayer) adjacent to the surface. Within this region, the fluid may be imagined as being made up of thin layers sliding over each other at increasing velocities at increasing distances from the plate. The force per unit area parallel to the surface, or shearing stress τ, required to maintain their velocities is proportional

Fig. 2.6 *Velocity profile, flow of air along a flat plate. [Page et al.: Ind. Eng. Chem., 44, 424 (1952).]*

to the velocity gradient,

$$\tau g_c = -\mu \frac{du}{dz} \tag{2.45}$$

where μ is the viscosity and z is measured as increasing in the direction toward the surface. This may be written as

$$\tau g_c = -\frac{\mu}{\rho} \frac{d(u\rho)}{dz} = -\nu \frac{d(u\rho)}{dz} \tag{2.46}$$

where ν is the kinematic viscosity, μ/ρ.

The kinematic viscosity has the same dimensions as diffusivity, length²/time, while the quantity $u\rho$ may be looked upon as a volumetric momentum concentration. The quantity τg_c is the rate of momentum transfer per unit area, or flux of momentum. Equation (2.46) is therefore a rate equation analogous to Eq. (2.1) for mass flux. In the transfer of momentum in this manner there is of course no bulk flow of fluid from one layer to the other in the z direction. Instead, molecules in one layer, in the course of traveling in random directions, will move from a fast-moving layer to an adjacent, more slowly moving layer, thereby transmitting momentum corresponding to the difference in velocities of the layers. Diffusion in the z direction occurs by the same mechanism. At high molecular concentrations, such as in gases at high pressures or even more so in liquids, the molecular diameter becomes appreciable in comparison with the molecular movement between collisions, and momentum may be imagined as being transmitted directly through the molecules themselves.[1] Visualize, for example, a number of billiard balls arranged in a group in close contact with each other on a table. A moving cue ball colliding with one of the outermost balls of the packed group will transmit its momentum very rapidly to one of the balls on the opposite side of the group, which will then be propelled from its original position. On the other hand, the cue ball is unlikely to move bodily through the group because of the large number of collisions it would experience. Thus, at high molecular concentrations the direct parallelism between molecular diffusivity and momentum diffusivity (or kinematic viscosity) breaks down: diffusion is much the slower process. It is interesting to note that a relatively simple kinetic theory predicted that both mass and momentum diffusivities are given by the same expression,

$$D_{AA} = \frac{\mu_A}{\rho_A} = \frac{w\lambda}{3} \tag{2.47}$$

where w is the average molecular velocity and λ is the mean free path of molecule. The Schmidt number, which is the dimensionless ratio of the two diffusivities, $Sc = \mu/\rho D$, should by this theory equal unity for a gas. A more sophisticated kinetic theory[7] gives values from 0.67 to 0.83, which is just the range found experimentally at moderate pressures. For binary gas mixtures, Sc may range up to 5. For liquids, as might be expected, Sc is much higher: approximately 297 for self-diffusion in water at 77°F, for example, and ranging into the thousands for more viscous liquids and even for water with slowly diffusing solutes.

Heat transfer

When a temperature gradient exists between the fluid and the plate, the rate of heat transfer in the laminar region of Fig. 2.6 is

$$q = -k \frac{dt}{dz} \tag{2.48}$$

where k is the thermal conductivity of the fluid. This may also be written as

$$q = -\frac{k}{C_p \rho} \frac{d(tC_p \rho)}{dz} = -\alpha \frac{d(tC_p \rho)}{dz} \tag{2.49}$$

where C_p is the specific heat at constant pressure. The quantity $tC_p \rho$ may be looked upon as a volumetric thermal concentration, and $\alpha = k/C_p \rho$ is the thermal diffusivity, which, like momentum and mass diffusivities, has dimensions length^2/time. Equation (2.49) is therefore a rate equation analogous to the corresponding equations for momentum and mass transfer.

In a gas at relatively low pressure the heat energy is transferred from one position to another by the molecules traveling from one layer to another at a lower temperature. A simplified kinetic theory leads to the expression

$$\alpha = \frac{k}{C_p \rho} = \frac{1}{3} w\lambda \frac{C_v}{C_p} \tag{2.50}$$

Equations (2.47) and (2.50) would give the dimensionless ratio $v/\alpha = C_p \mu/k$ equal to C_p/C_v. A more advanced kinetic theory modifies the size of the ratio, known as the Prandtl number Pr, and experimentally it has the range 0.65 to 0.9 for gases at low pressure, depending upon the molecular complexity of the gas. At high molecular concentrations, the process is modified. Thus for most liquids, Pr is larger (Pr = 7.02 for water at 68°F, for example).

The third dimensionless group, formed by dividing the thermal by the mass diffusivity, is the Lewis number, Le $= \alpha/D =$ Sc/Pr, and it plays an important part in problems of simultaneous heat and mass transfer, as will be developed later.

We may summarize this brief discussion of the similarity among momentum, heat, and mass transfer as follows. An elementary consideration of the three processes leads to the conclusion that in certain simplified situations, there is a direct analogy among them. In general, however, when three- rather than one-dimensional transfer is considered, the momentum-transfer process is of a sufficiently different nature for the analogy to break down. Modification of the simple analogy is also necessary when, for example, mass and momentum transfer occur simultaneously. Thus, if there were a net mass transfer toward the surface of Fig. 2.6, the momentum transfer of Eq. (2.46) would have to include the effect of the net diffusion. Similarly, mass transfer must inevitably have an influence on the velocity profile. Nevertheless, even the limited analogies which exist are put to important practical use.

NOTATION FOR CHAPTER 2

Generally, consistent units in either the cgs or the English system may be used. It has become the custom to express pressure in the diffusion equations as atmospheres, in either system. Certain empirical equations may be used with specific units only, and these are marked in the text and in the following list.

c = concentration, g moles/cu cm or lb moles/cu ft
C_p = heat capacity at constant pressure, cal/(g)(°C) or Btu/(lb)(°F)
C_v = heat capacity at constant volume, cal/(g)(°C) or Btu/(lb)(°F)
d = differential operator
D = diffusivity, sq cm/sec or sq ft/hr; in Eqs. (2.37) and (2.44), only sq cm/sec
f = a function
g_c = conversion factor, 980(g mass)(cm)/(g force)(sec)^2 or 4.17(10^8)(lb mass)(ft)/(lb force)(hr)^2
J = flux of diffusion relative to the molar average velocity, g moles/(sec)(sq cm) or lb moles/(hr)(sq ft)
k = thermal conductivity, (cal)(cm)/(sec)(sq cm)(°C) or (Btu)(ft)/(hr)(sq ft)(°F)
$\mathbf{k}$ = Boltzmann constant = 1.38(10^{-16}) erg/°K [Eqs. (2.37), (2.39), Fig. 2.5, and Table 2.2]
ln = natural logarithm
Le = Lewis number = $k/\rho D C_p$, dimensionless
M = molecular weight, g/g mole or lb/lb mole
n = number of moles
N = flux of diffusion relative to a fixed surface, g moles/(sec)(sq cm) or lb moles/(hr)(sq ft)
p = partial pressure, atm
P_t = total pressure, atm
Pr = Prandtl number = $C_p \mu/k$, dimensionless
q = flux of heat transfer, cal/(sec)(sq cm) or Btu/(hr)(sq ft)
r = molecular separation at collision, Å [Eqs. (2.37), (2.38), and Table 2.2]
R_i = rate of production of component i, g moles/(sec)(cu cm) or lb moles/(hr)(cu ft)
R = (with no subscript) universal gas constant, 82.06 cu cm(atm)/(g mole)(°K) or 0.729 cu ft (atm)/(lb mole)(°R)
Sc = Schmidt number = $\mu/\rho D$, dimensionless
T = absolute temperature, °K or °R; in Eqs. (2.37), (2.39), and (2.44), and Fig. 2.5, only °K
T_b = normal boiling point, °K [Eq. (2.39)]
u = linear velocity, cm/sec or ft/hr
v = liquid molal volume, cu cm/g mole [Eqs. (2.38) and (2.44)]
V = volume, cu cm or cu ft
w = average molecular velocity, cm/sec or ft/hr
x = (with no subscript) distance in the x direction, cm or ft
x_i = mole fraction concentration of component i in a liquid
y = (with no subscript) distance in the y direction, cm or ft
y_i = mole fraction concentration of component i in a gas
y_i' = mole fraction concentration of component i, diffusing-solute-free basis.
z = distance in the z direction, cm or ft
α = thermal diffusivity, sq cm/sec or sq ft/hr
∂ = partial differential operator
Δ = difference
ϵ = energy of molecular interaction, ergs [Eqs. (2.37), (2.39), Table 2.2, and Fig. 2.5]
θ = time, sec or hr
λ = mean free path of a molecule, cm or ft
μ = viscosity, g mass/cm sec or lb mass/ft hr
μ' = viscosity, centipoises [Eq. (2.44)]
v = kinematic viscosity or momentum diffusivity = μ/ρ, sq cm/sec or sq ft/hr

ρ = density, g mass/cu cm or lb mass/cu ft
τ = shearing stress, g force/sq cm or lb force/sq ft
ϕ = dissociation factor for solvent

Subscripts:

A = component A
B = component B
i = component i
n = the last of n components
m = effective
M = mean
x = in the x direction
y = in the y direction
z = in the z direction
1 = beginning of diffusion path
2 = end of diffusion path

REFERENCES

   1. Bosworth, R. C. L.: "Physics in the Chemical Industry," Macmillan and Co., Ltd., London, 1950.
   2. Bird, R. B., W. E. Stewart, and E. N. Lightfoot: "Transport Phenomena," John Wiley & Sons, Inc., New York, 1960.
   3. Chapman, S., and T. G. Cowling: "Mathematical Theory of Non-uniform Gases," Cambridge University Press, London, 1939.
   4. Gilliland, E. R.: *Ind. Eng. Chem.*, **26**, 681 (1934).
   5. Harned, H. S., and B. B. Owen: "The Physical Chemistry of Electrolytic Solutions," 3d ed., Reinhold Publishing Corporation, New York, 1958.
   6. Hirschfelder, J. O., R. B. Bird, and E. L. Spotz: *Trans. ASME*, **71**, 921 (1949); *Chem. Rev.*, **44**, 205 (1949).
   7. Hirschfelder, J. O., C. F. Curtis, and R. B. Bird: "Molecular Theory of Gases and Liquids," John Wiley & Sons, Inc., New York, 1954.
   8. "International Critical Tables," vol. V, McGraw-Hill Book Co., New York, 1929.
   9. Johnson, P. A., and A. L. Babb: *Chem. Rev.*, **56**, 387 (1956).
   10. Perry, R. H., C. H. Chilton, and S. D. Kirkpatrick (eds.): "The Chemical Engineers' Handbook," 4th ed., pp. 14-22—14-26, McGraw-Hill Book Co., New York, 1963.
   11. Reid, R. C., and T. K. Sherwood: "The Properties of Gases and Liquids," 2d ed., McGraw-Hill Book Co., New York, 1966.
   12. Scheibel, E. G.: *Ind. Eng. Chem.*, **46**, 2007 (1954).
   13. Stuel, L. I., and G. Thodos: *AIChE J.*, **10**, 266 (1964).
   14. Wilke, C. R.: *Chem. Eng. Progr.*, **45**, 218 (1949).
   15. Wilke, C. R., and P. Chang: *AIChE J.*, **1**, 264 (1955).
   16. Wilke, C. R., and C. Y. Lee: *Ind. Eng. Chem.*, **47**, 1253 (1955).
   17. Wintergeist, E.: *Ann. Physik.*, **4**, 323 (1930).

PROBLEMS

2.1. In an oxygen-nitrogen gas mixture at 1 atm, 25°C, the concentrations of oxygen at two planes 0.2 cm apart are 10 and 20 vol%, respectively. Calculate the rate of diffusion of the oxygen, expressed as g moles oxygen/(sq cm)(sec) for the case where:

   a. The nitrogen is nondiffusing.
   b. There is equimolar counterdiffusion of the two gases.

2.2. Repeat the calculations of Prob. 2.1 for a total pressure of 10 atm.

2.3. Estimate the diffusivities of the following gas mixtures:
a. Acetone–air, 1 atm, 0°C.
b. Nitrogen–carbon dioxide, 1 atm, 25°C.
c. Hydrogen chloride–air, 2 atm, 25°C.
d. Toluene–air, 1 atm, 25°C. **Ans.:** 0.0817 sq cm/sec.
e. Hydrogen–methane, 1 atm, 25°C.

2.4. Ammonia is diffusing through a stagnant gas mixture consisting of one-third nitrogen and two-thirds hydrogen by volume. The total pressure is 30 psia, and the temperature 130°F. Calculate the rate of diffusion of the ammonia, as lb/(hr)(sq ft), through a film of gas 0.5 mm thick when the concentration change across the film is 10 to 5% ammonia by volume.

2.5. Estimate the following liquid diffusivities:
a. Ethyl alcohol in dilute water solution, 10°C.
b. Carbon tetrachloride in dilute solution in methyl alcohol, 15°C [obsvd value = $1.69(10^{-5})$ sq cm/sec]. **Ans.:** $1.50(10^{-5})$ sq cm/sec.
c. Self-diffusion in water, 25°C.

2.6. Calculate the rate of diffusion of NaCl at 18°C through a stagnant film of water 0.1 cm thick when the concentrations are 20 and 10%, respectively, on either side of the film.

2.7. At 14.7 psia and 212°F, the density of air is 0.0592 lb/cu ft, the viscosity 0.0218 centipoise, the thermal conductivity 0.0183 (Btu)(ft)/(hr)(sq ft)(°F), and the specific heat at constant pressure 0.250 Btu/(lb)(°F). At 77°F, the viscosity is 0.0179 centipoise.
a. Calculate the kinematic viscosity at 212°F, sq ft/hr.
b. Calculate the thermal diffusivity at 212°F, sq ft/hr.
c. Calculate the Prandtl number at 212°F.
d. Assuming that for air at 1 atm Pr = Sc and that Sc is constant with changing temperature, calculate D for air at 77°F, sq ft/hr. Compare with the value of D for the system O_2–N_2, at 1 atm, 77°F, from the data of Table 2.1.

2.8. Ammonia is being cracked on a solid catalyst according to the reaction

$$2NH_3 \rightarrow N_2 + 3H_2$$

At one place in the apparatus, where the pressure is 1 atm abs and the temperature 200°C, the analysis of the bulk gas is 33.33% NH_3 (*A*), 16.67% N_2 (*B*), and 50.00% H_2 (*C*) by volume. The circumstances are such that NH_3 diffuses from the bulk-gas stream to the catalyst surface, and the products of of the reaction diffuse back, as if by molecular diffusion through a gas film in laminar flow 0.1 cm thick. Estimate the maximum local rate of cracking, lb NH_3/(hr) (sq ft catalyst surface), which might be considered to occur if the reaction is diffusion-rate controlled (chemical reaction rate very rapid) with the concentration of NH_3 at the catalyst surface equal to zero. **Ans.:** 9.43 lb/(hr)(sq ft).

2.9. A crystal of copper sulfate $CuSO_4 \cdot 5H_2O$ falls through a large tank of pure water at 20°C. Estimate the rate at which the crystal dissolves, lb/(hr)(sq ft crystal surface).
Data and assumptions. Molecular diffusion occurs through a film of water uniformly $1(10^{-4})$ ft thick, surrounding the crystal. At the inner side of the film, adjacent to the crystal surface, the concentration of copper sulfate is its solubility value, 0.0229 mole fraction $CuSO_4$ (solution density = 74.5 lb/cu ft). The outer surface of the film is pure water. The diffusivity of $CuSO_4$ is $2.82(10^{-5})$ sq ft/hr.

CHAPTER THREE
MASS-TRANSFER
COEFFICIENTS

We have seen that when a fluid flows past a surface under conditions such that turbulence generally prevails, there is a thin film of fluid in laminar flow immediately adjacent to the surface. This is followed by a transition, or buffer, zone where the flow gradually changes to the turbulent condition existing in the outer regions of the fluid. We have noted also that the rate of transfer of dissolved substance through the three regions will necessarily depend upon the nature of the fluid motion prevailing in each region.

In the turbulent region, particles of fluid no longer flow in the orderly manner found in the laminar film. Instead, relatively large portions of the fluid, called eddies, move rapidly from one position to the other with an appreciable component of their velocity in the direction perpendicular to the surface past which the fluid is flowing. These eddies bring with them dissolved material, and the eddy motion thus contributes considerably to the mass-transfer process. Since the eddy motion is rapid, mass transfer in the turbulent region is also rapid, much more so than that resulting from molecular diffusion in the laminar film. Because of the rapid eddy motion, the concentration gradients existing in the turbulent region will be smaller than those in the film, and Fig. 3.1 shows concentration gradients of this sort. In the experiment

Fig. 3.1 *Evaporation of water into air.*[37]

for which these are the data, air in turbulent motion flowed past a water surface, and water evaporated into the air.   Samples of the air were taken at various distances from the surface, and the water-vapor concentration was determined by analysis. At the water surface, the water concentration in the gas was the same as the vapor pressure of pure water at the prevailing temperature.   It was not possible to sample the gas very close to the water surface, but the rapid change in concentration in the laminar film, and the slower change in the outer turbulent region, are nevertheless unmistakable.   It is important also to note the general similarity of data of this sort to the velocity distribution shown in Fig. 2.6.

It is also useful to compare the data for mass transfer with similar data for heat transfer.   Thus, in Fig. 3.2 are plotted the temperatures at various distances from the surface when air flowed past a heated plate.   The large temperature gradient in the laminar film and the lesser gradient in the turbulent region are again evident.   It will generally be convenient to keep the corresponding heat-transfer process in mind when the mass-transfer process is discussed, since in many instances the methods of reasoning used to describe the latter are borrowed directly from those found to be successful with the former.

Mass-transfer coefficients

The mechanism of the flow process involving the movements of the eddies in the turbulent region is not thoroughly understood.   On the other hand, the mechanism of molecular diffusion, at least for gases, is fairly well known, since it can be described in terms of a kinetic theory to give results which agree well with experience.   It is natural therefore to attempt to describe the rate of mass transfer through a combination of laminar film and turbulent zone, including the intervening buffer zone, in the same manner found useful for laminar flow.   Thus, the $D_{AB}c/z$ of Eq. (2.22), which is

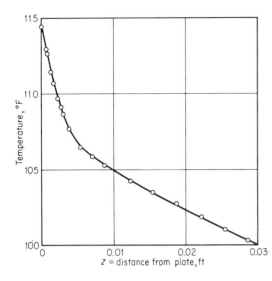

Fig. 3.2   *Heat transfer, flow of air past a heated plate.*[25]

characteristic of molecular diffusion, is replaced by F, a mass-transfer coefficient.[1,6] For binary solutions,

$$N_A = \frac{N_A}{N_A + N_B} F \ln \frac{N_A/(N_A + N_B) - c_{A2}/c}{N_A/(N_A + N_B) - c_{A1}/c} \tag{3.1}$$

where c_A/c is the mole-fraction concentration, x_A for liquids, y_A for gases. As in the case of molecular diffusion, the ratio $N_A/(N_A + N_B)$ is ordinarily established by nondiffusional considerations.

.Since the surface through which the transfer takes place may not be plane, so that the diffusion path in the fluid may be of variable cross section, N is defined as the *flux at the phase interface*, or *boundary*, where substance leaves or enters the phase for which F is the mass-transfer coefficient. N_A is positive when c_{A1} is at the beginning of the transfer path and c_{A2} at the end. In any case, one of these concentrations will be at the phase boundary. The manner of defining the concentration of A in the fluid will influence the value of F, and this is usually established arbitrarily. If mass transfer takes place between a phase boundary and a large quantity of unconfined fluid, as, for example, when a drop of water evaporates while falling through a great volume of air, the concentration of diffusing substance in the fluid is usually taken as the constant value found at large distances from the phase boundary. If the fluid is in a confining duct, so that the concentration is not constant along any position of the transfer path, the bulk-average concentration $\bar{c}_A$, as found by mixing all the fluid passing a given point, is usually used. In Fig. 3.3, where a liquid evaporates into the flowing gas, the concentration c_A of the vapor in the gas varies continuously from c_{A1} at the liquid surface to the value at $z = Z$. In this case c_{A2} in Eq. (3.1) would usually be taken as $\bar{c}_A$, defined by

$$\bar{c}_A = \frac{1}{\bar{u}_y S} \int_0^S u_y c_A \, dS \tag{3.2}$$

where $u_y(z)$ is the velocity distribution in the gas across the duct (the time average of u_y in the case of turbulence), $\bar{u}_y$ is the bulk-average velocity (volumetric rate/duct cross section), and S is the duct cross-sectional area. In any case, one must know how the mass-transfer coefficient is defined in order to use it properly.

The F of Eq. (3.1) is a *local* mass-transfer coefficient, defined for a particular location on the phase-boundary surface. Since the value of F depends on the local nature of the fluid motion, which may vary along the surface, an average value F_{av} is sometimes used in Eq. (3.1) with constant c_{A1} and c_{A2}, which takes into account these variations in F. The effect of variation in c_{A1} and c_{A2} on the flux must be accounted for separately.

Equation (3.1) is adapted to multicomponent systems by replacing $N_A + N_B$ by $\sum_{i=1}^{n} N_i$, where n is the number of components.

The two situations noted in Chap. 2, equimolar counterdiffusion and transfer of one substance through another which is not transferred, occur so frequently that special mass-transfer coefficients are usually used for them. These are defined by equations of the form

$$\text{Flux} = \text{coefficient (concentration difference)}$$

Since concentration may be defined in a number of ways and standards have not been established, we have a variety of coefficients for each situation:

Transfer of A through Nontransferring B $[N_B = 0, N_A/(N_A + N_B) = 1]$

Gases: $\qquad N_A = k_G(p_{A1} - p_{A2}) = k_y(y_{A1} - y_{A2}) = k_c(c_{A1} - c_{A2})$ $\qquad$ (3.3)

Liquids: $\qquad N_A = k_x(x_{A1} - x_{A2}) = k_L(c_{A1} - c_{A2})$ $\qquad$ (3.4)

Equimolar Countertransfer $[N_A = -N_B, N_A/(N_A + N_B) = \infty]$

Gases: $\qquad N_A = k'_G(p_{A1} - p_{A2}) = k'_y(y_{A1} - y_{A2}) = k'_c(c_{A1} - c_{A2})$ $\qquad$ (3.5)

Liquids: $\qquad N_A = k'_x(x_{A1} - x_{A2}) = k'_L(c_{A1} - c_{A2})$ $\qquad$ (3.6)

These are, of course, analogous to the definition of a heat-transfer coefficient h: $q = h(t_1 - t_2)$. Whereas the concept of the heat-transfer coefficient is generally applicable, at least in the absence of mass transfer, the coefficients of Eqs. (3.3) and

Fig. 3.3 *Mass transfer to a confined fluid.*

(3.4) are more restricted. Thus, k_c of Eq. (3.3) can be considered as a replacement of D_{AB}/z in an integration of Eq. (2.1), and the bulk-flow term of Eq. (2.4) has been ignored in equating this to N_A. The coefficients of Eqs. (3.3) and (3.4) are therefore generally useful only for low mass-transfer rates. Values measured under one level of transfer rate should be converted to F for use with Eq. (3.1) before being applied to another. To obtain the relation between F and the k's, note that for gases, for example, F replaces $D_{AB}P_t/RTz$ in Eq. (2.25) and that k_G replaces $D_{AB}P_t/RTzp_{BM}$ in Eq. (2.30). From this it follows that $F = k_G p_{BM}$. In this manner the conversions of Table 3.1 have been obtained. Since the bulk-flow term $N_A + N_B$ of Eq. (2.4) is zero for equimolal countertransfer, $F = k'_y$ (gases) and $F = k'_x$ (liquids), and Eqs. (3.5) and (3.6) are identical with Eq. (3.1) for this case.

Table 3.1 Relations among mass-transfer coefficients

Rate equation		Units of coefficient
Equimolal counterdiffusion	Diffusion of A through nondiffusing B	
Gases		$\dfrac{\text{Moles transferred}}{\text{Time(area)(pressure)}}$
$N_A = k'_G \, \Delta p_A$	$N_A = k_G \, \Delta p_A$	
$N_A = k'_y \, \Delta y_A$	$N_A = k_y \, \Delta y_A$	$\dfrac{\text{Moles transferred}}{\text{Time(area)(mole fraction)}}$
$N_A = k'_c \, \Delta c_A$	$N_A = k_c \, \Delta c_A$	$\dfrac{\text{Moles transferred}}{\text{Time(area)(moles/vol)}}$
	$W_A = k_Y \, \Delta Y_A$	$\dfrac{\text{Mass transferred}}{\text{Time(area)(mass }A\text{/mass }B)}$

Conversions

$$F = k_G p_{BM} = k_y \frac{p_{BM}}{P_t} = k_c \frac{p_{BM}}{RT} = \frac{k_Y}{M_B} = k'_G P_t = k'_y = k'_c \frac{P_t}{RT} = k'_c c$$

Liquids		$\dfrac{\text{Moles transferred}}{\text{Time(area)(moles/vol)}}$
$N_A = k'_L \, \Delta c_A$	$N_A = k_L \, \Delta c_A$	
$N_A = k'_x \, \Delta x_A$	$N_A = k_x \, \Delta x_A$	$\dfrac{\text{Moles transferred}}{\text{Time(area)(mole fraction)}}$

Conversions

$$F = k_x x_{BM} = k_L x_{BM} c = k'_L c = k'_L \frac{\rho}{M} = k'_x$$

Many data on mass transfer where $N_A/(N_A + N_B)$ is neither unity nor infinity have nevertheless been described in terms of the k-type coefficients. Before these can be used for other situations, they must be converted to F's.

Mass-transfer coefficients can, in a few limited situations, be deduced from theoretical principles. In the great majority of cases, however, we depend upon direct measurement under known conditions, for use later in design.

MASS-TRANSFER COEFFICIENTS IN LAMINAR FLOW

In principle, at least, we do not need mass-transfer coefficients for laminar flow, since molecular diffusion prevails, and the relationships of Chap. 2 can be used to compute mass-transfer rates. A uniform method of dealing with both laminar and turbulent flow is nevertheless desirable.

Mass-transfer coefficients for laminar flow should be capable of computation. To the extent that the flow conditions are capable of description and the mathematics remains tractable, this is so. These are, however, severe requirements, and frequently the simplification required to permit mathematical manipulation is such that the results fall somewhat short of reality. It is not our purpose to develop these methods in detail, since they are dealt with extensively elsewhere.[2,3] We shall choose one relatively simple situation to illustrate the general technique and to provide some basis for considering turbulent flow.

Mass transfer from a gas into a falling liquid film

Figure 3.4 shows a liquid falling in a thin film in laminar flow down a vertical flat surface while being exposed to a gas A, which dissolves in the liquid. The liquid contains a uniform concentration of A, c_{A0}, at the top. At the liquid surface, the concentration of the dissolved gas is c_{Ai}, in equilibrium with the pressure of A in the gas phase. Since $c_{Ai} > c_{A0}$, gas dissolves in the liquid. The problem is

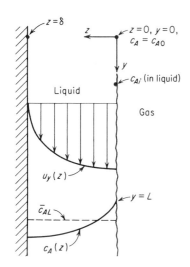

Fig. 3.4 *Falling liquid film.*

to obtain the mass-transfer coefficient k_L, with which the amount of gas dissolved after the liquid falls the distance L can be computed.

The problem is solved by simultaneous solution of the equation of continuity for component A, Eq. (2.17), with the equations describing the liquid motion, the Navier-Stokes equations. The simultaneous solution of this formidable set of partial differential equations becomes possible only when several simplifying assumptions are made. For present purposes, assume the following:

1. There is no chemical reaction. R_A of Eq. (2.17) $= 0$.
2. Conditions do not change in the x direction (perpendicular to the plane of the paper, Fig. 3.4). All derivatives with respect to x of Eq. (2.17) $= 0$.
3. Steady-state conditions prevail. $\partial c_A/\partial\theta = 0$.
4. The rate of absorption of gas is very small. This means that u_z in Eq. (2.17) due to diffusion of A is essentially zero.
5. Diffusion of A in the y direction is negligible in comparison with the movement of A downward due to bulk flow. Therefore, $D_{AB}\,\partial^2 c_A/\partial y^2 = 0$.
6. Physical properties (D_{AB}, ρ, μ) are constant.

Equation (2.17) then reduces to

$$u_y \frac{\partial c_A}{\partial y} = D_{AB}\frac{\partial^2 c_A}{\partial z^2} \tag{3.7}$$

which states that any A added to the liquid running down at any location z, over an increment in y, got there by diffusion in the z direction. The equations of motion under these conditions reduce to

$$\mu\frac{d^2 u_y}{dz^2} + \rho g = 0 \tag{3.8}$$

The solution to Eq. (3.8), with the conditions that $u_y = 0$ at $z = \delta$ and that $du_y/dz = 0$ at $z = 0$, is well known

$$u_y = \frac{\rho g \delta^2}{2\mu}\left[1 - \left(\frac{z}{\delta}\right)^2\right] = \frac{3}{2}\bar{u}_y\left[1 - \left(\frac{z}{\delta}\right)^2\right] \tag{3.9}$$

where $\bar{u}_y$ is the bulk-average velocity. The film thickness is then

$$\delta = \left(\frac{3\bar{u}_y\mu}{\rho g}\right)^{1/2} = \left(\frac{3\mu\Gamma}{\rho^2 g}\right)^{1/3} \tag{3.10}$$

where Γ is the mass rate of liquid flow per unit of film width in the x direction. Substituting Eq. (3.9) into (3.7),

$$\frac{3}{2}\bar{u}_y\left[1 - \left(\frac{z}{\delta}\right)^2\right]\frac{\partial c_A}{\partial y} = D_{AB}\frac{\partial^2 c_A}{\partial z^2} \tag{3.11}$$

which is to be solved under the following conditions:

1. At $z = 0$, $c_A = c_{Ai}$ at all values of y.
2. At $z = \delta$, $\partial c_A/\partial z = 0$ at all values of y, since no diffusion takes place into the solid wall.
3. At $y = 0$, $c_A = c_{A0}$ at all values of z.

The solution results in a general expression (an infinite series) giving c_A for any z and y, thus providing a concentration distribution $c_A(z)$ at $y = L$, as shown in Fig. 3.4. The bulk-average $\bar{c}_{AL}$ at $y = L$ can then be found in the manner of Eq. (3.2). The result is[17]

$$\frac{c_{Ai} - \bar{c}_{AL}}{c_{Ai} - c_{A0}} = 0.7857e^{-5.1213\eta} + 0.1001e^{-39.318\eta} + 0.03599e^{-105.64\eta} + \cdots \tag{3.12}$$

where $\eta = 2D_{AB}L/3\delta^2\bar{u}_y$. The total rate of absorption is then $\bar{u}_y\delta(\bar{c}_{AL} - c_{A0})$ per unit width of liquid film.

Alternatively, to obtain a local mass-transfer coefficient, we can combine Eq. (2.4) for the case of negligible bulk flow in the z direction ($N_A + N_B = 0$) with Eq. (3.4), keeping in mind that mass-transfer coefficients use fluxes at the phase interface ($z = 0$)

$$N_A = -D_{AB}\left(\frac{\partial c_A}{\partial z}\right)_{z=0} = k_L(c_{Ai} - \bar{c}_{AL}) \tag{3.13}$$

In this case, however, because of the nature of the series which describes c_A, the derivative is undefined at $z = 0$. It is better therefore to proceed with an average coefficient for the entire liquid-gas surface. The rate at which A is carried by the liquid at any y, per unit width in the x direction, is $\bar{u}_y\delta\bar{c}_A$ moles/time. Over a distance dy, per unit width, therefore, the rate of solute absorption is, in moles/time,

$$\bar{u}_y\delta\, d\bar{c}_A = k_L(c_{Ai} - \bar{c}_A)\, dy \tag{3.14}$$

$$\bar{u}_y\delta \int_{\bar{c}_A=c_{A0}}^{\bar{c}_A=\bar{c}_{AL}} \frac{d\bar{c}_A}{c_{Ai} - \bar{c}_A} = \int_0^L k_L\, dy = k_{L,\mathrm{av}}\int_0^L dy \tag{3.15}$$

$$k_{L,\mathrm{av}} = \frac{\bar{u}_y\delta}{L}\ln\frac{c_{Ai} - c_{A0}}{c_{Ai} - \bar{c}_{AL}} \tag{3.16}$$

which defines the average coefficient. Now for small rates of flow or long times of contact of the liquid with the gas (usually for film Reynolds numbers Re $= 4\Gamma/\mu$ less than 100), only the first term of the series of Eq. (3.12) need be used. Substituting in Eq. (3.16),

$$k_{L,\mathrm{av}} = \frac{\bar{u}_y\delta}{L}\ln\frac{e^{5.1213\eta}}{0.7857} = \frac{\bar{u}_y\delta}{L}(0.241 + 5.1213\eta) \doteq 3.41\frac{D_{AB}}{\delta} \tag{3.17}$$

$$\frac{k_{L,\mathrm{av}}\delta}{D_{AB}} = \mathrm{Sh}_{\mathrm{av}} \doteq 3.41 \tag{3.18}$$

where Sh represents the Sherwood number, the mass-transfer analog to the Nusselt number of heat transfer. A similar development for large Reynolds numbers or short contact time[31] leads to

$$k_{L,\mathrm{av}} = \left(\frac{6D_{AB}\Gamma}{\pi\rho\delta L}\right)^{1/2} \tag{3.19}$$

$$\mathrm{Sh}_{\mathrm{av}} = \left(\frac{3}{2\pi}\frac{\delta}{L}\,\mathrm{Re\ Sc}\right)^{1/2} \tag{3.20}$$

The product Re Sc is the Péclet number Pe.

These average k_L's may be used to compute the total absorption rate. Thus the average flux $N_{A,\mathrm{av}}$ for the entire gas-liquid surface, per unit width, is the difference in rate of flow of A in the liquid at $y = L$ and at $y = 0$, divided by the liquid surface. This may be used with some mean concentration difference

$$N_{A,\mathrm{av}} = \frac{\bar{u}_y\delta}{L}(\bar{c}_{AL} - c_{A0}) = k_{L,\mathrm{av}}(c_{Ai} - \bar{c}_A)_M \tag{3.21}$$

Substitution for $k_{L,\mathrm{av}}$ from Eq. (3.16) shows that the logarithmic average of the difference at the top and bottom of the film is required

$$(c_{Ai} - \bar{c}_A)_M = \frac{(c_{Ai} - c_{A0}) - (c_{Ai} - \bar{c}_{AL})}{\ln\left[(c_{Ai} - c_{A0})/(c_{Ai} - \bar{c}_{AL})\right]} \tag{3.22}$$

The experimental data[31] show that the $k_{L,av}$ realized may be as much as twice as large as the above theoretical values at high film Reynolds numbers, even for low mass-transfer rates, owing to ripples and waves formed in the liquid surface which were not considered in the mathematical analysis. Rapid absorption, as for very soluble gases, produces important values of u_z, and this will cause further discrepancies, owing to alteration of the velocity profile in the film. The velocity profile may also be altered by flow of the gas, so that even in the simplest case, when both fluids move, k_L should depend on both flow rates.

Illustration 3.1. Estimate the rate of absorption of carbon dioxide into a water film flowing down a vertical wall 2 ft long at the rate of 150 lb/hr per ft of width, at 25°C. The gas is pure CO_2 at 1 atm. The water is initially CO_2-free.

Solution. The solubility of CO_2 in water at 25°C, 1 atm, is $c_{Ai} = 0.0021$ lb mole/cu ft soln; $D_{AB} = 7.59(10^{-5})$ sq ft/hr; soln density $\rho = 62.3$ lb/cu ft; and viscosity $\mu = 0.894$ centipoise $= 2.16$ lb/(ft)(hr). $\Gamma = 150$ lb/(hr)(ft), $L = 2$ ft.

$$\delta = \left(\frac{3\mu\Gamma}{\rho^2 g}\right)^{1/3} = \left[\frac{3(2.16)150}{(62.3)^2(4.17)(10^8)}\right]^{1/3} = 0.000843 \text{ ft}$$

$$\text{Re} = \frac{4\Gamma}{\mu} = \frac{4(150)}{2.16} = 278$$

Consequently Eq. (3.19) should apply.

$$k_{L,av} = \left(\frac{6D_{AB}\Gamma}{\pi\rho\delta L}\right)^{1/2} = \left[\frac{6(7.59)(10^{-5})(150)}{\pi(62.3)(0.000843)(2)}\right]^{1/2}$$

$$= 0.455 \frac{\text{lb mole}}{\text{hr(sq ft)(lb mole/cu ft)}}$$

$$\bar{u}_y = \frac{\Gamma}{\rho\delta} = \frac{150}{62.3(0.000843)} = 2,850 \text{ ft/hr}$$

At the top, $c_{Ai} - \bar{c}_A = c_{Ai} - c_{A0} = c_{Ai} = 0.0021$ lb mole/cu ft.
At the bottom, $c_{Ai} - \bar{c}_{AL} = 0.0021 - \bar{c}_{AL}$ lb mole/cu ft.
The flux of absorption is given by Eqs. (3.21) and (3.22)

$$\frac{2,850(0.000843)\bar{c}_{AL}}{2} = \frac{0.455[0.0021 - (0.0021 - \bar{c}_{AL})]}{\ln [0.0021/(0.0021 - \bar{c}_{AL})]}$$

$$\therefore \quad \bar{c}_{AL} = 0.00066 \text{ lb mole/cu ft}$$

The rate of absorption is therefore estimated to be

$$\bar{u}_y\delta(\bar{c}_{AL} - c_{A0}) = 2,850(0.000843)(0.00066 - 0) = 0.001585 \text{ lb mole/(hr)(ft width)}$$

The actual value may be substantially larger.

MASS-TRANSFER COEFFICIENTS IN TURBULENT FLOW

Most practically useful situations involve turbulent flow, and for these it is generally not possible to compute mass-transfer coefficients owing to inability to describe the flow conditions mathematically. Instead, we rely principally on experimental data. The data are, however, limited in scope, with respect to circumstances and situations as well as to range of fluid properties. Therefore it is important to be able to extend their applicability to situations not covered experimentally and to draw upon knowledge of other transfer processes (of heat, particularly) for help.

To this end, there are many theories which attempt to interpret or explain the behavior of mass-transfer coefficients, such as the film, penetration, surface-renewal, and other theories. They are all speculations, and are continually being revised. It is helpful to keep in mind that transfer coefficients, for both heat and mass transfer, are expedients used to deal with situations which are not fully understood. They include in one quantity effects which are the result of both molecular and turbulent diffusion. The relative contribution of these effects, and indeed the detailed character of the turbulent diffusion itself, differs from one situation to another. The ultimate interpretation or explanation of the transfer coefficients will come only when the problems of the fluid mechanics are solved, at which time it will be possible to abandon the concept of the transfer coefficient.

Eddy diffusion

It will be useful first to describe briefly an elementary view of fluid turbulence, as a means of introducing the definitions of terms used in describing transfer under turbulent conditions. Turbulence is characterized by motion of the fluid particles which is irregular with respect both to direction and time. Thus, for a fluid flowing turbulently in a duct (Fig. 3.5), the flow is, in the net, in the axial (or x) direction. At any location 2 within the central region of the cross section, the time average of the velocity may be u_x, but at any instant the velocity will actually be $u_x + u'_{ix}$, where u'_{ix} is the *deviating* or *fluctuating* velocity. Values of u'_{ix} will vary with time through a range of positive and negative values, the time average being zero, although u'_x, the square root of the time average of $(u'_{ix})^2$, will be finite. Although the time-average value of $u_z = 0$, since the net flow is axially directed, the deviating velocity in the z direction will be u'_{iz} at any instant.

In Fig. 3.5, consider a second location 1, where the x velocity is larger than at 2 by an amount $\Delta u_x = -l\, du_x/dz$. The distance l, the *Prandtl mixing length*, is defined such that $u'_x = \Delta u_x = -l\, du_x/dz$. Owing to the z-directed fluctuating velocity, a particle of fluid, an eddy, may move from 2 to 1 at a velocity u'_{iz}, but it will be replaced by an eddy of equal volume moving from 1 to 2. It is imagined, in the Prandtl theory, that the eddies retain their identity during the interchange but

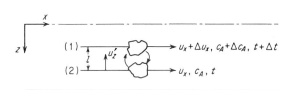

Fig. 3.5 *Eddy diffusion.*

blend into the fluid at their new locations.   This is recognized as a great oversimplification, since an eddy must likely lose at least part of its identity as soon as it moves from its original location even an infinitesimal distance (G. I. Taylor theory[16]).

The mass velocity of eddy interchange is then $\rho u'_{iz}$, and owing to the different velocities at 1 and 2, there will be a momentum transfer flux $\rho u'_{iz} u'_{ix}$.   If u'_{iz} and u'_{ix} are essentially equal, there results an average shear stress due to the turbulent eddy interchange,

$$\tau_{\text{turb}} g_c = \rho \, |u'_{iz} u'_{ix}| = \rho u'_z u'_x = \rho (u'_x)^2 = \rho l^2 \left(\frac{du_x}{dz}\right)^2 \tag{3.23}$$

Molecular motion, of course, still also contributes to the shear stress, as given by Eq. (2.45), so that the *total* shear stress becomes

$$\tau g_c = -\mu \frac{du_x}{dz} + \rho l^2 \left(\frac{du_x}{dz}\right)^2 = -\left[\mu + \rho l^2\left(-\frac{du_x}{dz}\right)\right]\frac{du_x}{dz} = -\left(\frac{\mu}{\rho} + E_v\right)\frac{d(u_x \rho)}{dz} \tag{3.24}$$

E_v is the eddy momentum diffusivity, length²/time.   While μ or $\nu = \mu/\rho$ is a constant for a given fluid at fixed temperature and pressure, E_v will depend on the local degree of turbulence.   In the various regions of the duct, ν predominates near the wall, while in the turbulent core E_v predominates, to an extent depending upon the degree of turbulence.

The eddies bring about a transfer of dissolved solute, as we have mentioned before.   The average concentration gradient between 1 and 2 in Fig. 3.5 is $\Delta c_A/l$, proportional to a local gradient, $-dc_A/dz$.   The flux of A due to the interchange, $u'_z \Delta c_A$, and the concentration gradient may be used to define an eddy diffusivity of mass E_D, length²/time

$$E_D = \frac{b_1 u'_z \Delta c_A}{\Delta c_A/l} = \frac{J_{A,\text{turb}}}{-dc_A/dz} \tag{3.25}$$

where b_1 is a proportionality constant.   The *total* flux of A, due both to molecular and eddy diffusion, then will be

$$J_A = -(D_{AB} + E_D)\frac{dc_A}{dz} \tag{3.26}$$

As in the case of momentum transfer, D is a constant for a particular solution at fixed conditions of temperature and pressure, while E_D depends on the local turbulence intensity. D predominates in the region near the wall, E_D in the turbulent core.

In similar fashion, an eddy thermal diffusivity E_H, length²/time, can be used to describe the flux of heat as a result of a temperature gradient,

$$E_H = \frac{b_2 u'_z \Delta(\rho C_p t)}{\Delta(\rho C_p t)/l} = \frac{q_{\text{turb}}}{-d(\rho C_p t)/dz} \tag{3.27}$$

where b_2 is a proportionality constant.   The *total* heat flux due to conduction and eddy motion is

$$q = -(k + E_H \rho C_p)\frac{dt}{dz} = -(\alpha + E_H)\frac{d(t\rho C_p)}{dz} \tag{3.28}$$

As before, α for a given fluid is fixed for fixed conditions of temperature and pressure, but E_H varies with the degree of turbulence and hence with location.

The three eddy diffusivities of momentum, heat, and mass are then each proportional to $u'_z l$. They may be computed from measured velocity, temperature, and concentration gradients, respectively, in that order of increasing difficulty of measurement. The data, very meager, indicate that the proportionality constants are not all the same. For ordinary fluids flowing in a pipe, E_D/E_v and E_H/E_v may be in the range 1.2 to 1.8, varying with position, while for liquid metals (high k, low Pr), E_H/E_v is much less than unity because of heat leak from the metal eddies as they move from place to place.[24,32] Within the limitations of the data, except for liquid metals, it appears that E_D is, for a given situation, essentially the same as E_H.

Just as for laminar flow or for stagnant fluids, the ratios of the diffusivities are significant. Thus, we may speak of a molecular Schmidt number $\mathrm{Sc} = v/D_{AB}$, a turbulent Schmidt number E_v/E_D, and a total Schmidt number $(v + E_v)/(D_{AB} + E_D)$. Similarly, the ratios of total to molecular diffusivity,

$$\frac{v + E_v}{v} = 1 + \frac{E_v}{v} \tag{3.29}$$

$$\frac{\alpha + E_H}{\alpha} = 1 + \mathrm{Pr}\,\frac{E_H}{v} \tag{3.30}$$

$$\frac{D + E_D}{D} = 1 + \mathrm{Sc}\,\frac{E_D}{v} \tag{3.31}$$

are significant in that they indicate the relative importance of turbulence and laminar flow. Assuming that the eddy diffusivities are about the same, then a small amount of turbulence. as near a solid surface $(E_v/v \ll 1)$, will not influence the ratio of Eq. (3.29) and therefore the velocity distribution very greatly. If Pr and Sc both equal unity, the influence on the heat and mass transfer will also be small. But for large Pr and Sc, the influence will be profound, and the relative influence on heat and mass transfer will clearly depend upon the relative size of Pr and Sc. Only for fluids whose $\mathrm{Pr} = \mathrm{Sc}$ will the percentage change in heat- and mass-transfer flux be the same for a given change in the degree of turbulence, and only for $\mathrm{Pr} = \mathrm{Sc} = 1$ will all three total diffusivities be the same.

Mass-transfer coefficients covering the transfer of material from an interface to the turbulent zone will clearly depend upon the total diffusivity $D + E_D$. Success in estimating this theoretically in the manner used for laminar flow will depend on knowledge of how the ratio E_D/D varies throughout the diffusion path. Knowledge of how the ratio E_v/v varies will be of direct help only provided $E_D = E_v$, which is evidently not generally true. But knowledge of the heat-transfer coefficients, which depend upon E_H/v, should be useful in predicting the mass-transfer coefficient, since E_H and E_D are evidently essentially equal except for the liquid metals.

Film theory

This is the oldest[18] and most obvious picture of the meaning of the mass-transfer coefficients. When a fluid flows in turbulent flow past a solid surface, the fluid

Fig. 3.6   *Film theory.*

velocity being zero at the surface itself, there must be a viscous layer, or film, in the fluid adjacent to the surface.   Since the eddy diffusivity is not infinite in the turbulent region of the fluid, there is a concentration gradient for any diffusing solute between the surface and the fluid which extends into the turbulent core.   That part lying within the viscous layer is characteristic of molecular diffusion.   This is shown by the full curve of Fig. 3.6 for the case of a solute diffusing into the fluid.   The film theory imagines the concentration to follow the broken curve of the figure, such that the entire concentration difference, $c_{A1} - c_{A2}$, is described by molecular diffusion, and defines an "effective" film thickness z_F whose resistance to molecular diffusion is the same as the actual resistance to mass transfer in the true viscous layer, buffer region, and turbulent core combined.   It was early recognized[19] that if this picture were to be valid, the effective film would have to be very thin, so that the quantity of solute within the film would be small relative to the amount passing through it or that the concentration gradient would have to be set up quickly.   The concentration gradient in the film is that characteristic of steady state.

In Eq. (3.1), it is clear that F has merely replaced the group $D_{AB}c/z$ of Eq. (2.22). The film theory states that z of Eq. (2.21) is z_F, the effective film thickness, whose thickness depends upon the nature of the flow conditions.   Similarly, the z's of Eqs. (2.26), (2.30), (2.34), (2.40), (2.41), and (2.43) are interpreted to be z_F, incorporated into the k's of Eqs. (3.3) to (3.6).

The film theory predicts therefore that F and the k-type mass-transfer coefficients for different solutes being transferred under the same fluid-flow conditions are directly proportional to the D's for the solutes.   On the other hand, we observe for turbulent flow a much smaller dependency, proportional to D^n, where n may be anything from nearly zero to 0.8 or 0.9, depending upon the circumstances.   The simple film theory has therefore been largely discredited, except as a limiting case.   Nevertheless, mass-transfer coefficients are still frequently called "film" coefficients.

Penetration theory

Higbie[15] emphasized that in many situations the time of exposure of a fluid to mass transfer is short, so that the concentration gradient of the film theory, characteristic of steady state, would not have time to develop. His theory was actually conceived to describe the contact of two fluids, as in Fig. 3.7. Here, as Higbie depicted it in Fig. 3.7a, a bubble of gas rises through a liquid which absorbs the gas. A particle of the liquid b, initially at the top of the bubble, is in contact with the gas for the time θ required for the bubble to rise a distance equal to its diameter while the liquid particle slips along the surface of the bubble. An extension to cases where the liquid may be in turbulent motion, as in Fig. 3.7b,[7] shows an eddy b rising from the turbulent depths of the liquid and remaining exposed for a time θ to the action of the gas. In this theory the time of exposure is taken as constant for all such eddies or particles of liquid.

Initially, the concentration of dissolved gas in the eddy is uniformly c_{A0}, and internally the eddy is considered to be stagnant. When the eddy is exposed to the gas at the surface, the concentration in the liquid at the gas-liquid surface is c_{Ai}, which may be taken as the equilibrium solubility of the gas in the liquid. During the time θ, the liquid particle is subject to unsteady-state diffusion or penetration of solute in the z direction, and, as an approximation, Eq. (2.18) may be applied

$$\frac{\partial c_A}{\partial \theta} = D_{AB} \frac{\partial^2 c_A}{\partial z^2} \tag{3.32}$$

For short exposure times, and with slow diffusion in the liquid, the molecules of dissolving solute are never able to reach the depth z_b corresponding to the thickness of the eddy, so that from the solute point of view, z_b is essentially infinite. The conditions on Eq. (3.32) then are

$$c_A = \begin{cases} c_{A0} & \text{at } \theta = 0 \text{ for all } z \\ c_{Ai} & \text{at } z = 0 \text{ for } \theta > 0 \\ c_{A0} & \text{at } z = \infty \text{ for all } \theta \end{cases}$$

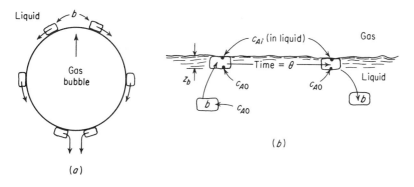

(a)

(b)

Fig. 3.7 *Penetration theory.*

and its solution is

$$c_A = c_{A0} + (c_{Ai} - c_{A0})\left(1 - \frac{2}{\pi}\int_0^{z/2(\theta D_{AB})^{0.5}} e^{-\eta^2}\,d\eta\right) \tag{3.33}$$

which gives the concentration profile $c_{\cdot A}(z)$ for any time. The flux at the surface at time θ, if absorption rates are small ($N_A + N_B \to 0$), is

$$N_{A,z=0} = -D_{AB}\left(\frac{\partial c_A}{\partial z}\right)_{z=0} = (c_{Ai} - c_{A0})\sqrt{\frac{D_{AB}}{\pi\theta}} \tag{3.34}$$

where the concentration gradient has been obtained by differentiating Eq. (3.33). The average flux over the time of exposure is then

$$N_{A,\text{av}} = \frac{\int_0^\theta (c_{Ai} - c_{A0})\sqrt{\dfrac{D_{AB}}{\pi\theta}}\,d\theta}{\theta - 0} = 2(c_{Ai} - c_{A0})\sqrt{\frac{D_{AB}}{\pi\theta}} \tag{3.35}$$

and comparison with Eq. (3.4) shows

$$k_{L,\text{av}} = 2\sqrt{\frac{D_{AB}}{\pi\theta}} \tag{3.36}$$

with $k_{L,\text{av}}$ proportional to $D_{AB}^{0.5}$ for different solutes under the same circumstances. This indicated dependence on D is typical of short exposure times, where the depth of solute penetration is small relative to the depth of the absorbing pool [compare Eq. (3.19)]. As pointed out above, experience shows a range of exponents on D from nearly zero to 0.8 or 0.9.

Surface-renewal theory

Danckwerts[7] pointed out that the Higbie theory with its constant time of exposure of the eddies of fluid at the surface is a special case of what may be a more realistic picture, where the eddies are exposed for varying lengths of time. The liquid-gas interface is then a mosaic of surface elements of different exposure-time histories, and since the rate of solute penetration depends on the exposure time, the average rate for unit surface area must be determined by summing up the individual values. If $\phi\,d\theta$ is the area of surface elements having residence times between θ and $\theta + d\theta$, then unit surface area becomes $1 = \int_0^\infty \phi\,d\theta$. On the assumption that the chance of a surface element's being replaced by another is quite independent of how long it has been in the surface, and if s is the fractional rate of replacement of elements belonging to any age group, Danckwerts finds $\phi = se^{-s\theta}$. Consequently, the mean rate of absorption per unit of surface is, using Eq. (3.35),

$$N_{A,\text{av}} = (c_{Ai} - c_{A0})\int_0^\infty \sqrt{\frac{D_{AB}}{\pi\theta}}\,se^{-s\theta}\,d\theta = (c_{Ai} - c_{A0})\sqrt{D_{AB}s} \tag{3.37}$$

and therefore

$$k_{L,av} = \sqrt{D_{AB}s} \qquad (3.38)$$

Danckwerts pointed out that all theories of this sort, derived with the original boundary conditions on Eq. (3.33), will lead to $k_{L,av}$ proportional to $D_{AB}^{0.5}$, regardless of the nature of the surface-renewal rate s which may apply.

Combination film–surface-renewal theory

Dobbins,[9] concerned with the rate of absorption of oxygen into flowing streams and rivers, pointed out that the film theory ($k_L \propto D_{AB}$) assumes a time of exposure of the surface elements sufficiently long for the concentration profile within the film to be characteristic of steady state, whereas the penetration and surface-renewal theories ($k_L \propto D_{AB}^{0.5}$) assume the surface elements to be of essentially infinite depth, the diffusing solute never reaching the region of constant concentration below. The observed dependency, $k_L \propto D_{AB}^n$ with n dependent upon circumstances, might be explained by allowing for a finite depth of the surface elements or eddies for a limited time.

Accordingly he replaced the third boundary condition on Eq. (3.32) by $c_A = c_{A0}$ for $z = z_b$, where z_b is finite. Higbie's requirement of constant exposure time then produced

$$k_{L,av} = \frac{D_{AB}}{z_b}\left(1 - \frac{z_b^2}{3D_{AB}\theta} - \frac{2z_b^2}{\pi^2 D_{AB}\theta}\sum_{n=1}^{\infty}\frac{1}{n^2}e^{-\pi^2 n^2 D_{AB}\theta/z_b^2}\right) \qquad (3.39)$$

which, as Fig. 3.8a shows, reduces to $k_{L,av} = D_{AB}/z_b$ for values of $D_{AB}\theta/z_b^2$ greater than about 0.6. In other words, for rapid penetration (D_{AB} large), long exposure time (θ large), or thin surface elements, a steady-state concentration gradient within the surface element is produced, and the penetration theory reverts to the film theory. Similarly, with Danckwerts' rate of renewal of the surface elements, he obtained

$$k_{L,av} = \sqrt{D_{AB}s}\,\coth\sqrt{\frac{sz_b^2}{D_{AB}}} \qquad (3.40)$$

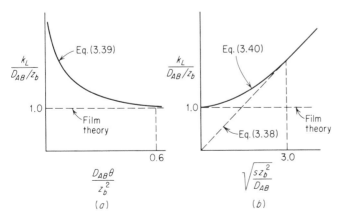

Fig. 3.8 *Film-surface renewal theory. (a) Constant exposure time. (b) Random replacement of surface elements. (After Dobbins.[9])*

which is shown in Fig. 3.8b. Here, as the rate of surface renewal becomes small (s approaches zero) or with large diffusivities, the mass-transfer coefficient takes on the character of the film theory, whereas for slow penetration (D_{AB} small) or rapid surface renewal (s large), it follows Eq. (3.38). Consequently $k_L \propto D_{AB}^n$, where n may have any value between the limits of 0.5 and 1.0, which will account for many observations. Toor and Marchello[36] have made similar suggestions.

By simulating the turbulences developed in a river, Dobbins[10] has absorbed gases into water and observed values of n in the range 0.985 to 0.65, smaller with increasing turbulence (larger s), and has measured both s and z_b by writing Eq. (3.40) with measured k_L's for gases of different diffusivities and solving simultaneously. The observations could not be accounted for by Eq. (3.39).

Flow past solids; boundary layers

In the case of the theories discussed above, where the interfacial surface is formed between two fluids, the velocity at that surface will not normally be zero. But when one of the phases is a solid, the fluid velocity parallel to the surface at the interface must of necessity be zero, and consequently the two circumstances are inherently different.

In Fig. 3.9 a fluid with uniform velocity u_0 and uniform solute concentration c_{A0} meets up with a flat solid surface AK. Since the velocity u_x is zero at the surface and rises to u_0 at some distance above the plate, the curve $ABCD$ separates the region of velocity u_0 from the region of lower velocity, called the boundary layer. The boundary layer may be characterized by laminar flow, as below the curve AB, but if the velocity u_0 is sufficiently large, for values of $\text{Re}_x = xu_0\rho/\mu$ in excess of about $5(10^5)$ the flow in the bulk of the boundary layer will be turbulent, as below the curve CD. Below the turbulent boundary layer there will be a thinner region, the viscous sublayer, extending from the plate to the curve FG. The equations of motion (Navier-Stokes equations) have been solved to provide the velocity distribution, u_x and u_z as functions

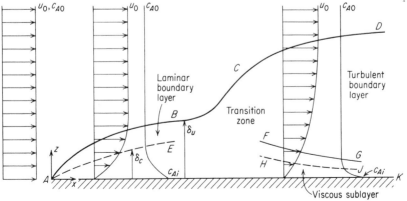

Fig. 3.9 *Boundary layers on a flat plate.*

of x and z, within the laminar boundary layer. For the turbulent region, exact solutions are not known for lack of complete knowledge of the turbulence, although approximations can be made. Boundary layers also occur for flow at the entrance to circular pipes, for flow along the outside of cylinders, and the like.

If mass transfer from the surface into the fluid occurs, as with a solid subliming into a gas or a solid dissolving into a liquid, the solute concentration in the fluid at the solid surface is everywhere c_{Ai}, greater than c_{A0}. There will be a curve AE, and also one HJ, which separates regions of uniform concentration c_{A0} from regions of higher values of c_A, corresponding to a concentration boundary layer. In the region where only a laminar velocity boundary layer exists, the equations of motion and of mass transfer can be solved simultaneously to yield the concentration profile and, from its slope at the surface, the laminar mass-transfer coefficient.[3] This is a fairly complex problem particularly if account is taken of the influence of the flux of mass of A in the z direction on the velocity profile. If this influence is negligible, and if mass transfer begins at the leading edge A, it develops that the thickness of the velocity boundary layer δ_u and that of the concentration boundary layer δ_c are in the ratio $\delta_u/\delta_c = Sc^{1/3}$. The average mass-transfer coefficient from the leading edge to a distance x is given by

$$Sh_{av} = \frac{k_{L,av}x}{D_{AB}} = 0.664\ Re_x^{1/2}\ Sc^{1/3} \tag{3.41}$$

This shows the mass-transfer coefficient to vary as $D_{AB}^{2/3}$, which is typical of the results of boundary-layer calculations.

In the regions where a turbulent boundary layer and a viscous sublayer exist, similar calculations cannot be made because the fluid motion cannot be described, except after rather drastic simplifying assumptions. While it has usually been assumed that the viscous sublayer is a *laminar* sublayer, attempts have been made to describe the mass-transfer characteristics by picturing eddies entering the sublayer from the turbulent region, even to the solid surface, somewhat in the manner of the surface-renewal theory. This idea was first proposed by Murphree[23] in 1932 and has more recently been revived by others.[8,14,20,29,38] As explained earlier (see page 49), such eddies may have important influence on the mass-transfer rate without strongly affecting the velocity profile.

When the surface over which the fluid passes is curved convexly in the direction of flow, as in flow at right angles to the outside of a cylinder and past a sphere, well-developed boundary layers form at very low rates of flow, which are amenable to theoretical treatment. At higher rates of flow, however, the boundary layer separates from the surface, and eddies form in the wake behind the object. Theoretical computation of the mass-transfer coefficient cannot then be made.

MASS-, HEAT-, AND MOMENTUM-TRANSFER ANALOGIES

In laminar flow past a solid surface, as for the two-dimensional laminar boundary layer of Fig. 3.9, for example, the momentum balance or equation of motion

(Navier-Stokes equation) for the x direction becomes[3]

$$u_x \frac{\partial u_x}{\partial x} + u_z \frac{\partial u_x}{\partial z} = v\left(\frac{\partial^2 u_x}{\partial x^2} + \frac{\partial^2 u_x}{\partial z^2}\right) \tag{3.42}$$

If there is mass transfer without chemical reaction, Eq. (2.17) gives the equation of continuity for substance A

$$u_x \frac{\partial c_A}{\partial x} + u_z \frac{\partial c_A}{\partial z} = D_{AB}\left(\frac{\partial^2 c_A}{\partial x^2} + \frac{\partial^2 c_A}{\partial z^2}\right) \tag{3.43}$$

and if there is heat transfer between the fluid and the plate, Eq. (2.19) provides

$$u_x \frac{\partial t}{\partial x} + u_z \frac{\partial t}{\partial z} = \alpha\left(\frac{\partial^2 t}{\partial x^2} + \frac{\partial^2 t}{\partial z^2}\right) \tag{3.44}$$

which are to be solved simultaneously, together with the equation of continuity (2.14). It is clear that these equations are all of the same form, with u_x, c_A, and t and the three diffusivities of momentum v, mass D_{AB}, and heat α replacing each other in appropriate places in the equations.

In solving these, dimensionless forms of the variables are usually substituted

$$\frac{u_x - (u_{x,z=0} = 0)}{u_0 - (u_{x,z=0} = 0)}$$

$$\frac{c_A - c_{Ai}}{c_{A0} - c_{Ai}} \quad \text{and} \quad \frac{t - t_i}{t_0 - t_i}$$

Then the boundary conditions become identical. Thus, for Fig. 3.9, at $z = 0$ all three dimensionless variables are zero, and at $z = \infty$, all three equal unity. Consequently the form of the solutions, which provide dimensionless velocity, concentration, and temperature profiles, are the same. Indeed, if all three diffusivities are equal, so that $Sc = Pr = 1$, the profiles in dimensionless form are identical. The initial slopes of the concentration, temperature, and velocity profiles provide the means of computing the corresponding local transfer coefficients

$$N_A = -D_{AB}\left(\frac{\partial c_A}{\partial z}\right)_{z=0} = k_L(c_{Ai} - c_{A0}) \tag{3.45}$$

$$q = -\alpha\left[\frac{\partial(t C_p \rho)}{\partial z}\right]_{z=0} = h(t_i - t_0) \tag{3.46}$$

$$\tau_i g_c = v\left[\frac{\partial(u_x \rho)}{\partial z}\right]_{z=0} = \frac{f}{2}u_0(\rho u_0 - 0) \tag{3.47}$$

where f is the dimensionless friction factor and $fu_0/2$ might be considered a momentum-transfer coefficient. When the coefficients are computed and arranged as dimensionless groups, the results are all of the same form, as might be expected. In particular, for the flat plate of Fig. 3.9 at low mass-transfer rates,

$$\frac{\text{Nu}}{\text{Re}_x \, \text{Pr}^{\frac{1}{3}}} = \frac{\text{Sh}}{\text{Re}_x \, \text{Sc}^{\frac{1}{3}}} = \frac{f}{2} = 0.332 \, \text{Re}_x^{-\frac{1}{2}} \tag{3.48}$$

and the average coefficients provide Nu_{av} and Sh_{av} given by the same expressions with 0.332 replaced by 0.664 [compare Eq. (3.41)].   The same procedure may be followed with any laminar-flow case, with similarly analogous expressions resulting.   In these cases, the friction factor corresponds to a skin-friction drag along the surface.   For flow where separation occurs, such as for flow past a sphere or at right angles to a cylinder or any bluff object, one might expect the friction factor based on total drag, which includes not only skin friction but form drag due to flow separation as well, to follow a function different from that of the mass- and heat-transfer groups.

In the case of turbulent flow, the differential equations will contain time-averaged velocities and in addition the eddy diffusivities of momentum, mass, and heat transfer. The resulting equations cannot be solved for lack of information about the eddy diffusivities, but one might expect results of the form

$$\frac{\text{Sh}}{\text{Re} \, \text{Sc}} = \psi_1\left(\frac{f}{2}, \text{Sc}, \frac{E_v}{E_D}\right) = \psi_2\left(\frac{f}{2}, \text{Sc}, \frac{E_D}{\nu}\right) \tag{3.49}$$

$$\frac{\text{Nu}}{\text{Re} \, \text{Pr}} = \psi_1\left(\frac{f}{2}, \text{Pr}, \frac{E_v}{E_H}\right) = \psi_2\left(\frac{f}{2}, \text{Pr}, \frac{E_H}{\nu}\right) \tag{3.50}$$

Successful completion of an analogy requires, therefore, knowledge of how the ratios E_v/ν, E_D/E_v, and E_H/E_v vary with distance from the fluid interface.   It is customary arbitrarily to set $E_D/E_v = E_H/E_v = 1$, despite experimental evidence to the contrary (see page 49) and to make some arbitrary decision about E_v/ν.   With these assumptions, however, experimental velocity profiles permit prediction of the profiles and coefficients for mass and heat transfer.   Further, assuming only $E_D = E_H$ (which is much more reasonable) permits information on heat transfer to be converted directly for use in mass-transfer calculations and vice versa.

Let us sum up and further generalize what can be done with the analogies:

1. For analogous circumstances, temperature and concentration profiles in dimensionless form and heat- and mass-transfer coefficients in the form of dimensionless groups, respectively, are given by the same functions.   To convert equations or correlations of data on heat transfer and temperatures to corresponding mass transfer and concentrations, the dimensionless groups of the former are replaced by the corresponding groups of the latter.   Table 3.2 lists the commonly appearing dimensionless groups.   The limitations are:

a. The flow conditions and geometry must be the same.

b. Most heat-transfer data are based on situations involving no mass transfer. Use of the analogy would then produce mass-transfer coefficients corresponding to no net mass transfer, in turn corresponding most closely to k'_G, k'_c, or k'_y ($= F$). Sherwood numbers are commonly written in terms of any of the coefficients, but when

Table 3.2. Corresponding dimensionless groups of mass and heat transfer

No.	Mass transfer	Heat transfer
1	$\dfrac{c_A - c_{A1}}{c_{A2} - c_{A1}}$	$\dfrac{t - t_1}{t_2 - t_1}$
2	Reynolds number $$\text{Re} = \frac{lu\rho}{\mu}$$	Reynolds number $$\text{Re} = \frac{lu\rho}{\mu}$$
3	Schmidt number $$\text{Sc} = \frac{\mu}{\rho D_{AB}} = \frac{\nu}{D_{AB}}$$	Prandtl number $$\text{Pr} = \frac{C_p \mu}{k} = \frac{\nu}{\alpha}$$
4	Sherwood number $$\text{Sh} = \frac{Fl}{c D_{AB}}, \frac{k_G p_{BM} RTl}{P_t D_{AB}},$$ $$\frac{k_c p_{BM} l}{P_t D_{AB}}, \frac{k_c' l}{D_{AB}}, \frac{k_y' RTl}{P_t D_{AB}}, \text{etc.}$$	Nusselt number $$\text{Nu} = \frac{hl}{k}$$
5	Grashof number† $$\text{Gr} = \frac{g l^3 \Delta\rho}{\rho}\left(\frac{\rho}{\mu}\right)^2$$	Grashof number† $$\text{Gr} = g l^3 \beta\, \Delta t \left(\frac{\rho}{\mu}\right)^2$$
6	Péclet number $$\text{Pe} = \text{Re Sc} = \frac{lu}{D_{AB}}$$	Péclet number $$\text{Pe} = \text{Re Pr} = \frac{C_p lu\rho}{k} = \frac{lu}{\alpha}$$
7	Stanton number $$\text{St} = \frac{\text{Sh}}{\text{Re Sc}} = \frac{\text{Sh}}{\text{Pe}} = \frac{F}{cu},$$ $$\frac{F}{G}, \frac{k_G p_{BM} M_{av}}{\rho u}, \text{etc.}$$	Stanton number $$\text{St} = \frac{\text{Nu}}{\text{Re Pr}} = \frac{\text{Nu}}{\text{Pe}} = \frac{h}{C_p u\rho}$$
8	$j_D = \text{St Sc}^{2/3}$	$j_H = \text{St Pr}^{2/3}$

† The Grashof number appears in cases involving natural convection; $\Delta\rho = |\rho_1 - \rho_2|$, $\Delta t = |t_1 - t_2|$, in the same phase.

derived by replacement of Nusselt numbers for use where the net mass transfer is not zero, they should be taken as $\text{Sh} = Fl/c D_{AB}$, and the F used with Eq. (3.1). Further, the result will be useful only in the absence of chemical reaction.

    c. The boundary conditions which would be used to solve the corresponding differential equations must be analogous. For example, in the case of the mass-transfer problem of the falling film of Fig. 3.4, the analogous circumstances for heat transfer would require heat transfer from the gas (not from the solid wall) to the liquid, the wall to be impervious to the transfer of heat, heat transfer beginning at the same value of y as mass transfer (in this case at $y = 0$), a constant temperature for the liquid-gas interface, and constant fluid properties.

d. For turbulent flow, $E_H = E_D$ at any location.

2. Friction factors and velocity profiles can be expected to correlate with the corresponding heat- and mass-transfer quantities only if $E_v = E_H = E_D$ in turbulent flow, and in extension to viscous sublayers only if $E_v/\nu = E_H/\alpha = E_D/D_{AB}$. For either laminar or turbulent flow, the friction factors must indicate skin friction and not form drag as well. In general, it is safest to avoid the friction analogy to mass and heat transfer.

These analogies are particularly useful in extending the very considerable amount of information on heat transfer to yield corresponding information on mass transfer, which is more likely to be lacking. Alternatively, local mass-transfer coefficients can be measured with relative ease through sublimation or dissolution of solids, and these can be converted to the analogous local heat-transfer coefficients, which are difficult to obtain.[34]

Illustration 3.2. What is the heat-transfer analog to Eq. (3.12)?

Solution. The equation remains the same with the dimensionless concentration ratio replaced by $(t_i - t_L)/(t_i - t_0)$; the dimensionless group

$$\eta = \frac{2D_{AB}L}{3\delta^2 \bar{u}_y} = \frac{2}{3}\frac{D_{AB}}{\delta \bar{u}_y}\frac{L}{\delta} = \frac{2}{3}\frac{L}{Pe}\frac{L}{\delta}$$

for mass transfer is replaced by

$$\eta = \frac{2}{3}\frac{L}{Pe}\frac{L}{\delta} = \frac{2}{3}\frac{\alpha}{\delta \bar{u}_y}\frac{L}{\delta} = \frac{2\alpha L}{3\delta^2 \bar{u}_y} \quad \text{Ans.}$$

Illustration 3.3. For flow of a fluid at right angles to a circular cylinder, the average heat-transfer coefficient (averaged around the periphery) for fluid Reynolds numbers in the range 1 to 4,000 is given by[11]

$$\mathrm{Nu}_{av} = 0.43 + 0.532\,\mathrm{Re}^{0.5}\,\mathrm{Pr}^{0.31}$$

where Nu and Re are computed with the cylinder diameter and fluid properties are taken at the mean of the cylinder and bulk-fluid temperatures.

Estimate the rate of sublimation of a cylinder of uranium hexafluoride, UF_6, $\frac{1}{4}$ in. diam, exposed to an air stream flowing at a velocity of 10 ft/sec. The surface temperature of the solid is $43°C$, at which temperature the vapor pressure of UF_6 is 400 mm Hg. The bulk air is at 1 atm pressure, $60°C$.

Solution. The analogous expression for the mass-transfer coefficient is

$$\mathrm{Sh}_{av} = 0.43 + 0.532\,\mathrm{Re}^{0.5}\,\mathrm{Sc}^{0.31}$$

Along the mass-transfer path (cylinder surface to bulk air) the average temperature is $51.5°C$, and the average partial pressure of UF_6 is 200 mm Hg, corresponding to $200/760 = 0.263$ mole fraction UF_6, 0.737 mole fraction air. The corresponding physical properties of the gas, at the mean temperature and composition, are estimated to be: density = 0.256 lb/cu ft, viscosity = 0.027 centipoise = 0.0653 lb/(ft)(hr), diffusivity = 0.35 sq ft/hr.

$$\text{Re} = \frac{du\rho}{\mu} = \frac{(0.25/12)(10)(3600)(0.256)}{0.0653} = 2{,}940$$

$$\text{Sc} = \frac{\mu}{\rho D} = \frac{0.0653}{0.256(0.35)} = 0.728$$

$$\therefore \quad \text{Sh}_{av} = 0.43 + 0.532(2{,}940)^{0.5}(0.728)^{0.31} = 26.5 = \frac{F_{av}d}{cD_{AB}}$$

$$c = \frac{1}{359}\frac{492}{460 + 124.7} = 0.00234 \text{ lb mole/cu ft}$$

$$F_{av} = \frac{\text{Sh}_{av}\, cD_{AB}}{d} = \frac{26.5(0.00234)(0.35)}{0.25/12} = 10.4 \text{ lb moles/(hr)(sq ft)}$$

In this case, N_B (air) = 0, so that $N_A/(N_A + N_B) = 1.0$. Since $c_A/c = p_A$ atm, Eq. (3.1) provides

$$N_A = 10.4 \ln\frac{1 - 0}{1 - {}^{400}\!/_{760}} = 7.78 \text{ lb moles UF}_6/(\text{hr})(\text{sq ft})$$

which is the mass-transfer flux based on the entire cylinder area.

Note 1: The calculated N_A is an instantaneous flux. Mass transfer will rapidly reduce the cylinder diameter, so that the Reynolds number and hence F will change with time. Furthermore, the surface will not remain in the form of a circular cylinder owing to the variation of the local F about the perimeter, so that the empirical correlation for Nu_{av} and Sh_{av} will then no longer apply.

Note 2: Use of k_c or k_G computed from a simple definition of Sh produces incorrect results because of the relatively high mass-transfer rate, which is not allowed for in the heat-transfer correlation. Thus, $k_c = k_G RT = \text{Sh}_{av}\, D_{AB}/d = 26.5(0.35)/(0.25/12) = 4{,}440$ lb moles/(hr)(sq ft)(lb mole/cu ft), or $k_G = 4{,}440/0.729(460 + 124.7) = 10.4$ lb moles/(hr)(sq ft)(atm). This leads to [Eq. (3.3)] $N_A = 10.4({}^{400}\!/_{760} - 0) = 5.48$ lb moles/(hr)(sq ft), which is too low. However, if k_G is taken to be $10.4 P_t/p_{BM}$, the correct answer will be given by Eq. (3.3).

Turbulent flow in circular pipes

A prodigious amount of effort has been spent in developing the analogies among the three transport phenomena for this case, beginning with Reynolds' original concept of the analogy between momentum and heat transfer in 1874.[28] The number of well-known relationships proposed is in the dozens, and new ones of increasing complexity are continually being proposed. Space limitations will not permit discussion of this interesting development, and we shall confine ourselves to a few of the results.

Although fairly elaborate measurements have been made of velocity distributions for this case, which should permit determination of the eddy viscosity and its variation with distance from the pipe wall and Reynolds number, nevertheless the quality of the data does not permit very accurate determination of this quantity, especially near the pipe wall. Even the assumption that all three eddy diffusivities are everywhere the same is then not enough to establish a good basis from which to compute mass or heat transfer from friction data. This is because for large values of Sc and Pr the computed mass- and heat-transfer coefficients are very sensitive to the variations of eddy diffusivity of mass and heat with distance from the wall (see page 49). Consequently either the variation of eddy viscosity with distance must be assumed, empirically or with the help of some other theory or other, for extension of the friction data, or the variations of those for heat and mass must be assumed.

Assuming that in the viscous sublayer E_v and E_H are both zero and that elsewhere the molecular diffusivities are of negligible importance, with $E_v = E_H$, Prandtl[27] and Taylor[35] deduced

$$\text{St}_{av} = \frac{\text{Nu}_{av}}{\text{Re Pr}} = \frac{h_{av}}{C_p \bar{u}_x \rho} = \frac{\frac{1}{2} f}{1 - u_{xF}/\bar{u}_x + (u_{xF}/\bar{u}_x)\,\text{Pr}} \qquad (3.51)$$

where u_{xF} is the axially directed velocity at the edge of the viscous sublayer. The mass-transfer analog can be immediately written. As a result of the assumptions, including neglect of the gradual, rather than abrupt, transition from the viscous sublayer to the turbulent core, the equation does not represent the observed data very well except for Pr (and Sc) near unity. The remarkably simple empirical modification by Colburn[5] represents the data extremely well (Colburn analogy)

$$\text{St}_{av} = \frac{h_{av}}{C_p \bar{u}_x \rho} = \frac{\frac{1}{2} f}{\text{Pr}^{\frac{2}{3}}} \qquad (3.52)$$

The group $\text{St}_{av}\,\text{Pr}^{\frac{2}{3}}$ is called j_H

$$\text{St}_{av}\,\text{Pr}^{\frac{2}{3}} = \frac{h_{av}}{C_p \bar{u}_x \rho}\,\text{Pr}^{\frac{2}{3}} = j_H = \frac{1}{2} f = \psi(\text{Re}) \qquad (3.53)$$

The mass-transfer analog (Chilton-Colburn analogy)[4] is

$$\text{St}_{av}\,\text{Sc}^{\frac{2}{3}} = \frac{\text{Sh}_{av}}{\text{Re Sc}}\,\text{Sc}^{\frac{2}{3}} = \frac{F_{av}}{c \bar{u}_x}\,\text{Sc}^{\frac{2}{3}} = j_D = \frac{1}{2} f = \psi(\text{Re}) \qquad (3.54)$$

which, as will be shown, agrees well with experimental data. Many much more elaborate analogies have been proposed,[8,20] based on a variety of assumed relations between E_D/ν and distance from the wall, even in the viscous sublayer [Eq. (3.54) has been shown[38] to be consistent with Murphree's early suggestion[23] that E_D/ν varies as the cube of the distance from the wall in the sublayer]. For most purposes, Eq. (3.54) serves amply well.

Experimental data have come from so-called wetted-wall towers (Fig. 3.10) and flow of liquids through soluble pipes. In Fig. 3.10, a volatile pure liquid is permitted to flow down the inside surface of a circular pipe while a gas is blown upward or downward through the central core. Measurement of the rate of evaporation of the liquid into the gas stream over the known surface permits calculation of the mass-transfer coefficients for the gas phase. Use of different gases and liquids provides variation of Sc. In this way, Sherwood and Gilliland[30] covered values of Re from 2,000 to 35,000, Sc from 0.6 to 2.5, and gas pressures from 0.1 to 3 atm. Linton and Sherwood[21] caused water to flow through a series of pipes made by casting molten benzoic acid and other sparingly soluble solids. In this way the range of Sc was extended to

Feed reservoir

Pipe wall

Liquid film

Wetted-wall section

Calming section

Liquid out

Gas

Fig. 3.10   *Wetted-wall tower.*

3,000.   All the data are empirically correlated by†

$$\text{Sh}_{\text{av}} = \frac{k_{c,\text{av}} p_{BM} d}{P_t D_{AB}} = \frac{k_{L,\text{av}} d}{D_{AB}} = 0.023 \, \text{Re}^{0.83} \, \text{Sc}^{\frac{1}{3}} \tag{3.55}$$

Over the range of Re $= 5{,}000$ to $200{,}000$, the friction factor for flow in smooth pipes can be expressed as

$$\tfrac{1}{2} f = 0.023 \, \text{Re}^{-0.20} \tag{3.56}$$

Substitution in Eq. (3.55) then gives

$$\frac{\text{Sh}_{\text{av}}}{\text{Re}^{1.03} \, \text{Sc}} \, \text{Sc}^{\frac{2}{3}} = \tfrac{1}{2} f \tag{3.57}$$

which may be compared with Eq. (3.54).

MASS-TRANSFER DATA FOR SIMPLE SITUATIONS

Table 3.3 provides a few of the correlations taken from the literature for relatively simple situations.   Others more appropriate to particular types of mass-transfer equipment will be introduced as needed.

† $k_c p_{BM}/P_t = k_c'$, which then corrects for the mass-transfer flux.   Consequently, Sh_{av} may be written also as $F_{\text{av}} d/c D_{AB}$ for cases where Eq. (3.1) must be applied.   The data for gases only are better correlated with 0.44 replacing $\frac{1}{3}$ as the exponent on Sc.

Table 3.3. Mass transfer[a] for simple situations

Fluid motion	Range of conditions	Equation	Ref.
1. Inside circular pipes	$Re = 4{,}000\text{--}60{,}000$ $Sc = 0.6\text{--}3{,}000$	$j_D = 0.023\,Re^{-0.17}$ $Sh_{av} = 0.023\,Re^{0.83}\,Sc^{1/3}$	21, 30
2. Perpendicular to circular cylinders (gases only)	$Re' = 400\text{--}25{,}000$ $Sc = 0.6\text{--}2.6$	$\dfrac{k_{G,av} P_t}{G}\,Sc^{0.56} = 0.281\,Re'^{-0.4}$	1, 26
3. Parallel to flat plates[b]	Transfer begins at leading edge $Re_x < 80{,}000$ $Re_x > 500{,}000$	$j_H = 0.664\,Re_x^{-0.5}$ $j_H = 0.036\,Re_x^{-0.2}$	22, 31
4. Past single spheres	$Sc = 0.6\text{--}3{,}200$ $Re''\,Sc^{0.5} = 1.8\text{--}600{,}000$	$Sh_{av} = Sh_o + 0.347(Re''\,Sc^{0.5})^{0.62}$ $Gr\,Sc < 10^8$: $Sh_o = 2.0 + 0.569(Gr\,Sc)^{0.250}$ $Gr\,Sc > 10^8$: $Sh_o = 2.0 + 0.0254(Gr\,Sc)^{0.333}\,Sc^{0.244}$	33
5. Through fixed beds of pellets (gases only)[c,d]	$Sc = 0.6$ $Re'' = 90\text{--}4{,}000$ $Re'' = 5{,}000\text{--}10{,}300$	$j_D = \dfrac{2.06}{\epsilon}\,(Re'')^{-0.575}$ $j_D = \dfrac{20.4}{\epsilon}\,(Re'')^{-0.815}$	13
6. Through fixed beds of pellets (liquids only)[d,e]	$Sc = 159\text{--}13{,}260$ $\dfrac{Re''}{\epsilon} = 0.08\text{--}125$ $\dfrac{Re''}{\epsilon} = 125\text{--}5{,}000$	$\dfrac{F}{G}\,Sc^{0.58} = 2.40\left(\dfrac{Re''}{\epsilon}\right)^{-0.66}$ $\dfrac{F}{G}\,Sc^{0.58} = 0.442\left(\dfrac{Re''}{\epsilon}\right)^{-0.31}$	12, 39

[a] Average mass-transfer coefficients throughout, for constant solute concentrations at the phase surface. Generally, fluid properties are evaluated at the average conditions between the phase surface and the bulk fluid. The heat- mass-transfer analogy is valid throughout except for flow of fluids through fixed beds of pellets.

[b] Mass-transfer data for this case scatter badly but are reasonably well represented by setting $j_D = j_H$.

[c] A transition in the range $Re = 4{,}000\text{--}5{,}000$ is indicated. Not all investigators confirm this. For a complete review, see J. J. Barker, *Ind. Eng. Chem.*, **57**(4), 43; (5), 33 (1965).

[d] For fixed beds, the relation between ϵ and d_p is

$$a = \frac{6(1-\epsilon)}{d_p}$$

where a is the specific solid surface, sq ft/cu ft of bed.

[e] The heat- mass-transfer analogy is not confirmed in this case.

Experimental data are usually obtained by blowing gases over various shapes wet with evaporating liquids or causing liquids to flow past solids which dissolve. Average, rather than local, mass-transfer coefficients are usually obtained. In most cases, the data are reported in terms of k_G, k_c, k_L, and the like, coefficients applicable to the binary systems used with $N_B = 0$, without details concerning the actual concentrations of solute during the experiments. Fortunately, the solute concentrations during the experiments are usually fairly low, so that if necessary, conversion of the data to the corresponding F is usually at least approximately possible by simply taking p_{BM}/P_t, x_{BM}, etc., equal to unity (see Table 3.1).

In many cases, particularly when only gases have been studied, the range of Schmidt numbers covered is relatively small; sometimes only one Sc (0.6 for air-water vapor) is studied. The j_D of Eq. (3.54) has been so successful in dealing with turbulent flow in pipes that many data of small Sc range have been put in this form without actually establishing the validity of the $\frac{2}{3}$ exponent on Sc for the situation at hand. Extension to values of Sc far outside the original range of the experiments, particularly for liquids, must therefore be made with the understanding that a considerable approximation may be involved. Some data, as for flow past spheres, for example, cannot be put in the j_D form, and it is likely that many of the correlations using j_D may not be very general.

For situations not covered by the available data, it seems reasonable to assume that the mass-transfer coefficients can be estimated as functions of Re from the corresponding heat-transfer data, if available. If necessary, in the absence of a known effect of Pr, the heat-transfer data may be put in the j_H form and the analog completed by equating j_D to j_H at the same Re. This should serve reasonably well if the range of extrapolation of Sc (or Pr) is not too large.

Illustration 3.4. It is desired to estimate the rate at which water will evaporate from a wetted surface of unusual shape when hydrogen at 1 atm, 100°F, is blown over the surface at a superficial velocity of 50 ft/sec. No mass-transfer measurements have been made, but heat-transfer measurements indicate that for air at 100°F, 1 atm, the heat-transfer coefficient h between air and the surface is given empirically by

$$h = 0.072 G'^{0.6}$$

where G' is the superficial air mass velocity, lb/(hr)(sq ft). Estimate the required mass-transfer coefficient. Physical-property data are:

	100°F, 1 atm	
	Air	H₂
Density ρ, lb/cu ft	0.071	0.00495
Viscosity μ, centipoise	0.0185	0.009
Thermal conductivity k, (Btu)(ft)/(hr)(sq ft)(°F)	0.01576	0.1069
Heat capacity C_p, Btu/(lb)(°F)	0.24	3.45
Diffusivity with water vapor, sq ft/hr		3.0

Solution. The experimental heat-transfer data do not include effects of changing Prandtl number. It will therefore be necessary to assume that the j_H group will satisfactorily describe the effect.

$$j_H = \frac{h}{C_p \rho u}\, Pr^{\frac{2}{3}} = \frac{h}{C_p G'}\, Pr^{\frac{2}{3}} = \psi(Re)$$

$$h = \frac{C_p G'}{Pr^{\frac{2}{3}}}\, \psi(Re) = 0.072 G'^{0.6} \quad \text{for air}$$

The $\psi(Re)$ must be compatible with $0.072 G'^{0.6}$. Therefore, let $\psi(Re) = b\, Re^n$ and define Re as lG'/μ, where l is a characteristic linear dimension of the solid body.

$$\therefore \quad h = \frac{C_p G'}{Pr^{\frac{2}{3}}}\, b\, Re^n = \frac{C_p G'}{Pr^{\frac{2}{3}}}\, b\left(\frac{lG'}{\mu}\right)^n = \frac{bC_p}{Pr^{\frac{2}{3}}}\left(\frac{l}{\mu}\right)^n G'^{1+n} = 0.072 G'^{0.6}$$

$$\therefore \quad 1 + n = 0.6 \qquad n = -0.4$$

$$\frac{bC_p}{Pr^{\frac{2}{3}}}\left(\frac{l}{\mu}\right)^{-0.4} = 0.072$$

$$b = \frac{0.072\, Pr^{\frac{2}{3}}}{C_p}\left(\frac{l}{\mu}\right)^{0.4}$$

Using the data for air at 100°F, 1 atm,

$$Pr = \frac{C_p \mu}{k} = \frac{0.24(0.0185)(2.42)}{0.01576} = 0.681$$

$$b = \frac{0.072(0.681)^{\frac{2}{3}}}{0.24}\left[\frac{l}{0.0185(2.42)}\right]^{0.4} = 0.810 l^{0.4}$$

$$j_H = \frac{h}{C_p G}\, Pr^{\frac{2}{3}} = \frac{0.810 l^{0.4}}{Re^{0.4}} = \psi(Re)$$

The heat- mass-transfer analogy will be used to estimate the mass-transfer coefficient ($j_D = j_H$).

$$j_D = \frac{k_G p_{BM} M_{av}}{\rho u}\, Sc^{\frac{2}{3}} = \psi(Re) = \frac{0.810 l^{0.4}}{Re^{0.4}}$$

$$k_G p_{BM} = F = \frac{0.810 l^{0.4}\, \rho u}{Re^{0.4}\, M_{av}\, Sc^{\frac{2}{3}}} = \frac{0.810 (\rho u)^{0.6} \mu^{0.4}}{M_{av}\, Sc^{\frac{2}{3}}}$$

For H_2–H_2O, 100°F, 1 atm, $Sc = \mu/\rho D = 0.009(2.42)/0.00495(3) = 1.468$. At $u = 50(3,600) = 180,000$ ft/hr, and assuming the density, mol wt, and viscosity of the gas are essentially those of H_2,

$$k_G p_{BM} = F = \frac{0.810[0.00495(180,000)]^{0.6}[0.009(2.42)]^{0.4}}{2.02(1.468)^{\frac{2}{3}}}$$

$$= 3.98 \text{ lb moles/(hr)(sq ft)} \quad \textbf{Ans.}$$

Flux variation with concentration

In many situations the concentrations of solute in the bulk fluid, and even at the fluid interface, may vary in the direction of flow. Further, the mass-transfer coefficients depend upon fluid properties and rate of flow, and if these vary in the direction of flow, the coefficients will also. The flux N_A of Eqs. (3.1) and (3.3) to (3.6) is therefore a local flux and will generally vary with distance in the direction of flow. This problem was dealt with, in part, in the development leading to Illustration 3.1. In solving problems where something other than the local flux is required, allowance must be made for these variations. This normally requires some considerations of material balances, but there is no standard procedure. An example is offered below, but it must be emphasized that generally some sort of improvisation for the circumstances at hand will be required.

Illustration 3.5. Nickel carbonyl is to be produced by passing carbon monoxide gas downward through a bed of nickel spheres, 0.5 in. diam. The bed is 1 sq ft in cross section and is packed so that there are 30% voids. Pure CO enters at 50°C, 1 atm, at the rate of 15 lb moles/hr. The reaction is

$$Ni + 4CO \rightarrow Ni(CO)_4$$

For present purposes, the following simplifying assumptions will be made:

1. The reaction is very rapid, so that the partial pressure of CO at the metal surface is essentially zero. The carbonyl forms as a gas, which diffuses as fast as it forms from the metal surface to the bulk-gas stream. The rate of reaction is controlled entirely by the rate of mass transfer of CO from the bulk gas to the metal surface and that of the $Ni(CO)_4$ to the bulk gas.
2. The temperature remains at 50°C and the pressure at 1 atm throughout.
3. The viscosity of the gas $= 0.024$ centipoise, and the Schmidt number $= 2.0$ throughout.
4. The size of the nickel spheres remains constant.

Estimate the bed depth required to reduce the CO content of the gas to 0.5%.
Solution. Let $A = CO$, $B = Ni(CO)_4$. $N_B = -N_A/4$, and $N_A/(N_A + N_B) = \frac{1}{3}$. In Eq. (3.1), $c_{A2}/c = y_{Ai}$ at the metal interface $= 0$, and $c_{A1}/c = y_A =$ mole fraction CO in the bulk gas. Equation (3.1) therefore becomes

$$N_A = \frac{1}{3} F \ln \frac{\frac{1}{3}}{\frac{1}{3} - y_A} = \frac{1}{3} F \ln \frac{4}{4 - 3y_A} \tag{3.58}$$

where N_A is the mass-transfer flux based on the metal surface. Since y_A varies with position in the bed, Eq. (3.58) gives a local flux N_A, and to determine the total mass transfer, allowance must be made for the variation of y_A and F with bed depth.
Let $G =$ moles of gas/(hr)(sq ft bed cross section) flowing at any depth z from the top. The CO content of this gas is $y_A G$ moles CO/(hr)(sq ft bed). The change in CO content in passing through a depth dz of bed is $-d(y_A G)$ moles/(hr)(sq ft). If a is the specific metal surface, sq ft/cu ft of bed, a depth dz and a cross section of 1 sq ft (volume $= dz$ cu ft) has a metal surface $a\, dz$ sq ft. Therefore $N_A = -d(y_A G)/a\, dz$ moles CO/(hr)(sq ft metal surface). For each mole of CO consumed, $\frac{1}{4}$ mole $Ni(CO)_4$ forms, representing a net loss of $\frac{3}{4}$ mole per mole CO consumed. The CO consumed through bed depth z is therefore $(G_0 - G)4/3$ moles, where G_0 is the molar superficial mass velocity at the top, and the CO content at depth z is $G_0 - (G_0 - G)4/3$. Therefore,

$$y_A = \frac{G_0 - (G_0 - G)4/3}{G} \qquad G = \frac{G_0}{4 - 3y_A}$$

$$d(y_A G) = \frac{4G_0\, dy_A}{(4 - 3y_A)^2}$$

Substituting in Eq. (3.58),

$$-\frac{4G_0\, dy_A}{(4 - 3y_A)^2 a\, dz} = \frac{4}{3} F \ln \frac{4}{4 - 3y_A} \tag{3.59}$$

F is given by item 5 of Table 3.3 and is dependent upon y_A. At depth z, the CO mass velocity $= [G_0 - (G_0 - G)4/3]28.0$, and the Ni(CO)$_4$ mass velocity $= [(G_0 - G)1/3]170.7$, making a total mass velocity $G' = 47.6G_0 - 19.6G$ lb/(hr)(sq ft). Substituting for G,

$$G' = 47.6G_0 - \frac{19.6G_0}{4 - 3y_A} = G_0\left(47.6 - \frac{19.6}{4 - 3y_A}\right) \text{ lb/(hr)(sq ft)}$$

With 0.5-in. spheres, $d_p = 0.5/12 = 0.0416$ ft; $\mu = 0.024(2.42) = 0.0580$ lb/(ft)(hr).

$$\text{Re}'' = \frac{d_p G'}{\mu} = 0.0416G_0 \frac{47.6 - 19.6/(4 - 3y_A)}{0.0580}$$

$$= G_0\left(34.2 - \frac{14.06}{4 - 3y_A}\right)$$

With $G_0 = 15$ lb moles/(hr)(sq ft) and y_A in the range 1 to 0.005, the range of Re$''$ is 302 to 461. Therefore (Table 3.3),

$$j_D = \frac{F}{G} \text{Sc}^{\frac{2}{3}} = \frac{2.06}{\epsilon} \text{Re}''^{-0.575}$$

For Sc $= 2$ and $\epsilon = 0.3$ void fraction, this becomes

$$F = \frac{2.06}{0.3(2)^{\frac{2}{3}}}\left(\frac{G_0}{4 - 3y_A}\right)\left[G_0\left(34.2 - \frac{14.06}{4 - 3y_A}\right)\right]^{-0.575} \tag{3.60}$$

Equation (3.60) may be substituted in Eq. (3.59). Since $a = 6(1 - \epsilon)/d_p = 6(1 - 0.3)/0.0416 = 101$ sq ft/cu ft and $G_0 = 15$ lb moles/(hr)(sq ft), the result, after consolidation and rearrangement for integration, is

$$Z = \int_0^Z dz = -0.0325 \int_{1.0}^{0.005} \frac{[34.2 - 14.06/(4 - 3y_A)]^{0.575}}{(4 - 3y_A) \ln [4/(4 - 3y_A)]} dy_A$$

The integration is most readily done graphically, by plotting the integrand as ordinate vs. y_A as abscissa and determining the area under the resulting curve between the indicated limits. As a result, $Z = 0.475$ ft, or say 6-in. bed depth. **Ans.**

SIMULTANEOUS MASS AND HEAT TRANSFER

Mass transfer may occur simultaneously with the transfer of heat, either as a result of an externally imposed temperature difference or because of the absorption or evolution of heat which generally occurs when a substance is transferred from one phase to another. In such cases, within one phase, the heat transferred is a result not only of the conduction (convection) by virtue of the temperature difference which would happen in the absence of mass transfer but also includes the sensible heat carried by the diffusing matter.

Consider the situation shown in Fig. 3.11. Here a fluid consisting of substances A and B flows past a second phase under conditions causing mass transfer. The total mass transferred is given by the following variation of Eq. (3.1):

$$N_A + N_B = F \ln \frac{N_A/(N_A + N_B) - c_{Ai}/c}{N_A/(N_A + N_B) - c_{A1}/c} \tag{3.61}$$

As usual, the relationship between N_A and N_B is fixed by other considerations. As a result of the temperature difference, there is a heat flux described by the ordinary

Fig. 3.11   *Effect of mass transfer on heat transfer.*[6]

heat-transfer coefficient h in the absence of mass transfer.   If we think in terms of the film theory, this heat flux is $h(-dt/dz)z_F$.   The total sensible heat flux q_s to the interface must include in addition the sensible heat brought there by the movement of matter through the temperature difference.   Thus,

$$q_s = h\left(-\frac{dt}{dz}\right)z_F + (N_A M_A C_{pA} + N_B M_B C_{pB})(t - t_i) \tag{3.62}$$

Rearranging and integrating,

$$\int_{t_i}^{t_1} \frac{dt}{q_s - (N_A M_A C_{pA} + N_B M_B C_{pB})(t - t_i)} = \frac{1}{h z_F} \int_{z_F}^{0} dz \tag{3.63}$$

$$q_s = \frac{N_A M_A C_{pA} + N_B M_B C_{pB}}{1 - e^{-(N_A M_A C_{pA} + N_B M_B C_{pB})/h}} (t_1 - t_i) \tag{3.64}$$

The first term after the equals sign in Eq. (3.64) may be considered as a heat-transfer coefficient corrected for mass transfer.

The *total* heat release at the interface q_t will then include additionally the effect produced when the transferred mass passes through the interface.   This may be a latent heat of vaporization, a heat of solution, or both, depending upon the circumstances.   Thus,

$$q_t = q_s + \lambda_A N_A + \lambda_B N_B \tag{3.65}$$

where λ is the molar heat evolution.   In some cases the heat released at the interface continues to flow to the left in Fig. 3.11, owing to a temperature drop in the adjacent phase.   In others, where the mass transfer in the fluid is in the opposite direction to the sensible heat transfer, it is possible that the diffusing mass may carry heat from the interface into the fluid as fast as it is released, in which case no heat enters the adjacent phase.

Illustration 3.6. An air–water vapor mixture flows upward through a vertical copper tube, 1 in. OD, 0.065 in. wall thickness, which is surrounded by flowing cold water.   As a result, the water

vapor condenses and flows as a liquid down the inside surface of the tube.   At one level in the apparatus, the average velocity of the gas is 15 ft/sec, its bulk-average temperature 150°F, the pressure 1 atm,
and the bulk-average partial pressure of water vapor = 0.24 atm.   The film of condensed liquid is
such that its heat-transfer coefficient = 2,000 Btu/(hr)(sq ft)(°F).   The cooling water has a bulk-
average temperature of 75°F and a heat-transfer coefficient = 100 Btu/(hr)(sq ft)(°F) (see Fig. 3.12).
Compute the local rate of condensation of water from the air stream.

Solution. For the metal tube, ID = $1 - 0.065(2) = 0.870$ in. = 0.0725 ft.   Av   diam =
$(1 + 0.870)/2 = 0.935$ in.

For the gas mixture, A = water, B = air. $N_B = 0$, $N_A/(N_A + N_B) = 1$; $y_{A1} = 0.24$, $y_{Ai} =$
p_{Ai} = vapor pressure of water at the interface temperature t_i. $M_{av} = 0.24(18.02) + 0.76(29) =$
26.4; $\rho = (26.4/359)[492/(460 + 150)] = 0.0594$ lb/cu ft; $\mu = (0.0175$ centipoise)(2.42) = 0.0424
lb/(ft)(hr). $C_{pA} = 0.45$, C_p of the mixture = 0.274 Btu/(lb)(°F).   Sc = 0.60, Pr = 0.75.

$$G' = \text{mass velocity} = u\rho = 15(3,600)(0.0594) = 3,205 \text{ lb/(hr)(sq ft)}$$

$$G = \text{molar mass velocity} = \frac{G'}{M_{av}} = \frac{3,205}{26.4} = 121.5$$

$$\text{Re} = \frac{dG'}{\mu} = \frac{0.0725(3,205)}{0.0424} = 5,490$$

The mass-transfer coefficient is given by item 1, Table 3.3

$$j_D = \text{St Sc}^{\frac{2}{3}} = \frac{F}{G} \text{Sc}^{\frac{2}{3}} = 0.023 \text{ Re}^{-0.17} = 0.023(5,490)^{-0.17} = 0.00532$$

$$F = \frac{0.00532G}{\text{Sc}^{\frac{2}{3}}} = \frac{0.00532(121.5)}{(0.60)^{\frac{2}{3}}} = 0.910 \text{ lb mole/(hr)(sq ft)}$$

The heat-transfer coefficient in the absence of mass transfer will be estimated through $j_D = j_H$.

$$j_H = \text{St Pr}^{\frac{2}{3}} = \frac{h}{C_p G'} \text{Pr}^{\frac{2}{3}} = 0.00532$$

$$h = \frac{0.00532C_p G'}{\text{Pr}^{\frac{2}{3}}} = \frac{0.00532(0.274)(3,205)}{(0.75)^{\frac{2}{3}}} = 5.66 \text{ Btu/(hr)(sq ft)(°F)}$$

The sensible heat-transfer flux to the interface is given by Eq. (3.64), with $N_B = 0$.   This is combined with Eq. (3.65) to produce

$$q_t = \frac{N_A(18.02)(0.45)}{1 - e^{-N_A(18.02)(0.45)/5.66}} (150 - t_i) + \lambda_{Ai}N_A \qquad (3.66)$$

Cold
water
$t = 75°F$
$h = 100$

Copper
tube wall

Condensed
water film
$h = 2,000$

Air–water
vapor
$t_1 = 150°F$
$p_{A1} = 0.24$

t_i
p_{Ai}

Fig. 3.12   *Illustration* 3.6.

where λ_{Ai} is the molal latent heat of vaporization of water at t_i.   All the heat arriving at the interface is carried to the cold water. U is the overall heat-transfer coefficient, interface to cold water, based on the inside tube surface

$$\frac{1}{U} = \frac{1}{2,000} + \frac{0.065/12}{220}\frac{0.870}{0.935} + \frac{1}{100}\frac{0.870}{1.00}$$

where 220 is the thermal conductivity of the copper.

$$U = 108.5 \text{ Btu/(hr)(sq ft)(°F)}$$

$$q_t = 108.5(t_i - 75) \tag{3.67}$$

The rate of mass transfer is given by Eq. (3.61) with $N_B = 0$, $c_{Ai}/c = p_{Ai}$, $c_{A1}/c = y_{A1} = 0.24$.

$$N_A = 0.910 \ln\frac{1 - p_{Ai}}{1 - 0.24} \tag{3.68}$$

Equations (3.66) to (3.68) are solved simultaneously by trial with the vapor-pressure curve for water, which relates p_{Ai} and t_i, and the latent-heat data.   It is easiest to assume t_i, which is checked when q_t from Eqs. (3.66) and (3.67) agree.

As a final trial, assume $t_i = 107.5$°F, whence $p_{Ai} = 0.0806$ atm, $\lambda_{Ai} = 18,630$ Btu/lb mole, and [Eq. (3.68)] $N_A = 0.1740$ lb mole/(hr)(sq ft).   By Eq. (3.67) $q_t = 3,520$; by Eq. (3.66) $q_t = 3,512$ Btu/(hr)(sq ft), a sufficiently close check.   The local rate of condensation of water is therefore 0.1740 lb mole/(hr)(sq ft).   **Ans.**

Note: In this case, the true q_s [Eq. (3.62)] $= 272$ Btu/(hr)(sq ft), whereas the uncorrected h gives $5.66(150 - 107.5) = 240$ Btu/(hr)(sq ft).

Illustration 3.7. Recalculate the example of Illustration 3.6 under the following circumstances. The bulk air stream is free of water vapor, at 150°F, 1 atm, and flowing at $G' = 3,205$ lb/(hr)(sq ft). The tube is thoroughly insulated on the outside against transfer of heat.   The liquid film at the tube wall is supplied from the top.

Solution. In this case, sensible heat transfers by convection from the warm gas to the cooler liquid surface.   Heat does not penetrate the liquid.   Water evaporates into the gas at a rate sufficient to take away the heat arriving at the surface. q_t of Eq. (3.65) $= 0$.

For the gas, $G' = 3,205$, $G = 3,205/29 = 110.5$ lb moles/(hr)(sq ft); $\mu = (0.0195$ centipoise$)$ $(2.42) = 0.0472$ lb/(ft)(hr);   Re $= 0.0725(3,205)/(0.0472) = 4,930$; $N_B = 0$; $N_A/(N_A + N_B) = 1.0$.

$$j_D = \frac{F}{G}\text{Sc}^{2/3} = 0.023\,\text{Re}^{-0.17} = 0.023(4,930)^{-0.17} = 0.0054$$

$$F = \frac{0.0054G}{\text{Sc}^{2/3}} = \frac{0.0054(110.5)}{(0.60)^{2/3}} = 0.84 \text{ lb mole/(hr)(sq ft)}$$

$$j_H = j_D = \frac{h}{C_pG'}\text{Pr}^{2/3} = 0.0054$$

$$h = \frac{0.0054C_pG'}{\text{Pr}^{2/3}} = \frac{0.0054(0.24)(3,205)}{(0.75)^{2/3}} = 5.04 \text{ Btu/(hr)(sq ft)}$$

Eqs. (3.64) and (3.65):

$$q_t = \frac{N_A(18.02)(0.45)}{1 - e^{-N_A(18.02)(0.45)/5.04}}(150 - t_i) + \lambda_{Ai}N_A = 0$$

Eq. (3.61):

$$N_A = 0.84 \ln\frac{1 - p_{Ai}}{1 - 0}$$

These are solved by trial.   As a final trial, assume $t_i = 70$°F, whence $\lambda_{Ai} = 19,000$ Btu/lb mole, $p_{Ai} = 0.0247$ atm, $N_A = -0.0210$ lb mole/(hr)(sq ft), and $q_t = 0$ (check).   The local rate of evaporation is 0.0210 lb mole/(hr)(sq ft).   **Ans.**

NOTATION FOR CHAPTER 3

Consistent units in either cgs or the English system may be used. Pressures in mass-transfer equations are ordinarily expressed in atmospheres in either system.

a = specific surface of a fixed bed of pellets, pellet surface/volume of bed, sq cm/cu cm or sq ft/ cu ft

b_1, b_2 = constants

c = solute concentration (if subscripted), molar density of a solution (if not subscripted), g moles/cu cm or lb moles/cu ft

$\bar{c}$ = bulk-average concentration, g moles/cu cm or lb moles/cu ft

C_p = heat capacity at constant pressure, cal/(g)(°C) or Btu/(lb)(°F)

d = differential operator

        = diameter, cm or ft

d_c = diameter of a cylinder, cm or ft

d_p = diameter of a sphere; for nonspherical particles, diameter of a sphere of the same surface as the particle; cm or ft

D = molecular diffusivity, sq cm/sec or sq ft/hr

E_D = eddy mass diffusivity, sq cm/sec or sq ft/hr

E_H = eddy thermal diffusivity, sq cm/sec or sq ft/hr

E_v = eddy momentum diffusivity, sq cm/sec or sq ft/hr

f = friction factor; Fanning friction factor for flow through circular pipes; dimensionless

F = mass-transfer coefficient, g moles/(sec)(sq cm) or lb moles/(hr)(sq ft)

g = acceleration due to gravity, cm/sq sec or ft/sq hr

g_c = conversion factor, 980 (g mass)(cm)/(g force)(sq sec), or $4.17(10^8)$(lb mass)(ft)/(lb force) (sq hr)

G = molar mass velocity, g moles/(sec)(sq cm) or lb moles/(hr)(sq ft)

G' = mass velocity, g mass/(sec)(sq cm) or lb mass/(hr)(sq ft)

Gr   = Grashof number, dimensionless

h = heat-transfer coefficient, cal/(sec)(sq cm)(°C) or Btu/(hr)(sq ft)(°F)

j_D = mass-transfer dimensionless group, St Sc$^{2/3}$

j_H = heat-transfer dimensionless group, St Pr$^{2/3}$

J = mass-transfer flux, g moles/(sec)(sq cm) or lb moles/(hr)(sq ft)

k = thermal conductivity, (cal)(cm)/(sec)(sq cm)(°C) or (Btu)(ft)/(hr)(sq ft)(°F)

k_c, k_G, k_x, k_y, etc. = mass-transfer coefficients, g moles/(sec)(sq cm)(concentration difference) or lb moles/(hr)(sq ft)(concentration difference); see Table 3.1

l = a length; Prandtl mixing length, cm or ft

L = length of wetted-wall tower, cm or ft

M = molecular weight, g mass/g mole or lb mass/lb mole

n = a number, dimensionless

N = mass-transfer flux at a phase boundary, g moles/(sec)(sq cm) or lb moles/(hr)(sq ft)

Nu   = Nusselt number, dimensionless

p = partial pressure, atm

P_t = total pressure, atm

Pe   = Péclet number, dimensionless

Pr   = Prandtl number, dimensionless

q = heat-transfer flux, cal/(sec)(sq cm) or Btu/(hr)(sq ft)

R = universal gas constant, 82.06 (cu cm)(atm)/(g mole)(°K) or 0.729 (cu ft)(atm)/(lb mole)(°R)

Re   = Reynolds number, dimensionless

Re'   = Reynolds number for flow outside a cylinder, $d_c G'/\mu$, dimensionless

Re''   = Reynolds number for flow past a sphere, $d_p G'/\mu$, dimensionless

Re$_x$ = Reynolds number computed with x as the length dimension, dimensionless

s = fractional rate of surface-element replacement, 1/sec or 1/hr

S = cross-sectional area of a duct, sq cm or sq ft
Sh = Sherwood number, dimensionless
St = Stanton number, dimensionless
t = temperature, °C or °F
T = absolute temperature, °K or °R
u = local velocity, cm/sec or ft/hr
$\bar{u}$ = bulk-average velocity, cm/sec or ft/hr
u' = root-mean-square deviating velocity, cm/sec or ft/hr
u_i' = instantaneous deviating velocity, cm/sec or ft/hr
x, y, z (no subscript) = distances in the x, y, z direction, respectively, cm or ft
x_A = concentration of component A in a liquid, mole fraction
y_A = concentration of component A in a gas, mole fraction
z_b = depth of penetration (film and surface-renewal theories), cm or ft
z_F = effective film thickness (film theory), cm or ft
α = thermal diffusivity = $k/C_p\rho$, sq cm/sec or sq ft/hr
β = volumetric coefficient of expansion, 1/°C or 1/°F
Γ = mass rate of flow per unit width, g mass/(cm)(sec) or lb mass/(ft)(hr)
δ = thickness of a layer, cm or ft
Δ = difference
ϵ = fractional void volume in a fixed bed of pellets = $1 - d_p a/6$, dimensionless
θ = time, sec or hr
λ = molar heat evolution on passing through an interface, cal/g mole or Btu/lb mole
μ = viscosity, g mass/(cm)(sec) or lb mass/(ft)(hr)
ν = kinematic viscosity = μ/ρ, sq cm/sec or sq ft/hr
π = 3.1416
ρ = density, g mass/cu cm or lb mass/cu ft
τ = shear stress, g force/sq cm or lb force/sq ft
ϕ = area of surface elements (surface-renewal theory), sq cm/(sq cm)(sec) or sq ft/(sq ft)(hr)
ψ_1, ψ_2 = functions

Subscripts:

av = average
A = component A
B = component B
c = concentration
i = interface; instantaneous when used for velocity
M = logarithmic mean
s = sensible heat
t = total
turb = turbulent
x, y, z = in the x, y, and z direction, respectively
0 = approach, or initial, value
1 = at beginning of mass-transfer path
2 = at end of mass-transfer path

REFERENCES

1. Bedingfield, C. H., and T. B. Drew: *Ind. Eng. Chem.*, **42**, 1164 (1950).
2. Bennett, C. O., and J. E. Myers: "Momentum, Heat, and Mass Transfer," McGraw-Hill Book Company, New York, 1962.
3. Bird, R. B., W. E. Stewart, and E. N. Lightfoot: "Transport Phenomena," John Wiley & Sons, Inc., New York, 1960.

4. Chilton, T. H., and A. P. Colburn: *Ind. Eng. Chem.*, **26**, 1183 (1934).
5. Colburn, A. P.: *Trans. AIChE*, **29**, 174 (1933).
6. Colburn, A. P., and T. B. Drew: *Trans. AIChE*, **33**, 197 (1937).
7. Danckwerts, P. V.: *AIChE J.*, **1**, 456 (1955); *Ind. Eng. Chem.*, **43**, 1460 (1951).
8. Deissler, R. G.: *NACA Rept.* **1210**, 1955.
9. Dobbins, W. E.: pt. 2-1, in McCabe and Eckenfelder (eds.), "Biological Treatment of Sewage and Industrial Wastes," Reinhold Publishing Corporation, New York, 1956.
10. Dobbins, W. E.: "International Conference on Water Pollution Research, London, September, 1962," p. 61, Pergamon Press, New York, 1964.
11. Eckert, E. R. G., and R. M. Drake: "Heat and Mass Transfer," 2d ed., McGraw-Hill Book Company, New York, 1959.
12. Gaffney, B. J., and T. B. Drew: *Ind. Eng. Chem.*, **42**, 1120 (1950).
13. Gupta, A. S., and G. Thodos: *AIChE J.*, **9**, 751 (1963); *Ind. Eng. Chem. Fundamentals*, **3**, 218 (1964).
14. Hanratty, T. J.: *AIChE J.*, **2**, 359 (1956).
15. Higbie, R.: *Trans. AIChE*, **31**, 365 (1935).
16. Hinze, J. O.: "Turbulence," McGraw-Hill Book Company, New York, 1959.
17. Johnstone, H. F., and R. L. Pigford: *Trans. AIChE*, **38**, 25 (1952).
18. Lewis, W. K.: *Ind. Eng. Chem.*, **8**, 825 (1916).
19. Lewis, W. K., and W. Whitman: *Ind. Eng. Chem.*, **16**,1215 (1924).
20. Lin, C. S., R. W. Moulton, and G. L. Putnam: *Ind. Eng. Chem.*, **45**, 636 (1953).
21. Linton, W. H., and T. K. Sherwood: *Chem. Eng. Progr.*, **46**, 258 (1950).
22. McAdams, W. H.: "Heat Transmission," 3d ed., McGraw-Hill Book Company, New York, 1954.
23. Murphree, E. V.: *Ind. Eng. Chem.*, **24**, 726 (1932).
24. Opfell, J. B., and B. H. Sage: in T. B. Drew and J. W. Hoopes (eds.), "Advances in Chemical Engineering," vol. 1, p. 241, Academic Press, Inc., New York, 1956.
25. Page, F., W. G. Schlinger, D. K. Breaux, and B. H. Sage: *Ind. Eng. Chem.*, **44**, 424 (1952).
26. Powell, R. W.: *Trans. Inst. Chem. Engrs.* (*London*), **13**, 175 (1935); **18**, 36 (1940).
27. Prandtl, T. L.: *Z. Physik*, **11**, 1072 (1910); **29**, 487 (1928).
28. Reynolds, O.: "Scientific Papers of Osborne Reynolds," vol. II, Cambridge University Press, New York, 1901.
29. Ruckenstein, E.: *Chem. Eng. Sci.*, **7**, 265 (1958); **18**, 233 (1963).
30. Sherwood, T. K., and E. R. Gilliland: *Ind. Eng. Chem.*, **26**, 516 (1934).
31. Sherwood, T. K., and R. L. Pigford: "Absorption and Extraction," 2d ed., McGraw-Hill Book Company, New York, 1952.
32. Sleicher, C. A.: in A. Acrivos (ed.), "Modern Chemical Engineering," vol. I, p. 45, Reinhold Publishing Corporation, New York, 1963.
33. Steinberger, R. L., and R. E. Treybal: *AIChE J.*, **6**, 227 (1960).
34. Stynes, S. K., and J. E. Myers: *AIChE J.*, **10**, 437 (1964).
35. Taylor, G. I.: *Rept. Mem., Brit. Advisory Comm. Aeronaut.*, **272**, 423 (1916).
36. Toor, H. L., and J. M. Marchello: *AIChE J.*, **4**, 97 (1958).
37. Towle, W. L., and T. K. Sherwood: *Ind. Eng. Chem.*, **31**, 457 (1939).
38. Vieth, W. R., J. H. Porter, and T. K. Sherwood: *Ind. Eng. Chem. Fundamentals*, **2**, 1 (1963).
39. Williams, J. E., K. E. Bazaire, and C. J. Geankoplis: *Ind. Eng. Chem. Fundamentals*, **2**, 126 (1963).

PROBLEMS

3.1. Estimate the mass-transfer coefficient and effective film thickness to be expected in the absorption of ammonia from air by a 2 N sulfuric acid solution in a wetted-wall tower under the following circumstances:

Air flow $= 41.4$ g/min (air only)
Av partial pressure ammonia in air $= 30.8$ mm Hg
Total pressure $= 760$ mm Hg
Av gas temp $= 25°C$
Av liquid temp $= 25°C$
Diam tower $= 1.46$ cm

For absorption of ammonia in sulfuric acid of this concentration, the entire mass-transfer resistance lies within the gas, and the partial pressure of ammonia at the interface is negligible. *Note:* The circumstances correspond to run 47 of Chambers and Sherwood [*Trans. AIChE*, **33**, 579 (1937)], who observed $d/z_F = 16.6$.

3.2. Powell[26] evaporated water from the outside of cylinders into an air stream flowing parallel to the axes of the cylinders. The air temperature was $25°C$, and the total pressure atmospheric. The results are given by

$$\frac{wl}{p_w - p_a} = 3.17(10^{-8})(ul)^{0.8}$$

where $w =$ water evaporated, g/(sec)(sq cm)
$p_a =$ partial pressure of water in air stream, mm Hg
$p_w =$ water vapor pressure at surface temp, mm Hg
$u =$ velocity of air stream, cm/sec
$l =$ length cylinder, cm

a. Transform the equation into the form $j_D = \psi(Re_l)$, where Re_l is a Reynolds number based on the cylinder length.

b. Calculate the rate of sublimation from a cylinder of naphthalene 3 in. in diam, 24 in. long, into a stream of pure carbon dioxide at a velocity of 20 ft/sec, 1 atm, $100°C$. The vapor pressure of naphthalene at the surface temperature may be taken as 10 mm Hg, and its diffusivity in carbon dioxide as 0.0515 sq cm/sec at $0°C$, 1 atm. Express the results as grams naphthalene evaporated/hr. **Ans.:** 345.

3.3. Water flows down the inside wall of a wetted-wall tower of the design of Fig. 3.10, while air flows upward through the core. In a particular case, the inside diameter is 1 in., and dry air enters at the rate 5,000 lb/(hr)(sq ft of inside cross section). Assume the air is everywhere at its average temperature, $97°F$, the water at $70°F$, and the mass-transfer coefficient constant. Pressure $= 1$ atm. Compute the average partial pressure of water in the air leaving, if the tower is 3 ft long. **Ans.:** 0.015 atm.

3.4. Winding and Cheney [*Ind. Eng. Chem.*, **40**, 1087 (1948)] passed air through a bank of rods of naphthalene. The rods were of "streamline" cross section, arranged in staggered array, with the air flowing at right angles to the axes of the rods. The mass-transfer coefficient was determined by measuring the rate of sublimation of the naphthalene. For a particular shape, size, and spacing of the rods, with air at $100°F$, 1 atm, the data could be correlated empirically by

$$k_G = 0.00663G'^{0.56}$$

where $G' =$ superficial mass velocity of air, lb/(hr)(sq ft)
$k_G =$ lb moles/(hr)(sq ft)(atm)

Estimate the mass-transfer coefficient to be expected for evaporation of water into hydrogen gas for the same geometrical arrangement, when the hydrogen flows at a superficial velocity of 50 ft/sec, $100°F$, 2 atm pressure. D for naphthalene-air, 1 atm, $100°F = 0.272$ sq ft/hr; for water-hydrogen, $32°F$, 1 atm $= 2.9$ sq ft/hr.

3.5. For the dissolution of crystals of soluble anhydrous solids into water in an agitated tank, Barker and Treybal [*AIChE J.*, **6**, 289 (1960)] obtained the following expression for the mass-transfer coefficient:

$$\frac{k_{L,av}T}{D_{AB}} = 0.052 \, Re_s^{0.833} \, Sc^{0.5}$$

where T = tank diameter
        Re_s = Reynolds number of stirrer
c_{A1}[Eq. (3.4)] = solubility of solute in water
        c_{A2} = solute concentration in the bulk liquid, lb moles/cu ft

A tank 3 ft in diameter, 4 ft deep, contains 1,250 lb water and is agitated with the 8-in.-diam stirrer at a stirrer Reynolds number Re_s = 100,000. Two hundred fifty pounds $CuSO_4 \cdot 5H_2O$ in the form of uniform crystals, $\frac{1}{4}$ in. diam, are suddenly dropped into the tank.

    a. Estimate the initial rate of dissolving, lb hydrate/hr.
    b. Estimate the time required to (1) dissolve all but 10 lb of the crystals and (2) completely dissolve the crystals.   **Ans.:** (1) 0.328 hr, (2) 0.548 hr.

    Data and assumptions. Assume the temperature remains at 20°C. For $CuSO_4$ in water D = $0.73(10^{-5})$ sq cm/sec. The density of the hydrate crystals = 143 lb/cu ft. For present purposes, assume that the kinematic viscosity of the solution remains at 1 centistoke and the solution density at 62.4 lb/cu ft. The crystals are assumed to be uniform spheres which remain spherical as they dissolve, without break-up of the crystals. Assume F remains constant for all crystal sizes. The solubility of $CuSO_4$ in water = 0.0229 mole fraction $CuSO_4$ at 20°C.

    3.6. The free-fall terminal velocity of water drops in air at atmospheric pressure is given by the following table of data:[31]

Diam, mm	0.05	0.2	0.5	1.0	2.0	3.0
Velocity, ft/sec	0.18	2.3	7.0	12.7	19.2	23.8

A water drop of initial diam 1.0 mm falls in quiet dry air at 1 atm, 100°F. The liquid temperature may be taken as 58°F. Assume the drop remains spherical and that the atmospheric pressure remains constant at 1 atm.

    a. Calculate the initial rate of evaporation.
    b. Calculate the time and distance of free fall for the drop to evaporate to a diameter of 0.2 mm.
Ans.: 0.0276 hr, 830 ft.
    c. Calculate the time for the above evaporation, assuming that the drop is suspended without motion (as from a fine thread) in still air.

    3.7. The temperature variation of rate of a chemical reaction which involves mass transfer is sometimes used to determine whether the rate of mass transfer or that of the chemical reaction "controls" or is the dominating mechanism.

    Consider a fluid flowing through a 1.0-in.-ID circular tube, where the transferred solute is ammonia in dilute solution. Compute the mass-transfer coefficient for each of the following cases:

    a. The fluid is a dilute solution of ammonia in air, 25°C, 1 atm, flowing at a Reynolds number = 10,000. D_{AB} = 0.226 sq cm/sec.
    b. Same as (*a*) (same mass velocity), but temperature = 35°C.
    c. The fluid is a dilute solution of ammonia in liquid water, 25°C, flowing at a Reynolds number = 10,000. D_{AB} = $2.65(10^{-5})$ sq cm/sec.
    d. Same as (*c*) (same mass velocity), but temperature = 35°C.

    In the case of both gas and liquid, assuming that the mass-transfer coefficient follows an Arrhenius-type equation, compute the "energy of activation" of mass transfer. Are these high or low, in comparison with the energy of activation of typical chemical reactions? Note that, for dilute solutions, the identity of the diffusing solute need not have been specified in order to obtain the "energy of activation" of mass transfer. What other method might be used to determine whether reaction rate or mass-transfer rate controls?

    3.8. A gas consisting of 50% air, 50% steam, by volume, flows at 200°F, 1 atm pressure at 25 ft/sec av velocity through a horizontal, square duct 1 ft wide. A horizontal copper tube, 1 in. OD, 0.065 in. wall thickness, passes through the center of the duct from one side to the other, at right angles to the duct axis, piercing the duct walls.   Cold water flows inside the tube at an average temperature of 60°F, velocity 10 ft/sec.   Estimate the rate of condensation on the outside of the copper tube.   **Ans.:** 5.54 lb/hr.

   Data. McAdams,[22] p. 338, gives the heat-transfer coefficient for the condensate film on the tube as

$$h_{av} = 1.51 \left(\frac{k^3 \rho^2 g}{\mu^2} \right)^{1/3} \left(\frac{\mu L}{4W} \right)^{1/3}$$

where W = lb/hr condensate
       L = tube length, ft

The fluid properties are to be evaluated at the mean temperature of the condensate film.   Data for the group $(k^3 \rho^2 g / \mu^2)^{1/3}$ for water are listed in McAdams, Table A-27, p. 484, for convenience.

CHAPTER FOUR
DIFFUSION IN SOLIDS

It was indicated in Chap. 1 that certain of the diffusional operations such as leaching, drying, adsorption, and the "membrane" operations of dialysis and gaseous effusion involve contact of fluids with solids. In such operations the diffusion must involve the solid phase and may proceed according to several mechanisms. Diffusion through a solid when the solute is dissolved to form a homogeneous solid solution may be termed "structure-insensitive" diffusion, and this form is most nearly similar to diffusion through fluids. A porous or granular solid, however, may permit flow of a liquid or gas through the interstices and capillaries, and diffusion by this mechanism may be termed "structure-sensitive." Diffusion may occur even along the surface of a solid with nothing but superficial penetration of the solute into the solid itself, which may be important in certain adsorption operations.

STRUCTURE-INSENSITIVE DIFFUSION

This type of diffusion may occur when the diffusing substance dissolves in the solid to form a homogeneous solution. The actual mechanisms of the diffusion may be quite complex and very different for diverse substances. For example, in the diffusion of hydrogen through palladium metal the hydrogen molecules evidently dissociate and enter the metal crystal lattice as atoms. On the other hand, nitrogen or oxygen when diffusing through metals forms compounds, and it is the progressive decomposition of these nitrides or oxides which results in the passage of the gas. Helium and hydrogen may diffuse through the anionic network of a glass, while gases such as argon and air diffuse along faults in the structure. The diffusion of metals into each other, such as the diffusion of gold through silver, follows a different mechanism from that of the diffusion of gases through membranes or rubber and other polymers or of ammonia and water through certain zeolitic crystals.

Steady-state diffusion

When the concentration gradient remains unchanged with passage of time, so that the rate of diffusion is constant, Fick's law may be applied in the form used in Chap. 2 for cases where the diffusivity is independent of concentration and where there is no bulk flow. Thus N_A, the rate of diffusion of substance A per unit cross section of solid, is proportional to the concentration gradient in the direction of diffusion, $-dc_A/dz$,

$$N_A = -D_{AB}\frac{dc_A}{dz} \tag{4.1}$$

where D_{AB} is the diffusivity of A through B. If D_{AB} is constant, integration of Eq. (4.1) for *diffusion through a flat slab* of thickness z results in

$$N_A = \frac{D_{AB}(c_{A1} - c_{A2})}{z} \tag{4.2}$$

which parallels the expressions obtained for fluids in a similar situation. Here c_{A1} and c_{A2} are the concentrations at opposite sides of the slab. For other solid shapes, the rate is given by

$$w = N_A S_{av} = \frac{D_{AB}S_{av}(c_{A1} - c_{A2})}{z} \tag{4.3}$$

with appropriate values of the average cross section for diffusion, S_{av}, to be applied. Thus, for *radial diffusion through a solid cylinder* of inner and outer radii a_1 and a_2, respectively, and of length l,

$$S_{av} = \frac{2\pi l(a_2 - a_1)}{\ln(a_2/a_1)} \tag{4.4}$$

and
$$z = a_2 - a_1 \tag{4.5}$$

For *radial diffusion through a spherical shell* of inner and outer radii a_1 and a_2,

$$S_{av} = 4\pi a_1 a_2 \tag{4.6}$$

$$z = a_2 - a_1 \tag{4.7}$$

Illustration 4.1. Hydrogen gas at 2 atm pressure, 25°C, is flowing through a pipe made of a vulcanized neoprene rubber, whose ID and OD are 1 and 2 in., respectively. The solubility of the hydrogen is 0.053 cu cm H_2 at standard conditions per cubic centimeter rubber per atmosphere, and the diffusivity of the hydrogen through the rubber is 0.18(10^{-5}) sq cm/sec. Estimate the rate of loss of hydrogen by diffusion per foot of pipe length.

Solution. At 2 atm hydrogen pressure, the solubility is 0.053(2) = 0.106 cu ft H_2 at standard conditions per cubic foot rubber. Therefore concentration c_{A1} at the inner surface of the pipe = 0.106/359 = 0.000295 lb mole H_2/cu ft.

At the outer surface, c_{A2} = 0 (assuming that the resistance to diffusion of the H_2 away from the surface is negligible).

$$D_{AB} = 0.18(10^{-5})(3.87) = 0.696(10^{-5}) \text{ sq ft/hr}$$

$$z = a_2 - a_1 = \frac{2-1}{2(12)} = 0.0417 \text{ ft} \qquad l = 1 \text{ ft}$$

Eq. (4.4): $\quad S_{av} = \dfrac{2\pi(1)(1-0.5)}{12 \ln(1/0.5)} = 0.377 \text{ sq ft}$

Eq. (4.3): $\quad w = \dfrac{D_{AB}S_{av}(c_{A1} - c_{A2})}{z} = \dfrac{0.696(10^{-5})(0.377)(0.000295 - 0)}{0.0417}$

$$= 1.86(10^{-8}) \text{ lb mole } H_2/\text{hr} \quad \textbf{Ans.}$$

Unsteady-state diffusion

Since solids are not so readily transported through equipment as fluids are, the application of batch and semibatch processes and consequently unsteady-state diffusional conditions arise much more frequently than in the case of fluids. Even in continuous operation, as in the case of a continuous drier, the history of each solid piece as it passes through equipment is representative of the unsteady state. These cases are therefore of considerable importance.

For the case where there is no bulk flow, and in the absence of chemical reaction, Fick's second law, Eq. (2.18), can be used to solve problems of unsteady-state diffusion by integration with appropriate boundary conditions. For some simple cases, Newman[6] has summarized the results most conveniently.

1. *Diffusion from a slab with sealed edges.* Consider a slab of thickness 2a, with sealed edges on four sides, so that diffusion can take place only toward and from the flat parallel faces, a cross section of which is shown in Fig. 4.1. Suppose initially the concentration of solute throughout the slab is uniform, c_{A0}, and that the slab is immersed in a medium so that the solute will diffuse out of the slab. Let the concentration at the surfaces be $c_{A\infty}$, invariant with passage of time. If the diffusion were allowed to continue indefinitely, the concentration would fall to the uniform value $c_{A\infty}$, and $c_{A0} - c_{A\infty}$ is a measure of the amount of solute removed. On the other hand, if diffusion from the slab were stopped at time θ, the distribution of solute would be given by the curve marked c, which by internal diffusion would level off to the uniform concentration $c_{A\theta}$, where $c_{A\theta}$ is the average concentration at time θ. The quantity $c_{A\theta} - c_{A\infty}$ is a measure of the amount of solute still unremoved. The fraction unremoved, E, is given by integration of Eq. (2.18),

$$E = \frac{c_{A\theta} - c_{A\infty}}{c_{A\theta} - c_{A\infty}} = f\left(\frac{D\theta}{a^2}\right)$$

$$= \frac{8}{\pi^2}\left(e^{-D\theta\pi^2/4a^2} + \tfrac{1}{9}e^{-9D\theta\pi^2/4a^2} + \tfrac{1}{25}e^{-25D\theta\pi^2/4a^2} + \cdots\right) = E_a \qquad (4.8)$$

The function is shown graphically in Fig. 4.2.

2. *Diffusion from a rectangular bar with sealed ends.* For a rectangular bar of thickness $2a$ and width $2b$, with sealed ends,

$$E = f\left(\frac{D\theta}{a^2}\right) f\left(\frac{D\theta}{b^2}\right) = E_a E_b \tag{4.9}$$

3. *Diffusion for a rectangular parallelepiped.* For a brick-shaped bar, of dimensions $2a$, $2b$, and $2c$, with diffusion from all six faces,

$$E = f\left(\frac{D\theta}{a^2}\right) f\left(\frac{D\theta}{b^2}\right) f\left(\frac{D\theta}{c^2}\right) = E_a E_b E_c \tag{4.10}$$

4. *Diffusion from a sphere.* For a sphere of radius a,

$$E = f'\left(\frac{D\theta}{a^2}\right) = E_s \tag{4.11}$$

5. *Diffusion from a cylinder with sealed ends.* For a cylinder of radius a, with plane ends sealed,

$$E = f''\left(\frac{D\theta}{a^2}\right) = E_r \tag{4.12}$$

6. *Diffusion from a cylinder.* For a cylinder of radius a and length $2c$, with diffusion from both ends as well as from the cylindrical surface,

$$E = f\left(\frac{D\theta}{c^2}\right) f''\left(\frac{D\theta}{a^2}\right) = E_c E_r \tag{4.13}$$

The functions $f'(D\theta/a^2)$ and $f''(D\theta/a^2)$ are also shown in Fig. 4.2.

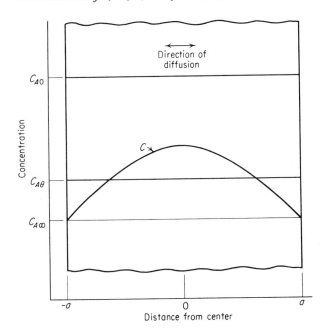

Fig. 4.1   *Unsteady-state diffusion in a slab.*

Fig. 4.2 *Unsteady-state diffusion.*

For solid shapes where the diffusion takes place from one rather than two oppo-site faces, the functions are calculated as if the thickness were twice the true value. For example, if diffusion occurs through only one face of the flat slab of thickness $2a$, edges sealed, the calculation is made with $D\theta/4a^2$. The equations may also be used for diffusion into, as well as out of, the various shapes.

It is important to note that Eqs. (4.8) to (4.13) and Fig. 4.2 all assume constant diffusivity, initially uniform concentration within the solid, and constancy of the edge concentration $c_{A\infty}$. The last is the same as assuming (1) that there is no resistance to diffusion in the fluid surrounding the solid and (2) that the quantity of such fluid is so large that its concentration does not change with time or (3) that the fluid is contin-uously replenished. In many instances, the diffusional resistance within the solid is so large that the assumption of absence of any in the fluid is quite reasonable. In any case, however, integrations of Eq. (2.18) involving varying D^{11} and the effect of added diffusional resistance[1,4-6] have been developed. It is useful to note that Eq. (2.18) is of the same form as Fourier's equation for heat conduction, with molecular rather than thermal diffusivity and concentration rather than temperature. Consequently the lengthy catalog of solutions to the problems of heat transfer of Carslaw and Jaeger[3] may be made applicable to diffusion by appropriate substitutions. Crank's book[4] deals particularly with problems of this sort for diffusion.

Illustration 4.2. A 5% agar gel containing a uniform concentration of 5 g urea/100 cu cm is molded in the form of a 3-cm cube. One face of the cube is exposed to a running supply of fresh water into which the urea diffuses. The other faces are protected by the mold. The temperature is 5°C. At the end of 68 hr, the average urea concentration in the gel has fallen to 3 g/100 cu cm. The resistance to diffusion may be considered as residing wholly within the gel.

a. Calculate the diffusivity of the urea in the gel.

b. How long would it have taken for the average concentration to fall to 1 g/100 cu cm?

c. Repeat (b) for the case where two opposite faces of the cube are exposed.

Solution. a. c_A can be calculated in terms of g/100 cu cm. $c_{A0} = 5$ g/100 cu cm; $c_{A\theta} = 3$, $c_{A\infty} = 0$ since pure water was the leaching agent. $a = \frac{3}{2} = 1.5$ cm; $\theta = 68(3,600) = 245,000$ sec.

$$\frac{c_{A\theta} - c_{A\infty}}{c_{A0} - c_{A\infty}} = \frac{3}{5} = 0.6 = E$$

The abscissa read from Fig. 4.2, which is $D\theta/4a^2$ for diffusion from only one exposed face, is 0.128

$$D = \frac{0.128(4)a^2}{\theta} = \frac{0.128(4)(1.5)^2}{245,000} = 4.70(10^{-6}) \text{ sq cm/sec}$$

b. For $c_{A\theta} = 1$ g/100 cu cm

$$\frac{c_{A\theta} - c_{A\infty}}{c_{A0} - c_{A\infty}} = \frac{1}{5} = 0.20 \qquad \frac{D\theta}{4a^2} = 0.568 \qquad \text{from Fig. 4.2}$$

$$\theta = \frac{0.568(4)a^2}{D} = \frac{0.568(4)(1.5)^2}{4.70(10^{-6})} = 1,087,000 \text{ sec, or 302 hr}$$

c. For two opposite faces exposed, $a = 1.5$ cm, $c_{A\theta}/c_{A0} = 0.2$, and $D\theta/a^2 = 0.568$.

$$\theta = \frac{0.568a^2}{D} = \frac{0.568(1.5)^2}{4.70(10^{-6})} = 222,000 \text{ sec, or 61.5 hr}$$

Diffusivity and permeability

While a great many measurements of diffusivity have been made, these are largely in connection with systems not of immediate interest here. The diffusivity in metals, for example, is of great interest to the metallurgist in problems of carburizing, nitriding or powder metallurgy, but of little value in the diffusional operations of the chemical engineer. A great many data on the diffusivity of gases through membranes have been gathered, a few typical values of which are listed in Table 4.1 in order to indicate order of magnitude. In connection with diffusion through membranes particularly, it is common to cite the so-called permeability P, rather than the diffusivity.[10] Permeability is defined as

$$P = \frac{V}{-dp/dz} \tag{4.14}$$

Table 4.1. Diffusivity of gases in vulcanized rubber,[1] 25°C

Diffusing substance (A)	D_{AB}, sq cm/sec	Solubility, cu cm gas, 0°C, 1 atm (cu cm rubber)(atm)
H_2	$0.85(10^{-5})$	0.040
O_2	$0.21(10^{-5})$	0.070
N_2	$0.15(10^{-5})$	0.035
CO_2	$0.11(10^{-5})$	0.90

where V is the volume of gas (at some specified temperature and pressure, frequently 1 atm, 0°C) diffusing per unit time (area) under the pressure gradient $-dp/dz$. The maximum concentration of solute gas in the solid is its solubility, which varies with the pressure of the gas in contact with the membrane.

Illustration 4.3. From the data of Table 4.1, calculate the rate of diffusion of carbon dioxide, CO_2, through a membrane of the rubber 1 mm thick at 25°C if the partial pressure of the CO_2 is 1 cm Hg on one side and zero on the other. Calculate also the permeability of the membrane.

Solution. At a pressure of 1 cm Hg ($\frac{1}{76}$ atm) the solubility of CO_2 in the rubber is $0.90/76 = 0.01184$ cu cm gas (measured at 0°C, 1 atm) per cu cm rubber, or $0.01184/22,400$ g mole CO_2/cu cm. On the downstream face of the membrane the CO_2 concentration is zero. The thickness $z = 0.1$ cm. Therefore

$$V = 22,400 N_A = \frac{22,400 D_{AB}\, \Delta c}{z} = \frac{0.11(10^{-5})(0.01184)}{0.1}$$

$$= 0.13(10^{-6}) \text{ cu cm } (0°C, 1 \text{ atm}) \text{ per sec/sq cm}$$

Eq. (4.14): $$P = \frac{V}{-dp/dz} = \frac{0.13(10^{-6})}{(1/76)/0.1}$$

$$= 0.99(10^{-6}) \text{ cu cm } (0°C, 1 \text{ atm}) \text{ per sec/(sq cm)(atm/cm)}$$

Note that $P = D_{AB}$ (solubility) $= 0.11(10^{-5})(0.90) = 0.99(10^{-6})$.

Diffusivities in solids may vary very rapidly with temperature, much more so than with liquids or gases. For example, D for nitrogen through a vulcanized chloroprene-polymer membrane is cited as $0.019(10^{-5})$ sq cm/sec at 27.1°C and $0.450(10^{-5})$ sq cm/sec at 84.3°C.[1] Usually, log D is linear with reciprocal absolute temperature for solid diffusion. The diffusivity may vary considerably with concentration; it may be anisotropic; for example, the diffusivity through crystals may vary depending upon the direction with respect to the various crystallographic axes. Observations such as these make it understandable that it is now impossible to predict the diffusivity in solids, as we did for liquids or gases, and it is necessary in practice to measure the diffusivity experimentally under the desired conditions.

STRUCTURE-SENSITIVE DIFFUSION

This is a most complex subject, owing to the great variety of solid structures and diffusing solutes which may have to be studied. Only a few of the situations can be considered in any detail.

Diffusion through a uniformly porous solid

Consider a rigid solid which is uniformly porous throughout, i.e., where the nature and percentage of voids are constant in all directions and in every part of the solid, as might be the case with an idealized clay brick. Suppose the pores and interstices of such a solid are filled with a solution, such as a solution of salt in water. If the solid is now immersed in water, one may imagine a continuous liquid path leading from the depths within the solid to the surrounding liquid through the myriad interstices formed by the rigid solid structure. Since a concentration gradient of dissolved salt exists within the liquid path, diffusion occurs, and in time the salt will completely diffuse from the solid into the surrounding fresh water.

To such a system the previous equations applicable to solid solutions may be applied. Since the liquid path along which the diffusion takes place is relatively very long and in general not known, one may characterize the operation by use of an effective diffusivity to be used in the equations of the preceding section, which could be expected to be smaller than the ordinary diffusivities for the solute in the solvent in the absence of a constraining solid structure. As an alternative,[7] one may define a "pore-shape factor" K, characteristic of the number, size, and nature of the pores in the solid, which when multiplied by the ordinary solid thickness provides a measure of the true length of the diffusion path. The factor is independent of solute and solvent, concentration, time, or any other variable affecting the rate of diffusion. Use of the preceding equations then requires, as before, constancy of the diffusivity, or the use of a correct average or integral diffusivity, over the concentration range experienced.

Under certain limited conditions, the previous relations may also be used to describe the change in average moisture content of a solid during drying: under conditions such that internal diffusion of moisture controls the rate of drying, and in cases where the solid structure contains very fine interstices. Coarse sands do not fall into the latter category, and the drying of wood on occasions may be complicated by the variation of diffusivity with direction, i.e., with or across the grain. These matters are considered in greater detail in Chap. 12. Applications to leaching are discussed in Chap. 13. For applications in catalysis, see the book by Satterfield and Sherwood.[8]

Illustration 4.4. Porous alumina spheres, 1 cm diameter, 25% voids, were thoroughly impregnated with an aqueous potassium chloride, KCl, solution concentration 0.25 g/cu cm. When immersed in pure running water, they lost 90% of their salt content in 4.75 hr. The temperature was 25°C. At this temperature the average diffusivity of KCl in water over the indicated concentration range is $1.84(10^{-5})$ sq cm/sec.

Estimate the time for removal of 90% of the dissolved solute if the spheres had been impregnated with potassium chromate, K_2CrO_4, solution at a concentration 0.28 g/cu cm, when immersed in a running stream of water containing 0.02 g K_2CrO_4/cu cm. The average diffusivity of K_2CrO_4 in water at 25°C is $1.14(10^{-5})$ sq cm/sec.

Solution. For these spheres, $a = 0.5$ cm, and, for the KCl diffusion, $\theta = 4.75(3,600) = 17,000$ sec. When the spheres are surrounded by pure water, the ultimate concentration in the spheres, $c_{A\infty} = 0$.

$$\therefore \quad \frac{c_{A\theta} - c_{A\infty}}{c_{A0} - c_{A\infty}} = 0.1 \quad \text{for 90\% removal of KCl}$$

From Fig. 4.2, $D\theta/(Ka)^2 = 0.18$, where K is the pore-shape factor.

$$K^2 = \frac{D\theta}{a^2(0.18)} = \frac{1.84(10^{-5})(17,000)}{0.5^2(0.18)} = 6.95$$

For the K_2CrO_4 diffusion, $c_{A0} = 0.28$ g/cu cm; $c_{A\infty} = 0.02$, and $c_{A\theta} = 0.1(0.28) = 0.028$.

$$\therefore \quad E = \frac{c_{A\theta} - c_{A\infty}}{c_{A0} - c_{A\infty}} = \frac{0.028 - 0.02}{0.28 - 0.02} = 0.0308 = E_s$$

From Fig. 4.2, $D\theta/(Ka)^2 = 0.30$.

$$\theta = \frac{0.30(Ka)^2}{D} = \frac{0.30(6.95)(0.5)^2}{1.14(10^{-5})} = 45,800 \text{ sec, or 12.2 hr} \quad \textbf{Ans.}$$

Illustration 4.5. A slab of wood, 15.2 by 15.2 by 1.90 cm, of initial uniform moisture content 39.7% water, was exposed to relatively dry air.[9]   The thin edges were sealed, and drying took place from the two large flat faces by internal diffusion of liquid water to the surface and evaporation at the surface.   The moisture content at the surface remained constant at 8.0%.   At the end of 7 hr 40 min, the average moisture content had fallen to 24.0%.

   a.   Calculate the effective diffusivity, sq cm/sec.

   b.   Assuming D remains constant and is the same for diffusion in all directions, what average water content would have resulted had the slab been dried from one face only, and from all six faces, for the same length of time?

   c.   What average water content would be had for a cylinder 1 ft long, 6 in. diameter, drying from all surfaces for a period of 7 days?

   Solution. a. Let ρ = dry density of wood, lb dry wood/cu ft, assumed constant.   If X is mass fraction of water, concentration in lb moles/cu ft $= \rho \dfrac{X}{1 - X} \dfrac{1}{18.02}$.   Since the factor $\rho/18.02$ then appears in all such concentrations, E may be computed in terms of lb water/lb dry wood, $X/(1 - X)$.

$$c_{A0} = \frac{0.397}{1 - 0.397} = 0.658 \text{ lb water/lb dry wood}$$

$$c_{A\infty} = \frac{0.08}{1 - 0.08} = 0.087 \text{ lb water/lb dry wood}$$

$$c_{A\theta} = \frac{0.240}{1 - 0.240} = 0.316 \text{ lb water/lb dry wood}$$

At $\theta = 7.67(3,600) = 27,600$ sec,

$$E = \frac{c_{A\theta} - c_{A\infty}}{c_{A0} - c_{A\infty}} = \frac{0.316 - 0.087}{0.658 - 0.087} = 0.40 = E_a$$

From Fig. 4.2, $D\theta/a^2 = 0.287$.   Since $a = 1.90/2 = 0.95$ cm,

$$\text{Effective diffusivity} = D = \frac{0.287a^2}{\theta} = \frac{0.287(0.95)^2}{27,600} = 9.38(10^{-6}) \text{ sq cm/sec}$$

   b.   For diffusion through one face only,

$$\frac{D\theta}{4a^2} = \frac{9.38(10^{-6})(27,600)}{4(0.95)^2} = 0.0718$$

From Fig. 4.2, $E = E_a = 0.7$.

$$\therefore \quad 0.7 = \frac{c_{A0} - 0.087}{0.658 - 0.087} \qquad c_{A0} = 0.487 \text{ lb water/lb dry wood}$$

corresponding to

$$\frac{0.487}{1.487} \, 100 = 32.8\% \text{ water}$$

For diffusion through six faces, $a = 0.95$ cm, $b = c = 15.2/2 = 7.6$ cm.

$$\frac{D\theta}{a^2} = \frac{9.38(10^{-6})(27,600)}{(0.95)^2} = 0.287$$

$$\frac{D\theta}{b^2} = \frac{D\theta}{c^2} = \frac{9.38(10^{-6})(27,600)}{(7.6)^2} = 0.00448$$

From Fig. 4.2, $E_a = 0.4$, $E_b = E_c = 0.94$.

Eq. (4.10): $\qquad E = E_a E_b E_c = 0.4(0.94)(0.94) = 0.353$

$$0.353 = \frac{c_{A\theta} - 0.087}{0.658 - 0.087}$$

$$c_{A\theta} = 0.291 \text{ lb water/lb dry wood } (22.5\% \text{ water})$$

c. For 7 days, $\theta = 7(24) = 168$ hr.

$$D = 9.38(10^{-6})(3.87) = 36.3(10^{-6}) \text{ sq ft/hr}$$

$$a = \frac{0.5}{2} = 0.25 \text{ ft} \qquad c = \frac{1}{2} = 0.5 \text{ ft}$$

$$\frac{D\theta}{a^2} = \frac{36.3(10^{-6})(168)}{(0.25)^2} = 0.0975 \qquad E_r = 0.405$$

$$\frac{D\theta}{c^2} = \frac{36.3(10^{-6})(168)}{(0.5)^2} = 0.0244 \qquad E_c = 0.82$$

Eq. (4.13): $\quad E = E_c E_r = 0.82(0.405) = 0.332$

$$0.332 = \frac{c_{A\theta} - 0.087}{0.658 - 0.087} \qquad c_{A\theta} = 0.277 \text{ lb water/lb dry wood } (21.7\% \text{ water})$$

Flow of gases through porous solids[2]

If there exists a concentration difference, i.e., a pressure difference, for a gas across a porous solid, a flow of the gas through the solid will take place. Under ordinary conditions, this is not a diffusional flow in the usual sense; yet since it may be described according to the methods of diffusion, it is sometimes so considered. Let us for the moment simplify the structure of the porous solid and consider it to be a series of straight capillary tubes of constant diameter d, and of length l, reaching from the high-pressure to the low-pressure side of the solid. At ordinary pressures, the flow of the gas in the capillaries may be either streamline or turbulent, depending upon whether the dimensionless Reynolds number, $du\rho/\mu$, is below or above 2,100. For the present purposes, where the diameter of the capillaries is small, and the pressure difference and hence the velocity are small, flow will be streamline and is described by

Poiseuille's law for a compressible fluid obeying the perfect-gas law,

$$N_A = \frac{d^2 g_c}{32 \mu l R T} p_{av} (p_1 - p_2) \tag{4.15}$$

where

$$p_{av} = \frac{p_1 + p_2}{2} \tag{4.16}$$

This assumes that the entire pressure difference is due to friction in the capillaries and ignores entrance and exit losses and kinetic-energy effects, which is satisfactory for present purposes. The capillaries leading through the porous solid are not of constant diameter, and their length is on the average some multiple of the solid thickness z. Only a fraction of the surface of the solid is open to the gas. The equation may then be written

$$RTN_A = \frac{k p_{av} (p_1 - p_2)}{z} \tag{4.17}$$

If the rate of flow is measured in terms of a gas volume V at the average pressure flowing per unit time per unit cross section of the solid, then Eq. (4.17) becomes

$$p_{av} V = \frac{P p_{av} (p_1 - p_2)}{z} \tag{4.18}$$

where P is the permeability of the solid to gas flow by Poiseuille's law. It is possible to compute average capillary sizes in membranes and porous barriers by measurements made according to this equation.

Under certain conditions, a different type of flow will occur, however. If the capillary diameters are small in comparison with the mean free path of the gas molecules λ (say $d \leq 0.1\lambda$), flow takes place by molecular effusion, following Knudsen's law. For a single straight capillary, this becomes

$$N_A = k' \sqrt{\frac{g_c}{2\pi M R T}} \frac{d}{l} (p_1 - p_2) \tag{4.19}$$

where k' is a correction to take care of reflection of the molecule from the capillary wall. This may be written

$$RTN_A = k' \sqrt{\frac{g_c R T}{2\pi M}} \frac{d}{l} (p_1 - p_2) \tag{4.20}$$

or since, as before, the capillaries are of variable diameter nor is their length the same as the thickness of the solid,

$$p_{av} V = \frac{P'(p_1 - p_2)}{z} \tag{4.21}$$

where P' is now the permeability of the solid to molecular streaming. The mean free path of the molecules can be estimated from the relation

$$\lambda = \frac{3.2\mu}{p} \sqrt{\frac{RT}{2\pi g_c M}} \tag{4.22}$$

Flow according to Knudsen's law is a function of the molecular weight of the gas, and consequently the components of a gas mixture will pass through a porous solid barrier at different rates. This has been used as a method for analyzing gas mixtures and is the basis of the separation process of gaseous effusion.

In a given capillary, flow will occur according to both laws: at very low pressures or in extremely fine capillaries Knudsen flow predominates, while at higher pressures Poiseuille flow predominates. In a porous solid with capillaries of various diameters, the different types may predominate in different capillaries within the same solid. In any case, the equations show that the rate of flow as measured by the quantity $p_{av}V$ is proportional to the pressure difference and inversely proportional to the thickness, as in true diffusion in solution. The effect of temperature on the permeability may be used to indicate which type of flow predominates.[1] For flow according to Poiseuille's law, the permeability varies inversely as the gas viscosity, which in turn increases with temperature; P then decreases with increased temperature. For Knudsen flow, P' varies as $\sqrt{T}$ and therefore increases with increased temperature. Further, it will be remembered that, should diffusion in solid solution occur, the temperature dependence of P depends upon those of D and the solubility. All these effects may occur at once and the resulting temperature dependence may therefore be very complex.

Finally it should be remembered that, should the pressure difference become very large, the possibility of turbulent flow exists, which follows still a different law.

Illustration 4.6. A porous carbon diaphragm 1 in. thick, of average pore diameter 100 μ, permitted the flow of nitrogen at the rate of 9.0 cu ft (measured at 1 atm, 80°F) per square foot per minute with a pressure difference across the diaphragm of 2 in. of water. The temperature was 80°F, and the downstream pressure was 1 atm. Calculate the flow to be expected at 250°F, with the same pressure difference.

Solution. At 80°F, 1 atm, the viscosity of nitrogen is 0.018 centipoise.

$$\mu = 0.018(\tfrac{1}{100}) = 0.00018 \text{ g/(cm)(sec)} \qquad R = 84{,}780 \text{ (g force)(cm)/(°K)(g mole)}$$

$$p = 1(1{,}033.2) = 1{,}033.2 \text{ g/sq cm} \qquad g_c = 980 \text{ (g mass)(cm)/(g force)(sq sec)}$$

$$T = (80 + 460)\frac{1}{1.8} = 300°K \qquad M = 28.02$$

Eq. (4.22):
$$\lambda = \frac{3.2\mu}{p}\sqrt{\frac{RT}{2\pi g_c M}} = \frac{3.2(0.00018)}{1{,}033.2}\sqrt{\frac{84{,}780(300)}{2\pi(980)(28.02)}}$$

$$= 0.00000557 \text{ cm, or } 0.0557\mu$$

With capillary diameters of 100 μ, flow is therefore according to Poiseuille's law. For the first condition,

$$V_2 = 9.0 \text{ cu ft/(sq ft)(min)} \qquad \text{at 80°F, 1 atm}$$

$$p_2 = 1 \text{ atm} = 14.7(144) = 2{,}120 \text{ lb/sq ft}$$

$$p_1 - p_2 = \tfrac{2}{12}(62.2) = 10.4 \text{ lb/sq ft}$$

$$p_{av} = 2{,}120 + \frac{10.4}{2} = 2{,}125 \text{ lb/sq ft}$$

Eq. (4.18):
$$\frac{P}{z} = \frac{p_2 V_2}{p_{av}(p_1 - p_2)} = \frac{2{,}120(9.0)}{2{,}125(10.4)} \cdot$$

$$= 0.864 \text{ cu ft/(min)(sq ft)(lb/sq ft) for 1-in. thickness at 80°F}$$

At 250°F, the viscosity of nitrogen is 0.022 centipoise, and the new permeability becomes

$$\frac{P}{z} = 0.864 \, \frac{0.018}{0.022} = 0.706$$

$$\therefore \quad V_2 = P\frac{p_{av}(p_1 - p_2)}{zp_2} = \frac{0.706(2,125)(10.4)}{2,120}$$

$$= 7.36 \text{ cu ft/(min)(sq ft)}$$

measured at 250°F, 1 atm

NOTATION FOR CHAPTER 4

Consistent units in either the cgs or the English system may be used throughout.

a = one-half thickness or radius, cm or ft
b = one-half width, cm or ft
c = concentration, g moles/cu cm or lb moles/cu ft
    = one-half length, cm or ft
d = diameter of a capillary, cm or ft
    = differential operator
D = diffusivity, sq cm/sec or sq ft/hr
e = 2.7183
E = fraction of solute unremoved, dimensionless
f, f', f'' = functions
g_c = conversion factor, 980 (g mass)(cm)/(g force)(sq sec) or 4.17(10^8)(lb mass)(ft)/(lb force) (sq hr)
k, k' = constants
K = pore-shape factor, dimensionless
l = length, cm or ft
$\ln$ = natural logarithm
M = molecular weight, g/g mole or lb/lb mole
N = rate of diffusion, g moles/(sec)(sq cm) or lb moles/(hr)(sq ft)
p = pressure, g force/sq cm or lb force/sq ft (unless otherwise indicated)
P = permeability = rate of diffusion per unit pressure gradient, cu cm/(sec)(sq cm)(g force/ sq cm/cm) or cu ft/(hr)(sq ft)(lb force/sq ft/ft) (frequently also in other pressure units)
R = universal gas constant, 84,780 (g force)(cm)/(g mole)(°K) or 1,543 ft-lb force/(lb mole)(°R)
S = cross-sectional area, sq cm or sq ft
T = absolute temperature, °K or °R
u = linear velocity, cm/sec or ft/hr
V = volumetric rate of flow, cu cm/(sec)(sq cm) or cu ft/(hr)(sq ft)
w = rate of diffusion, g moles/sec or lb moles/hr
z = distance in the direction of diffusion, cm or ft
Δ = difference
θ = time, sec or hr
λ = molecular mean free path, cm or ft
μ = viscosity, g mass/(cm)(sec)(= poises) or lb mass/(ft)(hr)
π = 3.1416
ρ = density, g mass/cu cm or lb mass/cu ft

Subscripts:

av   = average
A, B = components A, B

θ = at time θ
0   = initial (at time zero)
1, 2 = positions 1, 2
∞ = at time ∞; at equilibrium

REFERENCES

1.   Barrer, R. M.: "Diffusion in and through Solids," Cambridge University Press, London, 1941.

2.   Carman, P. C.: "Flow of Gases through Porous Media," Academic Press Inc., New York, 1956.

3.   Carslaw, H. S., and J. C. Jaeger: "Conduction of Heat in Solids," 2d ed., Oxford University Press, Fair Lawn, N.J., 1959.

4.   Crank, J.: "The Mathematics of Diffusion," Oxford University Press, Fair Lawn, N.J., 1956.

5.   Jost, W.: "Diffusion in Solids, Liquids, and Gases," Academic Press Inc., New York, 1952.

6.   Newman, A. B.: *Trans. AIChE*, **27**, 203, 310 (1931).

7.   Piret, E. L., R. A. Ebel, C. T. Kiang, and W. P. Armstrong: *Chem. Eng. Progr.*, **47**, 405, 628 (1951).

8.   Satterfield, C. N., and T. K. Sherwood: "The Role of Diffusion in Catalysts," Addison-Wesley Publishing Company, Inc., Reading, Mass., 1963.

9.   Sherwood, T. K.: *Ind. Eng. Chem.*, **21**, 12, 976 (1929).

10. Tuwiner, S. B.: "Diffusion and Membrane Technology," Reinhold Publishing Corporation, New York, 1962.

11. Van Arsdel, W. B.: *Chem. Eng. Progr.*, **43**, 13 (1947).

PROBLEMS

4.1. Removal of soybean oil impregnating a porous clay plate by contact with a solvent for the oil has been shown to be a matter of internal diffusion of the oil through the solid [Boucher, Brier, and Osburn, *Trans. AIChE*, **38**, 967 (1942)].   Such a clay plate, $\frac{1}{16}$ in. thick by 1.80 in. long by 1.08 in. wide, thin edges sealed, was impregnated with soybean oil to a uniform concentration of 0.229 lb oil/lb dry clay.   It was immersed in a flowing stream of pure tetrachloroethylene at 120°F, whereupon the oil content of the plate was reduced to 0.048 lb oil/lb dry clay in 1 hr.   The resistance to diffusion may be taken as residing wholly within the plate and the final ultimate oil content of the clay as zero when contacted with pure solvent.

a. Calculate the effective diffusivity.

b. A cylinder of the same clay, 0.5-in. diameter, 1 in. long, both ends sealed, contains an initial uniform concentration of 0.17 lb oil/lb clay.   When immersed in a flowing stream of pure tetrachloroethylene at 120°F, to what concentration will the oil content fall in 10 hr?   **Ans.:** 0.0748.

c. Recalculate (*b*) for the cases where only one end of the cylinder is sealed and where neither end is sealed.

d. How long will it take for the concentration to fall to 0.01 lb oil/lb clay for the cylinder of (*b*) with neither end sealed?

4.2. A slab of clay, such as that used to make brick, 2 in. thick, was dried from both flat surfaces with the four thin edges sealed, by exposure to dry air.   The initial uniform moisture content was 15%.   The drying took place by internal diffusion of the liquid water to the surface, followed by evaporation at the surface.   The diffusivity may be assumed to be constant with varying water concentration, and uniform in all directions.   The surface moisture content was 3%.   In 5 hr the average moisture content had fallen to 10.2%.

a. Calculate the diffusivity, sq ft/hr.

b. Under the same drying conditions, how much longer would it have taken to reduce the average water content to 6%?

c. How long would it require to dry a sphere of 6-in. radius from 15 to 6% under the same drying conditions?

d. How long would it require to dry a cylinder 1 ft long, 6-in. diameter, drying from all surfaces, to a moisture content of 6%? **Ans.:** 47.5 hr.

4.3. An unglazed porcelain plate 0.5 cm thick has an average pore diameter of 0.2 μ. Pure oxygen gas at an absolute pressure of 2 cm Hg, 100°C, on one side of the plate passed through at a rate of 0.093 cu cm (at 2 cm Hg, 100°C) per second per square centimeter when the pressure on the downstream side was so low as to be considered negligible. Estimate the rate of passage of hydrogen gas at 25°C and a pressure of 1 cm Hg abs, with negligible downstream pressure.

CHAPTER FIVE
INTERPHASE
MASS TRANSFER

Thus far we have considered only the diffusion of substances within a single phase. In most of the mass-transfer operations, however, two insoluble phases are brought into contact in order to permit transfer of constituent substances between them. Therefore we are now concerned with the simultaneous application of the diffusional mechanism for each phase to the combined system. We have seen that the rate of diffusion within each phase is dependent upon the concentration gradient existing within it. At the same time the concentration gradients of the two-phase system are indicative of the departure from equilibrium which exists between the phases. Should equilibrium be established, the concentration gradients and hence the rate of diffusion will fall to zero. It is necessary, therefore, to consider both the diffusional phenomena and the equilibria in order to describe the various situations fully.

EQUILIBRIUM

It is convenient first to consider the equilibrium characteristics of a particular operation and then to generalize the result for others. As an example, consider the gas-absorption operation which occurs when ammonia is dissolved from an ammonia-air mixture by liquid water. Suppose a fixed amount of liquid water is placed in a closed container together with a gaseous mixture of ammonia and air, the whole arranged so that the system can be maintained at constant temperature and pressure. Since ammonia is very soluble in water, some ammonia molecules will instantly transfer from the gas into the liquid, crossing the interfacial surface separating the two phases. A portion of the ammonia molecules escapes back into the gas, at a rate proportional to their concentration in the liquid. As more ammonia enters the liquid, with consequent increase in concentration within the liquid, the rate at which ammonia returns to the gas increases, until eventually the rate at which it enters the liquid exactly equals that at which it leaves. At the same time, through the mechanism of diffusion, the concentrations throughout each phase become uniform. A dynamic equilibrium now exists, and while ammonia molecules continue to transfer back and forth from one phase to the other, the net transfer falls to zero. The concentrations within each phase no longer change. To the observer who cannot see the individual molecules the diffusion has apparently stopped.

If we now inject additional ammonia into the container, a new set of equilibrium concentrations will eventually be established, with higher concentrations in each phase than were at first obtained. In this manner we can eventually obtain the complete relationship between the equilibrium concentrations in both phases. If the ammonia is designated as substance A, the equilibrium concentrations in the gas and liquid, y_A and x_A mole fractions, respectively, give rise to an *equilibrium-distribution curve* of the type shown in Fig. 5.1. This curve results irrespective of the amounts of water and air that we start with and is influenced only by the conditions, such as temperature and pressure, imposed upon the three-component system. It is important to note that at equilibrium the concentrations in the two phases are not equal; rather the chemical potential of the ammonia is the same in both phases, and it will be recalled (Chap. 2) that it is equality of chemical potentials, not concentrations, which cause the net transfer of solute to stop.

The curve of Fig. 5.1 does not of course show all the equilibrium concentrations existing within the system. For example, the water will partially vaporize into the

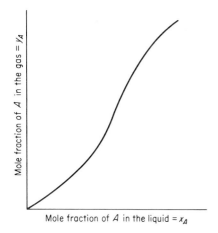

Mole fraction of A in the liquid = x_A

Fig. 5.1 *Equilibrium distribution of a solute between a gas and a liquid phase at constant temperature.*

gas phase, the components of the air will also dissolve to a small extent in the liquid, and equilibrium concentrations for these substances will also be established. For the moment we need not consider these equilibria, since they are of minor importance to the discussion at hand. Obviously also, concentration units other than mole fractions may be used to describe the equilibria.

Generally speaking, whenever a substance is distributed between two insoluble phases, a dynamic equilibrium of this type can be established. The various equilibria are peculiar to the particular system considered. For example, replacement of the water in the example considered above with another liquid such as benzene, or with a solid adsorbent such as activated carbon, or replacement of the ammonia with another solute such as sulfur dioxide will each result in new curves not at all related to the first. The equilibrium resulting for a two-liquid-phase system bears no relation to that for a liquid-solid system. A discussion of the characteristic shapes of the equilibrium curves for the various situations and the influence of conditions such as temperature and pressure must be left for the studies of the individual unit operations. Nevertheless the following principles are common to all systems involving the distribution of a substance between two insoluble phases:

1. At a fixed set of conditions, referring to temperature and pressure, there exists a set of equilibrium relationships which may be shown graphically in the form of an equilibrium-distribution curve by plotting the equilibrium concentrations in the two phases one against the other.

2. For a system in equilibrium, there is no net diffusion of the components between the phases.

3. For a system not in equilibrium, diffusion of the components between the phases will occur in such a manner as to bring the system to a condition of equilibrium. If sufficient time is available, equilibrium concentrations will eventually prevail.

DIFFUSION BETWEEN PHASES

Having established that departure from equilibrium provides the driving force for diffusion, the rates of diffusion in terms of the driving forces may now be studied. Many of the mass-transfer operations are carried out in steady-flow fashion, with continuous and invariant flow of the contacted phases, and under circumstances such that concentrations at any position in the equipment used do not change with time. It will be convenient to use one of these as an example with which to establish the principles and to generalize respecting other operations later. For this purpose, let us consider the absorption of a soluble gas such as ammonia (substance A) from a mixture such as air and ammonia, by liquid water as the absorbent, in one of the simplest of apparatus, the wetted-wall tower previously described in Chap. 3 (Fig. 3.10). The ammonia-air mixture may enter at the bottom and flow upward while the water flows downward around the inside of the pipe. The gas mixture changes its composition from a high- to a low-solute concentration as it flows upward, while the water dissolves the ammonia and leaves at the bottom as an aqueous ammonia

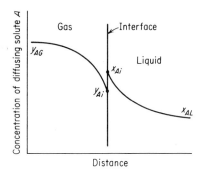

Fig. 5.2   *The two-resistance concept.*

solution.   Under steady-state conditions, the concentrations at any point in the apparatus do not change with passage of time.

Local two-phase mass transfer

Let us investigate the situation at a particular level along the tower, e.g., at a point midway between top and bottom.   Since the solute is diffusing from the gas phase into the liquid, there must be a concentration gradient in the direction of mass transfer within each phase.   This can be shown graphically in terms of the distance through the phases as in Fig. 5.2, where a section through the two phases in contact is shown. It will be assumed that no chemical reaction occurs.   The concentration of A in the main body of the gas is y_{AG} mole fraction, and it falls to y_{Ai} at the interface.   In the liquid, the concentration falls from x_{Ai} at the interface to x_{AL} in the bulk liquid. The bulk concentrations y_{AG} and x_{AL} are clearly not equilibrium values, since otherwise diffusion of the solute would not occur.   At the same time, these bulk concentrations cannot be used directly with a mass-transfer coefficient to describe the rate of interphase mass transfer, since the two concentrations are differently related to the chemical potential, which is the real "driving force" of mass transfer.

To get around this problem, Lewis and Whitman[5,10] assumed that the only diffusional resistances are those residing in the fluids themselves.   There is then no resistance to solute transfer across the interface separating the phases, and as a result the concentrations y_{Ai} and x_{Ai} are equilibrium values, given by the system's equilibrium-distribution curve.†   The reliability of this theory has been subjected to many tests.   As a result, it is now known that there are special situations where it is invalid. For example, if a solute diffuses to a solid interface, where it crystallizes, the molecules must orient themselves to fit into the crystal lattice, and since this is a time-consuming process, an interfacial "resistance" may result.   Certain substances tend to concentrate at the interface, and these may hinder the interphase transfer of solute.   For example, cetyl alcohol, when spread upon water in remarkably small concentrations, reduces the rate of evaporation of the water into air by as much as 95 percent.   It is

† This has been called the "two-film" theory, improperly so, because it is not related to, or dependent upon, the film theory of mass-transfer coefficients described in Chap. 3.   A more appropriate name would be the "two-resistance" theory.

Fig. **5.3** *Departure of bulk-phase concentrations from equilibrium.*

thought that this may occur by virtue of its adsorption at the surface, which then reduces the net area available for the mass transfer of the water.   Certain high-molecular-weight substances tend to adsorb at the interface between two insoluble liquids, and these tend to reduce the rate of transfer of an extractable solute.   These effects may be profound, but they are very specific; the theories of the actions are highly speculative.   In ordinary situations, the evidence is that equilibrium does indeed exist at the interface, and the interfacial concentrations of Fig. 5.2 are those given by a point on the equilibrium-distribution curve.

Referring again to Fig. 5.2, it is clear that the concentration rise at the interface, from y_{Ai} to x_{Ai}, is not a barrier to diffusion in the direction gas to liquid.   They are equilibrium concentrations, and hence correspond to equal chemical potentials of substance A in both phases at the interface.

The various concentrations may also be shown graphically, as in Fig. 5.3, whose coordinates are those of the equilibrium-distribution curve.   Point P represents the two bulk-phase concentrations and point M those at the interface.   For steady-state mass transfer, the rate at which A reaches the interface from the gas must equal that at which it diffuses to the bulk liquid, so that no accumulation or depletion of A at the interface occurs.   We may therefore write the flux of A in terms of the mass-transfer coefficients for each phase and the concentration changes appropriate to each (the development will be done in terms of the k-type coefficients, since this is simpler, and the results for F-type coefficients will be indicated later).   Thus, when k_y and k_x are the locally applicable coefficients,

$$N_A = k_y(y_{AG} - y_{Ai}) = k_x(x_{Ai} - x_{AL}) \tag{5.1}$$

and the differences in y's or x's are considered the "driving forces" for the mass transfer.   Rearrangement as

$$\frac{y_{AG} - y_{Ai}}{x_{AL} - x_{Ai}} = -\frac{k_x}{k_y} \tag{5.2}$$

provides the slope of the line PM.   If the mass-transfer coefficients are known, the interfacial concentrations and hence the flux N_A may be determined, either graphically by plotting the line PM or analytically by solving Eq. (5.2) with an algebraic expression for the equilibrium-distribution curve,

$$y_{Ai} = f(x_{Ai}) \tag{5.3}$$

Local overall mass-transfer coefficients

In experimental determinations of the rate of mass transfer, it is usually possible to determine the solute concentrations in the bulk of the fluids by sampling and analyzing. Successful sampling of the fluids at the interface, however, is ordinarily impossible, since the greatest part of the concentration differences, such as $y_{AG} - y_{Ai}$, takes place over extremely small distances. Any ordinary sampling device will be so large in comparison with this distance that it is impossible to approach the interface sufficiently closely. Sampling and analyzing, then, will provide y_{AG} and x_{AL} but not y_{Ai} and x_{Ai}. Under these circumstances, only an overall effect, in terms of the bulk concentrations, can be determined. The bulk concentrations are, however, not by themselves on the same basis in terms of chemical potential.

Consider the situation as shown in Fig. 5.4. Since the equilibrium-distribution curve for the system is unique at fixed temperature and pressure, then y_A^*, in equilibrium with x_{AL}, is as good a measure of x_{AL} as x_{AL} itself, and moreover it is on the same basis as y_{AG}. The entire two-phase mass-transfer effect may then be measured in terms of an overall mass-transfer coefficient K_y

$$N_A = K_y(y_{AG} - y_A^*) \tag{5.4}$$

From the geometry of the figure,

$$y_{AG} - y_A^* = (y_{AG} - y_{Ai}) + (y_{Ai} - y_A^*) = (y_{AG} - y_{Ai}) + m'(x_{Ai} - x_{AL}) \tag{5.5}$$

where m' is the slope of the chord CM. Substituting for the concentration differences

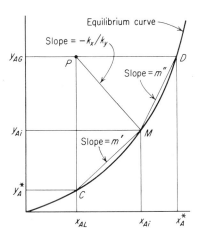

Fig. 5.4 *Overall concentration differences.*

their equivalents (flux/coefficient) as given by Eqs. (5.1) and (5.4),

$$\frac{N_A}{K_y} = \frac{N_A}{k_y} + \frac{m' N_A}{k_x} \tag{5.6}$$

or

$$\frac{1}{K_y} = \frac{1}{k_y} + \frac{m'}{k_x} \tag{5.7}$$

This shows the relationship among the individual-phase transfer coefficients and the overall coefficient to take the form of addition of resistances (hence the term "two-resistance" theory). In similar fashion, x_A^* is a measure of y_{AG} and may be used to define another overall coefficient K_x

$$N_A = K_x(x_A^* - x_{AL}) \tag{5.8}$$

and it is readily shown that

$$\frac{1}{K_x} = \frac{1}{m'' k_y} + \frac{1}{k_x} \tag{5.9}$$

where m'' is the slope of the chord MD on Fig. 5.4. Equations (5.7) and (5.9) lead to the following relationships among the mass-transfer resistances:

$$\frac{\text{Resistance in gas phase}}{\text{Total resistance, both phases}} = \frac{1/k_y}{1/K_y} \tag{5.10}$$

$$\frac{\text{Resistance in liquid phase}}{\text{Total resistance, both phases}} = \frac{1/k_x}{1/K_x} \tag{5.11}$$

Assuming that the numerical values of k_x and k_y are roughly the same, the importance of the slope of the equilibrium-curve chords can readily be demonstrated. If m' is small (equilibrium-distribution curve very flat), so that at equilibrium only a small concentration of A in the gas will provide a very large concentration in the liquid (solute A is very soluble in the liquid), the term m'/k_x of Eq. (5.7) becomes minor, the major resistance is represented by $1/k_y$, and it is said that the rate of mass transfer is gas-phase-controlled. In the extreme, this becomes

$$\frac{1}{K_y} \doteq \frac{1}{k_y} \tag{5.12}$$

or

$$y_{AG} - y_A^* \doteq y_{AG} - y_{Ai} \tag{5.13}$$

Under such circumstances, even fairly large percentage changes in k_x will not significantly affect K_y, and efforts to increase the rate of mass transfer would best be directed toward decreasing the gas-phase resistance. Conversely, when m'' is very large (solute A relatively insoluble in the liquid), with k_x and k_y nearly equal, the first term on the right of Eq. (5.9) becomes minor, and the major resistance to mass transfer resides within the liquid, which is then said to control the rate. Ultimately, this becomes

$$\frac{1}{K_x} \doteq \frac{1}{k_x} \tag{5.14}$$

$$x_A^* - x_{AL} \doteq x_{Ai} - x_{AL} \tag{5.15}$$

In such cases efforts to effect large changes in the rate of mass transfer are best directed to conditions influencing the liquid coefficient k_x. For cases where k_x and k_y are not nearly equal, Fig. 5.4 shows that it will be the relative size of the ratio k_x/k_y and of m' (or m'') which will determine the location of the controlling mass-transfer resistance.

It is sometimes useful to note that the effect of temperature is much larger for liquid mass-transfer coefficients than for those for gases (see Prob. 3.7, for example). Consequently a large effect of temperature on the overall coefficient, when it is determined experimentally, is usually a fairly clear indication that the controlling mass-transfer resistance is in the liquid phase.

For purposes of establishing the nature of the two-resistance theory and the overall coefficient concept, gas absorption was chosen as an example. The principles are applicable to any of the mass-transfer operations, however, and may be applied in terms of k-type coefficients using any concentration units, as listed in Table 3.1 (the F-type coefficients are considered separately below). For each case, the values of m' and m'' must be appropriately defined and used consistently with the coefficients. Thus, if the generalized phases are termed E (with concentrations expressed as i) and R (with concentrations expressed as j),

$$\frac{1}{K_E} = \frac{1}{k_E} + \frac{m'}{k_R} \tag{5.16}$$

$$\frac{1}{K_R} = \frac{1}{m''k_E} + \frac{1}{k_R} \tag{5.17}$$

$$m' = \frac{i_{Ai} - i_A^*}{j_{Ai} - j_{AR}} \qquad m'' = \frac{i_{AE} - i_{Ai}}{j_A^* - j_{Ai}} \tag{5.18}$$

$$i_A^* = f(j_{AR}) \qquad i_{AE} = f(j_A^*) \tag{5.19}$$

where f is the equilibrium-distribution function.

Local coefficients—General case

When we deal with situations which do not involve either diffusion of only one substance or equimolar counterdiffusion, or if mass-transfer rates are large, the F-type coefficients should be used. The general approach is the same, although the resulting expressions are more cumbersome than those developed above. Thus, in the case of a situation such as that shown in Figs. 5.2 to 5.4, the mass-transfer flux is

$$N_A = \frac{N_A}{\Sigma N} F_G \ln \frac{N_A/\Sigma N - y_{Ai}}{N_A/\Sigma N - y_{AG}} = \frac{N_A}{\Sigma N} F_L \ln \frac{N_A/\Sigma N - x_{AL}}{N_A/\Sigma N - x_{Ai}} \tag{5.20}$$

where F_G and F_L are the gas- and liquid-phase coefficients for substance A and $\Sigma N = N_A + N_B + N_C + \cdots$. Equation (5.20) then becomes[2]

$$\frac{N_A/\Sigma N - y_{Ai}}{N_A/\Sigma N - y_{AG}} = \left(\frac{N_A/\Sigma N - x_{AL}}{N_A/\Sigma N - x_{Ai}}\right)^{F_L/F_G} \tag{5.21}$$

The interfacial compositions y_{Ai} and x_{Ai} may be found by plotting Eq. (5.21) (with y_{Ai} replaced by y_A and x_{Ai} by x_A) on the distribution diagram (Fig. 5.3) and determining the intersection of the resulting curve with the distribution curve. This is, in general, a trial-and-error procedure, since $N_A/\Sigma N$ may not be known, and must be done in conjunction with Eq. (5.20). In the special cases for diffusion only of A and of equimolar counterdiffusion in two-components phases, no trial and error is required.

We may also define the overall coefficients F_{OG} and F_{OL} as

$$N_A = \frac{N_A}{\Sigma N} F_{OG} \ln \frac{N_A/\Sigma N - y_A^*}{N_A/\Sigma N - y_{AG}} = \frac{N_A}{\Sigma N} F_{OL} \ln \frac{N_A/\Sigma N - x_{AL}}{N_A/\Sigma N - x_A^*} \tag{5.22}$$

By a procedure similar to that used for the K's, it may be shown that the overall and individual phase F's are related:

$$\exp\left[\frac{N_A}{(N_A/\Sigma N)F_{OG}}\right] = \exp\left[\frac{N_A}{(N_A/\Sigma N)F_G}\right]$$

$$+ m'\frac{N_A/\Sigma N - x_{AL}}{N_A/\Sigma N - y_{AG}}\left\{1 - \exp\left[-\frac{N_A}{(N_A/\Sigma N)F_L}\right]\right\} \tag{5.23}$$

$$\exp\left[-\frac{N_A}{(N_A/\Sigma N)F_{OL}}\right] = \frac{1}{m''}\left(\frac{N_A/\Sigma N - y_{AG}}{N_A/\Sigma N - x_{AL}}\right)\left\{1 - \exp\left[\frac{N_A}{(N_A/\Sigma N)F_G}\right]\right\}$$

$$+ \exp\left[-\frac{N_A}{(N_A/\Sigma N)F_L}\right] \tag{5.24}$$

where $\exp Z$ means e^Z. These fortunately simplify for the two important special cases:

(a) *Diffusion of one component* $(\Sigma N = N_A, N_A/\Sigma N = 1.0)$†

$$e^{N_A/F_{OG}} = e^{N_A/F_G} + m'\left(\frac{1 - x_{AL}}{1 - y_{AG}}\right)(1 - e^{-N_A/F_L}) \tag{5.25}$$

$$e^{-N_A/F_{OL}} = \frac{1}{m''}\left(\frac{1 - y_{AG}}{1 - x_{AL}}\right)(1 - e^{N_A/F_G}) + e^{-N_A/F_L} \tag{5.26}$$

† Equations (5.25) and (5.26) may also be written in the following forms:

$$\frac{1}{F_{OG}} = \frac{1}{F_G}\frac{(1 - y_A)_{iM}}{(1 - y_A)_{*M}} + \frac{m'(1 - x_A)_{iM}}{F_L(1 - y_A)_{*M}} \tag{5.25a}$$

$$\frac{1}{F_{OL}} = \frac{1}{m''F_G}\frac{(1 - y_A)_{iM}}{(1 - x_A)_{*M}} + \frac{1}{F_L}\frac{(1 - x_A)_{iM}}{(1 - x_A)_{*M}} \tag{5.26a}$$

where

$(1 - y_A)_{iM}$ = logarithmic mean of $1 - y_{AG}$ and $1 - y_{Ai}$
$(1 - y_A)_{*M}$ = logarithmic mean of $1 - y_{AG}$ and $1 - y_A^*$
$(1 - x_A)_{iM}$ = logarithmic mean of $1 - x_{AL}$ and $1 - x_{Ai}$
$(1 - x_A)_{*M}$ = logarithmic mean of $1 - x_{AL}$ and $1 - x_A^*$

(*b*) *Equimolar counterdiffusion* $[\Sigma N = 0\ (F_G = k'_y,\ F_L = k'_x)]$

$$\frac{1}{F_{OG}} = \frac{1}{F_G} + \frac{m'}{F_L} \tag{5.27}$$

$$\frac{1}{F_{OL}} = \frac{1}{m''F_G} + \frac{1}{F_L} \tag{5.28}$$

Use of local overall coefficients

The concept of overall mass-transfer coefficients is in many ways similar to that of overall heat-transfer coefficients in the case of heat-exchanger design. And, as is the practice in heat transfer, the overall coefficients of mass transfer are frequently synthesized through the relationships developed above from the individual coefficients for the separate phases. These may be taken, for example, from the correlations of Chap. 3 or from those developed in later chapters for specific types of mass-transfer equipment. It is important to recognize the limitations inherent in this procedure.[3]

The hydrodynamic circumstances must be the same as those for which the correlations were developed. Especially in the case of two fluids, where motion in one may influence motion in the other, the individual correlations may make inadequate allowances for the effect on the transfer coefficients. On occasion, particularly in the transfer of solute between two liquids, an "interfacial turbulence," or extraordinary motion of the interface, occurs as a result of interfacial tension gradients peculiar to the two-phase system at hand, and this leads to unexpectedly high interphase mass transfer.[1,8] On other occasions adsorption of surface-active substances at the interface has caused a rigidity, or reduction of mobility, at the interface with consequent reduction in the expected mass-transfer rate.[1]

The mere presence of a mass-transfer resistance in one phase must have no influence on that in the other: the resistances must not interact, in other words. This may be important, since the individual-phase coefficient correlations are frequently developed under conditions where mass-transfer resistance in the second phase is nil, as when the second phase is a pure substance. The analysis of such situations is dependent upon the mechanism assumed for mass transfer (film, surface-renewal, etc., theories), and has been incompletely developed.

Average overall coefficients

As will be shown, in practical mass-transfer apparatus the bulk concentrations in the contacted phases normally vary considerably from place to place, so that a point such as *P* in Figs. 5.3 and 5.4 is just one of an infinite number which forms a curve on these figures. Thus, in the countercurrent wetted-wall gas absorber considered earlier, the solute concentrations in both fluids are small at the top and large at the bottom. In such situations, we may speak of an average overall coefficient applicable to the entire device. Such an average coefficient can be synthesized from constituent individual-phase coefficients by the same equations as developed above for local overall coefficients only, provided the quantity $m'k_E/k_R$ (or $m''k_R/k_E$) remains everywhere constant.[3]   Of course, variations in values of the coefficients and slope m' may occur in such a way that they are self-compensating.   But in practice, since average phase coefficients, assumed constant for the entire apparatus, are the only ones usually available, average overall coefficients generally will have meaning only when $m' = m'' = $ const, in other words, for cases of straight-line equilibrium-distribution curves. Obviously, also, the same hydrodynamic regime must exist throughout the apparatus for an average overall coefficient to have meaning.

Illustration 5.1. A wetted-wall absorption tower, 1 in. ID, is fed with water as the wall liquid and an ammonia-air mixture as the central-core gas.   At a particular level in the tower, the ammonia concentration in the bulk gas is 0.80 mole fraction, that in the bulk liquid 0.05 mole fraction.   The temperature $= 80°F$, the pressure 1 atm.   The rates of flow are such that the local mass-transfer coefficient in the liquid, from a correlation obtained with dilute solutions, is $k_L = 0.34$ lb mole/ (hr)(sq ft)(lb mole/cu ft), and the local Sherwood number for the gas is 40.   The diffusivity of ammonia in air $= 0.890$ sq ft/hr.   Compute the local mass-transfer flux for the absorption of ammonia, ignoring the vaporization of water.
    Solution. $y_{AG} = 0.80$, $x_{AL} = 0.05$ mole fraction ammonia.   Because of the large concentration of ammonia in the gas, F's rather than k's will be used.   Notation is that of Chap. 3.
    Liquid. From Table 3.1, $F_L = k_L x_{BM} c$.   Since the molecular weight of ammonia and water are so nearly the same, and the density of a dilute solution is practically that of water, the molar density $c = 62.3/18 = 3.44$ lb moles/cu ft.   Since the k_L was determined for dilute solutions, where x_{BM} is practically 1.0,

$$F_L = 0.34(1.0)(3.44) = 1.170 \text{ lb moles/(hr)(sq ft)}$$

Gas.

$$\text{Sh} = \frac{F_G d}{c D_A} = 40 \qquad d = \tfrac{1}{12} = 0.0833 \text{ ft}$$

$$c = \frac{1}{359} \frac{492}{460 + 80} = 0.00254 \text{ lb mole/cu ft}$$

$$D_A = 0.890 \text{ sq ft/hr}$$

$$F_G = \frac{40 c D_A}{d} = \frac{40(0.00254)(0.890)}{0.0833} = 1.085 \text{ lb moles/(hr)(sq ft)}$$

Mass-transfer flux. The equilibrium distribution of ammonia is taken from the data at 80°F in "The Chemical Engineers' Handbook," 4th ed., p. 3-66:

NH$_3$ mole fraction x_A	NH$_3$ partial pressure p_A, lb/sq in.	$y_A = \dfrac{p_A}{14.7}$
0	0	0
0.05	1.04	0.0707
0.10	1.98	0.1347
0.25	8.69	0.590
0.30	13.52	0.920

These are plotted as the equilibrium curve in Fig. 5.5.

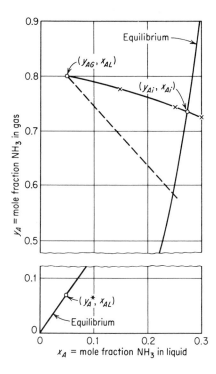

Fig. 5.5   *Construction for Illustration 5.1.*

For transfer of only one component, $N_A/\Sigma N = 1.0$.   Equation (5.21), with y_{Ai} and x_{Ai} replaced by y_A and x_A, becomes

$$y_A = 1 - (1 - y_{AG})\left(\frac{1 - x_{AL}}{1 - x_A}\right)^{F_L/F_G} = 1 - (1 - 0.8)\left(\frac{1 - 0.05}{1 - x_A}\right)^{1.078}$$

from which the following are computed:

x_A	0.05	0.15	0.25	0.30
y_A	0.80	0.780	0.742	0.722

These are plotted (as crosses) on Fig. 5.5, and the resulting curve intersects the equilibrium curve to give the interface compositions, $x_{Ai} = 0.274$, $y_{Ai} = 0.732$.   Therefore, Eq. (5.20) provides

$$N_A = 1(1.170)\ln\frac{1 - 0.05}{1 - 0.274} = 1(1.085)\ln\frac{1 - 0.732}{1 - 0.80} = 0.316 \text{ lb mole } NH_3$$

absorbed/(hr)(sq ft), local flux   **Ans.**

Overall coefficient.   Although it is not particularly useful in this case, the overall coefficient will be computed to demonstrate the method.   The gas concentration in equilibrium with the bulk liquid ($x_{AL} = 0.05$) is, from Fig. 5.5, $y_A^* = 0.0707$.   The chord slope m' is therefore

$$m' = \frac{y_{Ai} - y_A^*}{x_{Ai} - x_{AL}} = \frac{0.732 - 0.0707}{0.274 - 0.05} = 2.95$$

Note that, unless the equilibrium curve is straight, this cannot be obtained without first obtaining (y_{Ai}, x_{Ai}), in which case there is no need for an overall coefficient.   In Eq. (5.25), normally we would obtain F_{OG} by trial, by assuming N_A. Thus (with one eye on the answer obtained above), assume $N_A = 0.316$. Then Eq. (5.25) becomes

$$e^{0.316/F_{OG}} = e^{0.316/1.085} + 2.95 \frac{1 - 0.05}{1 - 0.80} (1 - e^{-0.316/1.170}) = 4.658$$

$$\therefore \quad F_{OG} = 0.205 \text{ lb mole/(hr)(sq ft)}$$

As a check of the trial value of N_A, Eq. (5.22) is

$$N_A = 1(0.205) \ln \frac{1 - 0.0707}{1 - 0.80} = 0.316 \quad \text{(check)}$$

Use of k-type coefficients. There are, of course, k's which are consistent with the F's and which will produce the correct result. Thus, $k_y = F_G P_t/p_{BM} = 4.64$ and $k_x = F_L/x_{BM} = 1.39$ will produce the same result as above. But these k's are specific for the concentration levels at hand, and the p_{BM} and x_{BM} terms, which correct for the bulk-flow flux [the $(N_A + N_B)$ term of Eq. (2.4)], cannot be obtained until x_{Ai} and y_{Ai} are first obtained as above.

However, if it had been assumed that the concentrations were dilute and that the bulk-flow terms were negligible, the Sherwood number *might* have been (incorrectly) interpreted as

$$\text{Sh} = \frac{k_y R T d}{P_t D_A} = 40 = \frac{k_y(0.729)(460 + 80)(0.0833)}{1(0.890)}$$

$$k_y = 1.085 \text{ lb moles/(hr)(sq ft)(mole fraction)}$$

and, in the case of the liquid,

$$k_x = k_L c = 0.34(3.44) = 1.170 \text{ lb moles/(hr)(sq ft)(mole fraction)}$$

These k's are suitable for small driving forces but are unsuitable here. Thus

$$-\frac{k_x}{k_y} = -\frac{1.170}{1.085} = -1.078$$

and a line of this slope (the dashed line of Fig. 5.5) drawn from (x_{AL}, y_{AG}) intersects the equilibrium curve at $x_A = 0.250$, $y_A = 0.585$. If this is interpreted to be (x_{Ai}, y_{Ai}), the calculated flux would be

$$N_A = k_x(x_{Ai} - x_{AL}) = 1.170(0.250 - 0.05) = 0.234$$

or

$$N_A = k_y(y_{AG} - y_{Ai}) = 1.085(0.8 - 0.585) = 0.234$$

The corresponding overall coefficient, with $m' = (0.585 - 0.0707)/(0.250 - 0.05) = 2.57$, would be

$$\frac{1}{K_y} = \frac{1}{k_y} + \frac{m'}{k_x} = \frac{1}{1.085} + \frac{2.57}{1.170}$$

$$K_y = 0.321 \text{ lb mole/(hr)(sq ft)(mole fraction)}$$

and

$$N_A = K_y(y_{AG} - y_A^*) = 0.321(0.8 - 0.0707) = 0.234$$

This value of N_A is of course incorrect. However, had the gas concentration been low, say 0.10 mole fraction NH_3, these k's would have been satisfactory and would have given the same flux as the F's.

MATERIAL BALANCES

The concentration-difference driving forces discussed above, as has been pointed out, are those existing at one position in the equipment used to contact the immiscible phases. In the case of a steady-state process, because of the transfer of solute from one phase to the other, the concentration within each phase changes as it moves through the equipment. Similarly, in the case of a batch process, the concentration in each phase changes with time. These changes produce corresponding variations in the driving forces, and these can be followed with the help of material balances. In what follows, all concentrations are the bulk-average values for the indicated streams.

Steady-state cocurrent processes

Consider any mass-transfer operation whatsoever conducted in a steady-state cocurrent fashion, as in Fig. 5.6, in which the apparatus used is represented simply as a rectangular box. Let the two insoluble phases be identified as phase E and phase R, and for the present consider only the case where a single substance A diffuses from phase R to phase E during their contact. The other constituents of the phases, solvents for the diffusing solutes, are then considered not to diffuse.

At the entrance to the device in which the phases are contacted, phase R contains R_1 moles per unit time of total substances, consisting of nondiffusing solvent R_S moles per unit time and diffusing solute A, whose concentration is x_1 mole fraction. As phase R moves through the equipment, A diffuses to phase E and consequently the total quantity of R falls to R_2 moles per unit time at the exit, although the rate of flow of nondiffusing solvent R_S is the same as at the entrance. The concentration of A has fallen to x_2 mole fraction. Similarly, phase E at the entrance contains E_1 moles per unit time total substances, of which E_S moles is nondiffusing solvent, and an A concentration of y_1 mole fraction. Owing to the accumulation of A to a concentration

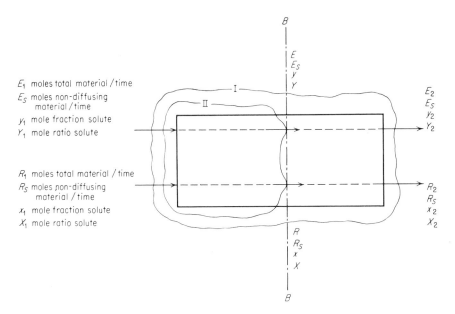

Fig. 5.6 *Steady-state cocurrent processes.*

y_2 mole fraction, phase E increases in amount to E_2 moles per unit time at the exit, although the solvent content E_S has remained constant.

Envelope I, the closed, irregular line drawn about the equipment, will help to establish a material balance for substance A, since an accounting for substance A must be made wherever the envelope is crossed by an arrow representing a flowing stream.   The A content of the entering R phase is R_1x_1, that of the E phase is E_1y_1. Similarly the A content of the leaving streams is R_2x_2 and E_2y_2, respectively.

Thus,
$$R_1x_1 + E_1y_1 = R_2x_2 + E_2y_2 \tag{5.29}$$

or
$$R_1x_1 - R_2x_2 = E_2y_2 - E_1y_1 \tag{5.30}$$

But
$$R_1x_1 = R_S \frac{x_1}{1 - x_1} = R_SX_1 \tag{5.31}$$

where X_1 is the mole-ratio concentration of A at the entrance, moles A/mole non-A. The other terms may be similarly described, and Eq. (5.30) becomes

$$R_S(X_1 - X_2) = E_S(Y_2 - Y_1) \tag{5.32}$$

The last is the equation of a straight line on X, Y coordinates, of slope $-R_S/E_S$, passing through two points whose coordinates are (X_1,Y_1) and (X_2,Y_2), respectively.

At any section B-B through the apparatus, the mole fractions of A are x and y and the mole ratios X and Y, in phases R and E, respectively, and if an envelope II is drawn so as to include all the device from the entrance to section B-B, the A balance becomes

$$R_S(X_1 - X) = E_S(Y - Y_1) \tag{5.33}$$

This is also the equation of a straight line on X, Y coordinates, of slope $-R_S/E_S$, through the points (X_1,Y_1) and (X,Y).   Since the two straight lines have the same slope and a point in common, they are the same straight line, and Eq. (5.33) is therefore a general expression relating the compositions of the phases in the equipment at any distance from the entrance.†

Since X and Y represent concentrations in the two phases, the equilibrium relationship may also be expressed in terms of these coordinates.   Figure 5.7 shows a representation of the equilibrium relationship as well as the straight line QP of Eqs. (5.32) and (5.33).   The line QP, called an *operating line*, should not be confused with the driving-force lines of the earlier discussion.   At the entrance to the apparatus, for example, the mass-transfer coefficients in the two phases may give rise to the driving-force line KP, where K represents the interface compositions at the entrance and the distances KM and MP represent, respectively, the driving forces in phase E and phase R.   Similarly, at the exit, point L may represent the interface composition and LQ the line representative of the driving forces.   If the apparatus were longer than that indicated in Fig. 5.6, so that eventually an equilibrium between the two phases

---

† Masses, mass fractions, and mass ratios may be substituted consistently for moles, mole fractions, and mole ratios in Eqs. (5.29) to (5.33).

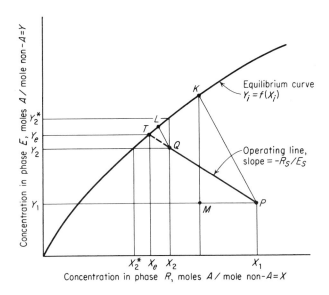

Fig. 5.7 *Steady-state cocurrent process, transfer of solute from phase R to phase E.*

were established, the corresponding equilibrium compositions X_e and Y_e are given by an extension of the operating line to intersection with the equilibrium curve at T. The driving forces, and therefore the diffusion rate, at this point will have fallen to zero. Should the diffusion be in the opposite direction, i.e., from phase E to phase R, the operating line will fall on the opposite side of the equilibrium curve, as in Fig. 5.8.

It must be emphasized that the graphical representation of the operating line as as a *straight* line is greatly dependent upon the units in which the concentrations of

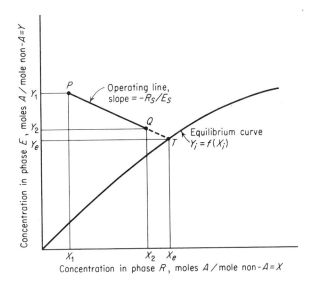

Fig. 5.8 *Steady-state cocurrent process, transfer of solute from phase E to phase R.*

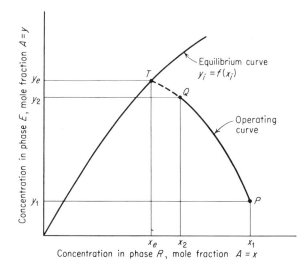

the material balance are expressed.   The representations of Figs. 5.7 and 5.8 are straight lines because the mole-ratio concentrations are based on the unchanging quantities E_S and R_S.   If Eq. (5.30) is plotted on mole-fraction coordinates, or if any concentration unit proportional to mole fractions such as partial pressure is used, for example, Fig. 5.9 indicates the nature of the operating *curve* obtained.   Extrapolation to locate the ultimate equilibrium conditions at T is of course much more difficult than for mole-ratio coordinates.   On the other hand, in any operation where the total quantities of each of the phases E and R remain constant while the compositions change owing to diffusion of several components, a diagram in terms of mole fraction will provide a straight-line operating line, as Eq. (5.30) indicates (let $E_2 = E_1 = E$; $R_2 = R_1 = R$).   If all the components diffuse so that the total quantities of each phase do not remain constant, the operating line will generally be curved.

To sum up, the cocurrent operating line is a graphical representation of the material balance.   A point on the line represents the bulk-average concentrations of the streams in contact with each other at any section in the apparatus.   Consequently the line passes from the point representing the streams entering the apparatus to that representing the effluent streams.

Steady-state countercurrent processes

If the same process as previously considered is carried out in countercurrent fashion, as in Fig. 5.10, where the subscripts 1 indicate that end of the apparatus where phase R enters and 2 that end where phase R leaves, the material balances become, by envelope I,†

$$E_2 y_2 + R_1 x_1 = E_1 y_1 + R_2 x_2 \qquad (5.34)$$

† Masses, mass ratios, and mass fractions may be substituted consistently for moles, mole ratios, and mole fractions in Eqs. (5.34) to (5.37).

and
$$R_S(X_1 - X_2) = E_S(Y_1 - Y_2) \tag{5.35}$$

and, for envelope II,
$$Ey + R_1x_1 = E_1y_1 + Rx \tag{5.36}$$

and
$$R_S(X_1 - X) = E_S(Y_1 - Y) \tag{5.37}$$

Equations (5.36) and (5.37) give the general relationship between concentrations in the phases at any section, while Eqs. (5.34) and (5.35) establish the entire material balance. Equation (5.35) is that of a straight line on X, Y coordinates, of slope R_S/E_S, through points of coordinates (X_1,Y_1), (X_2,Y_2), as shown in Fig. 5.11. The line will lie above the equilibrium-distribution curve if diffusion proceeds from phase E to phase R, below for diffusion in the opposite direction. For the former case, at a point where the concentrations in the phases are given by the point P, the driving-force line may be indicated by line PM, whose slope depends upon the relative diffusional resistances of the phases. The driving forces obviously change in magnitude from one end of the equipment to the other. If the operating line should touch the equilibrium curve anywhere, so that the contacted phases are in equilibrium, the driving force and hence the rate of mass transfer would become zero, and the time required for a finite material transfer would be infinite. This may be interpreted in terms of a limiting ratio of flow rates of the phases for the concentration changes specified.

As in the cocurrent case, linearity of the operating line depends upon the method of expressing the concentrations. The operating lines of Fig. 5.11 are straight because the mole-ratio concentrations X and Y are based on the quantities R_S and

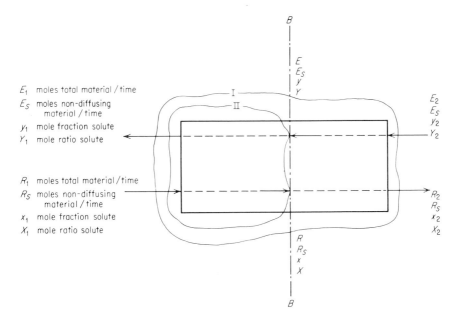

Fig. 5.10 *Steady-state countercurrent process.*

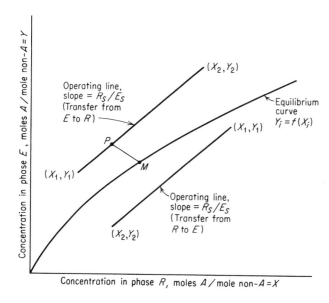

Fig. 5.11   *Steady-state counter-current process.*

E_S, which are stipulated to be constant.   If for this situation mole fractions (or quantities such as partial pressures, which are proportional to mole fractions) are used, the operating lines are curved, as indicated in Fig. 5.12.   However, for some operations should the total quantity of each of the phases E and R be constant while the compositions change, the mole-fraction diagram will provide the straight-line operating lines, as Eq. (5.34) would indicate (let $E = E_1 = E_2$; $R = R_1 = R_2$).   As

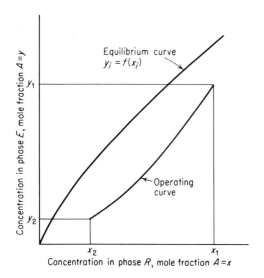

Fig. 5.12   *Steady-state countercurrent process, transfer of solute from phase R to phase E.*

in the cocurrent case, however, the operating line will generally be curved if all the components diffuse so that the total quantities of each phase do not remain constant.

The countercurrent operating line is a graphical representation of the material balance, passing from the point representing the streams at one end of the apparatus to the point representing the streams at the other. A point on the line represents the bulk-average concentrations of the streams passing each other at any section in the apparatus. It is useful to rearrange Eq. (5.36) to read

$$Ey - Rx = E_1 y_1 - R_1 x_1 \qquad (5.38)$$

The left-hand side represents the *net* flow rate of solute A to the left at section B-B in Fig. 5.10. The right-hand side is the net flow rate of solute out at the left end of the apparatus, or the difference in solute flow, out — in, and for steady state this is constant. Since the section B-B was taken to represent any section of the apparatus, at every point on the operating line the *net* flow rate of solute is constant, equal to the net flow out at the end.

STAGES

A *stage* is defined as any device or combination of devices in which two insoluble phases are brought into intimate contact, where mass transfer occurs between the phases tending to bring them to equilibrium, and where the phases are then mechanically separated. A process carried out in this manner is a *single-stage* process. An *ideal*, or *theoretical*, stage is one where the time of contact between phases is sufficient so that the effluents are indeed in equilibrium, and although in principle this cannot be attained, in practice we can frequently approach so close to equilibrium that the difference is unimportant.

Continuous cocurrent processes

Quite obviously the cocurrent process and apparatus of Fig. 5.6 is that of a single stage, and if the stage were ideal, the effluent compositions would be at point T on Fig. 5.7 or 5.8.

A *stage efficiency* is defined as the fractional approach to equilibrium which a real stage produces. Referring to Fig. 5.7, this might be taken as the fraction which the line QP represents of the line TP, or the rate of actual solute transfer to that if equilibrium were attained. The most frequently used expression, however, is the Murphree stage efficiency, the fractional approach of one leaving stream to equilibrium with the actual concentration in the other leaving stream.[6] Referring to Fig. 5.7, this may be expressed in terms of the concentrations in phase E or in phase R,

$$\mathbf{E}_{ME} = \frac{Y_2 - Y_1}{Y_2^* - Y_1} \qquad \mathbf{E}_{MR} = \frac{X_1 - X_2}{X_1 - X_2^*} \qquad (5.39)$$

These definitions are somewhat arbitrary since, in the case of a truly cocurrent operation such as that of Fig. 5.7, it would be impossible to obtain a leaving concentration in phase E higher than Y_e or one in phase R lower than X_e. They are nevertheless useful, as will be developed in later chapters. The two Murphree efficiencies are not normally equal for a given stage, and they can be simply related only when the equilibrium relation is a straight line. Thus, for a straight equilibrium line of slope $m = (Y_2^* - Y_2)/(X_2 - X_2^*)$, it can be shown that

$$\mathbf{E}_{ME} = \frac{\mathbf{E}_{MR}}{\mathbf{E}_{MR}(1 - S) + S} = \frac{\mathbf{E}_{MR}}{\mathbf{E}_{MR}(1 - 1/A) + 1/A} \tag{5.40}$$

The derivation is left to the student (Prob. 5.6). Here $A = R_S/mE_S$ is called the *absorption factor*, and its reciprocal, $S = mE_S/R_S$, is the *stripping factor*. As will be shown, these have great economic importance.

Batch processes

It is characteristic of batch processes that while there is no flow of the phases into and out of the equipment used, the concentrations within each phase change with time. When initially brought into contact, the phases will not be of equilibrium compositions, but they will approach equilibrium with passage of time. The material-balance equation (5.33) for the cocurrent steady-state operation then shows the relation between the concentrations X and Y in the phases which coexist at any time after the start of the operation, and Figs. 5.7 and 5.8 give the graphical representation of these compositions. Point T on these figures represents the ultimate compositions which are obtained at equilibrium. The batch operation is a single stage.

Cascades

A group of stages interconnected so that the various streams flow from one to the other is called a cascade. Its purpose is to increase the extent of mass transfer over and above that which is possible with a single stage. The fractional overall stage efficiency of a cascade is then defined as the number of ideal stages to which the cascade is equivalent divided by the number of real stages.

Two or more stages connected so that the flow is cocurrent between stages will, of course, never be equivalent to more than one ideal stage, although the overall stage efficiency can thereby be increased. For effects greater than one ideal stage, they may be connected for cross flow or countercurrent flow.

Cross-flow cascades

In Fig. 5.13, each stage is represented simply by a circle, and within each the flow is cocurrent. The R phase flows from one stage to the next, being contacted in each stage by fresh E phase. There may be different flow rates of the E to each stage, and each stage may have a different Murphree stage efficiency. The material balances are obviously merely a repetition of that for a single stage and the construction on the distribution diagram is obvious. Cross flow is used sometimes in adsorption, leaching, drying, and extraction operations but rarely in the others.

Countercurrent cascades

These are the most efficient arrangements, requiring fewest stages for a given change of composition and ratio of flow rates, and they are therefore most frequently used.

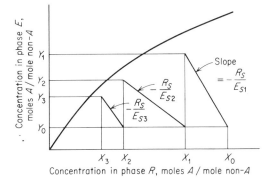

Fig. 5.13 *A cross-flow cascade of three real stages.*

Refer to Fig. 5.14, where a cascade of N_p ideal stages is shown. The flow rates and compositions are numbered corresponding to the effluent from a stage, so that Y_2 is the concentration in the E phase leaving stage 2, etc. Each stage is identical in its action to the cocurrent process of Fig. 5.6; yet the cascade as a whole has the characteristics of the countercurrent process of Fig. 5.10. The cocurrent operating lines for the first two stages are written beneath them on the figure, and since the stages are ideal, the effluents are in equilibrium (Y_2 in equilibrium with X_2, etc.). The graphical relations are shown in Fig. 5.15. Line PQ is the operating line for stage 1, MN for

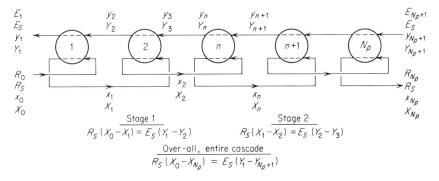

Fig. 5.14 *Countercurrent multistage cascade.*

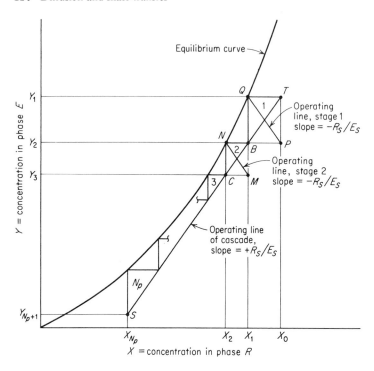

Fig. 5.15 *Countercurrent multistage cascade, solute transfer from phase R to phase E.*

stage 2, etc., and the coordinates (X_1, Y_1) fall on the equilibrium curve because the stage is ideal. Line ST is the operating line for the entire cascade, and points such as B, C, etc., represent compositions of streams passing each other between stages. We may therefore determine the number of ideal stages required for a countercurrent process by drawing the stairlike construction $TQBNC \cdots S$ (Fig. 5.15). If anywhere the equilibrium curve and cascade operating line should touch, the stages become *pinched*, and an infinite number are required to bring about the desired composition change. If the solute transfer is from E to R, the entire construction falls above the equilibrium curve of Fig. 5.15.

For most cases, because of either a curved operating line or equilibrium curve, the relation among number of stages, compositions, and flow ratio must be determined graphically, as shown. For the *special* case where both are straight, however, with the equilibrium curve continuing straight to the origin of the distribution graph, an analytical solution can be developed which will be most useful.

In Fig. 5.14, a solute balance for stages $n + 1$ through N_p is

$$E_S(Y_{n+1} - Y_{Np+1}) = R_S(X_n - X_{Np}) \tag{5.41}$$

If the equilibrium curve slope is $m = Y_{n+1}/X_{n+1}$, and if the absorption factor $A = R_S/mE_S$, then by substitution and rearrangement, Eq. (5.41) becomes

$$X_{n+1} - AX_n = \frac{Y_{Np+1}}{m} - AX_{Np} \tag{5.42}$$

This is a linear first-order finite-difference equation, whose solution is handled much like that of ordinary differential equations.[11]   Thus, putting it in operator form,

$$(D - A)X_n = \frac{Y_{Np+1}}{m} - AX_{Np} \tag{5.43}$$

where the operator D indicates the finite difference.   The characteristic equation is then

$$M - A = 0 \tag{5.44}$$

from which $M = A$.   Hence the general solution (here a little different from ordinary differential equations) is

$$X_n = C_1 A^n \tag{5.45}$$

with C_1 a constant.   Since the right-hand side of Eq. (5.43) is a constant, the particular solution is $X = C_2$, where C_2 is a constant.   Substituting this into the original finite-difference equation (5.42) provides

$$C_2 - AC_2 = \frac{Y_{Np+1}}{m} - AX_{Np} \tag{5.46}$$

from which

$$C_2 = \frac{Y_{Np+1}/m - AX_{Np}}{1 - A} \tag{5.47}$$

The complete solution is therefore

$$X_n = C_1 A^n + \frac{Y_{Np+1}/m - AX_{Np}}{1 - A} \tag{5.48}$$

To determine C_1, we set $n = 0$:

$$C_1 = X_0 - \frac{Y_{Np+1}/m - AX_{Np}}{1 - A}$$

and therefore we have

$$X_n = \left(X_0 - \frac{Y_{Np+1}/m - AX_{Np}}{1 - A} \right) A^n + \frac{Y_{Np+1}/m - AX_{Np}}{1 - A} \tag{5.49}$$

This result is useful to get the concentration X_n at any stage in the cascade, knowing the terminal concentrations.   Putting $n = N_p$ and rearranging provide the very useful forms which follow.

For transfer from R to E (stripping of R)

$A \neq 1$:

$$\frac{X_0 - X_{Np}}{X_0 - Y_{Np+1}/m} = \frac{(1/A)^{Np+1} - 1/A}{(1/A)^{Np+1} - 1} \tag{5.50}$$

$$N_p = \frac{\log \left[\dfrac{X_0 - Y_{Np+1}/m}{X_{Np} - Y_{Np+1}/m} (1 - A) + A \right]}{\log 1/A} \tag{5.51}$$

$A = 1$:

$$\frac{X_0 - X_{Np}}{X_0 - Y_{Np+1}/m} = \frac{N_p}{N_p + 1} \tag{5.52}$$

$$N_p = \frac{X_0 - X_{Np}}{X_{Np} - Y_{Np+1}/m} \tag{5.53}$$

For transfer from E to R (absorption into R).   A similar treatment yields

$A \neq 1$:
$$\frac{Y_{Np+1} - Y_1}{Y_{Np+1} - mX_0} = \frac{A^{Np+1} - A}{A^{Np+1} - 1} \qquad (5.54)$$

$$N_p = \frac{\log\left[\dfrac{Y_{Np+1} - mX_0}{Y_1 - mX_0}\left(1 - \dfrac{1}{A}\right) + \dfrac{1}{A}\right]}{\log A} \qquad (5.55)$$

$A = 1$:
$$\frac{Y_{Np+1} - Y_1}{Y_{Np+1} - mX_0} = \frac{N_p}{N_p + 1} \qquad (5.56)$$

$$N_p = \frac{Y_{Np+1} - Y_1}{Y_1 - mX_0} \qquad (5.57)$$

These are called the Kremser-Brown-Souders (or simply Kremser) equations, after those who derived them for gas absorption,[4,7] although apparently Turner[9] had used them earlier for leaching and solids washing.   They are plotted in Fig. 5.16, which then becomes very convenient for quick solutions.   We shall have many opportunities to use them for different operations.   In order to make them so generally useful, it is important to note that in the derivation, $A = R_S/mE_S = $ const, where R_S and E_S are the nonsolute molar flow rates with concentrations (X in R and Y in E) defined as mole ratios and $m = Y/X$ at equilibrium.   However, as necessary to keep A constant, A may be defined as R/mE, with R and E either as total molar flow rates, concentrations (x in R and y in E) as mole fractions, $m = y/x$, or as total mass flow rates and weight fractions, respectively.

We shall delay using the equations until specific opportunity arises.

Stages and mass-transfer rates

It is clear from the previous discussion that each process may be considered either in terms of the number of stages it represents or in terms of the appropriate mass-transfer rates.   A batch or continuous cocurrent operation, for example, is a single-stage operation, but the stage efficiency realized in the available contact time will depend upon the average mass-transfer rates prevailing.   A change of composition greater than that possible with one stage may be brought about by repetition of the cocurrent process, where one of the effluents from the first stage is brought again into contact with fresh treating phase.   Alternatively, a countercurrent multistage cascade can be arranged.   If, however, the countercurrent operation is carried out in continuous-contact fashion without repeated separation and recontacting of the phases in a stepwise manner, it is still possible to describe the operation in terms of the number of ideal stages to which it is equivalent.   But in view of the differential changes in composition which occur in such cases, it is more correct to characterize them in terms of average mass-transfer coefficients or equivalent.   Integration of the point mass-transfer rate equations must be delayed until the characteristics of each operation can be considered, but the computation of the number of ideal stages requires only the equilibrium and material-balance relationships.

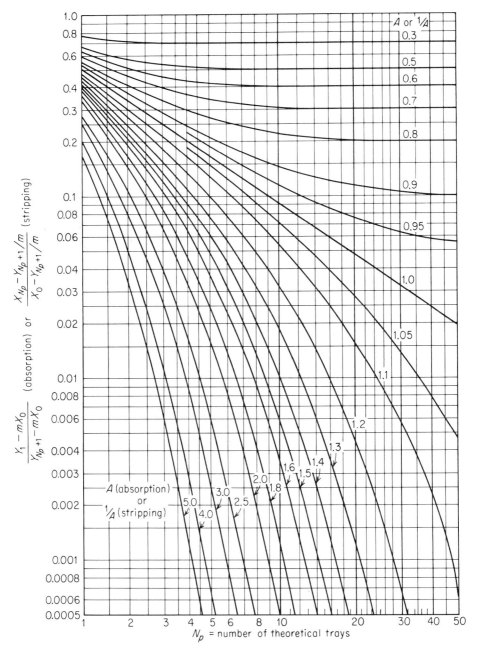

Fig. 5.16 *Number of theoretical stages for countercurrent cascades, with Henry's law equilibrium and constant absorption or stripping factors.* [*After Hachmuth and Vance, Chem. Eng. Progr.*, **48**, 523, 570, 617 (1952).]

Illustration 5.2. When a certain sample of moist soap is exposed to air at 120°F, 1 atm pressure, the equilibrium distribution of moisture between the air and soap is as follows:

Wt % moisture in soap	0	2.40	3.76	4.76	6.10	7.83	9.90	12.63	15.40	19.02
Partial pressure water in air, mm Hg	0	9.66	19.20	28.4	37.2	46.4	55.0	63.2	71.9	79.5

a. Ten pounds of wet soap containing 16.7% moisture by weight is placed in a vessel containing 150 cu ft moist air whose initial moisture content corresponds to a water-vapor partial pressure of 12 mm Hg. After the soap has reached a moisture content of 13.0%, the air in the vessel is entirely replaced by fresh air of the original moisture content and the system is then allowed to reach equilibrium. The total pressure and temperature are maintained at 1 atm and 120°F, respectively. What will be the ultimate moisture content of the soap?

b. It is desired to dry the soap from 16.7 to 4% moisture continuously in a countercurrent stream of air whose initial water-vapor partial pressure is 12 mm Hg. The pressure and temperature will be maintained throughout at 1 atm and 120°F. Per 1 lb initial wet soap per hour, what is the minimum amount of air required per hour?

c. If 30% more air than that determined in (*b*) is used, what will be the moisture content of the air leaving the drier? To how many ideal stages will the process be equivalent?

Solution. a. The process is a batch operation. Since air and soap are mutually insoluble, with water distributing between them, Eq. (5.32) applies. Let the E phase be air–water and the R phase be soap–water. Define Y as lb water/lb dry air and X as lb water/lb dry soap. It will be necessary to convert the equilibrium data to these units.

For a partial pressure of moisture $= p$ mm Hg and a total pressure of 760 mm Hg, $p/(760 - p)$ is the mole ratio of water to dry air. Multiplying this by the ratio of molecular weights of water to air then gives Y: $Y = [p/(760 - p)](18.02/29)$. Thus, at $p = 71.9$ mm Hg,

$$Y = \frac{71.9}{760 - 71.9}\frac{18.02}{29} = 0.0650 \text{ lb water/lb dry air}$$

In similar fashion the percent moisture content of the soap is converted to units of X. Thus, at 15.40% moisture,

$$X = \frac{15.40}{100 - 15.40} = 0.182 \text{ lb water/lb dry soap}$$

In this manner all the equilibrium data are converted to these units and the data plotted as the equilibrium curve of Fig. 5.17.

First operation. Initial air, $p = 12$ mm Hg:

$$Y_1 = \frac{12}{760 - 12}\frac{18.02}{29} = 0.00996 \text{ lb water/lb dry air}$$

Initial soap, 16.7% water:

$$X_1 = \frac{16.7}{100 - 16.7} = 0.2 \text{ lb water/lb dry soap}$$

Final soap, 13% water:

$$X_2 = \frac{13.0}{100 - 13.0} = 0.1493 \text{ lb water/lb dry soap}$$

$$R_S = 10(1 - 0.167) = 8.33 \text{ lb dry soap}$$

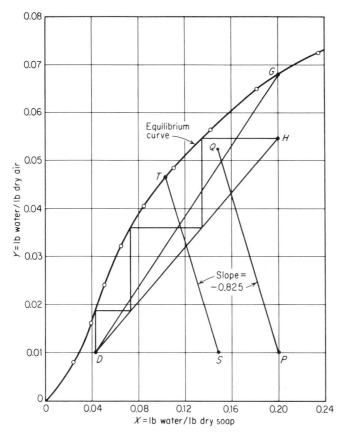

Fig. 5.17 *Solution to Illustration 5.2.*

E_S, the mass of dry air, is found by use of the perfect-gas law,

$$E_S = 150 \frac{760 - 12}{760} \frac{492}{460 + 120} \frac{29}{359} = 10.1 \text{ lb dry air}$$

$$\text{Slope of operating line} = \frac{-R_S}{E_S} = \frac{-8.33}{10.1} = -0.825$$

From point P, coordinates (X_1, Y_1), on Fig. 5.17, the operating line of slope -0.825 is drawn, to reach the abscissa $X_2 = 0.1493$ at point Q. The conditions at Q correspond to the end of the first operation.

Second operation. $X_1 = 0.1493$, $Y_1 = 0.00996$, which locate point S on the figure. The operating line is drawn parallel to the line PQ since the ratio $-R_S/E_S$ is the same as in the first operation. Extension of the line to the equilibrium curve at T provides the final value of $X_2 = 0.103$ lb water/lb dry soap.

$$\text{Final moisture content of soap} = \frac{0.103}{1.103} 100 = 9.33 \%$$

  b. Equation (5.35) and Fig. 5.10 apply

$$R_S = 1(1 - 0.167) = 0.833 \text{ lb dry soap/hr}$$

Entering soap: $X_1 = 0.20$ lb water/lb dry soap

Leaving soap: $X_2 = \dfrac{0.04}{1 - 0.04} = 0.0417$ lb water/lb dry soap

Entering air: $Y_2 = 0.00996$ lb water/lb dry air

$$\text{Slope of operating line} = \frac{R_S}{E_S} = \frac{\text{lb dry soap/hr}}{\text{lb dry air/hr}}$$

Point D, coordinates (X_2, Y_2), is plotted on Fig 5.17.   The operating line of least slope giving rise to equilibrium conditions will indicate the least amount of air usable.   Such a line is DG, which provides equilibrium conditions at $X_1 = 0.20$.   The corresponding value of $Y_1 = 0.068$ lb water/lb dry air is read from the figure at G.

Eq. (5.35): $0.833(0.20 - 0.0417) = E_S(0.068 - 0.00996)$

$$E_S = 2.27 \text{ lb dry air/hr}$$

This corresponds to

$$\frac{2.27}{29} \, 359 \, \frac{760}{760 - 12} \, \frac{460 + 120}{492} = 33.6 \text{ cu ft air/lb soap}$$

  c. $E_S = 1.30(2.27) = 2.95$ lb dry air/hr

Eq. (5.35) $0.833(0.20 - 0.0417) = 2.95(Y_1 - 0.00996)$

$$Y_1 = 0.0547 \text{ lb water/lb dry air}$$

This corresponds to operating line DH, where H has the coordinates $X_1 = 0.20$, $Y_1 = 0.0547$.   The ideal stages are marked on the figure and total three.

NOTATION FOR CHAPTER 5

Consistent units in either the cgs or the English system may be used.   In either system, pressures are customarily expressed as atmospheres in the mass-transfer equations.

A	= substance A, the diffusing solute
	= absorption factor, dimensionless
e	= 2.7183
E	= phase E; total rate of flow of phase E, g moles/sec or lb moles/hr
E_S	= rate of flow of nondiffusing solvent in phase E, g moles/sec or lb moles/hr
E_{ME}	= fractional Murphree stage efficiency for phase E
E_{MR}	= fractional Murphree stage efficiency for phase R
f	= equilibrium-distribution function
F_G	= gas-phase mass-transfer coefficient, g moles/(sec)(sq cm) or lb moles/(hr)(sq ft)
F_L	= liquid-phase mass-transfer coefficient, g moles/(sec)(sq cm) or lb moles/(hr)(sq ft)
F_{OG}	= overall gas mass-transfer coefficient, g moles/(sec)(sq cm) or lb moles/(hr)(sq ft)
F_{OL}	= overall liquid mass-transfer coefficient, g moles/(sec)(sq cm) or lb moles/(hr)(sq ft)
i	= generalized concentration in phase R
j	= generalized concentration in phase E
k_x	= liquid mass-transfer coefficient, g moles/(sec)(sq ft)(mole fraction) or lb moles/(hr)(sq ft) (mole fraction)
k_y	= gas mass-transfer coefficient, g moles/(sec)(sq ft)(mole fraction) or lb moles/(hr)(sq ft) (mole fraction)

K_x = overall liquid mass-transfer coefficient, g moles/(sec)(sq cm)(mole fraction) or lb moles/ (hr)(sq ft)(mole fraction)

K_y = overall gas mass-transfer coefficient, g moles/(sec)(sq cm)(mole fraction) or lb moles/ (hr)(sq ft)(mole fraction)

m = equilibrium curve slope, dimensionless

m', m'' = slopes of chords of the equilibrium curve, dimensionless

n = stage n

N = mass-transfer flux, g moles/(sec)(sq cm) or lb moles/(hr)(sq ft)

N_p = total number of ideal stages in a cascade

R = phase R; total rate of flow of phase R, g moles/sec or lb moles/hr

R_S = rate of flow of nondiffusing solvent in phase R, g moles/sec or lb moles/hr

S = stripping factor, dimensionless

x = concentration of A in a liquid or in phase R, mole fraction

X = concentration of A in phase R, moles A/mole non-A

y = concentration of A in a gas or in phase E, mole fraction

Y = concentration of A in phase E, moles A/mole non-A

Subscripts:

A = substance A

e = equilibrium

E = phase E

G = gas

i = interface

L = liquid

n = stage n

O = overall

R = phase R

0 = entering stage 1

1, 2 = positions 1 and 2; stages 1 and 2

Superscript:

$*$ = in equilibrium with bulk concentration in other phase

REFERENCES

   1. Davies, T. J.: in T. B. Drew, J. W. Hoopes, and T. Vermeulen (eds.), "Advances in Chemical Engineering," vol. 4, p. 1, Academic Press Inc., New York, 1963.

   2. Kent, E. R., and R. L. Pigford: *AIChE J.*, **2**, 363 (1956).

   3. King, C. J.: *AIChE J.*, **10**, 671 (1964).

   4. Kremser, A.: *Natl. Petrol. News*, **22**(21), 42 (1930).

   5. Lewis, W. K., and W. G. Whitman: *Ind. Eng. Chem.*, **16**, 1215 (1924).

   6. Murphree, E. V.: *Ind. Eng. Chem.*, **17**, 747 (1925).

   7. Souders, M., and G. G. Brown: *Ind. Eng. Chem.*, **24**, 519 (1932).

   8. Sternling, C. V., and L. E. Scriven: *AIChE J.*, **5**, 514 (1958).

   9. Turner, S. D.: *Ind. Eng. Chem.*, **21**, 190 (1929).

   10. Whitman, W. G.: *Chem. Met. Eng.*, **29**, 147 (1923).

   11. Wylie, C. R., Jr.: "Advanced Engineering Mathematics," 3d ed., McGraw-Hill Book Company, New York, 1966.

PROBLEMS

5.1. Repeat the calculations for the local mass-transfer flux of ammonia in Illustration 5.1, on the assumption that the gas pressure is 2 atm. The gas mass velocity, bulk-average gas and liquid concentrations, liquid flow rate, and temperature are unchanged.

5.2. In a certain apparatus used for the absorption of sulfur dioxide, SO_2, from air by means of water, at one point in the equipment the gas contained 10% SO_2 by volume and was in contact with liquid containing 0.4% SO_2 by weight (density = 61.8 lb/cu ft). The temperature was 50°C and the total pressure 1 atm. The overall mass-transfer coefficient based on gas concentrations was K_G = 0.055 lb mole SO_2 absorbed/(hr)(sq ft)(atm). Of the diffusional resistance 47% lay in the gas phase, 53% in the liquid. Equilibrium data at 50°C are as follows:

G SO_2/100 g water	0.2	0.3	0.5	0.7
Partial pressure SO_2, mm Hg	29	46	83	119

a. Calculate the overall coefficient based on liquid concentrations in terms of lb moles/cu ft.
b. Calculate the individual film coefficients for the gas film [expressed as k_G lb moles/(hr)(sq ft)(atm), k_y lb moles/(hr)(sq ft)(mole fraction), and k_c lb moles/(hr)(sq ft)(lb mole/cu ft)] and for the liquid film [expressed as k_L lb moles/(hr)(sq ft)(lb mole/cu ft) and k_x lb moles/(hr)(sq ft)(mole fraction)].
c. Determine the interfacial compositions in both phases.

5.3. The equilibrium partial pressure of water vapor in contact with a certain silica gel on which water is adsorbed is, at 25°C, as follows:

Partial pressure of water, mm Hg	0	2.14	4.74	7.13	9.05	10.9	12.6	14.3	16.7
Lb water/100 lb dry gel	0	5	10	15	20	25	30	35	40

a. Plot the equilibrium data as p = partial pressure of water vapor, mm Hg, against x = wt fraction water in the gel.
b. Plot the equilibrium data as X = lb moles water/lb dry gel, Y = lb moles water vapor/lb mole dry air, for a total pressure of 1 atm.
c. Ten pounds of silica gel containing 5 wt% adsorbed water is placed in a flowing air stream containing a partial pressure of water vapor of 12 mm Hg. The total pressure is 1 atm and the temperature 25°C. When equilibrium is reached, how many pounds of additional water will the gel have adsorbed? Air is not adsorbed.
d. One pound of silica gel containing 5 wt % adsorbed water is placed in a vessel in which there are 400 cu ft moist air whose partial pressure of water is 15 mm Hg. The total pressure and temperature are kept at 1 atm and 25°C, respectively. At equilibrium, what will be the moisture content of the air and gel and the weight of water adsorbed by the gel? **Ans.: 0.1335 lb water.**
e. Write the equation of the operating line for (*d*) in terms of X and Y. Convert this into an equation in terms of p and x, and plot the operating curve on the p, x coordinates.
f. One pound of silica gel containing 18% adsorbed moisture is placed in a vessel containing 500 cu ft dry air. The temperature and pressure are maintained at 1 atm and 25°C, respectively. Compute the final equilibrium moisture content of the air and gel.
g. Repeat (*f*) for a total pressure of 2 atm. (Note that the equilibrium curve in terms of X and Y previously used is not applicable.)

5.4. The equilibrium adsorption of benzene vapor on a certain activated charcoal at 33.3°C is as follows:

Cu cm benzene vapor adsorbed (measured at standard conditions)/g C	15	25	40	50	65	80	90	100
Partial pressure benzene, mm Hg	0.0010	0.0045	0.0251	0.115	0.251	1.00	2.81	7.82

a. A nitrogen–benzene vapor mixture containing 1.0% benzene by volume is to be passed countercurrently at the rate of 100 cu ft/min in contact with a moving stream of the activated charcoal so as to remove 95% of the benzene from the gas in a continuous process. The entering charcoal contains 15 cu cm benzene vapor (at standard conditions) adsorbed per gram charcoal. The temperature and total pressure are to be maintained at 33.3°C and 1 atm, respectively, throughout. The nitrogen is not adsorbed. What is the least amount of charcoal which may be used per hour? If twice as much is used, what will be the concentration of adsorbed benzene upon the charcoal leaving?

b. Repeat (*a*) for a cocurrent flow of gas and charcoal.

c. Charcoal which has adsorbed upon it 100 cu cm (at standard conditions) benzene vapor per gram charcoal is to be stripped at the rate of 100 lb/hr of its benzene to a concentration of 55 cu cm adsorbed benzene/g charcoal by continuous countercurrent contact with a stream of pure nitrogen gas at 1 atm. The temperature will be maintained at 33.3°C. What is the minimum rate of nitrogen flow, cu ft/hr? What will be the benzene content of the exit gas if twice as much nitrogen is fed? What will be the number of ideal stages? **Ans.:** Three ideal stages.

5.5. A mixture of hydrogen and air, 4 atm pressure, bulk-average concentration 50% H_2 by volume, flows through a circular reinforced tube of vulcanized rubber whose ID and OD are 1 and 1.125 in., respectively, at an average velocity of 10 ft/sec. Outside the pipe, hydrogen-free air at 1atm flows at right angles to the pipe at a velocity of 10 ft/sec. The temperature is everywhere 25°C. The solubility of hydrogen in the rubber is 0.053 cu cm H_2 (at standard conditions) per cu cm rubber per atm partial pressure, and its diffusivity in the rubber = $0.18(10^{-5})$ sq cm/sec. The diffusivity of H_2–air = 0.161 sq cm/sec at 0°C, 1 atm. Estimate the rate of loss of hydrogen from the pipe per foot of pipe length.

5.6. Assuming the equilibrium curve of Fig. 5.7 is straight, of slope *m*, derive the relation between the Murphree stage efficiencies E_{ME} and E_{MR}.

5.7. If the equilibrium distribution curve of the cross-flow plant of Fig. 5.13 is everywhere straight, of slope *m*, make a solute material balance about stage *n* + 1, and by following the procedures used to derive Eq. (5.51) show that

$$N_p = \frac{\log\,[(X_0 - Y_0/m)/(X_{Np} - Y_0/m)]}{\log\,(S + 1)}$$

where *S* is the stripping factor, mE_S/R_S, constant for all stages, and N_p is the total number of ideal stages.

PART TWO
GAS-LIQUID
OPERATIONS

The operations which include humidification and dehumidification, gas absorption and desorption, and distillation in its various forms all have in common the requirement that a gas and a liquid phase be brought into contact for the purpose of a diffusional interchange between them.

The order listed above is in many respects that of increasing complexity of the operations, and this is therefore the order in which they will be considered. Since in humidification the liquid is a pure substance, concentration gradients exist and diffusion of matter occurs only within the gas phase. In absorption, concentration gradients exist within both the liquid and the gas, and diffusion of at least one component occurs within both. In distillation, all the substances comprising the phases diffuse. These operations are also characterized by an especially intimate relationship between heat and mass transfer. The evaporation or condensation of a substance introduces consideration of latent heats of vaporization, sometimes heats of solution as well. In distillation, the new phase necessary for mass-transfer separation is created from the original by addition or withdrawal of heat. Our discussion must necessarily include consideration of these important heat quantities and their effects.

In the case of all these operations, the equipment used has as its principal function the contact of the gas and liquid in as efficient a fashion as possible, commensurate with the cost. In principle, at least, any type of equipment satisfactory for one of these operations is also suitable for the others, and the major types are indeed used for all. For this reason, our discussion begins with equipment.

CHAPTER SIX
EQUIPMENT FOR
GAS-LIQUID OPERATIONS

The purpose of the equipment used for the gas-liquid operations is to provide intimate contact of the two fluids in order to permit interphase diffusion of the constituents. The rate of mass transfer is directly dependent upon the interfacial surface exposed between the phases, and the nature and degree of dispersion of one fluid in the other are therefore of prime importance. The equipment may be broadly classified according to whether its principal action is to disperse the gas or the liquid, although in many devices both phases become dispersed.

I. GAS DISPERSED

In this group are included those devices, such as agitated vessels and the various types of tray towers, in which the gas phase is dispersed into bubbles or drops. The most important of the group are the tray towers.

Agitated vessels

The simplest method of dispersing the gas into a batch of liquid is to discharge it beneath the liquid surface through a perforated pipe, or sparger. The gas bubbles from such a sparger are relatively large, and the interfacial surface is correspondingly small therefore.   The degree of dispersion may be increased by forcing the gas through smaller openings such as those in porous ceramic or metallic plates, but the small openings require high gas pressures and are subject to clogging.   It is preferable to increase the degree of dispersion by use of a mechanical agitator, as in Fig. 6.1. Here the agitation is brought about by a turbine-type impeller.   The gas is introduced through submerged pipes against a "target," an open sleeve, which leads the gas into the bottom of the impeller at a position about halfway from the center to the periphery. This prevents formation of large gas bubbles at the center of the impeller and assists in the shearing of the gas into bubbles of small sizes by the impeller.   The hooded ring surrounding the impeller aids in projecting the stream downward and therefore provides a longer time of contact between gas and liquid.   In other arrangements the hooded ring is omitted, and instead four vertical baffles, projecting radially inward from the wall to a distance of one-tenth the tank diameter, extending for the full depth of the liquid, are used.   When a large part of the gas does not dissolve in one pass through the liquid, an impeller is sometimes used near the liquid surface to draw the gas down into the liquid from the gas space above.

Turbine impellers will finely subdivide gas introduced at superficial linear velocities less than 0.1 ft/sec based on vessel cross sections.   Agitated vessels are therefore primarily useful for dispersing small quantities into liquids, on a batch, semibatch, or continuous basis.   They are also especially useful for cases where the liquid contains a suspended solid, as, for example, in the precipitation of calcium carbonate by the absorption of carbon dioxide from flue gas into a lime slurry or in the hydrogenation of a liquid in the presence of a suspended solid catalyst.   They are frequently used in fermentation processes of the pharmaceutical industry, where oxygen from air is absorbed into liquids containing suspended microorganisms such as yeasts and molds, which require the oxygen for their life processes.

Fig. 6.1 *Turbo gas absorber.* *(General American Transportation Corporation.)*

Since a well-designed turbine impeller provides very thorough mixing of the liquid, it may reasonably be assumed that the concentration throughout the liquid phase in such devices is quite uniform.   The benefits of countercurrent flow for continuous operation cannot therefore be had with a single tank and agitator.   Multistage arrangements, with countercurrent flow of gas and liquid, require multiple vessels and agitators, piped to lead the gas from the top of one tank to the bottom of the next and the liquid from vessel to vessel in the opposite direction.

TRAY TOWERS

Tray towers are vertical cylinders in which the liquid and gas are contacted in stepwise fashion on trays or plates, in a manner shown schematically for one type (bubble-cap trays) in Fig. 6.2.   The liquid enters at the top and flows downward by gravity.   On the way, it flows across each tray and through a downspout to the tray below.   The gas passes upward through openings of one sort or another in the tray, then bubbles through the liquid to form a froth, disengages from the froth, and passes on to the next tray above.   The overall effect is a multiple countercurrent contact of gas and liquid, although each tray is characterized by a cross flow of the two.   Each tray of the tower is a stage, since on the tray the fluids are brought into intimate contact, interphase diffusion occurs, and the fluids are separated.

The number of theoretical trays (or stages) in a column or tower is dependent only upon the difficulty of the separation to be carried out and is determined solely from material balances and equilibrium considerations.   The stage or tray efficiency, and therefore the number of real trays, is determined by the mechanical design used and the conditions of operation.   The diameter of the tower, on the other hand, depends upon the quantities of liquid and gas flowing through the tower per unit time. Once the number of theoretical trays required has been determined, the principal problem in the design of the tower is to choose dimensions and arrangements which will represent the best compromise among several opposing tendencies, for it is generally found that conditions leading to high tray efficiencies will ultimately lead to operational difficulties.

In order that stage or tray efficiencies be high, the time of contact should be long, so as to permit the diffusion to occur, the interfacial surface between phases must be made large, and a relatively high intensity of turbulence is required to obtain high mass-transfer coefficients.   In order to provide long contact time, the liquid pool on each tray should be deep, so that bubbles of gas will require a relatively long time to rise through the liquid.   When the gas bubbles only slowly through the openings on the tray, the bubbles are large and the interfacial surface per unit of gas volume is small, the liquid is relatively quiescent, and much of it may even pass over the tray without having contacted the gas.   On the other hand, when the gas velocity is relatively high, it is dispersed very thoroughly into the liquid, which in turn is agitated into a froth.   This provides large interfacial surface areas.   For high tray efficiencies, therefore, we require deep pools of liquid and relatively high gas velocities.

These conditions, however, lead to a number of difficulties.   One of these is the

Shell

Tray

Downspout

Tray support ring

Tray stiffener

Vapor riser

Froth

Gas out

Liquid in

Bubble cap

Sidestream withdrawal

Intermediate feed

Gas in

Liquid out

Fig. 6.2 *Schematic section through a bubble-cap tray tower.*

mechanical entrainment of droplets of liquid in the rising gas stream.   At high gas velocities, when the gas is disengaged from the froth, small droplets of liquid will be carried by the gas to the tray above.   Liquid carried up the tower in this manner reduces the concentration change which is brought about by the mass transfer, and consequently adversely affects the tray efficiency.   And so the gas velocity may be limited by the reduction in tray efficiency due to liquid entrainment.

Furthermore, great liquid depths on the tray and high gas velocities both result in high pressure drop for the gas in flowing through the tray, and this in turn leads to a number of difficulties.   In the case of absorbers and humidifiers, high pressure drop results in high fan power to blow or draw the gas through the tower, and consequently high operating cost.   In the case of distillation, high pressure at the bottom of the tower results in high boiling temperatures, which in turn may lead to heating difficulties and possibly damage to heat-sensitive compounds.

Ultimately, purely mechanical difficulties arise.   High pressure drop may lead directly to a condition of *flooding*.   With a large pressure difference in the space between trays, the level of liquid leaving a tray at relatively low pressure and entering one of high pressure must necessarily assume an elevated position in the downspouts, as shown in Fig. 6.2.   As the pressure difference is increased owing to increased rate of flow of either gas or liquid, the level in the downspout will rise further to permit the liquid to enter the lower tray.   Ultimately the liquid level may reach that on the tray above.   Further increase in either flow rate then aggravates the condition rapidly, and the liquid will fill the entire space between the trays.   The tower is then flooded, the tray efficiency falls to a low value, the flow of gas is erratic, and liquid may be forced out of the exit pipe at the top of the tower.

For liquid-gas combinations which tend to foam excessively, high gas velocities may lead to a condition of *priming*, which is also an inoperative situation.   Here the foam persists throughout the space between trays, and a great deal of liquid is carried by the gas from one tray to the tray above.   This is an exaggerated condition of entrainment.   The liquid so carried recirculates between trays, and the added liquid-handling load increases the gas pressure drop sufficiently to lead to flooding.

We may summarize these opposing tendencies as follows.   Great depths of liquid on the trays lead to high tray efficiencies through long time of contact but also to high pressure drop per tray.   High gas velocities, within limits, provide good vapor-liquid contact through excellence of dispersion but lead to excessive entrainment and high pressure drop.   The various arrangements and dimensions chosen for design are those which experience has proved to be reasonably good compromises.   The general design procedure involves a somewhat empirical application of these followed by computational check to ensure that pressure drop and flexibility, i.e., ability of the tower to handle more than the immediately expected fluid quantities, are satisfactory.

General characteristics

Certain design features are common to the most frequently used types of trays (bubble-cap and sieve trays), and these will be dealt with first.

Shell and trays. The tower may be made of any of a number of materials, depending upon the corrosion conditions encountered.   Glass, glass-lined metal, impervious carbon, plastics, even wood, but most frequently metals are used.   For metal towers, the shells are usually cylindrical for reasons of cost.   If made in one piece, they are fitted with handholes or manholes to permit installation of trays and cleaning. Alternatively, they may be made of a number of flanged sections bolted together.

The trays of modern installations are ordinarily made of sheet metal, of special alloys if necessary, the thickness governed by the anticipated corrosion rate. The trays must be stiffened or supported, as in Fig. 6.2, and must be fastened to the shell to prevent movement due to surges of gas, with allowance for thermal expansion. This can be arranged by use of tray-support rings with slotted bolt holes, to which the trays are bolted. Large trays are made in sections for ease in installation and so that a man can climb from one tray to another during repair and cleaning. They should be installed level to within $\frac{1}{4}$ in.

Tray spacing. Tray spacing is usually chosen first on the basis of expediency in construction, maintenance, and cost, and later checked to be certain that adequate insurance against flooding is present. For special cases where headroom is a most important consideration, spacings of 6 in. have been used. For all except the smallest tower diameters, 18 in. would seem to be a more workable minimum from the point of view of cleaning the trays. Most petroleum-refinery installations use 18 to 20 in. for tower diameters up to 4 ft and increased spacing for greater diameters in order to facilitate cleaning and removal of trays through manholes in the shell. See Table 6.1 for a summary of recommended values.

Tower diameter. The tower diameter and consequently its cross section must be sufficiently large to handle the gas and liquid at velocities which will not cause flooding or excessive entrainment. For a given type of tray at flooding, the superficial velocity of the gas V_F (cu ft gas/sec divided by the "net" cross section for gas flow, A_n sq ft) is related to fluid densities by

$$V_F = C_F \left(\frac{\rho_L - \rho_G}{\rho_G} \right)^{1/2} \tag{6.1}$$

The net cross section A_n is the tower cross section A_t minus the area taken up by downspouts (one A_d in the case of a cross-flow tray as in Fig. 6.2). C_F is an empirical constant which will be considered later for individual tray types. Some appropriately smaller value of V is used for actual design, for nonfoaming liquids 80 to 85 percent of V_F (75 percent or less for foaming liquids), subject to check of entrainment and pressure-drop characteristics. For most circumstances, the diameter so chosen will be adequate, although occasionally the liquid flow may be limiting. A well-designed single-pass cross-flow tray can ordinarily be expected to handle up to 75 gal/min of liquid per foot of diameter [$q/d = 0.165$ cu ft/(sec)(ft)] without excessive liquid gradient. For most installations, considerations of cost make it impractical to vary the tower diameter to accommodate variations in liquid or gas flow from one end of the tower to the other, and the maximum flow quantities are used to set the design. When the variation in flow is considerable, and especially when expensive alloys are used in construction, two diameters are sometimes used.

The tower diameters may clearly be decreased by use of increased tray spacing so that tower cost, which depends on height as well as diameter, passes through a minimum at some optimum tray spacing.

Downspouts. The liquid is led from one tray to the next by means of downspouts, or downcomers. These may be circular pipes or, preferably, simply portions of the tower cross section set aside for liquid flow by vertical plates, as in Fig. 6.2. Since

Table 6.1. Recommended conditions and dimensions for tray towers

	General	

1. Tray spacing:

Tower diameter d, ft	Tray spacing t, in.
	6 in. minimum
4 or less	18–20
4–10	24
10–12	30
12–24	36

2. Liquid flow:
    a. Not over 0.165 cu ft/(sec)(ft diam) for single-pass cross-flow trays
    b. Not over 0.35 cu ft/(sec)(ft weir length) for others

3. Downspout holdup: 8 sec minimum (superficial)

4. Downspout seal: 0.5 in. minimum at no liquid flow

5. Weir length: Straight, rectangular weirs of cross-flow trays, 0.6d–0.8d

6. Liquid gradient: 0.5 in. (1.25 in. maximum)

7. Pressure drop per tray:

Pressure	Pressure drop
35 mm Hg abs	3 mm Hg or less
Atm	0.07–0.12 psi
300 psi	0.15 psi

	Bubble-cap trays

1. Liquid seal:

Pressure	Seal, in.
Vacuum	0.5–1.5
Atm	1.0–2.0
50–100 psi	1.5–3.0
200–500 psi	2.0–4.0

2. Skirt clearance: 0.5 in. minimum, 1.5 in. for dirty liquids

**Table 6.1. Recommended conditions and
dimensions for tray towers**   (*Continued*)

3. Flooding constant C_F [Eqs. (6.1), (6.2)]:

Range of $\dfrac{L'}{G'}\left(\dfrac{\rho_G}{\rho_L}\right)^{0.5}$	a	b
0.01–0.03 use values at 0.03		
0.03–0.2	$0.0041t + 0.0135$	$0.0047t + 0.068$
0.2–1.0	$0.0068t + 0.049$	$0.0028t + 0.044$

Perforated trays

Flooding constant C_F [Eqs. (6.1), (6.3)]

Range of $\dfrac{L'}{G'}\left(\dfrac{\rho_G}{\rho_L}\right)^{0.5}$	a	b
0.01–0.1 use values at 0.1		
0.1–1.0	$0.0062t + 0.0385$	$0.00253t + 0.05$

the liquid is agitated into a froth on the tray, adequate residence time must be allowed in the downspout to permit disengaging of the gas from the liquid so that only clear liquid enters the tray below.   A minimum residence, or holdup, time for the liquid of 8 sec [= total volume of downspout in cu ft/(cu ft liquid/sec)] will ordinarily ensure this.   Foamy liquids require more time.   The downspout must be brought sufficiently close to the tray below so as to seal into the liquid on that tray ($\frac{1}{2}$ to 1 in. below the outlet weir level), thus preventing gas bubbles from rising up the downspout to short-circuit the tray above.   Seal pots and seal-pot dams (inlet weirs) may be used, as in Fig. 6.3, but not if there is any tendency to accumulate sediment.

Weirs.   The depth of liquid on the tray required for gas contacting is maintained by an overflow weir (outlet weir), which may or may not be a continuation of the downspout plate.   The weir may be straight, rectangular, or notched; circular weirs which are extensions of circular pipes used as downspouts are not recommended.

Fig. 6.3   *Seal-pot arrangement.*

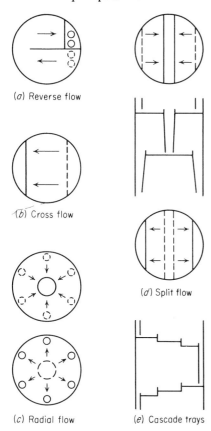

(a) Reverse flow

(b) Cross flow

(c) Radial flow

(d) Split flow

(e) Cascade trays

Fig. 6.4 *Tray arrangements. Arrows show direction of liquid flow.*

In order to ensure reasonably uniform distribution of liquid flow on single-pass trays, a weir length of 60 to 75 percent of the tower diameter is used. To assist the weir action, the openings on the tray for gas flow (particularly for bubble caps) are set from 3 to 5 in. from the weir, so that some vapor-disengaging space is provided before the liquid flows over the weir.

Liquid flow. An increase in liquid depth from the outlet to the inlet of the tray, the liquid *gradient* (by which is meant merely the difference in liquid depth), results from the resistance offered to flow of liquid by devices on the tray and the flow of gas. Excessive liquid gradient, as will be shown, leads to maldistribution of gas and other difficulties.

The liquid gradient may be minimized by reducing the distance along the tray through which the liquid must flow. For large-diameter towers, radial or split flow may be substituted for the simple cross flow thus far considered (see Fig. 6.4), although every attempt is usually made to use the cross-flow tray by reason of its lower cost. For very large diameters, cascade trays of several levels, each with its own weir, can be used, although their cost is considerable. For towers up to 4 ft in diameter, simple cross flow is probably best. In any case, the liquid gradient should be kept to about 0.5 in. with perhaps 1.25 in. as a maximum.

Bubble-cap trays

These have been known for well over a century. Because they can operate at high efficiency over a wide range of flow rates, they have been the most commonly used type of tray in the past, and their technology is probably the most advanced of all vapor-liquid contacting devices. A schematic arrangement is shown in Fig. 6.2. The vapor or gas rises through the openings in the tray (vapor risers) into bubble caps which surmount each riser. The periphery of each cap is slotted or serrated with a number of openings (slots) through which the gas bubbles into the liquid.

Tower diameter. The diameter is determined through the use of a gas velocity, appropriately smaller than that which causes flooding, as indicated earlier. The constant C_F of Eq. (6.1) has been correlated for the available data on flooding for nonfoaming systems, for cases where the weir height is less than 15 percent of the tray spacing, and for tray spacings $t = 12$ to 36 in.[17,19] The curves of the original papers can be adequately expressed by

$$C_F = \left[a \log \frac{1}{(L'/G')(\rho_G/\rho_L)^{0.5}} + b \right] \left(\frac{\sigma'}{20} \right)^{0.2} \tag{6.2}$$

and values of a and b are given in Table 6.1.

The caps are ordinarily circular, 3 to 6 in. diameter, or sometimes rectangular (tunnel caps), 3 to 6 in. wide by 12 in. or more long. They are most frequently made of thin metal by punching or spinning, less frequently by casting, but also from other materials such as plastics, glass, or carbon. Figure 6.5 shows some typical designs. The slots are arranged around the periphery (skirt) and are either of sawtooth design or cut so that they do not extend to the edge of the cap, leaving a *shroud ring*. Slots may be rectangular or triangular; the shape does not seem particularly important in influencing tray efficiency. The slots should be covered by a depth of liquid, the *liquid seal*, so as to ensure contact of liquid and gas. Typical values of liquid seal[4] are given in Table 6.1. The skirt of the cap may be placed directly on the tray, but it is preferable to allow at least 0.5 in. skirt clearance to prevent accumulation of sediment from the liquid and to allow for means of passing more than the expected amount of gas under the skirt if necessary. The vapor risers under the cap should extend above the top of the slots to reduce the tendency to *back trap* or *dump* (flow of liquid through the riser).

A typical cross-flow tray layout is shown in Fig. 6.6. The caps are set at the corners of equilateral triangles, arranged so that the liquid is adequately contacted by gas. The gas issuing from the slots is usually not projected more than about 1 in. from the cap, so that the distance between caps should be from 1 to 3 in., and for the same reason the clearance between caps and tower shell should be kept small. The

Fig. 6.5 *Typical bubble-cap designs. (With permission of The Pressed Steel Company.)*

arrangement is usually chosen by trial and error.   After the first arrangement is made, with perhaps 60 to 70 percent of the tray area allocated to bubble caps, a computation is made of the gas pressure drop, liquid gradient, the increase in level of liquid in the downspout, and gas distribution among the caps.   If not satisfactory, a new layout is chosen.   Detailed computation of the hydraulic characteristics of bubble-cap trays has been thoroughly developed by Bolles[4] and others,[48] and will not be covered here.

The difficulties that excessive liquid gradient can cause are shown schematically in Fig. 6.7.   The bulk of the gas flows through the row of caps nearest the outlet weir, while those caps nearest the liquid inlet do not function properly because the pressure due to liquid depth prevents the gas from opening the slots.   Back trapping is most injurious to tray efficiency, since on cross-flow trays the back-trapped liquid bypasses two trays.   In an existing tower, the difficulties are sometimes alleviated by raising the level of the caps and risers near the liquid inlet of the trays.

Properly designed bubble trays are able to handle a four- to fivefold range of gas flow, as well as liquid flows ranging from the maximum causing flooding to very low values (the ratio of maximum to minimum flow is termed *turndown*) since at all times the liquid level on the trays is maintained by the weir and the cap slots are covered.

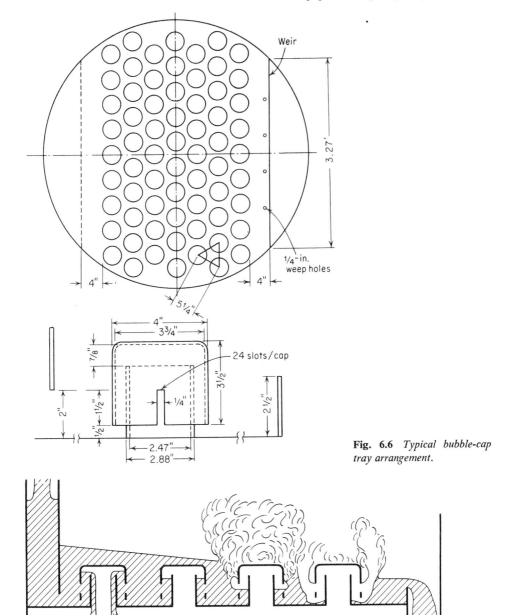

Fig. 6.6 *Typical bubble-cap tray arrangement.*

Fig. 6.7 *Effect of excessive liquid gradient.*

Perforated (sieve) trays

These have been known almost as long as bubble-cap trays, but they fell out of favor, particularly in the first half of this century. In recent years, because they are much less expensive than bubble-cap trays, interest in them has revived to the extent that they (or proprietary modifications) have nearly replaced bubble caps for new installations.

Perforated trays are built in the same general fashion as bubble-cap trays except that the area normally devoted to caps and risers is replaced by a sheet of metal perforated with small circular holes. If it were not for the rapid flow of gas up through the holes, liquid would rain down (*weep*) through them. The gas, dispersed into bubbles by the perforations, expands the liquid into a turbulent froth, characterized by very large interfacial surface for mass transfer. The trays are subject to flooding due to backup of liquid in the downspouts or excessive entrainment (priming) much as bubble-cap trays are.

Hole diameters from ⅛ to ½ in. are used, 3⁄16 in. perhaps most frequently, and the holes are placed on the corners of equilateral triangles at distances between centers (*pitch*) of from 2.5 to 5 hole diameters.[48] For most installations, stainless steel or other alloy perforated sheet, which is commercially available, is used rather than carbon steel, even though not particularly required for corrosion resistance. Sheet thickness is usually four-tenths to eight-tenths the hole diameter for stainless steel, somewhat larger for carbon steel or copper alloys.

Tower diameter. The flooding constant C_F of Eq. (6.1) has been correlated for the data available on flooding.[17,18] The original curves can be represented by

$$C_F = \left[a \log \frac{1}{(L'/G')(\rho_G/\rho_L)^{0.5}} + b \right] \left(\frac{\sigma'}{20} \right)^{0.2} \left(5 \frac{A_h}{A_a} + 0.5 \right) \qquad (6.3)$$

and the constants a and b are given in Table 6.1. The expression is limited to hole diameters not larger than ¼ in., to cases where the weir height does not exceed 15 percent of the tray spacing, and to nonfoaming systems. A_a is the active area of the tray, taken to be that between inlet downspout and the outlet weir on a cross-flow tray, and A_h is the hole area per tray. A velocity appropriately smaller than the flooding velocity of Eq. (6.1) is then chosen to fix the diameter of the tower (see Illustration 6.1).

Perforated-tray hydraulics

The design of a perforated tray must include not only the tray layout but also estimates of the gas pressure drop and approach to flooding as well as insurance against weeping and excessive entrainment.

Liquid depth. Liquid depths should not ordinarily be less than 2 in., to ensure good froth formation, or probably much greater than 4 in.,[28] although the recent tendency is to make the maximum figure larger. These limits refer to the sum of the weir height h_W plus the crest over the weir h_1, although the evidence is that in the perforated area the actual equivalent clear-liquid depth will be smaller than this.

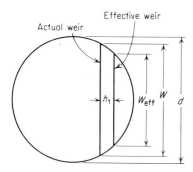

Fig. 6.8 *Schematic diagram of a cross-flow perforated tray.*

Weirs. Refer to Fig. 6.8, where a schematic representation of a cross-flow tray is shown. The crest of liquid over a straight rectangular weir may be estimated by the familiar Francis formula,

$$\frac{q}{W_{\text{eff}}} = 3.33\left(\frac{h_1}{12}\right)^{3/2} \tag{6.4}$$

where q = rate of liquid flow, cu ft/sec
W_{eff} = effective length of weir, ft
h_1 = liquid crest over weir, in.

Owing to the fact that the weir action is hampered by the curved sides of the circular tower, it is recommended[13] that W_{eff} be represented as a chord of the circle of diameter d, a distance h_1 farther from the center than the actual weir, as in Fig. 6.9. Equation (6.4) may then be rearranged to

$$h_1 = 5.38\left(\frac{W}{W_{\text{eff}}}\right)^{2/3}\left(\frac{q}{W}\right)^{2/3} \tag{6.5}$$

Fig. 6.9 *Effective weir length.*

Fig. 6.10 *Correction for effective weir length.*

The effective lengths of weirs have been calculated from the geometry of Fig. 6.9, and the correction is given by Fig. 6.10.

Pressure drop for the gas. For convenience, all gas-pressure drops will be expressed as equivalent heads, in inches, of clear liquid of density ρ_L lb/cu ft on the tray. The pressure drop for the gas h_G is the sum of the effects for flow of gas through the dry plate and those caused by the presence of liquid:

$$h_G = h_D + h_L + h_R \qquad (6.6)$$

where h_D = dry-plate pressure drop
   h_L = pressure drop due to the depth of liquid on the tray
   h_R = "residual" pressure drop

Although Fig. 6.8 shows a hydraulic gradient Δ, half of which should be used in Eq. (6.6), in practice this is so small, except for the very largest of trays, that it may reasonably be neglected.[24,33] Estimates of the gas-pressure drop summarized here are based on a critical study by Madigan[32] of all available data and the generally accepted methods. Most of the available data are for the air–water system, and extension to others is somewhat uncertain.

Dry pressure drop h_D. This is calculated on the basis that it is the result of a loss in pressure on entrance to the perforations, friction within the short tube formed by the perforation due to plate thickness, and an exit loss:[25]

$$h_D = 12C_o \frac{V_h{}^2 \rho_G}{2g\rho_L}\left[0.40\left(1.25 - \frac{A_h}{A_n}\right) + \frac{4lf}{d_h} + \left(1 - \frac{A_h}{A_n}\right)^2\right] \qquad (6.7)$$

The Fanning friction factor f is taken from a standard chart.[2] C_0 is an orifice coefficient which depends upon the plate thickness/hole diameter ratio.[34] Over the range $l/d_h = 0.2$ to 2.0,

$$C_O = 1.09 \left(\frac{d_h}{l} \right)^{0.25} \tag{6.8}$$

Hydraulic head h_L. In the perforated area of the tray, the liquid is actually in the form of a froth. The equivalent depth of clear liquid h_L is that which would be obtained if the froth collapsed. This is usually actually less than the height of the outlet weir, decreasing with increased gas rate. The methods available for estimating h_L are not well developed, and this is the poorest known of the several gas pressure drops. The recommended relationship is[21]

$$h_L = 0.24 + 0.725 h_W - 0.29 h_W V_a \rho_G^{0.5} + 4.48 \frac{q}{z} \tag{6.9}$$

where z is the average liquid flow width, which may be taken as $(d + W)/2$.

Residual gas pressure drop h_R. This is believed to be due largely to the necessity of overcoming surface tension as the gas issues from a perforation. A balance of the internal force in a static bubble required to overcome surface tension is

$$\frac{\pi d_p{}^2}{4} \Delta P_B = \pi d_p \sigma \tag{6.10}$$

or

$$\Delta P_B = \frac{4\sigma}{d_p} \tag{6.11}$$

where ΔP_B is the excess pressure in the bubble owing to surface tension. But the bubble of gas grows over a finite time when the gas flows, and by averaging over time[16] it develops that the appropriate value is ΔP_R:

$$\Delta P_R = \frac{6\sigma}{d_p} \tag{6.12}$$

Since d_p is not readily computed, we substitute as an approximation the diameter of the perforation, $d_h/12$, which leads to

$$h_R = 12 \frac{\Delta P_R}{\rho_L} \frac{g_c}{g} = 144(6) \frac{\sigma}{\rho_L d_h} \frac{g_c}{g} = 0.06 \frac{\sigma'}{\rho_L d_h} \tag{6.13}$$

where g_c/g is taken as 1.0.

Comparison of observed data with values of h_G calculated by these methods shows a standard deviation of 14.7 percent.[32]

Pressure loss at liquid entrance h_2. The flow of liquid under the downspout apron as it enters the tray incurs a pressure loss which may be estimated as three velocity heads:[10]

$$h_2 = \frac{12(3)}{2g} \left(\frac{q}{A_{da}} \right)^2 = 0.558 \left(\frac{q}{A_{da}} \right)^2 \tag{6.14}$$

where A_{da} is the smaller of the two areas, the downspout cross section or the free area between the downspout apron and the tray, and g is taken as 32.2 ft/sq sec. Friction in the downspout is negligible.

Backup in the downspout. Refer to Fig. 6.8. The distance h_3, the difference in liquid level inside and immediately outside the downspout, will be the sum of the pressure losses due to liquid and gas flow

$$h_3 = h_G + h_2 \tag{6.15}$$

Since the mass in the downspout will be partly froth carried over the weir from the tray above, not yet disengaged, whose average density may be estimated roughly as half of the clear liquid, safe design requires that the level of equivalent clear liquid in the downspout be no more than half the tray spacing. Neglecting Δ, the requirement is

$$h_W + h_1 + h_3 \leqslant \frac{t}{2} \tag{6.16}$$

Weeping. If the gas velocity through the holes is too small, liquid will drain through them and short-circuit part of the tray. The data on incipient weeping are meager, particularly for large liquid depths on the tray. A study of the available data[32] led to the following as the best representation of V_{hW}, the minimum gas velocity below which liquid weeping will occur,

$$\frac{V_{hW}\mu_G}{\sigma g_c} = 2.92(10^{-4}) \left(\frac{\mu_G^2}{\sigma g_c \rho_G d_h'} \frac{\rho_L}{\rho_G} 10^5 \right)^{0.379} \left(\frac{l}{d_h} \right)^{0.293} \left(\frac{2A_a d_h'}{\sqrt{3}p'^3} \right)^{2.8/(Z/d_h')^{0.724}} \tag{6.17}$$

where each of the ratios in parentheses is dimensionless. Available data for h_L, in the range 0.9 to 1.9 in., do not indicate h_L to be of influence. It may be for higher values.

Liquid entrainment. When liquid is carried by the gas up to the tray above, the entrained liquid is caught in the liquid on the upper tray, and the liquid flowing downward is then larger in amount by the entrainment. A convenient definition of the degree or extent of entrainment is the fraction of the liquid entering a tray which is carried by the gas to the tray above,[17]

$$\text{Fractional entrainment} = E = \frac{\text{moles liquid entrained/(hr)(sq ft)}}{L + \text{moles liquid entrained/(hr)(sq ft)}}$$

The important influence of entrainment on tray efficiency will be discussed later. Figure 6.11 represents a summary of sieve-tray entrainment data[17,18] with an accuracy of ± 20 percent.

Illustration 6.1. A dilute aqueous solution of methanol and water is to be stripped with steam in a perforated tray tower. The conditions chosen for design are (1) vapor, 700 moles/hr, 18 mole % methanol; (2) liquid, 2,100 moles/hr, 5 wt. % (2.9 mole %) methanol; (3) temperature 95°C, pressure 1 atm. Design a suitable perforated tray.

Solution. Mol wt methanol = 32, mol wt water = 18. Av mol wt gas = 0.18(32) + 0.82(18) = 20.5 lb/lb mole.

$$\rho_G = \frac{20.5}{359} \frac{273}{273 + 95} = 0.0424 \text{ lb/cu ft}$$

$$Q = \frac{700}{3,600} 359 \frac{273 + 95}{273} = 94 \text{ cu ft/sec, vapor rate}$$

$$\rho_L = 60 \text{ lb/cu ft}$$

$$\text{Av mol wt liquid} = 100/(\tfrac{5}{32} + \tfrac{95}{18}) = 18.43 \text{ lb/lb mole}$$

$$q = \frac{2,100(18.43)}{60(3,600)} = 0.1794 \text{ cu ft liquid/sec}$$

Perforations. Take $d_h = \frac{3}{16}$-in.-diameter (0.1875-in.) holes, on equilateral triangular pitch, 0.5 in. between hole centers, punched in sheet metal 0.078 in. thick (14 U.S. standard gauge). Each triangle has an area $(3)^{0.5}(0.5)^2/4 = 0.1085$ sq in., and contains one-half a hole of area $\pi(0.1875)^2/4 = 0.0276$ sq in. The perforated sheet has a ratio of hole to total area $= 0.0276/2(0.1085) = 0.1275$.

Tower diameter. Tentatively take $t = 20$ in tray spacing.

$$\frac{L'}{G'} \left(\frac{\rho_G}{\rho_L} \right)^{0.5} = \frac{q\rho_L}{Q\rho_G} \left(\frac{\rho_G}{\rho_L} \right)^{0.5} = \frac{q}{Q} \left(\frac{\rho_L}{\rho_G} \right)^{0.5} = \frac{0.1794}{94} \left(\frac{60}{0.0424} \right)^{0.5} = 0.0719$$

Table 6.1:
$$a = 0.0062(20) + 0.0385 = 0.1625$$
$$b = 0.00253(20) + 0.05 = 0.1006$$

Fig. **6.11** *Entrainment, sieve trays.*[17] *(With permission of Petro/Chemical Engineering.)*

In Eq. (6.3), since $\dfrac{L'}{G'}\left(\dfrac{\rho_G}{\rho_L}\right)^{0.5}$ is less than 0.1, use 0.1 (see Table 6.1).   Tentatively take $A_h/A_a = 0.1275$.
The surface tension is estimated as 40 dynes/cm.

$$C_F = \left(0.1625 \log \frac{1}{0.1} + 0.1006\right)\left(\frac{40}{20}\right)^{0.2}[5(0.1275) + 0.5] = 0.354$$

Eq. (6.1): $V_F = 0.354\left(\dfrac{60 - 0.0424}{0.0424}\right)^{0.5} = 13.31$ ft/sec at flooding

Using 80% of flooding, $V = 0.80(13.31) = 10.65$ ft/sec based on area A_n.

$$A_n = \frac{Q}{V} = \frac{94}{10.65} = 8.82 \text{ sq ft}$$

Tentatively choose a weir length $W = 0.7d$.   This makes the segmental area of one downspout 8.8% of the cross section of the circular tower.

$$A_t = \frac{8.82}{1 - 0.088} = 9.65 \text{ sq ft}$$

$d = [4(9.65)/\pi]^{0.5} = 3.5$ ft, tower diam

$W = 0.7(3.5) = 2.45$ ft weir length

$A_d = 0.088(9.65) = 0.850$ sq ft downspout cross section

$A_a = A_t - 2A_d = 9.65 - 2(0.850) = 7.95$ sq ft active area

Hole area A_h. Taking $A_h/A_t = 0.09$ to allow for a tray support ring, $A_h = 0.09(9.65) = 0.866$ sq ft hole area.

$$\text{Total area of perforated sheet} = \frac{0.866}{0.1275} = 6.80 \text{ sq ft}$$

True $A_h/A_a = 0.866/7.95 = 0.1095$, which will not alter the flooding coefficient C_F significantly.
Weir crest h_1. Try $h_1 = 1.0$ in. $\therefore h_1/d = 1/3.5 = 0.286$, and $W/d = 0.7$.   From Fig. 6.10, $(W/W_{\text{eff}})^{2/3} = 1.05$.

Eq. (6.5): $$h_1 = 5.38(1.05)\left(\frac{0.1794}{2.45}\right)^{2/3} = 0.98 \text{ in.   OK}$$

Set weir height $h_W = 2.0$ in.
Dry pressure drop h_D

Eq. (6.8): $$C_O = 1.09\left(\frac{0.1875}{0.078}\right)^{0.25} = 1.360$$

$$V_h = \frac{VA_n}{A_h} = 10.65\,\frac{8.82}{0.866} = 108.4 \text{ ft/sec}$$

$$\mu_G' = 0.0125 \text{ centipoise}$$

$$\text{Hole Reynolds number} = \frac{d_h' V_h \rho_G}{\mu_G} = \frac{0.1875(108.4)(0.0424)}{12(0.0125)(0.000672)} = 8,550$$

$\therefore\ f = 0.008$ ("The Chemical Engineers' Handbook," 4th ed., Fig. 5.25).

$$g = 32.2 \text{ ft/sec}^2 \qquad l = 0.078 \text{ in. plate thickness}$$

Substituting in Eq. (6.7) yields $h_D = 2.10$ in. liquid.
Hydraulic head h_L

$$V_a = \frac{VA_n}{A_a} = 10.65\,\frac{8.82}{7.95} = 11.81 \text{ ft/sec}$$

$$\rho_G = 0.0424 \text{ lb/cu ft} \qquad h_W = 2.0 \text{ in.}$$

$$q = 0.1794 \text{ cu ft/sec} \qquad z = \frac{d + W}{2} = 2.975 \text{ ft}$$

Substituting in Eq. (6.9) yields $h_L = 0.55$ in. liquid.
Residual pressure drop h_R.   Eq. (6.13):

$$h_R = \frac{0.06(40)}{60(0.1875)} = 0.213 \text{ in. liquid}$$

Total gas-pressure drop h_G.   Eq. (6.6):

$$h_G = 2.10 + 0.55 + 0.213 = 2.86 \text{ in. liquid}$$

Pressure loss at liquid entrance h_2. The downspout apron will be set at $h_W - 0.5 = 1.5$ in. above the tray.   The area for liquid flow under the apron $= 1.5W/12 = 1.5(2.45)/12 = 0.306$ sq ft.   Since this is smaller than A_d, $A_{da} = 0.306$ sq ft.

Eq. (6.14): $$h_2 = 0.558\left(\frac{0.1749}{0.306}\right)^2 = 0.192 \text{ in. liquid}$$

Backup in downspout. Eq. (6.15): $h_3 = 2.86 + 0.192 = 3.05$ in.
Check on flooding. $h_W + h_1 + h_3 = 2.0 + 0.98 + 3.05 = 6.03$ in., which is well below $t/2 = 10$ in.   OK.

Weeping velocity

$$\mu_G = 0.0125(0.000672) = 8.40(10^{-6}) \text{ lb/(ft)(sec)}$$

$$\sigma = 40(6.85)(10^{-5}) = 274(10^{-5}) \text{ lb/ft}$$

$$d_h' = \frac{0.1875}{12} = 0.0156 \text{ ft} \qquad p' = \frac{0.5}{12} = 0.0417 \text{ ft}$$

For $W/d = 0.7$, the weir is set 1.25 ft from the center of the tower. Therefore $Z = 2(1.25) = 2.50$ ft. All the other items of Eq. (6.17) have been previously evaluated, and the equation then yields $V_{hW} = 20$ ft/sec. The tray will not weep until the gas velocity through the holes is reduced to something close to this value.

Downspout residence time. The volume of the downspout $= A_d(t + h_W)/12 = 0.850(20 + 2)/12 = 1.56$ cu ft. Since the liquid flow rate is $q = 0.1794$ cu ft/sec, the superficial residence time $= 1.56/0.1794 = 8.7$ sec, which should be satisfactory.

Entrainment

$$\frac{V}{V_F} = 0.80 \qquad \frac{L'}{G'}\left(\frac{\rho_G}{\rho_L}\right)^{0.5} = 0.0719 \text{ (see Tower diameter)}$$

Fig. 6.11: $E = 0.042$

The recycling of liquid resulting from such entrainment is too small to influence the tray hydraulics appreciably.

The mass-transfer efficiency of this tray is estimated in Illustration 6.2.

Proprietary trays

Although for many decades the basic design of tray-tower internals remained relatively static, recent years have seen a great many innovations, only a few of which can be mentioned here. Figure 6.12 is a variation of the bubble-cap arrangement,[3,36] wherein the vapor issues from the slots in the direction of liquid flow. The structure shown extends across the entire area of the tray. As a result the backward splashing of liquid in the direction of the liquid inlet to the tray is much reduced in comparison with that for bubble caps. There is also a great variety of *valve trays*, which are, in effect, perforated trays with variable area of openings for gas flow. The perforations are relatively large, roughly 1.5 in. in diameter if circular, and they are covered with movable caps which rise as the flow rate of gas increases. At low gas rates and correspondingly small openings, the tendency to weep is reduced; at high gas rates the

Direction of liquid flow

Gas

Fig. 6.12 *Socony-Mobil Uniflux tray (schematic).*

←Hole in
tray deck

Fig. 6.13   *Glitsch Ballast Tray (schematic), a form of valve tray.   (Fritz W. Glitsch and Sons, Inc.)*

pressure drop remains low.   Figure 6.13 shows one variety, and there are many others.[38,42,50]   In most cases, the design of proprietary trays must be left to the supplier.

Tray efficiency

Tray efficiency is the fractional approach to an ideal or theoretical tray (see Chap. 5) which is attained by a real tray.   Ultimately, we require a measure of approach to equilibrium of all the vapor and liquid from the tray, but since the conditions at various locations on the tray may differ, we begin by considering the local, or *point*, efficiency of mass transfer at a particular place on the tray surface.

Point efficiency.   Figure 6.14 is a schematic representation of one tray of a multitray tower.   The tray n is fed from tray $n - 1$ above by liquid of average composition x_{n-1} mole fraction of transferred component, and it delivers liquid of average composition x_n to the tray below.   At the place under consideration, a pencil of gas of composition $y_{n+1,\text{local}}$ rises from below, and as a result of mass transfer, leaves with a concentration $y_{n,\text{local}}$.   At the place in question, it is assumed that the local liquid concentration x_{local} is constant in the vertical direction.   The point

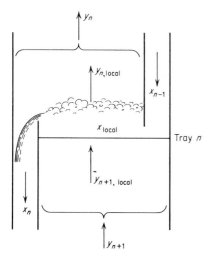

Fig. 6.14   *Tray efficiency.*

efficiency is then defined by

$$\mathbf{E}_{OG} = \frac{y_{n,\text{local}} - y_{n+1,\text{local}}}{y_{\text{local}}^* - y_{n+1,\text{local}}} \tag{6.18}$$

Here y_{local}^* is the concentration in equilibrium with x_{local}, and Eq. (6.18) then represents the change in gas concentration which actually occurs as a fraction of that which would occur if equilibrium were established. The subscript G signifies that gas concentrations are used, and the O emphasizes that $\mathbf{E}_{OG}$ is a measure of the overall resistance to mass transfer for both phases. As the gas passes through the openings of the tray and through the liquid and foam, it encounters several hydrodynamic regimes, each with different rates of mass transfer. The danger in attempting to describe the entire effect in terms of a single quantity, in cases of this sort, was pointed out in Chap. 5, but present information permits nothing better.

Consider that the gas rises at a rate G lb moles/(hr)(sq ft). Let the interfacial surface between gas and liquid be a sq ft/cu ft of liquid-gas foam. As the gas rises a differential height dh_L, the area of contact is $a\,dh_L$ per square feet of tray. If, while of concentration y, it undergoes a concentration change dy in this height, and if the total quantity of gas remains essentially constant, the rate of solute transfer is $G\,dy$:

$$G\,dy = K_y(a\,dh_L)(y_{\text{local}}^* - y) \tag{6.19}$$

Then

$$\int_{y_{n+1,\text{local}}}^{y_{n,\text{local}}} \frac{dy}{y_{\text{local}}^* - y} = \int_0^{h_L} \frac{K_y a\,dh_L}{G} \tag{6.20}$$

Since y_{local}^* is constant for constant x_{local},

$$-\ln \frac{y_{\text{local}}^* - y_{n,\text{local}}}{y_{\text{local}}^* - y_{n+1,\text{local}}} = -\ln\left(1 - \frac{y_{n,\text{local}} - y_{n+1,\text{local}}}{y_{\text{local}}^* - y_{n+1,\text{local}}}\right)$$

$$= -\ln(1 - \mathbf{E}_{OG}) = \frac{K_y a h_L}{G} \tag{6.21}$$

Therefore

$$\mathbf{E}_{OG} = 1 - e^{-K_y a h_L/G} = 1 - e^{-N_{tOG}} \tag{6.22}$$

The exponent on e is simplified to N_{tOG}, the number of overall gas-transfer units. Just as K_y contains both gas and liquid resistance to mass transfer, so also N_{tOG} is made up of the transfer units for the gas N_{tG} and those for the liquid N_{tL}. As will be shown in Chap. 8, these may be combined in the manner of Eq. (5.7):

$$\frac{1}{N_{tOG}} = \frac{1}{N_{tG}} + \frac{mG}{L}\frac{1}{N_{tL}} \tag{6.23}$$

The terms on the right represent, respectively, the gas and liquid mass-transfer resistances, which must be obtained experimentally. For example, by contacting a gas with a pure liquid on a tray, so that vaporization of the liquid occurs without mass-transfer resistance in the liquid, the vaporization efficiency provides N_{tG}, which may then be correlated in terms of fluid properties, tray design, and operating conditions.   Values of N_{tL} obtained through absorption of relatively insoluble gases into liquids (see Chap. 5) may be similarly correlated.

Murphree tray efficiency.   The bulk-average concentrations of all the local pencils of gas of Fig. 6.14 are y_{n+1} and y_n.   The Murphree efficiency of the entire tray is then [see Eq. (5.39)]

$$\mathbf{E}_{MG} = \frac{y_n - y_{n+1}}{y_n^* - y_{n+1}} \tag{6.24}$$

where y_n^* is the value in equilibrium with the leaving liquid of concentration x_n.

The relationship between $\mathbf{E}_{MG}$ and $\mathbf{E}_{OG}$ can then be derived by integrating the local $\mathbf{E}_{OG}$'s over the surface of the tray.   Clearly, if all the gas entering were uniformly mixed and fed uniformly to the entire tray cross section, and if the mechanical contacting of gas and liquid were everywhere uniform, the uniformity of concentration of exit gas $y_{n+1,\text{local}}$ would then depend on the uniformity of liquid concentration on the tray.   Liquid on the tray is splashed about by the action of the gas, some of it even being thrown backward in the direction from which it enters the tray (back mixing).   The two extreme cases which might be visualized are:

1. Liquid completely back mixed, everywhere of uniform concentration x_n. In this case, Eq. (6.24) reverts to Eq. (6.18), and

$$\mathbf{E}_{MG} = \mathbf{E}_{OG} \tag{6.25}$$

2. Liquid in "plug flow," with no mixing, each particle remaining on the tray for the same length of time.   In this case, it has been shown that[30]

$$\mathbf{E}_{MG} = \frac{L}{mG} (e^{\mathbf{E}_{OG} mG/L} - 1) \tag{6.26}$$

and $\mathbf{E}_{MG} > \mathbf{E}_{OG}$.

In the more likely intermediate case, the transport of solute by the mixing process can be described in terms of an eddy diffusivity D_E, whereupon[7]

$$\frac{\mathbf{E}_{MG}}{\mathbf{E}_{OG}} = \frac{1 - e^{-(\eta + \text{Pe})}}{(\eta + \text{Pe})[1 + (\eta + \text{Pe})/\eta]} + \frac{e^\eta - 1}{\eta[1 + \eta/(\eta + \text{Pe})]} \tag{6.27}$$

where

$$\eta = \frac{\text{Pe}}{2}\left[\left(1 + \frac{4mG\mathbf{E}_{OG}}{L\,\text{Pe}}\right)^{0.5} - 1\right] \tag{6.28}$$

$$\text{Pe} = \frac{Z^2}{D_E \theta_L} \tag{6.29}$$

Here θ_L is the liquid residence time on tray and Z the length of liquid travel.   Pe is a Péclet number (see Chap. 3), as can be seen better by writing it as $\dfrac{Z}{D_E} \dfrac{Z}{\theta_L}$, whence

Z/θ_L becomes the average liquid velocity. Pe $= 0$ corresponds to complete back mixing ($D_E = \infty$), while Pe $= \infty$ corresponds to plug flow ($D_E = 0$). Large values of Pe result when mixing is not extensive and for large values of Z (large tower diameters).

Entrainment. A further correction is required for the damage done by entrainment. Entrainment represents a form of back mixing, which acts to destroy the concentration changes produced by the trays. It can be shown[11,18] that the Murphree efficiency corrected for entrainment is

$$E_{MGE} = \frac{E_{MG}}{1 + E_{MG}[E/(1 - E)]} \tag{6.30}$$

Data. Experimental information on N_{tG}, N_{tL}, and D_E is needed to use the relations developed above. Many data have been published, particularly for bubble-cap trays, and an excellent review is available.[48] Perhaps the best-organized information results from a research program sponsored by the American Institute of Chemical Engineers.[7] Most of the work was done with bubble-cap trays, but the relatively fewer data together with subsequent information from sieve trays[22] indicate that the empirical expressions below represent the performance of sieve trays reasonably well. No attempt will be made here to outline in detail the range of conditions covered by these expressions, which should be used with caution, especially if the original report is not consulted.

Sieve Trays

$$N_{tG} = \frac{0.776 + 0.116h_W - 0.290V_a\rho_G^{0.5} + 9.72q/Z}{Sc_G^{0.5}} \tag{6.31}$$

$$N_{tL} = 7.31(10^5)D_L^{0.5}(0.26V_a\rho_G^{0.5} + 0.15)\theta_L \tag{6.32}$$

$$D_E = \left(0.774 + 1.026V_a + 67.2\frac{q}{Z} + 0.900h_W\right)^2 \tag{6.33}$$

$$\theta_L = \frac{\text{cu ft liquid on tray}}{\text{liquid rate, cu ft/hr}} = \frac{(h_L/12)zZ}{3,600q} = \frac{2.31(10^{-5})h_L zZ}{q} \tag{6.34}$$

Illustration 6.2. Estimate the tray efficiency of the stripping tray of Illustration 6.1.
Solution. From the results of Illustration 6.1, we have

Vapor rate $= 700$ lb moles/hr	Liquid rate $= 2,100$ lb moles/hr
$\rho_G = 0.0424$ lb/cu ft	$h_L = 0.55$ in.
$q = 0.1794$ cu ft/sec	$h_W = 2.0$ in.
$V_a = 11.81$ ft/sec	$Z = 2.50$ ft
$z = 2.975$ ft	$E = 0.042$

In addition, by the methods of Chap. 2, the following may be estimated: $Sc_G = 0.865$, $D_L = 2.3(10^{-4})$ sq ft/hr. The vapor-liquid equilibria yield $m = 6.2$ ("The Chemical Engineers' Handbook," 4th ed.,

p. 13-5).   Substitution of these directly in Eqs. (6.31) to (6.34) then yields

$$\theta_L = 52.7(10)^{-5} \text{ hr} \qquad N_{tG} = 0.955$$
$$N_{tL} = 3.79 \qquad D_E = 351 \text{ sq ft/hr}$$

Eq. (6.23):

$$\frac{1}{N_{tOG}} = \frac{1}{0.955} + \frac{6.2(700)}{2,100} \frac{1}{3.79}$$

$$N_{tOG} = 0.628$$

Eq. (6.22): $\mathbf{E}_{OG} = 1 - e^{-0.628} = 0.466$

Eq. (6.29): $$\text{Pe} = \frac{(2.50)^2}{351(52.7)(10^{-5})} = 33.7$$

Eq. (6.28): $\eta = 0.944$

Eq. (6.27): $\dfrac{\mathbf{E}_{MG}}{\mathbf{E}_{OG}} = 1.55 \qquad \mathbf{E}_{MG} = 1.55(0.466) = 0.727$

Eq. (6.30): $\mathbf{E}_{MGE} = 0.70$ **Ans.**

Overall tray efficiency.   Another method of describing the performance of a tray tower is through the overall tray efficiency,

$$\mathbf{E}_O = \frac{\text{number of ideal trays required}}{\text{number of real trays required}} \tag{6.35}$$

While reliable information on such an efficiency is most desirable and convenient to use, it must be obvious that so many variables enter into such a measure that really reliable values of $\mathbf{E}_O$ for design purposes would be most difficult to come by.   As will be shown in Chap. 8, $\mathbf{E}_O$ may be derived from the individual tray efficiencies in certain simple situations.

Provided that only standard tray designs are used and operation is within the standard ranges of liquid and gas rates, some success in correlating $\mathbf{E}_O$ with conditions might be expected.   O'Connell[39] was successful in doing this for absorption and distillation in bubble-cap-tray towers, and his correlations are shown in Figs. 6.15 and 6.16.   These must be used with great caution, but for rough estimates they are most useful.

II. LIQUID DISPERSED

In this group are included those devices in which the liquid is dispersed into thin films or drops, such as wetted-wall towers, sprays and spray towers, the various packed towers, and the like.   The packed towers are the most important of the group.

Venturi scrubbers

In these devices, which are similar to ejectors, the gas is drawn into the throat of a venturi by a stream of absorbing liquid sprayed into the convergent duct section.

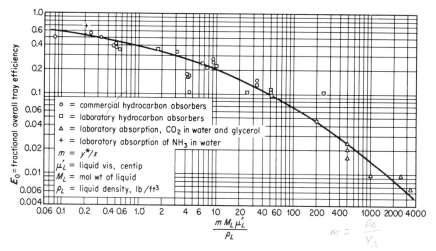

Fig. 6.15 *Overall tray efficiencies of bubble-tray absorbers. (After O'Connell.[39])*

The cocurrent flow produces a single stage,[23] although multistage countercurrent effects may be obtained by using several venturis.

Wetted-wall towers

A thin film of liquid running down the inside of a vertical pipe, with gas flowing either cocurrently or countercurrently, constitutes a wetted-wall tower.   Such devices have been used for theoretical studies of mass transfer, as described in Chap. 3, because the interfacial surface between the phases is readily kept under control and is measurable.

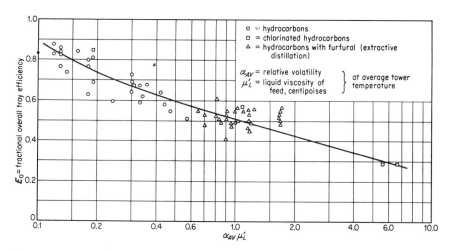

Fig. 6.16 *Overall tray efficiencies for bubble-tray distillation towers separating hydrocarbons and similar mixtures. (After O'Connell.[39])*

Industrially, they have been used as absorbers for hydrochloric acid, where absorption is accompanied by a very large evolution of heat. In this case the wetted-wall tower is surrounded with rapidly flowing cooling water. Multitube devices have also been used for distillation, where the liquid film is generated at the top by partial condensation of the rising vapor. Gas pressure drop in these towers is probably lower than in any other gas-liquid contacting device, for a given set of operating conditions.

Spray towers and spray chambers

The liquid may be sprayed into a gas stream by means of a nozzle which disperses the liquid into a fine spray of drops. The flow may be countercurrent, as in vertical towers with the liquid sprayed downward, or parallel, as in horizontal spray chambers (see Chap. 7). These devices have the advantage of low pressure drop for the gas but also have a number of disadvantages. There is a relatively high pumping cost for the liquid, owing to the pressure drop through the spray nozzle. The tendency for entrainment of liquid by the gas leaving is considerable, and mist eliminators will almost always be necessary. Unless the diameter/length ratio is very small, the gas will be fairly thoroughly mixed by the spray, and full advantage of countercurrent flow cannot be taken. The diameter/length ratio, however, cannot ordinarily be made very small since then the spray would quickly reach the walls of the tower and become ineffective as a spray.

Baffle towers and shower trays

In a tower of the design shown in Fig. 6.17, the gas flows upward through curtains of liquid falling from the edges of the baffles. The liquid dispersion is not so good as with sprays, but countercurrent contact is more readily maintained. The shower tray of Fig. 6.18, for which pressure drops as low as 0.015 psi (0.75 mm Hg) are possible,[27] is sometimes used in vacuum distillations.

Fig. 6.17 *Section through disk-and-doughnut baffle column.*

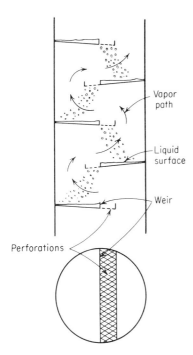

Fig. 6.18 *Shower tray.*

Packed towers

Packed towers, used for continuous countercurrent contact of liquid and gas, are vertical columns which have been filled with packing or devices of large surface, as in Fig. 6.19.   The liquid is distributed over, and trickles down through, the packed bed, thus exposing a large surface to contact the gas.

Packing. The tower packing, or *fill*, should offer the following characteristics:

1. Provide for large interfacial surface between liquid and gas.   The surface of the packing per unit volume of packed space a_p should be large but not in a microscopic sense.   Lumps of coke, for example, have a large surface owing to their porous structure, but most of this would be covered by the trickling film of liquid.   The specific packing surface a_p in any event is almost always larger than the interfacial liquid-gas surface.

2. Possess desirable fluid-flow characteristics.   This ordinarily means that the fractional void volume ϵ, or fraction of empty space, in the packed bed should be large.   The packing must permit passage of large volumes of fluid through small tower cross sections without loading or flooding (see below) and with low pressure drop for the gas.   Furthermore, gas pressure drop should be largely the result of skin friction if possible, since this is more effective than form drag in promoting high values of the mass-transfer coefficients (see Wetted-wall towers, page 151).

Fig. 6.19 *Packed tower.*

3. Be chemically inert to fluids being processed.
4. Have structural strength to permit easy handling and installation.
5. Represent low cost.

Packings are of two major types, random and regular.

Random packings. Random packings are those which are simply dumped into the tower during installation and allowed to fall at random. In the past such readily available materials as broken stone, gravel, or lumps of coke were used, but although inexpensive, these are not desirable for reasons of small surface and poor fluid-flow characteristics. Random packings most frequently used at present are manufactured, and the common types are shown in Fig. 6.20. Raschig rings are hollow cylinders, as shown, of diameters ranging from ¼ to 4 in. or more. They may be made of chemical stoneware or porcelain, which are useful in contact with most liquids except alkalies and hydrofluoric acid; of carbon, which is useful except in strongly oxidizing atmospheres; of metals; or of plastics. Thin-walled metal rings offer the advantage of lightness in weight. Lessing rings and others with internal partitions are less frequently used. The saddle-shaped packings, Berl and Intalox saddles, are available in sizes from ½ to 3 in., ordinarily made of chemical stoneware although they may be made of any material which can be stamped into shape. Generally the random packings offer larger specific surface (and larger gas pressure drop) in the smaller sizes, but they cost less per cubic foot in the larger sizes. For industrial work the 1- to 2-in. sizes are most popular. During installation the packings are poured into

(*a*) Raschig ring   (*b*) Lessing ring   (*c*) Partition ring   (*d*) Berl saddle (Courtesy, Maurice A. Knight)   (*e*) Intalox saddle (Courtesy, United States Stoneware Co.)

(*f*) Tellerette (Courtesy, Ceilcote Company, Inc.)   (*g*) Pall ring (Courtesy, United States Stoneware Co.)

Fig. 6.20 *Random tower packings.*

the tower to fall at random, and in order to prevent breakage of the more fragile packings, the tower may be first filled with water to reduce the velocity of fall.

Regular packings. These may be of the type shown in Fig. 6.21, or they may be those devices known generally as *counterflow trays*, which will be mentioned later. The regular packings offer the advantages of lower pressure drop and greater possible throughput of fluids, usually at the expense at least of more costly installation than random packings.   The larger sizes of Raschig rings (3 in. or larger) may be carefully stacked, as in Fig. 6.21*a*.   Rings are also available with internal spirals, as in Fig. 6.21*b*, and these may be stacked one upon the other to provide continuous passages for the gas.   The packing of Fig. 6.21*c*, Spraypak and Panapak, is made of sheets of several layers of expanded metal lath which have been formed into wave-shaped surfaces.[43]   Wood grids (Fig. 6.21*d*) or hurdles are inexpensive, and both the arrangement shown and many variants are used in filling water-cooling towers.   Drip-point ceramic grid tiles are large and easily stacked; they provide very effective contact at low gas pressure drop.

(*a*) Raschig rings, stacked staggered
(Top view)

(*b*) Double spiral ring
(Courtesy, United States Stoneware Co.)

Direction of flow: liquid↓, gas↑

(*c*) Section through expanded metal lath packing

Multi-layer bent sheet

(*d*) Wood grids

No. 6146

No. 6295

(*e*) Drip-point grids
(Courtesy, General Refractories Co.)

Fig. 6.21 *Regular, or stacked, packings.*

Gas   Liquid

Fig. 6.22 *Multibeam support plate.* (*The United States Stoneware Company.*)

The packings shown in Figs. 6.20 and 6.21 are by no means the only ones used, but they are probably the most popular.   Many others offer particular advantages, e.g., low pressure drop or very effective gas-liquid contact.   Among these are packings made of Fiberglas[52] and Dowpac[1] for large towers.   For laboratory or pilot-plant installations, there are McMahon packing,[35] a sort of Berl saddle made of wire gauze; Cannon packing,[8] a semiring of punched metal; and Heli-Pak and Heli-Grid of wound-wire construction.[40]

Tower shells. These may be of wood, metal, chemical stoneware, acidproof brick, glass, plastic, plastic- or glass-lined metal, or other material depending upon the corrosion conditions.   For ease of construction, they are usually circular in cross section.

Packing supports. An open space at the bottom of the tower is necessary for ensuring good distribution of the gas into the packing.   Consequently the packing must be supported above the open space.   The support must, of course, be sufficiently strong to carry the weight of a reasonable height of packing, and it must have ample free area to allow for flow of liquid and gas with a minimum of restriction.   A bar grid, of the sort shown in Fig. 6.19, may be used, but specially designed supports which provide separate passageways for gas and liquid are preferred.   Figure 6.22 shows one variety whose free area for flow is of the order of 85 percent, which may be made in various modifications and of many different materials including metals, ceramics, and plastics.

Liquid distribution. The importance of adequate initial distribution of the liquid at the top of the packing is indicated in Fig. 6.23.   Dry packing is of course completely ineffective for mass transfer, and various devices are used for liquid distribution. Spray nozzles generally result in too much entrainment of liquid in the gas to be useful.   The arrangement shown in Fig. 6.19 or a ring of perforated pipe may be used

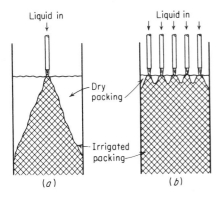

Fig. 6.23 *Liquid distribution and packing irrigation. (a) Inadequate; (b) adequate.*

in small towers.   For large diameters, a distributor of the type shown in Fig. 6.24 may be used.   It is generally considered necessary to provide at least five points of introduction of liquid for each square foot of tower cross section for large towers ($d \geqslant 4$ ft) and a greater number for smaller diameters.

Random packing size and liquid redistribution. In the case of random packings, the packing density, i.e., the number of packing pieces per cubic foot, is ordinarily less in the immediate vicinity of the tower walls, and this leads to a tendency of the liquid to segregate toward the walls and the gas to flow in the center of the tower (channeling).   This tendency is much less pronounced provided the diameter of the individual packing pieces is smaller than at least one-eighth the tower diameter, but it is recommended that, if possible, the ratio d_p/d not exceed 1:15.[12]   Even so it is customary to provide for redistribution of the liquid at intervals varying from three

Fig. 6.24 *Weir-trough liquid distributor.* (*The United States Stoneware Company.*)

to ten times the tower diameter, but at least every 20 ft.   With proper attention to liquid distribution, packed towers are successfully built to diameters of 20 ft or more.

Packing restrainers. These are necessary when gas velocities are high, and they are generally desirable to guard against lifting of packing during a sudden gas surge. Heavy screens or bars may be used.

Entrainment eliminators. Especially at high gas velocities, the gas leaving the top of the packing may carry off droplets of liquid as a mist.   This may be removed by mist eliminators, through which the gas must pass, installed above the liquid inlet. A layer of wire mesh several inches thick[9,53] or 2 or 3 ft of dry random packing are very effective.

Flow of fluids through packing. For most random packings, the pressure drop suffered by the gas is influenced by the gas and liquid flow rates in a manner similar to that shown in Fig. 6.25.   The slope of the line for dry packing is usually in the range 1.8 to 2.0, indicating turbulent flow for most practical gas velocities.

At a fixed gas velocity, the gas pressure drop increases with increased liquid rate, owing principally to the reduced free cross section available for flow of gas resulting from the presence of the liquid.   In the region of Fig. 6.25 below A, the liquid holdup, i.e., the quantity of liquid contained in the packed bed, is reasonably constant with changing gas velocity, although it increases with liquid rate.   In the region between A and B, the liquid holdup increases rapidly with gas rate, the free area for gas flow becomes smaller, and the pressure drop rises more rapidly.   This is known as *loading*.   As the gas rate is increased to B at fixed liquid rate, one of a number of changes occurs: (1) a layer of liquid, through which the gas bubbles, may appear at the top of the packing; (2) liquid may fill the tower, starting at the bottom or at any intermediate restriction such as a packing support, so that there is a change from gas–continuous liquid–dispersed to liquid–continuous gas–dispersed (inversion);

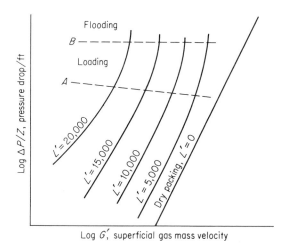

Fig. 6.25 *Typical gas pressure drop for counterflow of liquid and gas in random packings.*

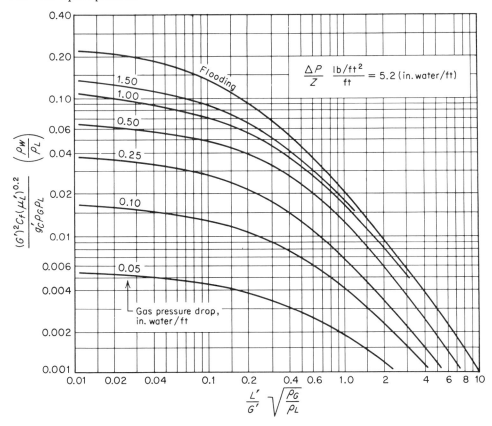

Fig. 6.26 *Flooding and pressure drop in packed towers.* (*The United States Stoneware Company.*)

or (3) slugs of foam may rise rapidly upward through the packing.   At the same time, entrainment of liquid by the effluent gas increases rapidly, and the tower is *flooded*. The gas pressure drop then increases very rapidly.   The change in conditions in the region *A* to *B* of Fig. 6.25 is gradual, and initial loading and flooding are frequently determined by the change in slope of the pressure-drop curves rather than through any visible effect.   It is not practical to operate a tower in a flooded condition; most towers operate just below, or in the lower part of, the loading region.

Flooding and loading. Flooding velocities in random packings are well correlated by the upper curve of Fig. 6.26.[12,51]† The lower limit of loading will occur at a gas

---

† The generalized correlation of flooding in this basic form was first made by Sherwood et al.,[45] who used a_p/ε^3 calculated from the packing geometry as the method of characterizing the packings. Later it was found that this quantity varied greatly, depending upon the method of packing (wet or dry) and with settling of the packing,[31] and finally it was found best to use an empirical characterization C_f chosen to fit the data.[12]   The original correlation did not include ρ_W/ρ_L. This was added as $(\rho_W/\rho_L)^2$ to handle the pressure-drop data,[29] but subsequently it was found better[12] to reduce the exponent on this group to 1.

pressure drop of about 0.5 in. water/ft of packed depth, and flooding at about 2 to 3 in. water/ft.   Values of C_f, which characterize the packing, are given in Table 6.2. They depend strongly on the method of installing the packing.   Flooding velocities for regular or stacked packings will generally be considerably greater than for random packing.

Pressure drop for single-phase flow. The pressure drop suffered by a single fluid in flowing through a bed of packed solids, when it alone fills the voids in the bed, is reasonably well correlated by the Ergun equation[15]

$$\frac{\Delta P}{Z} \frac{g_c' \epsilon^3 \, d_p \rho_G}{(1 - \epsilon) G'^2} = \frac{\Delta P}{Z} \frac{6 g_c' \rho_G}{C_f' G'^2} = \frac{150(1 - \epsilon)}{\text{Re}} + 1.75 \qquad (6.36)$$

Here the terms on the right are friction factors, the first for purely laminar flow, the second for completely turbulent flow.   There is a gradual transition from one type of flow to the other, the two terms changing their relative importance as the flow rate increases. $\text{Re} = d_p G'/\mu_G$, and d_p is the effective diameter of the particle, the diameter of a sphere of the same surface/volume ratio as the packing in place.   If the packing surface is a_p sq ft/cu ft of packed bed, the surface per unit volume of the particles is $a_p/(1 - \epsilon)$, and from the properties of a sphere,

$$d_p = \frac{6(1 - \epsilon)}{a_p} \qquad (6.37)$$

This will not normally be the same as the nominal size of the particles.   For the hollow manufactured packings of Table 6.2, operating at gas rates above 500 lb/(hr)(sq ft), the right-hand side of Eq. (6.36) may be taken simply as 1.75.   Reasonably good results are then obtained by using values of C_f' about twice those for C_f in Table 6.2.

Pressure drop for two-phase flow. For simultaneous countercurrent flow of liquid and gas, the pressure-drop data of various investigators show wide discrepancies, sometimes as much as 60 percent for the same type of packing and rates of flow, presumably owing to differences in packing density.   Estimates cannot therefore be expected to be very accurate.   For most purposes, the generalized correlation of Leva[29] shown as modified in Fig. 6.26 will serve.   Here the value of C_f in Table 6.2 should be used directly.   More elaborate data for particular packings are available from the manufacturers.

Illustration 6.3. Sulfur dioxide is to be removed from gas of the characteristics of air by scrubbing with an aqueous ammonium salt solution in a tower packed with 1-in. ceramic Raschig rings.   The gas, entering at the rate of 100,000 cu ft/hr (80°F, 1 atm), contains 7.0% SO_2, which is to be nearly completely removed.   The washing solution will enter at the rate of 30,000 lb/hr and has a density 77 lb/cu ft, viscosity 2.5 centipoises.

    a.   Choose a suitable tower diameter.

    b.   If the irrigated packed height is 25 ft, and if 3 ft of 1-in. Raschig rings is used above the liquid inlet as an entrainment separator, estimate the power requirement to overcome the gas pressure drop. The overall efficiency of fan and motor is 60%.

Table 6.2. Characteristics of random packings†

Packing	Nominal size, in.										
	¼	⅜	½	⅝	¾	1	1¼	1½	2	3	3½
Raschig rings:											
Ceramic:‡											
C_f	1,000	750	640	380	255	160	125	95	65	37	
ϵ	0.73	0.68	0.63	0.68	0.73	0.73	0.74	0.71	0.74	0.78	
a_p	240	155	111	100	80	58	45	38	28	19	
Metal:											
⅟₃₂-in. wall:											
C_f	700		300	258	185	115					
ϵ	0.69		0.84		0.88	0.92					
a_p	236		128		83.5	62.7					
⅟₁₆-in. wall:											
C_f			340	290	230	145	110	82	57	37	
ϵ			0.73		0.78	0.85	0.87	0.90	0.92	0.95	
a_p			118		71.8	56.7	49.3	41.2	31.4	20.6	
Pall rings:											
Plastic:											
C_f				97		52		32	25		16
ϵ				0.88		0.90		0.905	0.91		
a_p				110		63.0		39	31		23.4
Metal:											
C_f				71		48		28	20		
ϵ				0.902		0.938		0.953	0.964		
a_p				131.2		66.3		48.1	36.6		
Intalox saddles, ceramic											
C_f	600		265		130	98		52	40		
ϵ	0.75		0.78		0.77	0.775		0.81	0.79		
a_p	300		190		102	78		59.5	36		
Berl saddles, ceramic:											
C_f	900		380		170	110		65	45		
ϵ	0.60		0.63		0.66	0.69		0.75	0.72		
a_p	274		142		82	76		44	32		

Tellerettes,§ ¾ × 2 in., plastic:
  High density:
    $C_f = 57$
    $\epsilon = 0.87$
  Low density:
    $C_f = 65$
    $\epsilon = 0.83$

† Table from the United States Stoneware Company. Data are for wet dumped packing in 16- and 30-in. ID towers.
  ‡ Nominal size and wall thickness, in inches, for ceramic Raschig rings are, respectively, ¼, ⅟₃₂; ⅜, ⅟₁₆; ½ to ¾, ³⁄₃₂; 1, ⅛; 1¼ and 1½, ³⁄₁₆; 2, ¼; 3, ⅜.
  § Teller and Ford: *Ind. Eng. Chem.*, **50**, 1201 (1958).

Solution. a. Since the larger flow quantities are at the bottom for an absorber, the diameter will be chosen for the bottom conditions.

$$\text{Av mol wt gas in} = 0.07(64) + 0.93(29) = 31.4 \text{ lb/lb mole}$$

$$\text{Gas in} = 100{,}000(^{492}\!/_{520})(^1\!/_{359}) = 254 \text{ lb moles/hr or } 254(31.4) = 7{,}980 \text{ lb/hr}$$

$$\rho_G = \frac{7{,}980}{100{,}000} = 0.0798 \text{ lb/cu ft}$$

Assuming essentially complete absorption, SO_2 removed $= 254(0.07)(64) = 1{,}139$ lb/hr.

$$\text{Liquid leaving} = 30{,}000 + 1{,}139 = 31{,}140 \text{ lb/hr}$$

$$\frac{L'}{G'}\left(\frac{\rho_G}{\rho_L}\right)^{0.5} = \frac{31{,}140}{7{,}980}\left(\frac{0.0798}{77}\right)^{0.5} = 0.126$$

At flooding the ordinate of Fig. 6.26 is 0.13. For 1-in. ceramic Raschig rings, $C_f = 160$ (Table 6.2). Therefore,

$$G' \text{ at flooding} = \left(\frac{0.13 g_c' \rho_G \rho_L}{C_f \mu_L'^{0.2}} \frac{\rho_L}{\rho_W}\right)^{0.5}$$

$$= \left[\frac{0.13(4.18)(10^8)(0.0798)(77)^2}{160(2.5)^{0.2}(62.3)}\right]^{0.5}$$

$$= 1{,}470 \text{ lb/(hr)(sq ft)}$$

For 60% of the flooding rate, $G' = 0.60(1{,}470) = 882$ lb/(hr)(sq ft). The tower cross section is therefore $7{,}980/882 = 9.05$ sq ft.

$d = [4(9.05)/\pi]^{0.5} = 3.37$ ft, or say $d = 3.5$ ft diam. **Ans.**

b. For 3.5-ft diameter, the cross section $= 9.60$ sq ft.

$$G' = \frac{7{,}980}{9.6} = 830 \text{ lb/(hr)(sq ft)}$$

$$\frac{G'^2 C_f \mu_L'^{0.2}}{g_c' \rho_G \rho_L} \frac{\rho_W}{\rho_L} = \frac{(830)^2(160)(2.5)^{0.2}(62.3)}{4.18(10^8)(0.0798)(77)^2} = 0.0418$$

With this ordinate and 0.126 as abscissa, the pressure drop for the irrigated packing is estimated from Fig. 6.26 as 0.4 in. water/ft or $0.4(5.2)(25) = 52$ lb/sq ft for the 25 ft of packing.

For the dry packing, the gas flow rate is $(7{,}980 - 1{,}139)/9.60 = 713$ lb/(hr)(sq ft), at a pressure $14.7 - {}^{52}\!/_{144} = 14.3$ psi. The gas density is

$$\rho_G = \frac{29}{359}\frac{492}{540}\frac{14.3}{14.7} = 0.0682 \text{ lb/cu ft}$$

Using Eq. (6.36) with the right-hand side simplified to 1.75 since $G' > 500$ and with $C_f' = 2C_f = 320$, we have

$$\frac{\Delta P}{Z}\frac{6(4.18)(10^8)(0.0682)}{320(713)^2} = 1.75$$

$$\frac{\Delta P}{Z} = 1.66 \text{ lb/(sq ft)(ft)}$$

For a 3-ft packed depth, $\Delta P = 1.66(3) = 5.0$ lb/sq ft.

The total pressure drop for the packing is therefore $52 + 5 = 57$ lb/sq ft. To estimate fan power, to this must be added the pressure drop for the packing supports and liquid distributor and inlet expansion and outlet contraction losses for the gas. For a well-designed packing support (85 % free area) and liquid distributor, the pressure drop should be negligible. For a gas velocity in the inlet and outlet pipes of 25 ft/sec, the expansion and contraction losses would amount to, at most, 1.5 velocity heads, or $1.5(25)^2/2(32.2) = 14.6$ ft-lb/lb or $14.6(0.0682) = 1.0$ lb/sq ft.

The fan power output for the tower is therefore estimated to be

$$\frac{(57 + 1)(7,980)}{0.0682(3,600)} = 1,885 \text{ ft-lb/sec}$$

The power for the fan motor is then $1,885/(550)(0.6) = 5.7$ hp. **Ans.**

Mass-transfer coefficients for packed towers

When a packed tower is operated in the usual manner as a countercurrent absorber or stripper for transfer of solute between the gas and liquid, the rate of solute transfer may be computed from measured values of the rate of gas and liquid flow and the bulk concentrations of solute in the entering and leaving streams. As explained in Chap. 5, because of the impossibility of measuring solute concentrations at the gas-liquid interface, the resulting rates of mass transfer can be expressed only as overall coefficients, rather than as coefficients for the individual fluids. Further, since the interfacial area between gas and liquid is not directly measured in such experiments, the *flux* of mass transfer cannot be determined, but instead only the rate as the product of the flux and the total interfacial area. By dividing these rates by the volume of the packing, the results appear as "volumetric overall coefficients," $K_x a$, $K_y a$, $K_G a$, $F_{OG} a$, $F_{OL} a$, etc., where a is the interfacial surface per cubic foot of packed volume.

The individual fluid mass-transfer coefficients (k_x, k_y, F_L, F_G) and the interfacial area a which make up these overall volumetric coefficients are differently dependent upon fluid properties, flow rates, and type of packing. The overall volumetric coefficients are therefore useful only in the design of towers filled with the same packing and handling the same chemical system at the same flow rates and concentrations as existed during the measurements. For general design purposes, the individual coefficients and the interfacial area are necessary.

To obtain individual coefficients, the general approach has been to choose experimental conditions such that the resistance to mass transfer in the gas phase is negligible in comparison with that in the liquid. This is the case for the absorption or desorption of very insoluble gases, e.g., oxygen or hydrogen in water [see Eq. (5.14)].[44] Measurements in such systems then lead to values of $k_x a$, $k_L a$, and $F_L a$, which can be correlated in terms of system variables. There are evidently no systems involving absorption or desorption where the solute is so soluble in the liquid that the liquid-phase resistance is entirely negligible. But by subtracting the known liquid resistance from the overall resistances (see Chap. 5), it is possible to arrive at the gas-phase coefficients $k_y a$, $k_G a$, and $F_G a$, and to correlate these in terms of system variables.

Another approach to obtaining pure gas-phase coefficients is to make measurements when a pure liquid evaporates into a gas. Here there is no liquid resistance since there is no concentration gradient within the liquid. The resulting volumetric coefficients $k_y a$ and $F_G a$, however, do not agree with those obtained in the manner first described above. The reason is the different effective interfacial areas, as explained below.

Liquid holdup. Holdup refers to the liquid retained in the tower as films wetting the packing and as pools caught in the crevices between packing particles. It is found that the total holdup ϕ_t is made up of two parts,

$$\phi_t = \phi_o + \phi_s \tag{6.38}$$

where ϕ_s is the "static" and ϕ_o the operating, or moving, holdup, each expressed as cu ft liquid/cu ft packed volume. The moving holdup consists of liquid which continually moves through the packing, continually replaced regularly and rapidly by new liquid flowing from above. On stopping the gas and liquid flow, the moving holdup drains from the packing. The static holdup is liquid retained as pools in protected interstices in the packing, largely stagnant, and only slowly replaced by fresh liquid. On stopping the flows, the static holdup does not drain.

When absorption or desorption of a solute occurs, involving transfer of a solute between the bulk liquid and gas, the liquid of the static holdup rapidly comes to equilibrium with the adjacent gas, and thereafter its interfacial surface contributes nothing to mass transfer except as it is slowly replaced. For absorption and desorption, therefore, the smaller area offered by the moving holdup is effective. When evaporation or condensation occurs with the liquid phase a single, pure component, however, the area offered by the total holdup is effective since the liquid then offers no resistance to mass transfer.

Mass transfer. Shulman[46] and his coworkers, in an extensive work, have established the nature of the gas-phase mass-transfer coefficients characteristic of Raschig rings and Berl saddles by passing gases through beds packed with packings made with naphthalene, which sublimes into the gas. By comparing these with $k_G a$'s from aqueous absorption[20] and other systems, the interfacial areas for absorption and vaporization were obtained. The data on $k_L a$'s[44] then provided the correlation for k_L, the liquid-phase coefficient. Their work is summarized as follows.

For Raschig rings and Berl saddles, the gas-phase coefficient is given by[†]

$$\frac{F_G \, \mathrm{Sc}_G^{2/3}}{G} = \frac{k_G p_{BM} \, \mathrm{Sc}_G^{2/3}}{G} = 1.195 \left[\frac{d_s G'}{\mu_G''(1 - \epsilon_o)} \right]^{-0.36} \tag{6.39}$$

where ϵ_o, the operating void space in the packing, is given by

$$\epsilon_o = \epsilon - \phi_t \tag{6.40}$$

and d_s is the diameter of a sphere of the same surface as a single packing particle (not the same as d_p). The fluid properties should be evaluated at the average conditions

† The j form of Eq. (6.39), with the $2/3$ exponent on Sc_G, correlates the data well, although it has been pointed out that, in principle at least, the nature of the function should probably change with degree of turbulence.[49]

between interface and bulk gas. The liquid coefficient is given by

$$\frac{k_L d_s}{D_L} = 25.1 \left(\frac{d_s L'}{\mu''_L}\right)^{0.45} Sc_L^{0.5} \tag{6.41}$$

Since the liquid data were obtained at very low solute concentrations, k_L may be converted to F_L through $F_L = k_L c$, where c is the molar density of the solvent liquid.

Table 6.3. Interfacial areas for absorption, desorption, aqueous liquids†

For gases of density approximating 0.075 lb/cu ft, and below loading, $a_{AW} = mG'^n L'^p$. For other gases, substitute $G'(0.075/\rho_G)^{0.5}$ for G'. (Note: The original data cover L' up to 4,500 lb/(hr)(sq ft). Extrapolation to $L' = 7,500$ has been suggested.[46])

Packing	Size, in.	Range of L', lb/(hr)(sq ft)	m	n	p
Raschig rings	0.5	500–1,500	8,200	$3.15(10^{-4})L' - 0.30$	−1.04
		1,500–4,500	9.32	$0.151(10^{-4})L' + 0.148$	−0.111
	1	500–1,500	0.274	0	0.552
		1,500–4,500	463	$0.528(10^{-4})L' - 0.0793$	−0.47
	1.5	500–1,500	1.82	$0.675(10^{-4})L' - 0.1013$	0.274
		1,500–4,500	4.85	$0.148(10^{-4})L' - 0.022$	0.140
	2	500–1,500	0.401	0	0.481
		1,500–4,500	0.95	0	0.362
Berl saddles	0.5	500–1,500	0.0336	0.0529	0.761
		1,500–4,500	2.54	0.0529	0.170
	1‡	500–1,500	15.89	$0.686(10^{-4})L' - 0.1029$	0
		1,500–4,500	238	$0.420(10^{-4})L' - 0.0630$	−0.359
	1.5‡	500–1,500	0.613	−0.0508	0.455
		1,500–4,500	46.5	$0.325(10^{-4})L' - 0.0996$	−0.1355

† Data of Shulman et al.[46]
‡ For $G' < 800$ lb/(hr)(sq ft) only. For higher values, see Shulman, *AIChE J.*, **1**, 253 (1955), Figs. 16 and 17.

The interfacial areas for absorption and desorption with water (or very dilute aqueous solutions) a_{AW} are given for conditions below loading by Shulman in an extensive series of graphs. These are well represented by the empirical expressions of Table 6.3. For absorption or desorption with nonaqueous liquids, the area is a_A, given by

$$a_A = a_{AW} \frac{\phi_o}{\phi_{oW}} \tag{6.42}$$

and for contact of a gas with a pure liquid, as in vaporization, the areas are

$$a_V = 0.85 a_A \frac{\phi_t}{\phi_o} \tag{6.43a}$$

$$a_{VW} = 0.85 a_{AW} \frac{\phi_{tW}}{\phi_{oW}} \tag{6.43b}$$

The subscript W indicates water as the liquid.   The holdup data are summarized in Table 6.4.   Although these data are based on work with absorption, desorption, and vaporization, the evidence is that the same coefficients apply to distillation in packed towers.[37]   In distillation, a_A's should be used.

Many other volumetric mass-transfer-coefficient data are available, often covering wider ranges of flow rates and for packings other than those given here.   Excellent summaries of these are available.[14,48]

Illustration 6.4. A tower packed with 1.5-in. Berl saddles is to used for absorbing benzene vapor from a dilute mixture with an inert gas.   The circumstances are:

Gas: Av mol wt = 11, viscosity = 0.01 centipoise, 80°F, 800 mm Hg, $D_G = 0.504$ sq ft/hr, flow rate = $G' = 528$ lb/(hr)(sq ft).

Liquid: Av mol wt = 260, viscosity = 2.0 centipoises, sp gr = 0.84 g/cu cm, surface tension = 30 dynes/cm, $D_L = 1.85(10^{-5})$ sq ft/hr, flow rate = 2,000 lb/(hr)(sq ft).

Compute the volumetric mass-transfer coefficients.

Solution. For the gas,

$$\mu_G'' = 0.01(2.42) = 0.0242 \text{ lb/(ft)(hr)}$$

$$\rho_G = \frac{11}{359} \frac{800}{760} \frac{492}{460 + 80} = 0.0294 \text{ lb/cu ft}$$

$$Sc_G = \frac{\mu_G''}{\rho_G D_G} = \frac{0.0262}{0.0294(0.504)} = 1.63$$

$$G' = 528 \text{ lb/(hr)(sq ft)} \qquad G = {}^{528}\!/_{11} = 48.0 \text{ lb moles/(hr)(sq ft)}$$

For the liquid,

$$L' = 2,000 \text{ lb/(hr)(sq ft)}$$

$$\rho_L = 62.3(0.84) = 52.4 \text{ lb/cu ft} \qquad \mu_L' = 2.0 \text{ centipoises}$$

$$Sc_L = \frac{\mu_L''}{\rho_L D_L} = \frac{2(2.42)}{52.4(1.85)(10^{-5})} = 5,000$$

$$\sigma' = 30 \text{ dynes/cm}$$

Holdup. Table 6.4:

$$d_s = 0.155 \text{ ft}$$

$$\beta = 0.965 d_s^{0.376} = 0.477$$

$$\phi_{tW} = \frac{2.55(10^{-5})L'^{0.477}}{d_s^2} = 0.0394 \text{ cu ft/cu ft}$$

$$\phi_{sW} = \frac{0.00032}{d_s^{1.56}} = 0.000428 \text{ cu ft/cu ft}$$

$$\phi_{oW} = \phi_{tW} - \phi_{sW} = 0.0394 - 0.00043 = 0.0390$$

$$H = \frac{1.291 L'^{0.57} \mu_L'^{0.13}}{\rho_L^{0.84}(0.212 L'^{0.413} - 1)} \left(\frac{\sigma'}{73}\right)^{1.033-0.262 \log L'} = 1.375$$

$$\phi_o = \phi_{oW} H = 0.0390(1.375) = 0.0536 \text{ cu ft/cu ft}$$

$$\phi_s = \frac{1.641(10^{-4})\mu_L'^{0.04}\sigma'^{0.55}}{d_s^{1.56}\rho_L^{0.37}} = 0.00034 \text{ cu ft/cu ft}$$

$$\phi_t = \phi_o + \phi_s = 0.0536 + 0.00034 = 0.0539 \text{ cu ft/cu ft}$$

Table 6.4. Liquid holdup in packed towers†

$\phi_t = \phi_o + \phi_s \qquad \phi_{tW} = \phi_{oW} + \phi_{sW} \qquad \phi_o = \phi_{oW}H$

Packing	Nominal size, in.	d_s, ft	ϕ_s	Water (ordinary temperatures)	μ_L', centipoise	H
Ceramic Raschig rings	0.5 1 1.5 2	0.0582 0.1167 0.1740 0.238	$\dfrac{6.85(10^{-5})\mu_L'^{0.02}\sigma'^{0.99}}{d_s^{1.21}\rho_L^{0.37}}$	$\phi_{tW} = \dfrac{2.25(10^{-5})L'^\beta}{d_s^2}$ $\phi_{sW} = \dfrac{0.00104}{d_s^{1.21}}$ $\beta = 0.965 d_s^{0.376}$	<12 >12	$\dfrac{0.897L'^{0.57}\mu_L'^{0.13}}{\rho_L^{0.84}(0.1183L'^{0.430}-1)}\left(\dfrac{\sigma'}{73}\right)^{0.925-0.262\log L'}$ $\dfrac{0.575L'^{0.57}\mu_L'^{0.31}}{\rho_L^{0.84}(0.1183L'^{0.430}-1)}\left(\dfrac{\sigma'}{73}\right)^{0.925-0.262\log L'}$
Carbon Raschig rings	1 1.5 2	0.0427 0.178 0.235	$\dfrac{6.36(10^{-3})\mu_L'^{0.02}\sigma'^{0.23}}{d_s^{1.21}\rho_L^{0.37}}$	$\phi_{tW} = \dfrac{7.90(10^{-5})L'^\beta}{d_s^2}$ $\phi_{sW} = \dfrac{0.00250}{d_s^{1.21}}$ $\beta = 0.706 d_s^{0.376}$	<12 >12	$\dfrac{0.375L'^{0.57}\mu_L'^{0.13}}{\rho_L^{0.84}(0.174L'^{0.315}-1)}\left(\dfrac{\sigma'}{73}\right)^{0.925-0.262\log L'}$ $\dfrac{0.239L'^{0.57}\mu_L'^{0.31}}{\rho_L^{0.84}(0.174L'^{0.315}-1)}\left(\dfrac{\sigma'}{73}\right)^{0.925-0.262\log L'}$
Ceramic Berl saddles	0.5 1 1.5	0.0532 0.1050 0.155	$\dfrac{1.641(10^{-4})\mu_L'^{0.04}\sigma'^{0.55}}{d_s^{1.56}\rho_L^{0.37}}$	$\phi_{tW} = \dfrac{2.50(10^{-5})L'^\beta}{d_s^2}$ $\phi_{sW} = \dfrac{0.00032}{d_s^{1.56}}$ $\beta = 0.965 d_s^{0.376}$	<20 >20	$\dfrac{1.291L'^{0.57}\mu_L'^{0.13}}{\rho_L^{0.84}(0.212L'^{0.413}-1)}\left(\dfrac{\sigma'}{73}\right)^{1.033-0.262\log L'}$ $\dfrac{0.752L'^{0.57}\mu_L'^{0.31}}{\rho_L^{0.84}(0.212L'^{0.413}-1)}\left(\dfrac{\sigma'}{73}\right)^{1.033-0.262\log L'}$

† Data of Shulman et al.[46]

Interfacial area. Use

$$G' = 528 \left(\frac{0.075}{0.0294} \right)^{0.5} = 843$$

$$m = 46.5 \qquad n = 0.325(10^{-4})L' - 0.0996 = -0.0346$$

$$p = -0.1355 \qquad a_{AW} = mG'^n L'^p = 13.13 \text{ sq ft/cu ft}$$

Eq. (6.42):

$$a_A = a_{AW} \frac{\phi_o}{\phi_{oW}} = 13.13 \frac{0.0536}{0.0390} = 18.1 \text{ sq ft/cu ft}$$

Table 6.2:

$$\epsilon = 0.75$$

Eq. (6.40):

$$\epsilon_o = \epsilon - \phi_t = 0.75 - 0.0539 = 0.696$$

Eq. (6.39):

$$\frac{F_G(1.63)^{2/3}}{48} = 1.195 \left[\frac{0.155(528)}{0.0242(1 - 0.696)} \right]^{-0.36}$$

$$F_G = 1.443 \text{ lb moles/(hr)(sq ft)} = k_G p_{BM}$$

Eq. (6.41):

$$\frac{k_L(0.155)}{1.85(10^{-5})} = 25.1 \left[\frac{0.155(2,000)}{2(2.42)} \right]^{0.45} (5,000)^{0.5}$$

$$k_L = 1.375 \text{ lb moles/(hr)(sq ft)(lb mole/cu ft)}$$

Since the data for k_L were taken at very low concentrations, this may be converted to $F_L = k_L c$ where here $c = 0.84(62.3)/260 = 0.201$ lb mole/cu ft molar density. Therefore $F_L = 1.375(0.201) = 0.276$ lb mole/(hr)(sq ft) $= k_L x_{BM} c$.

The volumetric coefficients are

$$F_G a_A = 1.443(18.1) = 26.1 \text{ lb moles/(hr)(cu ft)} = k_G a_A p_{BM}$$

$$F_L a_A = 0.276(18.1) = 5.00 \text{ lb moles/(hr)(cu ft)} = k_L a_A x_{BM} c$$

Illustration 6.5. A tower packed with 2-in. ceramic Raschig rings is to be used for dehumidification of air by countercurrent contact with water. At the top of the tower, the conditions are to be: water flow rate = 4,000 lb/(hr)(sq ft), temp = 60°F; air flow rate = 800 lb/(hr)(sq ft), at 70°F, 1 atm, essentially dry. Compute the transfer coefficients for the top of the tower.

Solution. For the gas, $G' = 800$ lb/(hr)(sq ft), $G = {}^{800}\!/_{29} = 27.6$ lb moles/(hr)(sq ft). $\mu'_G = 0.018$ centipoise, $Sc_G = 0.6$ for air–water vapor, and

$$\rho_G = \frac{29}{359} \left(\frac{492}{530} \right) = 0.0750 \text{ lb/cu ft}$$

For the liquid, $L' = 4,000$ lb/(hr)(sq ft).

Table 6.4:

$$d_s = 0.238 \text{ ft}$$

$$\beta = 0.965 d_s^{0.376} = 0.541$$

$$\phi_{tW} = \frac{2.25(10^{-5})L'^{\beta}}{d_s^2} = 0.0353 \text{ cu ft/cu ft}$$

$$\phi_{sW} = \frac{0.00104}{d_s^{1.21}} = 0.0059 \text{ cu ft/cu ft}$$

$$\phi_{oW} = \phi_{tW} - \phi_{sW} = 0.0353 - 0.0059 = 0.0294 \text{ cu ft/cu ft}$$

Table 6.3: $m = 0.95$ $n = 0$ $p = 0.362$

$$a_{AW} = mG'^n L'^p = 19.1 \text{ sq ft/cu ft}$$

Eq. (6.43b): $a_{VW} = 0.85 a_{AW} \dfrac{\phi_{tW}}{\phi_{oW}} = 0.85(19.1)\dfrac{0.0353}{0.0294}$

$$= 19.5 \text{ sq ft/cu ft}$$

Table 6.2: $\epsilon = 0.74$ $\epsilon_o = \epsilon - \phi_t = 0.74 - 0.0353 = 0.705$

Eq. (6.39): $\dfrac{F_G(0.6)^{\frac{2}{3}}}{27.6} = 1.195\left[\dfrac{0.238(800)}{0.018(2.42)(1 - 0.705)}\right]^{-0.36} = 0.0393$

$$F_G = 1.527 \text{ lb moles/(hr)(sq ft)}$$
$$F_G a_{VW} = 1.527(19.5) = 29.8 \text{ lb moles/(hr)(cu ft)}$$
$$= k_G a_{VW} p_{BM}$$

There is no mass-transfer coefficient for the liquid, since it is pure water. However, for such processes (see Chap. 7), we need convection heat-transfer coefficients for both gas and liquid. These may be estimated, in the absence of directly applicable data, through the heat- mass-transfer analogy. Thus, from Eq. (6.39), $j_D = 0.0393$, and assuming $j_H = j_D$,

$$j_H = \frac{h_G}{C_p G'} \text{Pr}_G^{\frac{2}{3}} = 0.0393$$

For air, $C_p = 0.24 \text{ Btu/(lb)(°F)}$, $\text{Pr}_G = 0.74$.

$$h_G = \frac{0.0393 C_p G'}{\text{Pr}_G^{\frac{2}{3}}} = \frac{0.0393(0.24)(800)}{(0.74)^{\frac{2}{3}}} = 9.24 \text{ Btu/(hr)(sq ft)(°F)}$$

Similarly, the heat-transfer analog of Eq. (6.41) is

$$\text{Nu} = \frac{h_L d_s}{k} = 25.1\left(\frac{d_s L'}{\mu_L''}\right)^{0.45} \text{Pr}_L^{0.5}$$

where $k = $ thermal conductivity of water $= 0.339 \text{ (Btu)(ft)/(hr)(sq ft)(°F)}$, and $\text{Pr}_L = C_p \mu_L''/k = 1.0(1.12)(2.42)/0.339 = 8.0$. Therefore,

$$h_L = 25.1 \frac{k}{d_s}\left(\frac{d_s L'}{\mu_L''}\right)^{0.45} \text{Pr}_L^{0.5}$$

$$= \frac{25.1(0.339)}{0.238}\left[\frac{0.238(4,000)}{1.12(2.42)}\right]^{0.45}(8.0)^{0.5}$$

$$= 1415 \text{ Btu/(hr)(sq ft)(°F)}$$

The corresponding volumetric coefficients are

$$h_G a_V = 9.24(19.5) = 180 \text{ Btu/(hr)(cu ft)(°F)}$$
$$h_L a_V = 1415(19.5) = 27,600 \text{ Btu/(hr)(cu ft)(°F)}$$

End Effects and Axial Mixing. In addition to that which occurs within the packed volume, there will be mass transfer where the liquid is introduced by sprays or other distributors and where it drips off the lower packing support. These constitute the "end effects."   For proper evaluation of the packing itself, correction of experimental data must be made for these, usually by operating at several packing heights followed by extrapolation of the results to zero height. New equipment designed with uncorrected data will be conservatively designed if shorter than the experimental equipment but underdesigned if taller. Alternatively, equipment designed with corrected data will include a small factor of safety represented by the end effects. The data represented by Eqs. (6.38) to (6.43) and Tables 6.3 and 6.4 are believed to be reasonably free of end effects.

As will be clear in later chapters, the equations usually used for design, which are the same as those used for computing mass-transfer coefficients from laboratory measurements, are based on the assumption that the gas and liquid flow in "piston," or "plug," flow, with a flat velocity profile across the tower and with each portion of the gas or liquid having the same residence time in the tower. Such is not actually the case. Nonuniformity of packing and maldistribution of liquid may lead to "channeling," or regions where the liquid flow is abnormally great; the liquid in the static holdup moves forward much more slowly than that in the moving holdup; drops of liquid falling from a packing piece may be blown upward by the gas. Similarly the resistance to gas flow at the tower walls, and in relatively dry regions of the packing, is different from that elsewhere; the downward movement of liquid induces downward movement of the gas. As a result, the purely piston-type flow does not occur, and there is a relative movement within each fluid parallel to the axis of the tower, described as "axial mixing." The transport of solute by axial mixing tends to reduce the concentration differences for interphase mass transfer. The axial solute transport has been described in terms of an eddy diffusivity, although the precise method of incorporating this idea into the mass-transfer equations is not yet certain. In any event, the true mass-transfer coefficients for interphase solute transfer are undoubtedly larger than those which we customarily use, since the latter have not been corrected for axial mixing. A good introduction to the literature and some experimental data are given by Brittan and Woodburn.[6]

Counterflow trays

These are proprietary traylike devices which resemble packings in the sense that the gas and liquid flow countercurrently through the same openings. Separate liquid downspouts are not used. Turbo-Grids[47] are of several varieties: parallel rods or bars arranged horizontally across the tower or sheet metal stamped with slotted openings form the trays, and these are installed so that alternate trays have the openings at right angles. Kittel trays[41,54] are slotted double trays arranged so that liquid movement on the tray is influenced by passage of the gas. Ripple trays[26] are perforated sheets bent into a sinusoidal wave, and alternate trays are installed with the waves at right angles. These devices all have low gas pressure drop and high liquid-flow capacity.

NOTATION FOR CHAPTER 6

a = specific interfacial surface for mass transfer, sq ft/cu ft

a_A = specific interfacial surface for absorption, desorption, and distillation, sq ft/cu ft packed volume

a_p	=	specific packing surface, sq ft/cu ft packed volume
a_V	=	specific interfacial surface for contact of a gas with a pure liquid, sq ft/cu ft packed volume
A_a	=	active area of a tray $= A_t - 2A_d$ for cross-flow trays, sq ft/tray
A_d	=	downspout cross-sectional area, sq ft
A_{da}	=	smaller of the two areas, A_d or free area between downspout apron and tray, sq ft
A_h	=	perforation area, sq ft/tray
A_n	=	net tower cross-sectional area for gas flow $= A_t - A_d$ for cross-flow trays. sq ft/tray
A_t	=	tower cross-sectional area, sq ft
c	=	concentration, lb moles/cu ft
C_f	=	characterization factor of packing, two-phase flow
C_f'	=	characterization factor of packing, single-phase flow
C_F	=	flooding constant for trays
C_O	=	orifice constant, dimensionless
d	=	tower diameter, ft
d_h	=	hole diameter, in.
d_h'	=	hole diameter, ft
d_p	=	bubble or particle diameter, ft; for particles, d_p is given by Eq. (6.37)
d_s	=	diameter of a sphere of same surface as a single packing particle, ft
D	=	molecular diffusivity, sq ft/hr
D_E	=	eddy diffusivity of back mixing, sq ft/hr
E	=	fractional entrainment, moles entrained liquid/moles (entrained liquid + net liquid flow)
E_{MG}	=	Murphree gas-phase tray efficiency, fractional
E_{MGE}	=	Murphree gas-phase tray efficiency, corrected for entrainment, fractional
E_O	=	overall tray efficiency, fractional
E_{OG}	=	point gas-phase tray efficiency, fractional
f	=	Fanning friction factor, dimensionless
F	=	mass-transfer coefficient, lb moles/(hr)(sq ft)
F_O	=	overall mass-transfer coefficient, lb moles/(hr)(sq ft)
g	=	acceleration due to gravity, ft/sq sec
g_c	=	conversion constant, 32.2 (lb mass)(ft)/(lb force)(sq sec)
g_c'	=	conversion constant, 4.18(10⁸)(lb mass)(ft)/(lb force)(sq hr)
G	=	superficial molar gas velocity, lb moles/(hr)(sq ft)
G'	=	superficial gas mass velocity, lb/(hr)(sq ft)
h_D	=	dry-plate gas pressure drop, as head of clear liquid, in.
h_G	=	gas pressure drop for a perforated tray, as head of clear liquid, in.
h_L	=	gas pressure drop due to liquid holdup on a tray, as head of clear liquid, in.
h_R	=	residual gas pressure drop, as head of clear liquid, in.
h_W	=	weir height, in.
h_1	=	weir crest, in.
h_2	=	head loss due to liquid flow under downspout apron, in.
h_3	=	backup of liquid in downspout, in.
H	=	correction factor, dimensionless
k_G	=	gas-phase mass-transfer coefficient, lb moles/(hr)(sq ft)(atm)
k_L	=	liquid-phase mass-transfer coefficient, lb moles/(hr)(sq ft)(lb mole/cu ft)
k_x	=	liquid-phase mass-transfer coefficient, lb moles/(hr)(sq ft)(mole fraction)
k_y	=	gas-phase mass-transfer coefficient, lb moles/(hr)(sq ft)(mole fraction)
K_x	=	overall liquid mass-transfer coefficient, lb moles/(hr)(sq ft)(mole fraction)
K_y	=	overall gas mass-transfer coefficient, lb moles/(hr)(sq ft)(mole fraction)
l	=	plate thickness, in.
ln	=	natural logarithm
log	=	common logarithm
L	=	superficial molar liquid velocity, lb moles/(hr)(sq ft)

L'	=	superficial liquid mass velocity, lb/(hr)(sq ft)
m	=	slope of chord of equilibrium curve (see Chap. 5), mole fraction in gas/mole fraction in liquid, for Eqs. (6.23) to (6.28)
	=	empirical constant, for Table 6.3
n	=	empirical constant
N_{tG}	=	number of gas-phase transfer units
N_{tL}	=	number of liquid-phase transfer units
N_{tOG}	=	number of overall gas transfer units
p	=	empirical constant
p'	=	pitch; center-to-center hole spacing, ft
p_{BM}	=	logarithmic mean partial pressure of nondiffusing gas, atm
ΔP	=	gas pressure drop, lb force/sq ft
ΔP_R	=	residual gas pressure drop, lb force/sq ft
Pe	=	Péclet number for liquid mixing, dimensionless
q	=	liquid flow rate, cu ft/sec
Q	=	gas flow rate, cu ft/sec
Sc	=	Schmidt number, $\mu''/\rho D$, dimensionless
t	=	tray spacing, in.
V	=	velocity of gas through net tower area A_n, ft/sec
V_a	=	velocity of gas through active tray area A_a, ft/sec
V_F	=	velocity of gas through net tower area A_n at flooding, ft/sec
V_h	=	velocity of gas through perforations, ft/sec
V_{hW}	=	velocity of gas through perforations at incipient weeping, ft/sec
W	=	weir length, ft
W_{eff}	=	effective weir length, ft
x	=	concentration in liquid, mole fraction
y	=	concentration in gas, mole fraction
z	=	average flow width for liquid on a tray, ft
Z	=	length of travel on a tray, ft
	=	depth of packing, ft
Δ	=	hydraulic gradient, in.
ϵ	=	fractional void volume in a dry packed bed, cu ft voids/cu ft packed volume
ϵ_o	=	fractional void volume in irrigated packing, cu ft voids/cu ft packed volume
θ_L	=	time of residence of liquid on a tray, hr
μ	=	viscosity, lb mass/(ft)(sec) = $0.000672\mu'$
μ'	=	viscosity, centipoises
μ''	=	viscosity, lb mass/(ft)(hr) = $2.42\mu'$
ρ	=	density, lb mass/cu ft
σ	=	surface tension, lb force/ft = $6.85(10^{-5})\sigma'$
σ'	=	surface tension, dynes/cm
ϕ	=	volume fraction liquid, cu ft liquid/cu ft packed volume

Other subscripts;

G	=	gas
L	=	liquid
n	=	tray number
o	=	operating, or moving
s	=	static
W	=	water

Superscript:

*	=	in equilibrium with bulk liquid

REFERENCES

1. Anon.: *Chem. Eng. News*, Oct. 23, 1961, p. 58.
2. Bolles, W. L.: *Petrol. Process.*, **11**(2), 64; (3), 82; (4), 72; (5), 109 (1956).
3. Bolles, W. L.: in B. D. Smith, "Design of Equilibrium Stage Processes," chap. 14, McGraw-Hill Book Company, New York, 1963.
4. Boucher, D. F., and G. E. Alves: in "The Chemical Engineers' Handbook," 4th ed., p. 5-20, McGraw-Hill Book Company, New York, 1963.
5. Bowles, V. O.: *Petrol. Refiner*, **34**(7), 118 (1955).
6. Brittan, M. I., and E. T. Woodburn: *AIChE J.*, **12**, 541 (1966).
7. "Bubble-tray Design Manual," American Institute of Chemical Engineers, New York, 1958.
8. Cannon, M. R.: *Ind. Eng. Chem.*, **41**, 1953 (1949).
9. Carpenter, C. L., and D. F. Othmer: *AIChE J.*, **1**, 549 (1955).
10. Cicalese, J. J., J. A. Davies, P. J. Harrington, G. S. Houghland, A. J. L. Huchinson, and T. J. Walsh: *Proc. Am. Petrol. Inst.*, **26**, sec. III, 180 (1946).
11. Colburn, A. P.: *Ind. Eng. Chem.*, **28**, 526 (1936).
12. Eckert, J. S.: *Chem. Eng. Progr.*, **57**(9), 54 (1961); **59**(5), 76 (1963).
13. Edmister, W. C.: *Petrol. Engr.*, **1948**(12), 193.
14. Emmett, R. E., and R. L. Pigford: sec. 14 in "The Chemical Engineers' Handbook," 4th ed., McGraw-Hill Book Company, New York, 1963.
15. Ergun, S.: *Chem. Eng. Progr.*, **48**, 89 (1952).
16. Eversole, W. G., G. H. Wagner, and E. Stackhouse: *Ind. Eng. Chem.*, **33**, 1459 (1941).
17. Fair, J. R.: *Petro/Chem. Eng.*, **33** (Sept.), 210 (1961).
18. Fair, J. R.: chap. 15 in B. D. Smith, "Design of Equilibrium Stage Processes," McGraw-Hill Book Company, New York, 1963.
19. Fair, J. R., and R. L. Matthews: *Petrol. Refiner*, **37**(4), 153 (1958).
20. Fellinger, L.: reported by T. K. Sherwood and R. L. Pigford, "Absorption and Extraction," 2d ed., McGraw-Hill Book Company, New York, 1952.
21. Foss, A. S., and J. A. Gerster: *Chem. Eng. Progr.*, **52**, 28 (1956).
22. Gerster, J. A.: *Chem. Eng. Progr.*, **59**, 35 (1963).
23. Harris, L. S., and G. S. Haun: *Chem. Eng. Progr.*, **60**(5), 100 (1964).
24. Hughmark, G. A., and H. E. O'Connell: *Chem. Eng. Progr.*, **53**, 127 (1957).
25. Hunt, C. d'A., D. N. Hanson, and C. R. Wilke: *AIChE J.*, **1**, 441 (1955).
26. Hutchinson, M. H., and R. F. Baddour: *Chem. Eng. Progr.*, **52**, 503 (1956).
27. Kraft, W. W.: *Ind. Eng. Chem.*, **40**, 807 (1948).
28. Liebson, I., R. E. Kelley, and L. A. Bullington: *Petrol. Refiner*, **36**(2), 127 (1957).
29. Leva, M.: *Chem. Eng. Progr. Symp. Ser.*, **50**(10), 51 (1954).
30. Lewis, W. K., Jr.: *Ind. Eng. Chem.*, **28**, 399 (1936).
31. Lobo, W. E., L. Friend, F. Hashmall, and F. Zenz: *Trans. AIChE*, **41**, 693 (1945).
32. Madigan, C. M.: Master of Chemical Engineering thesis, New York University, 1964.
33. Mayfield, F. D., W. L. Church, A. C. Green, D. C. Lee, and R. S. Rasmussen; *Ind. Eng. Chem.*, **44**, 2238 (1952).
34. McAllister, R. A., P. H. McGinnis, and C. A. Planck: *Chem. Eng. Sci.*, **9**, 25 (1958).
35. McMahon, H. O.: *Ind. Eng. Chem.*, **39**, 712 (1947).
36. Muller, H. M., and D. F. Othmer: *Ind. Eng. Chem.*, **51**, 625 (1959).
37. Norman, W. S., T. Cakaloz, A. Z. Fresco, and D. H. Sutcliffe: *Trans. Inst. Chem. Engrs. (London)*, **41**, 61 (1963).
38. Nutter, I. E.: *Chem. Eng.*, **61**(5), 176 (1954).
39. O'Connell, H. E.: *Trans. AIChE*, **42**, 741 (1946).
40. Podbielniak, W.: *Ind. Eng. Chem., Anal. Ed.*, **13**, 639 (1941).
41. Pollard, B.: *Chem. Ind. (London)*, **1958**, 1414.
42. Robin, B. J.: *Brit. Chem. Eng.*, **4**, 351 (1959).

43. Scofield, R. C.: *Chem. Eng. Progr.*, **46**, 405 (1950).
44. Sherwood, T. K., and F. A. L. Holloway: *Trans. AIChE*, **36**, 39 (1940).
45. Sherwood, T. K., G. H. Shipley, and F. A. L. Holloway: *Ind. Eng. Chem.*, **30**, 765 (1938).
46. Shulman, H. L. et al.: *AIChE J.*, **1**, 247, 253, 259 (1955); **3**, 157 (1957); **5**, 280, (1959); **6**, 175, 469 (1960); **9**, 479 (1963).
47. Staff, Shell Development Co.: *Chem. Eng. Progr.*, **50**, 57 (1954).
48. Teller, A. J., S. A. Miller, and E. G. Scheibel: sec. 18 in "The Chemical Engineers' Handbook," 4th ed., McGraw-Hill Book Company, New York, 1963.
49. Thoenes, D., and H. Kramers: *Chem. Eng. Sci.*, **8**, 271 (1958).
50. Thrift, G. C.: *Oil Gas J.*, **52**(51), 165 (1954); *Chem. Eng.*, **61**(5), 177 (1954).
51. United States Stoneware Company: "Packed Tower Design Manual," p. GR-109R4, Akron, Ohio, 1963.
52. Williams, G. C., R. B. Akell, and C. P. Talbott: *Chem. Eng. Progr.*, **43**, 585 (1947).
53. York, O. H.: *Chem. Eng. Progr.*, **50**, 421 (1954).
54. Zuiderweg, F. J., H. Verburg, and F. A. H. Gilissen: *Proc. Intern. Symp. Distillation, London, 1960*, p. 201.

PROBLEMS

Problems associated with tray efficiencies and mass-transfer coefficients for packed towers are to be found with Chaps. 7 to 9.

6.1. For the stripping operation of Illustration 6.1, determine suitable diameters of towers of the following designs, and compare with that of the perforated tray tower of Illustration 6.1:

a. Bubble-cap tray tower.

b. Tower packed with (1) 1-in. ceramic Raschig rings, (2) 1-in. Berl saddles, and (3) 1-in. Pall rings. For these use a gas pressure drop of 0.4 in. water/ft of packing.

6.2. A gas containing methane, propane, and butane is to be scrubbed countercurrently in a perforated-tray tower with a hydrocarbon oil to absorb principally the butane. It is agreed to design a tray for the circumstances existing at the bottom of the tower, where the conditions are:

Pressure = 50 psia

Temperature = 100°F

Gas—1,750 lb moles/hr, containing 85% methane, 10% propane, and 5% butane by volume.

Liquid—1,000 lb moles/hr, av mol wt = 150, density = 53.0 lb/cu ft, surface tension = 25 dynes/cm, viscosity = 1.60 centipoises.

Design a suitable perforated tray, and check for flooding by downspout backup, weeping, and downspout residence time.

6.3. A packed tower is to be designed for the countercurrent contact of a benzene–nitrogen gas mixture with kerosene to wash out the benzene from the gas. The circumstances are:

Gas in = 20 cu ft/sec, containing 5 mole % benzene, at 800 mm Hg abs, 75°F

Gas out = substantially pure nitrogen

Liquid in = 3.0 lb/sec, benzene-free, sp gr = 0.80, viscosity = 2.3 centipoises

The packing will be 1-in. Intalox saddles, and the tower diameter will be set to produce 0.4 in. water pressure drop per foot of irrigated packing.

a. Calculate the tower diameter to be used.

b. Assume that, for the diameter chosen, the irrigated packed depth will be 20 ft and that 3 ft of unirrigated packing will be placed above the liquid inlet to act as an entrainment separator. The blower-motor combination to be used at the gas inlet will have an overall efficiency of 60%. Calculate the power required to blow the gas through the packing.

6.4. A small water-cooling tower, 3 ft in diameter, packed with 2-in. ceramic Raschig rings, is fed with water at the rate of 20,000 lb/(hr)(sq ft), in at 105°F, out at 80°F. The water is contacted with air (85°F, 1 atm, essentially dry) drawn upward countercurrently to the water flow. Neglecting evaporation of the water, estimate the rate of air flow, cu ft/min, which would flood the tower.

CHAPTER SEVEN HUMIDIFICATION OPERATIONS

The operations considered in this chapter are concerned with the interphase transfer of mass and of energy which result when a gas is brought into contact with a pure liquid in which it is essentially insoluble. While the term "humidification operations" is used to characterize these in a general fashion, the purpose of such operations may include not only humidification of the gas but dehumidification and cooling of the gas, measurement of its vapor content, and cooling of the liquid as well. The matter transferred between phases in such cases is the substance comprising the liquid phase, which either vaporizes or condenses. As in all mass-transfer problems, it is necessary for a complete understanding of the operation to be familiar with the equilibrium characteristics of the systems. But since the mass transfer in these cases will invariably be accompanied by a simultaneous transfer of heat energy as well, some consideration must also be given to the enthalpy characteristics of the systems.

VAPOR-LIQUID EQUILIBRIUM AND ENTHALPY FOR A PURE SUBSTANCE

As indicated above, the substance undergoing interphase transfer in these operations is the material comprising the liquid phase, which diffuses in the form of a vapor.

The equilibrium vapor-pressure characteristics of the liquid are therefore of importance.

Vapor-pressure curve

Every liquid exerts an equilibrium pressure, the vapor pressure, to an extent depending upon the temperature. When the vapor pressures of a liquid are plotted against the corresponding temperatures, a curve such as *TBDC* (Fig. 7.1) results. The vapor-pressure curve for each substance is unique, but each exhibits characteristics generally similar to that in the figure. The curve separates two areas of the plot, representing, respectively, conditions where the substance exists wholly in the liquid state and wholly in the vapor state. If the conditions imposed upon the substance are in the liquid-state area, such as at point *A*, the substance will be entirely liquid. Under all conditions in the lower area, such as those at point *E*, the substance is entirely a vapor. At all conditions corresponding to points on the curve *TBDC*, however, liquid and vapor may coexist in any proportions indefinitely. Liquid and vapor represented by points on the vapor-pressure curve are called *saturated liquid* and *saturated vapor*, respectively. Vapor or gas at a temperature above that corresponding to saturation is termed *superheated*. The vapor-pressure curve has two abrupt end points, at *T* and *C*. Point *T*, from which originate curves *LT* and *ST* separating the conditions for the solid state from those for the liquid and vapor, is the *triple point*, at which all three states of aggregation may coexist. Point *C* is the *critical point*, or *state*, whose coordinates are the *critical pressure* and *critical temperature*. At the critical point, distinction between the liquid and vapor phases disappears, and all the properties of the liquid, such as density, viscosity, refractive index, etc., are identical with those of the vapor. The substance at a temperature above the

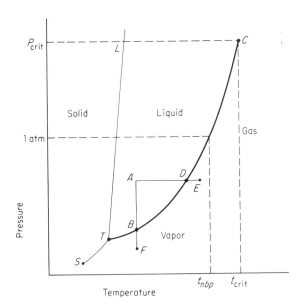

Fig. 7.1 *Vapor pressure of a pure liquid.*

critical is called a *gas*, and it will then not be liquefied regardless of how high a pressure may be imposed. This distinction between a gas and a vapor, however, is not always strictly adhered to, and the term gas is frequently used to designate merely a condition relatively far removed from the vapor-pressure curve. The temperature corresponding to each pressure on the curve is termed the boiling point of the liquid at the pressure in question, and that corresponding to 1 atm in particular is known as the *normal boiling point*, as at t_{nbp} on Fig. 7.1.

Whenever a process involves bringing a sample of fluid across the vapor-pressure curve, such as the isobaric process ADE or the isothermal process ABF, there will be a change of phase. This will be accompanied by the evolution (for condensation) or absorption (for vaporization) of the *latent heat of vaporization* at constant temperature, for example, at points B or D in the processes mentioned above. Heat added or given up with changing temperatures is called *sensible heat*.

Interpolation between data.   For such common liquids as water, many refrigerants, and others, the vapor pressure–temperature curve has been established at many points. For most liquids, however, only relatively few data are available, so that it is necessary frequently to interpolate between, or extrapolate beyond, the measurements. The curve on arithmetic coordinates (Fig. 7.1) is very inconvenient for this because of the curvature, and some method of linearizing the curve is needed. Most of the common methods stem from the Clausius-Clapeyron equation, which relates the slope of the vapor-pressure curve to the latent heat of vaporization

$$\frac{dP}{dT} = \frac{\lambda'}{T(v_G - v_L)} \tag{7.1}$$

where v_G and v_L are molal specific volumes of the saturated vapor and liquid, respectively, and λ' is the molal latent heat in units consistent with the rest of the equation. As a simplification, we may neglect v_L in comparison with v_G and express the latter by the ideal-gas law, to obtain

$$d \ln P = \frac{dP}{P} = \frac{\lambda' \, dT}{RT^2} \tag{7.2}$$

and if λ' may be considered reasonably constant over a short range of temperature,

$$\ln P = -\frac{\lambda'}{RT} + \text{const} \tag{7.3}$$

Equation (7.3) suggests that a plot of log P against $1/T$ will be straight for short temperature ranges. It also suggests a method of interpolating between points listed in a table of data.

Illustration 7.1.   A table lists the vapor pressure of benzene to be 100 mm Hg at 26.1°C and 400 mm Hg at 60.6°C. At what temperature is the vapor pressure 200 mm Hg?

Solution. At 26.1°C, $1/T = 1/299.1$ reciprocal °K; at 60.6°C, $1/T = 1/333.6$.

$$\frac{1/299.1 - 1/T}{1/299.1 - 1/333.6} = \frac{\log 100 - \log 200}{\log 100 - \log 400}$$

$$T = 315.4°K = 42.4°C$$

The correct value is 42.2°C.   Linear interpolation would have given 37.6°C.

Reference-substance plots[15]

Equation (7.2) may be rewritten for a second substance, a *reference substance*, at the same temperature,

$$d \ln P_r = \frac{\lambda'_r \, dT}{RT^2} \tag{7.4}$$

where the subscript r denotes the reference substance.   Dividing Eq. (7.2) by (7.4) provides

$$\frac{d \ln P}{d \ln P_r} = \frac{\lambda'}{\lambda'_r} = \frac{M\lambda}{M_r \lambda_r} \tag{7.5}$$

which, upon integration, becomes

$$\log P = \frac{M\lambda}{M_r \lambda_r} \log P_r + \text{const} \tag{7.6}$$

Equation (7.6) suggests that a linear graph will result if $\log P$ as ordinate is plotted against $\log P_r$ for the reference substance as abscissa, where for each plotted point the vapor pressures are taken at the same temperature.   Such a plot is straight over larger temperature ranges (but not near the critical temperature) than that based on Eq. (7.3) and, moreover, the slope of the curve gives the ratio of the latent heats at the same temperature.   The reference substance chosen is one whose vapor-pressure data are well known.

Illustration 7.2.   (*a*) Plot the vapor pressure of benzene over the range 15 to 180°C using water as reference substance according to Eq. (7.6).   (*b*) Determine the vapor pressure of benzene at 100°C.   (*c*) Determine the latent heat of vaporization of benzene at 25°C.

Solution. a.   Logarithmic graph paper is marked with scales for the vapor pressure of benzene and for water, as in Fig. 7.2.   The vapor pressure of benzene at 15.4°C is 60 mm Hg, and that for water at this temperature is 13.1 mm Hg.   These pressures provide the coordinates of the lowest point on the plot.   In similar fashion, additional data for benzene are plotted with the help of a steam table, thus providing the curve shown.   The line is very nearly straight over the temperature range used.

b.   At 100°C, the vapor pressure of water is 760 mm Hg.   Entering the plot at this value for the abscissa, the vapor pressure of benzene is read as 1,400 mm Hg.   Alternatively the abscissa can be marked with the temperatures corresponding to the vapor pressures of water, as shown, thus eliminating the necessity of referring to the steam table.

c.   The slope of the curve at 25°C is 0.775.   (*Note:* This is most conveniently determined with a millimeter rule.   If the coordinates are used, the slope will be $\Delta \log P / \Delta \log P_r$.)   At 25°C, the latent

Fig. 7.2 *Reference-substance plot for the vapor pressure of benzene.*

heat of vaporization of water is 1049.8 Btu/lb.   From Eq. (7.6),

$$\frac{\lambda M}{\lambda_r M_r} = \frac{\lambda(78.05)}{1,049.8(18.02)} = 0.775$$

$$\lambda = 187.5 \text{ Btu/lb} \qquad \text{for benzene at } 25°C$$

(The accepted value is 186.5 Btu/lb.)

Enthalpy

The internal energy U of a substance is the total energy residing in the substance owing to the motion and relative position of the constituent atoms and molecules. Absolute values of internal energy are not known, but numerical values relative to some arbitrarily defined standard state for the substance can be computed.   The sum of the internal energy and the product of pressure and volume of the substance, when both quantities are expressed in the same units, is defined as the *enthalpy* of the substance,

$$H = U + Pv$$

In a batch process at constant pressure, where work is done only in expansion against the pressure, the heat absorbed by the system is the gain in enthalpy,

$$Q = \Delta H = \Delta(U + Pv) \qquad (7.7)$$

In a steady-state continuous-flow process, the net transfer of energy to the system as heat and work will be the sum of its gains in enthalpy and potential and kinetic energies.   It frequently happens that the changes in potential and kinetic energies are insignificant in comparison with the enthalpy change and that there is no mechanical work done.   In such cases, Eq. (7.7) can be used to compute the heat added to the system, and such a calculation is termed a *heat balance*.   In *adiabatic* operations, where no exchange of heat between the system and its surroundings occurs, the heat balance becomes simply an equality of enthalpies in the initial and final condition.

Absolute values of the enthalpy of a substance, like the internal energy, are not known.   However, by arbitrarily setting the enthalpy of a substance at zero when it is in a convenient reference state, relative values of enthalpy at other conditions may be calculated.   To define the reference state, the temperature, pressure, and state of aggregation must be established.   For the substance water, the ordinary steam tables list the relative enthalpy at various conditions referred to the enthalpy of the substance at 32°F, the equilibrium vapor pressure at this temperature, and in the liquid state. For other substances, other reference conditions may be more convenient.

Figure 7.3 is a graphical representation of the relative enthalpy of a typical substance where the liquid, vapor, and gaseous states are shown.   The data are most conveniently shown on lines of constant pressure.   The curves marked "saturated liquid" and "saturated vapor," however, cut across the constant-pressure lines and show the enthalpies for these conditions at temperatures and pressures corresponding

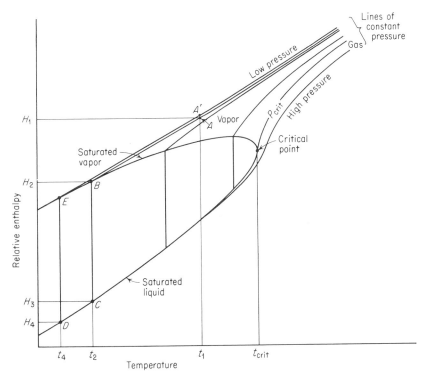

Fig. 7.3   *Typical enthalpy-temperature diagram for a pure substance.*

to the equilibrium vapor-pressure relationship for the substance. The vertical distance between the saturated-vapor and -liquid curves, such as the distance BC, represents the latent heat of vaporization at the corresponding temperature. The latent heat thus decreases with increased temperature, becoming zero at the critical point. In the vapor state at low pressures, the enthalpy is essentially a function of temperature; at all pressures where the ideal-gas law may be used to describe the Pvt relation, the lines of constant pressure are superimposed and the enthalpy is independent of pressure. Except near the critical temperature, the enthalpy of the liquid is also substantially independent of pressure until exceedingly high pressures are reached.

The change in enthalpy between two conditions, such as those at A and D, may be taken simply as the difference in ordinates corresponding to the points. Thus, to calculate the enthalpy of the substance in the superheated condition at point A relative to the saturated liquid at D, or $H_1 - H_4$, we may add the enthalpy change $H_1 - H_2$, the sensible heat of the vapor from the saturation temperature t_2 at the same pressure to the superheated condition at A; $H_2 - H_3$, the latent heat of vaporization at t_2; and $H_3 - H_4$, the sensible heat of the liquid from the final condition at D to the boiling point at the prevailing pressure t_2. For a liquid or vapor, the slope of the constant-pressure lines at any temperature is termed the *heat capacity*. The lines are not strictly straight, so that the heat capacity changes with temperature. By use of an average heat capacity or average slope, however, sensible heats are readily calculated. Thus, referring again to Fig. 7.3,

$$H_1 - H_2 = C(t_1 - t_2)$$

where C is the average heat capacity of the vapor at constant pressure over the indicated temperature range.

> **Illustration 7.3.** Compute the heat evolved when 10 lb of benzene as a superheated vapor at 94 mm Hg, 100°C, is cooled and condensed to a liquid at 10°C. The average heat capacity for the vapor may be taken as 0.30 and for the liquid 0.36 Btu/(lb)(°F).
>
> *Solution.* Refer to Fig. 7.2. When the pressure is 94 mm Hg, the saturation temperature for benzene is 25°C. The latent heat of vaporization at this temperature is 186.5 Btu/lb (Illustration 7.2). The initial condition corresponds to a point such as A on Fig. 7.3, the final condition to point D, the path of the process to $ABCD$. Using the notation of Fig. 7.3,
>
> $$H_1 - H_2 = C(t_1 - t_2) = 0.30(100 - 25)(1.8) = 40.5 \text{ Btu/lb}$$
> $$H_2 - H_3 = 186.5 \text{ Btu/lb}$$
> $$H_3 - H_4 = C(t_2 - t_4) = 0.36(25 - 10)(1.8) = 9.7 \text{ Btu/lb}$$
> $$\therefore \quad H_1 - H_4 = 40.5 + 186.5 + 9.7 = 236.7 \text{ Btu/lb}$$
> $$\therefore \quad \text{Heat evolved for 10 lb benzene} = 10(236.7) = 2367 \text{ Btu}$$

VAPOR-GAS MIXTURES

In what follows, the term *vapor* will be applied to that substance, designated as substance A, in the vaporous state which is relatively near its condensation temperature at the prevailing pressure. The term *gas* will be applied to substance B, which is a relatively highly superheated gas.

Absolute humidity

While the common concentration units (partial pressure, mole fraction, etc.) which are based on total quantity are useful, when operations involve changes in vapor content of a vapor-gas mixture without changes in the gas content, it is more convenient to use a unit based on the unchanging amount of gas.   The ratio mass of vapor/mass of gas is the *absolute humidity* Y'.   If the quantities are expressed in moles, the ratio is the *molal* absolute humidity Y.

$$Y = \frac{y_A}{y_B} = \frac{p_A}{p_B} = \frac{p_A}{P_t - p_A} \frac{\text{moles } A}{\text{moles } B}$$

$$Y' = Y\frac{M_A}{M_B} = \frac{p_A}{P_t - p_A}\frac{M_A}{M_B}\frac{\text{mass } A}{\text{mass } B}$$

(7.8)

In many respects the molal ratio is the more convenient, owing to the ease with which moles and volumes may be interrelated through the gas law, but the mass ratio has nevertheless become firmly established in the humidification literature.   The mass absolute humidity was first introduced by Grosvenor[5] and is sometimes called the Grosvenor humidity.

  Illustration 7.4. In a mixture of benzene vapor (A) and nitrogen gas (B) at a total pressure of 800 mm Hg and a temperature of 60°C, the partial pressure of benzene is 100 mm Hg.   Express the benzene concentration in other terms.
  Solution. $p_A = 100$, $p_B = 800 - 100 = 700$ mm Hg.
  a. Mole fraction.   Since the pressure fraction and mole fraction are identical for gas mixtures, $y_A = p_A/P_t = {}^{100}\!/_{800} = 0.125$ mole fraction benzene.   The mole fraction nitrogen $= y_B = 1 - 0.125 = {}^{700}\!/_{800} = 0.875$.
  b. Volume fraction of benzene equals the mole fraction, 0.125.
  c. Absolute humidity.

$$Y = \frac{y_A}{y_B} = \frac{p_A}{p_B} = \frac{0.125}{0.875} = \frac{100}{700} = 0.143 \text{ mole benzene/mole nitrogen}$$

$$Y' = Y\frac{M_A}{M_B} = 0.143\frac{78.05}{28.08} = 0.398 \text{ lb benzene/lb nitrogen}$$

Saturated vapor-gas mixtures

If an insoluble dry gas B is brought into contact with sufficient liquid A, the liquid will evaporate into the gas until ultimately, at equilibrium, the partial pressure of A in the vapor-gas mixture reaches its saturation value, the vapor pressure P_A at the prevailing temperature.   So long as the gas can be considered insoluble in the liquid, the partial pressure of vapor in the saturated mixture is independent of the nature of the gas and total pressure (except at very high pressures) and is dependent only upon the temperature and identity of the liquid.   However, the saturated molal absolute humidity $Y_s = P_A/(P_t - P_A)$ will depend upon the total pressure, and the saturated absolute humidity $Y_s' = Y_s M_A/M_B$ upon the identity of the gas as well.   Both saturated humidities become infinite at the boiling point of the liquid at the prevailing total pressure.

Illustration 7.5. A gas (B)–benzene (A) mixture is saturated at 1 atm, 50°C. Calculate the absolute humidity if (a) B is nitrogen and (b) if B is oxygen.

Solution. Since the mixture is saturated, the partial pressure of benzene p_A equals the equilibrium vapor pressure P_A of benzene at 50°C.   From Fig. 7.2, $P_A = 275$ mm Hg, or 0.362 atm.

$a.$ $Y_s = \dfrac{P_A}{P_t - P_A} = \dfrac{0.362}{1 - 0.362} = 0.568$ mole benzene/mole nitrogen

$\quad\quad Y_s' = \dfrac{Y_s M_A}{M_B} = \dfrac{0.568(78.05)}{28.02} = 1.583$ lb benzene/lb nitrogen

$b.$ $Y_s = \dfrac{P_A}{P_t - P_A} = \dfrac{0.362}{1 - 0.362} = 0.568$ mole benzene/mole oxygen

$\quad\quad Y_s' = \dfrac{Y_s M_A}{M_B} = \dfrac{0.568(78.05)}{32.00} = 1.387$ lb benzene/lb oxygen

Unsaturated vapor-gas mixtures

If the partial pressure of the vapor in a vapor-gas mixture is for any reason less than the equilibrium vapor pressure of the liquid at the same temperature, the mixture is unsaturated.

1. *Dry-bulb temperature.* This is the temperature of a vapor-gas mixture as ordinarily determined by immersion of a thermometer in the mixture.

2. *Relative saturation.* *Relative saturation*, also called *relative humidity*, expressed as a percentage is defined as $100 p_A/P_A$, where P_A is the vapor pressure at the dry-bulb temperature of the mixture.   For any vapor, the graphical representation of conditions of constant relative saturation may be easily constructed on a vapor pressure–temperature chart, as in Fig. 7.4a, by dividing the ordinates of the vapor-pressure

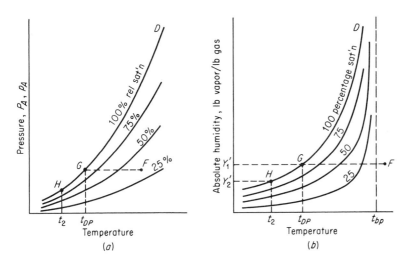

Fig. 7.4 *Forms of psychrometric charts.*

curve into appropriate intervals. Thus the curve for 50 percent relative saturation shows a vapor partial pressure equal to one-half the equilibrium vapor pressure at any temperature. A reference-substance plot, such as Fig. 7.2, could also be used for this.

3. *Percentage saturation. Percentage saturation,* or *percentage absolute humidity,* is defined as $100 Y/Y_s$ and $100 Y'/Y_s'$, where the saturated values are computed at the dry-bulb temperature of the mixture. Graphical representation of the quantity for any vapor may be made on a chart of Y vs. t (in which case the chart must be limited to a single total pressure) or one of Y' vs. t (for a single total pressure and a specific gas), as in Fig. 7.4b. On this chart, the saturation humidities are plotted from vapor-pressure data with the help of Eq. (7.8), to give curve GD. The curve for humidities at 50 percentage saturation is plotted at half the ordinate of curve GD, etc. All the curves of constant percentage saturation reach infinity at the boiling point of the liquid at the prevailing pressure.†

4. *Dew point.* This is the temperature at which a vapor-gas mixture becomes saturated when cooled at constant total pressure out of contact with a liquid. For example, if an unsaturated mixture such as that at F (Fig. 7.4) is cooled at constant pressure out of contact with liquid, the path of the cooling process follows the line FG, the mixture becoming more nearly saturated as the temperature is lowered, and fully saturated at t_{DP}, the dew-point temperature. All mixtures of absolute humidity Y_1' on this figure have the same dew point. If the temperature is reduced only an infinitesimal amount below t_{DP}, vapor will condense as a liquid dew. This is used as a method of humidity determination: a shiny metal surface is cooled in the presence of the gas mixture, and the appearance of a fog which clouds the mirrorlike surface indicates that the dew point has been reached.

If the mixture is cooled to a lower temperature, the vapor-gas mixture will continue to precipitate liquid, itself always remaining saturated, until at the final temperature t_2 (Fig. 7.4) the residual vapor-gas mixture will be at point H. The mass of vapor condensed per unit mass of dry gas will be $Y_1' - Y_2'$. Except under specially controlled circumstances supersaturation will not occur, and no vapor-gas mixture whose coordinates lie to the left of curve GD will result.

5. *Humid volume.* The humid volume v_H of a vapor-gas mixture is the volume in cubic feet of 1 lb of dry gas and its accompanying vapor at the prevailing temperature and pressure. For a mixture of absolute humidity Y' at $t_G°F$ and P_t atm, the ideal-gas law gives the humid volume as

$$v_H = \left(\frac{1}{M_B} + \frac{Y'}{M_A}\right) 359 \frac{t_G + 460}{492} \frac{1}{P_t} = 0.730 \left(\frac{1}{M_B} + \frac{Y'}{M_A}\right) \frac{t_G + 460}{P_t} \quad (7.9)$$

The humid volume of a saturated mixture is computed with $Y' = Y_s'$ and that for a

---

† For this reason curves of constant relative saturation are sometimes drawn on absolute humidity–temperature charts. Since relative saturation and percentage saturation are not numerically equal for an unsaturated mixture, the position of such curves must be computed by the methods of Illustration 7.6.

dry gas with $Y' = 0$. These values may then be plotted against temperature on a psychrometric chart. For partially saturated mixtures, v_H may be interpolated between values for 0 and 100 percentage saturation at the same temperature according to percentage saturation. When the mass of *dry* gas in a mixture is multiplied by the humid volume, the volume of *mixture* results.

6. *Humid heat.* The humid heat C_S is the heat required to raise the temperature of 1 lb of gas and its accompanying vapor 1°F at constant pressure. For a mixture of absolute humidity Y',

$$C_S = C_B + Y'C_A \qquad (7.10)$$

Provided neither vaporation nor condensation occurs, the heat in Btu required to raise the temperature of W_B lb dry gas *and* its accompanying vapor Δt°F will be

$$Q = W_B C_S \Delta t \qquad (7.11)$$

7. *Enthalpy.* The (relative) enthalpy of a vapor-gas mixture is the sum of the (relative) enthalpies of the gas and of the vapor content. Imagine 1 lb of a gas containing Y' lb vapor at dry-bulb temperature t_G°F. If the mixture is unsaturated, the vapor is in a superheated state, and we may calculate the enthalpy relative to the reference states gas and saturated liquid at t_0°F. The enthalpy of the gas alone is $C_B(t_G - t_0)$. The vapor at t_G is at a condition corresponding to point A on Fig. 7.3, and its reference state corresponds to point D. If t_{DP} is the dew point of the mixture (t_2 on Fig. 7.3) and λ_{DP} the latent heat of vaporization of the vapor at that temperature, the enthalpy per pound of vapor will be $C_A(t_G - t_{DP}) + \lambda_{DP} + C_{AL}(t_{DP} - t_0)$. Then the total enthalpy for the mixture, per pound of dry gas, is

$$H' = C_B(t_G - t_0) + Y'[C_A(t_G - t_{DP}) + \lambda_{DP} + C_{AL}(t_{DP} - t_0)] \qquad (7.12)$$

Refer again to Fig. 7.3. For the low pressures ordinarily encountered in humidification work, the point A which actually lies on a line of constant pressure corresponding to the partial pressure of the vapor in the mixture may, for all practical purposes, be considered as lying on the line whose pressure is the saturation pressure of the vapor at the reference temperature, or at A'. The vapor enthalpy may then be computed by following the path $A'ED$ and becomes, per pound of vapor, $C_A(t_G - t_0) + \lambda_0$, where λ_0 is the latent heat of vaporization at the reference temperature. The enthalpy of the mixture, per pound of dry gas, is then

$$H' = C_B(t_G - t_0) + Y'[C_A(t_G - t_0) + \lambda_0] = C_S(t - t_0) + Y'\lambda_0 \qquad (7.13)$$

Occasionally different reference temperatures are chosen for the dry gas and for the vapor. Note that the enthalpy H' for a mixture may be increased by increasing the temperature at constant humidity, by increasing the humidity at constant temperature, or by increasing both. Alternatively, under certain conditions H' may remain constant as t and Y' vary in opposite directions.

By substitution of Y'_s and the appropriate humid heat in Eq. (7.13), the enthalpy of saturated mixtures H'_s may be computed and plotted against temperature on the

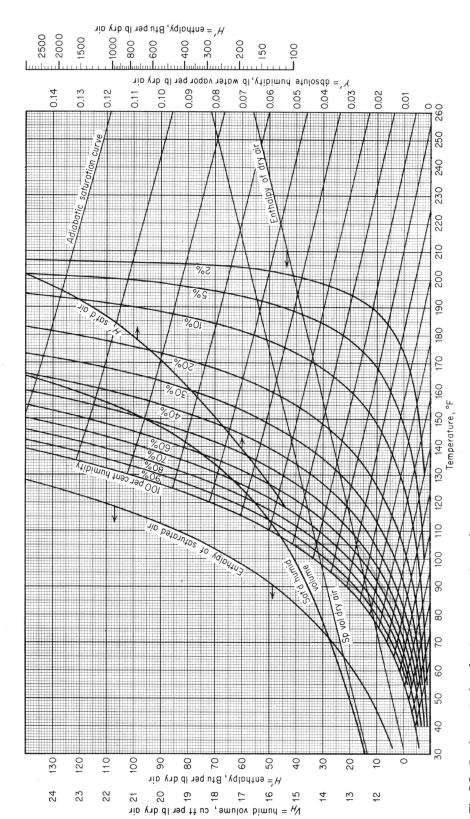

Fig. 7.5 *Psychrometric chart for air–water vapor, 1 atm abs.*

psychrometric chart.   Similarly H for the dry gas may be plotted.   Enthalpies for unsaturated mixtures may then be interpolated between the saturated and dry values at the same temperature according to the percentage saturation.

The system air–water

While psychrometric charts for any vapor-gas mixture may be prepared when circumstances warrant, the system air–water vapor occurs so frequently that unusually complete charts for this mixture are available.   Figure 7.5 is one such chart prepared for a total pressure of 1 atm.   For convenient reference, the various equations representing the curves are listed in Table 7.1.   It should be noted that all the

Table 7.1. Psychrometric relations for the system air (B)–water (A) at 1 atm pressure

$M_A = 18.02$, mol wt water

$M_B = 28.97$, mol wt air

$$Y' = 0.622 \frac{p_{H_2O}}{1 - p_{H_2O}} \qquad \text{lb water vapor/lb air}$$

$$Y'_s = 0.622 \frac{p_{H_2O}}{1 - p_{H_2O}} \qquad \text{lb water vapor/lb air at saturation}$$

$v_H = (0.0252 + 0.0405Y')(t_G + 460) \qquad$ cu ft mixture/lb air

$C_S = 0.24 + 0.45Y' \qquad$ Btu for mixture/(lb air)(°F)

$t_0 = 32$°F.

$\lambda_0 = 1075.8$ Btu/lb, latent heat of vaporization of water, 32°F

$H' = (0.24 + 0.45Y')(t_G - 32) + 1{,}075.8Y'$, relative enthalpy, Btu for mixture/lb air, referred to gaseous air and saturated liquid water at 32°F

quantities (absolute humidity, enthalpies, humid volumes) are plotted against temperature.   In the case of the enthalpies, gaseous air and saturated liquid water at 32°F were the reference conditions used so that the chart may be used in conjunction with the steam tables.   The data for enthalpy of saturated air were then plotted with two enthalpy scales to provide for the large range of values necessary.   The series of curves marked "adiabatic-saturation curves" on the chart were plotted according to Eq. (7.21), to be considered later.   For most purposes these may be considered as curves of constant enthalpy for the vapor-gas mixture per pound of gas.

Illustration 7.6. An air (B)–water vapor (A) sample has a dry-bulb temperature of 135°F and an absolute humidity 0.030 lb water/lb dry air at 1 atm pressure. Tabulate its characteristics.

Solution. The point of coordinates $t = 135$°F, $Y' = 0.030$ is located on the psychrometric chart (Fig. 7.5), a schematic version of which is shown in Fig. 7.6.   This is point D on Fig. 7.6.

a.   By vertical interpolation between the adjacent curves of constant percent humidity, the sample has a percent humidity of 22.9%.   Alternatively, the saturation humidity at 135°F is $Y'_s = 0.131$, and the percent humidity at D is therefore $(0.030/0.131)100 = 22.9\%$.

b.   The molal absolute humidity $= Y = Y'(M_B/M_A) = 0.030(28.97/18.02) = 0.0482$ mole water/mole dry air.

c.   The partial pressure of water vapor in the sample, by Eq. (7.8), is

$$p_A = \frac{YP_t}{1 + Y} = \frac{0.0482(1)}{1.0482} = 0.0460 \text{ atm}$$

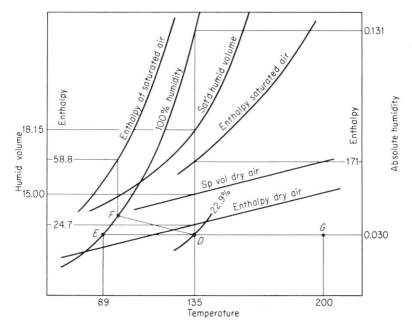

Fig. 7.6 *Solution to Illustrations 7.6 and 7.7.*

d. The vapor pressure of water at 135°F is 0.1727 atm = P_A (steam tables). The relative humidity = $p_A(100)/P_A$ = 0.0460(100)/0.1727 = 26.6%.

e. Dew point. From point D proceed at constant humidity to the saturation curve at point E, at which the dew-point temperature is 89°F.

f. Humid volume. At 135°F, the specific volume of dry air is 15.00 cu ft/lb dry air. The humid volume of saturated air is 18.15 cu ft/lb dry air. Interpolating for 22.9% humidity,

$$v_H = 15.00 + (18.15 - 15.00)(0.229) = 15.72 \text{ cu ft wet air/lb dry air}$$

g. Humid heat, Eq. (7.10)

$$C_S = C_B + Y'C_A = 0.24 + 0.45(0.030) = 0.254 \text{ Btu for wet air/(lb dry air)(°F)}$$

h. Enthalpy. At 135°F, the enthalpy of dry air is 24.7 Btu/lb dry air: that for saturated air is 171 Btu/lb dry air. Interpolating for 22.9% humidity,

$$H' = 24.7 + (171 - 24.7)0.229 = 58.2 \text{ Btu for wet air/lb dry air}$$

Alternatively, Eq. (7.13),

$$H' = C_S(t_G - t_0) + Y'\lambda_0 = 0.254(135 - 32) + 0.030(1,075.8) = 58.4 \text{ Btu/lb dry air}$$

Alternatively, line DF is drawn parallel to the adjacent adiabatic saturation curves. At F, the enthalpy is nearly the same as at D, or 58.8 Btu/lb dry air.

Illustration 7.7. One hundred cubic feet of the moist air of Illustration 7.6 is heated to 200°F. How many Btu are required?

Solution. After heating, the mixture will be at point G (Fig. 7.6).   The mass of dry air $= w_B = 100/v_H = 100/15.72 = 6.35$ lb.

Eq. (7.11): $$Q = w_B C_S \, \Delta t = 6.35(0.254)(200 - 135) = 105 \text{ Btu}$$

Alternatively, the enthalpy of the mixture at G, computed by the methods of Illustration 7.6, is 74.9 Btu/lb dry air.

$$Q = w_B(H'_G - H'_D) = 6.35(74.9 - 58.4) = 105 \text{ Btu}$$

Adiabatic-saturation curves

Consider the operation indicated schematically in Fig. 7.7.   Here the entering gas is contacted with liquid, for example, in a spray, and as a result of diffusion and heat transfer between gas and liquid the gas leaves at conditions of humidity and temperature different from those at the entrance.   The operation is adiabatic inasmuch as no heat is gained or lost to the surroundings.   A mass balance for substance A,

$$L' = G'_S(Y'_2 - Y'_1) \tag{7.14}$$

An enthalpy balance,

$$G'_S H'_1 + L' H_L = G'_S H'_2 \tag{7.15}$$

$$\therefore \quad H'_1 + (Y'_2 - Y'_1)H_L = H'_2 \tag{7.16}$$

This may be expanded by the definition of H' given in Eq. (7.13),

$$C_{S1}(t_{G1} - t_0) + Y'_1 \lambda_0 + (Y'_2 - Y'_1)C_{AL}(t_L - t_0) = C_{S2}(t_{G2} - t_0) + Y'_2 \lambda_0 \tag{7.17}$$

In the special case where the leaving gas-vapor mixture is saturated, and therefore at conditions t_{as}, Y'_{as}, H'_{as}, and the liquid enters at t_{as}, the gas is humidified by evaporation of liquid and cooled.   Equation (7.17) becomes, on expansion of the humid-heat terms,

$$C_B(t_{G1} - t_0) + Y'_1 C_A(t_{G1} - t_0) + Y'_1 \lambda_0 + (Y'_{as} - Y'_1)C_{AL}(t_{as} - t_0)$$
$$= C_B(t_{as} - t_0) + Y'_{as} C_A(t_{as} - t_0) + Y'_{as} \lambda_0 \tag{7.18}$$

By subtracting $Y'_1 C_A t_{as}$ from both sides and simplifying, this becomes

$$(C_B + Y'_1 C_A)(t_{G1} - t_{as}) = C_{S1}(t_{G1} - t_{as})$$
$$= (Y'_{as} - Y'_1)[C_A(t_{as} - t_0) + \lambda_0 - C_{AL}(t_{as} - t_0)] \tag{7.19}$$

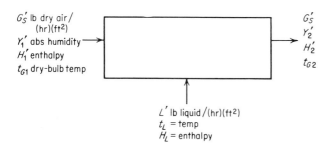

G'_S lb dry air/ (hr)(ft²)
Y'_1 abs humidity
H'_1 enthalpy
t_{G1} dry-bulb temp

G'_S
Y'_2
H'_2
t_{G2}

L' lb liquid/(hr)(ft²)
t_L = temp
H_L = enthalpy

Fig. 7.7 *Adiabatic gas-liquid contact.*

Reference to Fig. 7.3 shows the quantity in brackets to be equal to λ_{as}.   Consequently,

$$C_{S1}(t_{G1} - t_{as}) = (Y'_{as} - Y'_1)\lambda_{as} \qquad (7.20)$$

or

$$t_{G1} - t_{as} = (Y'_{as} - Y'_1)\frac{\lambda_{as}}{C_{S1}} \qquad (7.21)$$

This is the equation of a curve on the psychrometric chart, the "adiabatic-saturation curve"† which passes through the points (Y'_{as}, t_{as}) on the 100 percent saturation curve and (Y'_1, t_{G1}).   Since the humid heat C_{S1} contains the term Y'_1, the curve is not straight but instead slightly concave upward.   For any vapor-gas mixture there is an *adiabatic-saturation temperature* t_{as} such that if contacted with liquid at t_{as}, the gas will become humidified and cooled.   If sufficient contact time is available, the gas will become saturated at (Y'_{as}, t_{as}) but otherwise will leave unsaturated at (Y'_2, t_{G2}), a point on the adiabatic-saturation curve for the initial mixture.   Eventually, as Eq. (7.20) indicates, the sensible heat given up by the gas in cooling equals the latent heat required to evaporate the added vapor.

The psychrometric chart (Fig. 7.5) for air–water contains a family of adiabatic-saturation curves, as previously noted.   Each point on the curve represents a mixture whose adiabatic-saturation temperature is at the intersection of the curve with the 100 percent humidity curve.

Illustration 7.8.   Air at 190°F, $Y' = 0.030$ lb water/lb dry air, 1 atm is contacted with water at the adiabatic-saturation temperature and is thereby humidified and cooled to 90% saturation. What are the final temperature and humidity of the air?

Solution.   The point representing the original air is located on the psychrometric chart (Fig. 7.5). The adiabatic-saturation curve through the point reaches the 100% saturation curve at 105°F, the adiabatic-saturation temperature.   This is the water temperature.   On this curve, 90% saturation occurs at 108°F, $Y' = 0.0504$ lb water/lb air, the exit-air conditions.

Wet-bulb temperature

The wet-bulb temperature is the steady-state temperature reached by a small amount of liquid evaporating into a large amount of unsaturated vapor-gas mixture.   Under properly controlled conditions it can be used to measure the humidity of the mixture. For this purpose a thermometer whose bulb has been covered with a wick kept wet with the liquid is immersed in a rapidly moving stream of the gas mixture.   The temperature indicated by this thermometer will ultimately reach a value lower than the dry-bulb temperature of the gas if the latter is unsaturated, and from a knowledge of this the humidity is computed.

Consider a drop of liquid immersed in a rapidly moving stream of unsaturated vapor-gas mixture.   If the liquid is initially at a temperature higher than the gas dew point, the vapor pressure of the liquid will be higher at the drop surface than the

---

† The adiabatic-saturation curve is nearly one of constant enthalpy per pound of dry gas.   As Eq. (7.16) indicates, H'_{as} differs from H'_1 by the enthalpy of the evaporated liquid at its entering temperature t_{as} but this difference is usually unimportant.

partial pressure of vapor in the gas, and the liquid will evaporate and diffuse into the gas. The latent heat required for the evaporation will at first be supplied at the expense of the sensible heat of the liquid drop, which will then cool down. As soon as the liquid temperature is reduced below the dry-bulb temperature of the gas, heat will flow from the gas to the liquid, at an increasing rate as the temperature difference becomes larger. Eventually the rate of heat transfer from the gas to the liquid will equal the rate of heat requirement for the evaporation, and the temperature of the liquid will remain constant at some low value, the wet-bulb temperature t_w. The mechanism of the wet-bulb process is essentially the same as that governing the adiabatic saturation, except that in the case of the former the humidity of the gas is assumed not to change during the process.

Refer to Fig. 7.8, sketched in the manner of the film theory, where a drop of liquid is shown already at the steady-state conditions, and the mass of gas is so large as it passes the drop that its humidity is not measurably affected by the evaporation. The problem is very similar to that of Illustration 3.7, and Eq. (3.65) applies with $q_T = 0$ since no heat passes through the gas-liquid interface, and $N_B = 0$. Therefore†

$$q_s = \frac{N_A M_A C_A}{1 - e^{-N_A M_A C_A/h_G}} (t_G - t_w) \doteq h_G(t_G - t_w) \tag{7.22}$$

and the approximation of the right-hand side is usually satisfactory since ordinarily the rate of mass transfer is small. Further,

$$N_A = F \ln \frac{1 - P_{Aw}/P_t}{1 - P_{AG}/P_t} \doteq k_G(p_{AG} - P_{Aw}) \tag{7.23}$$

where the approximation on the right is usually satisfactory since N_A is small [the form of Eq. (7.23) reflects the fact that N_A is negative if q_s is taken to be positive]. P_{Aw} is the vapor pressure of A at t_w. Substituting Eqs. (7.22) and (7.23) into Eq. (3.65) with N_B and q_T equal to zero,

$$h_G(t_G - t_w) + \lambda_w M_A k_G(p_{AG} - P_{Aw}) = 0 \tag{7.24}$$

where λ_w is the latent heat at the wet-bulb temperature per unit of mass. From this,

$$t_G - t_w = \frac{\lambda_w M_A k_G(P_{Aw} - p_{AG})}{h_G} = \frac{\lambda_w M_B p_{BM} k_G(Y_w' - Y')}{h_G} \tag{7.25}$$

† For very careful measurements, the possibility of the liquid surface's receiving heat by radiation from either the gas itself or from the surroundings must also be considered. Assuming that the source of radiation is at temperature t_G, we then have

$$q_s = (h_G + h_R)(t_G - t_w)$$

where the radiative heat transfer is described by an equivalent convection-type coefficient h_R. In wet-bulb thermometry, the effect of radiation may be minimized by using radiation shields and maintaining a high velocity of gas to keep h_G relatively high (at least 15 to 20 ft/sec in the case of air–water vapor mixtures at ordinary temperatures). The relative size of h_G and h_R in any case may be estimated by standard methods.[9] It is necessary to observe the additional precaution of feeding the wick surrounding the thermometer bulb with an adequate supply of liquid preadjusted as nearly as practicable to the wet-bulb temperature.

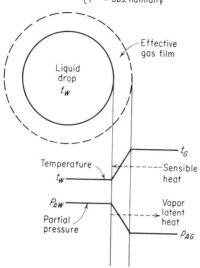

Vapor-gas mixture $\begin{cases} t_G = \text{dry-bulb temp.} \\ p_{AG} = \text{part. pres. of vapor} \\ Y' = \text{abs. humidity} \end{cases}$

Effective gas film

Liquid drop t_W

t_G

Temperature t_W

Sensible heat

p_{AW}

Partial pressure

Vapor latent heat

p_{AG}

Fig. 7.8 *The wet-bulb temperature.*

where p_{BM} is the average partial pressure of the gas.   Since (Table 3.1) $M_B p_{BM} k_G = k_Y$, Eq. (7.25) becomes

$$t_G - t_w = \frac{\lambda_w(Y'_w - Y')}{h_G/k_Y} \tag{7.26}$$

which is the form of the relationship commonly used.   The quantity $t_G - t_w$ is the *wet-bulb depression*.

In order to use Eq. (7.26) for determination of Y', it is necessary to have at hand appropriate values of h_G/k_Y, the *psychrometric ratio*.   Values of h_G and k_Y may be independently estimated for the particular shape of the wetted surface by correlations such as those of Table 3.3.   Alternatively, experimental values of the ratio for special circumstances may be employed.   For the case of *flow of gases past a wetted cylinder such as a wet-bulb thermometer*, a limited number of investigations have been made for a variety of vapors in several gases.   The best of the data show that so long as turbulent flow prevails there is no apparent effect of Reynolds number on the ratio. This is because for most gas-vapor mixtures the ratio Sc/Pr is not very far removed from unity (see page 49).   Bedingfield and Drew[2] made measurements over an extended range of Schmidt numbers, using cast cylinders of a volatile solid which sublimed into the gas stream.   They found, for air as the gas,

$$\frac{h_G}{k_Y} = 0.294 \, \text{Sc}^{0.56} \tag{7.27}$$

and, for other gases (see Table 3.3, item 2),

$$\frac{h_G}{k_Y} = C_S\left(\frac{k}{C_S \rho D_{AB}}\right)^{0.56} = C_S\left(\frac{\text{Sc}}{\text{Pr}}\right)^{0.56} \tag{7.28}$$

Fig. 7.9   *The ratio h_G/k_Y for wet-bulb thermometry in air-vapor systems.*

The ratio Sc/Pr is the Lewis number Le.   Figure 7.9 compares Eq. (7.27) with some of the better data culled from the literature, each different plotted symbol representing a different vapor.   For pure air, for which Sc = Pr = 0.702, h_G/k_Y should equal $C_S = 0.24$, and the line has been drawn through this point at A on the figure.[2]

A thorough study[16,17] of Dropkin's[3] carefully measured data on wet-bulb thermometers with air-water vapor led to the value $h_G/k_Y = 0.227$, which is recommended for this system.   This agrees very closely with Eq. (7.27) and also with the correlation of Lynch and Wilke.[8]

It will be noted that Eq. (7.26) is identical with Eq. (7.21) for the adiabatic-saturation temperature with, however, the replacement of C_{S1} by h_G/k_Y.   In the case of the air-water system at moderate humidities, C_{S1} is not greatly different from 0.227, and for many practical purposes the adiabatic-saturation curves of Fig. 7.5 may be used instead of Eq. (7.26).   For most other systems, however, the wet-bulb temperature of an unsaturated mixture will be higher than the corresponding adiabatic-saturation temperature.

Illustration 7.9.   For an air-water vapor mixture of dry-bulb temperature 150°F, a wet-bulb temperature of 90°F was determined under such conditions that the radiation coefficient may be considered negligible.   The total pressure was 1 atm.   Compute the humidity of the air.

Solution.   At $t_w = 90°F$, $\lambda_w = 1042.9$ Btu/lb, and $Y'_w = 0.031$ lb H_2O/lb dry air (Fig. 7.5); $h_G/k_Y = 0.227$, $t_G = 150°F$.

Eq. (7.26):
$$150 - 90 = \frac{1,042.9}{0.227}(0.031 - Y')$$

$$Y' = 0.0179 \text{ lb water/lb air}$$

Alternatively as an approximation, the adiabatic-saturation curve for $t_{as} = 90°F$ on Fig. 7.5 is followed down to a dry-bulb temperature 150°F, where Y' is read as 0.0170.

Illustration 7.10. Estimate the wet-bulb and adiabatic-saturation temperatures for a toluene–air mixture of 140°F dry-bulb temperature, $Y' = 0.050$ lb vapor/lb air, 1 atm.

Solution. a. Wet bulb temperature. $t_G = 140°F$ (60°C), $Y' = 0.050$ lb toluene/lb air. From Table 2.1 $D_{AB} = 0.092$ sq cm/sec at 59.0°C, 1 atm, or $0.092(3.87) = 0.356$ sq ft/hr. At 140°F, ρ for air $= 0.0663$ lb/cu ft, and $\mu = 0.0195$ centipoise, or 0.0472 lb/(ft)(hr).

Sc *should* be calculated for mean conditions between those of the gas-vapor mixture and the wet-bulb saturation conditions, but for dilute gas mixtures the values of ρ and μ for air are satisfactory.

$$\text{Sc} = \frac{\mu}{\rho D_{AB}} = \frac{0.0472}{0.0663(0.356)} = 2.00$$

Eq. (7.27):

$$\frac{h_G}{k_Y} = 0.294(2.00)^{0.56} = 0.431 \text{ Btu/(lb)(°F)} \qquad \text{(obsvd value} = 0.44)$$

Eq. (7.26):

$$140 - t_w = \frac{\lambda_w}{0.431}(Y'_w - 0.050)$$

Solution for t_w is by trial and error. Try $t_w = 90°F$. $\lambda_w = 183$ Btu/lb. The vapor pressure of toluene at 90°F $= 41.3$ mm Hg.

$$\therefore \quad Y'_w = \frac{41.3}{760 - 41.3}\frac{92.1}{29} = 0.1827 \text{ lb vapor/lb air}$$

and the equation gives $t_w = 83.8°F$ instead of the 90°F assumed. On repeated trials, t_w is computed to be 88°F.

b. Adiabatic-saturation temperature. $t_1 = 140°F$, $Y'_1 = 0.050$. C for toluene vapor $= 0.30$ Btu/(lb)(°F). $C_{S1} = 0.24 + 0.05(0.30) = 0.255$ Btu/(lb air)(°F).

Eq. (7.21):

$$140 - t_{as} = (Y'_{as} - 0.05)\frac{\lambda_{as}}{0.255}$$

In the same fashion as the wet-bulb temperature, t_{as} is calculated by trial and found to be 79°F.

The Lewis relation

We have seen that *for the system air–water vapor*, h_G/k_Y is approximately equal to C_S, or, approximately, $h_G/k_Y C_S = 1$. This is the so-called Lewis relation (after W. K. Lewis). Not only does this lead to near equality of the wet-bulb and adiabatic-saturation temperatures (as in the case of air–water vapor), but also to other simplifications to be developed later. It is important to recognize the circumstances which bring this about.

The heat-transfer coefficient h_G may be defined through Eq. (3.28):

$$h_G = \frac{q}{\Delta t} = -\frac{\alpha + E_H}{\Delta t}\frac{d(t\rho C)}{dz} = \frac{(\alpha + E_H)\rho C}{\Delta z} \tag{7.29}$$

Similarly, Eq. (3.26), if bulk flow is neglected ($J_A = N_A$), leads to the mass-transfer coefficient

$$k_c = \frac{N_A}{\Delta c} = -\frac{D + E_D}{\Delta c_A}\frac{dc_A}{dz} = \frac{D + E_D}{\Delta z} = \frac{k_Y RT}{p_{BM} M_B} \tag{7.30}$$

Consequently,

$$\frac{h_G}{k_Y} = \frac{(\alpha + E_H)\rho CRT}{(D + E_D)p_{BM} M_B} \tag{7.31}$$

and since $p_{BM}M_B/RT = \rho$, and $C \doteq C_S$,

$$\frac{h_G}{k_Y C_S} = \frac{\alpha + E_H}{D + E_D} \tag{7.32}$$

Now we have seen (page 49) that $E_D = E_H$. Consequently $h_G/k_Y C_S = 1$ only if $\alpha = D$, or $\mathrm{Pr} = \mathrm{Sc}$, or $\mathrm{Le} = 1.0$. For low concentrations of water vapor in air, $\mathrm{Sc} = 0.60$ and $\mathrm{Pr} = 0.702$, so that the Lewis relation is nearly followed. For other systems, Lewis numbers are roughly in the range 0.3 to 5, and the simplifications resulting from the Lewis relation will only rarely accrue.

GAS-LIQUID CONTACT OPERATIONS

Direct contact of a gas with a pure liquid may have any of several purposes:

1. *Cooling a hot gas.* Direct contact provides a nonfouling heat exchanger which is very effective, providing vaporization of some of the liquid into the gas is not objectionable.

2. *Humidifying a gas.* This may be used for controlling the moisture content of air for drying, for example.

3. *Dehumidifying a gas.* Contact of a warm vapor-gas mixture with cold liquid results in condensation of the vapor. This has applications in air conditioning, recovery of solvent vapors from gases used in drying, and the like.

4. *Cooling a liquid.* The cooling occurs by transfer of sensible heat and also by evaporation. The principal application is cooling of water by contact with atmospheric air (water cooling).

Although operations of this sort are simple in the sense that mass transfer is confined to the gas phase (there can be no mass transfer within the pure liquid), they are nevertheless complex owing to the very large heat effects which accompany evaporation or condensation. The discussion here will be confined to adiabatic operations, i.e., where no heat is added to, or removed from, the system except by the liquid and gas being contacted. There are important nonadiabatic operations also: "evaporative cooling,"[17] for example, where a liquid inside a pipe is cooled by water flowing in a film about the outside, the latter in turn being cooled by direct contact with air; dehumidification of a gas by contact with refrigerated tubes; and many others.

Fundamental relationships

The adiabatic operations are usually carried out countercurrently in a packed tower of some sort. Refer to Fig. 7.10, which shows a tower of unit cross-sectional area. A mass balance for substance A over the lower part of the tower (envelope I) is

$$L' - L_1' = G_S'(Y' - Y_1') \tag{7.33}$$

or

$$dL' = G_S' \, dY' \tag{7.34}$$

Similarly, an enthalpy balance is

$$L'H_L + G_S'H_1' = L_1'H_{L1} + G_S'H' \tag{7.35}$$

Fig. 7.10 *Continuous countercurrent adiabatic gas-liquid contact.*

These may be applied to the entire tower by putting subscript 2 on the unnumbered terms.

The rate relationships are fairly complex and will be developed in the manner of Olander.[14]   Refer to Fig. 7.11, which represents a section of the tower of differential height dZ and shows the liquid and gas flowing side by side, separated by the gas-liquid interface.   The changes in temperature, humidity, etc., are all differential over this section.

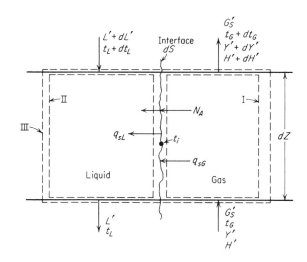

Fig. 7.11 *Differential section of a packed tower.*

The interfacial surface of the section is dS.   If the interfacial surface per unit volume of packing is a sq ft/cu ft (not the same as the packing surface a_p), since the volume of packing per unit tower cross section is dZ cu ft, then $dS = a\,dZ$.   If the packing is incompletely wetted by the liquid, the surface for mass transfer a_M, which is the liquid-gas interface, will be smaller than that for heat transfer a_H, since heat transfer may also occur between the packing and the fluids.   Note that a_M corresponds to a_V of Chap. 6.   The transfer rates are then:

Mass, as lb vapor/(hr)(sq ft tower cross section)

$$N_A M_A a_M\, dZ = -G'_S\, dY' = M_A F_G\left(\ln \frac{1 - P_{Ai}/P_t}{1 - p_{AG}/P_t}\right) a_M\, dZ \qquad (7.36)$$

Sensible heat, as Btu/(hr)(sq ft tower cross section)

Gas: $$q_{sG} a_H\, dZ = \frac{N_A M_A C_A}{1 - e^{-N_A M_A C_A/h_G}} (t_G - t_i) a_H\, dZ = h'_G a_H (t_G - t_i)\, dZ \qquad (7.37)$$

Liquid: $$q_{sL} a_H\, dZ = h_L a_H (t_i - t_L)\, dZ \qquad (7.38)$$

In Eq. (7.36), P_{Ai} is the vapor pressure of A at the interface temperature t_i, and p_{AG} is the partial pressure in the bulk gas.   In Eq. (7.37), radiation has been neglected, and the coefficient h'_G, which accounts for the effect of mass transfer on heat transfer, replaces the ordinary convection coefficient h_G (see Chap. 3).   The rate equations are written as if transfer were in the direction gas to interface to liquid, but they are directly applicable as written to all situations; correct signs for the fluxes will develop automatically.

We now require a series of enthalpy balances based on the envelopes sketched in Fig. 7.11.

Envelope I

Rate enthalpy in $= G'_S H'$

Rate enthalpy out $= G'_S(H' + dH') - (G'_S\, dY')[C_A(t_G - t_0) + \lambda_0]$

The second term is the enthalpy of the transferred vapor [recall N_A and $G_S\, dY$ have opposite signs in Eq. (7.36)].

Rate in $-$ rate out $=$ heat-transfer rate

$$G'_S H' - G'_S(H' + dH') + (G'_S\, dY')[C_A(t_G - t_0) + \lambda_0] = h'_G a_H (t_G - t_i)\, dZ \quad (7.39)$$

If dH', obtained by differentiation of Eq. (7.13), is substituted, this reduces to

$$-G'_S C_S\, dt_G = h'_G a_H (t_G - t_i)\, dZ \qquad (7.40)$$

Envelope II

$$\text{Rate enthalpy in} = (L' + dL')C_{AL}(t_L + dt_L - t_0) + (-G'_S\,dY')C_{AL}(t_i - t_0)$$

Here the second term is the enthalpy of the material transferred, now a liquid.

$$\text{Rate enthalpy out} = L'C_{AL}(t_L - t_0)$$

$$\text{Rate out} = \text{rate in} + \text{heat-transfer rate}$$

$$L'C_{AL}(t_L - t_0) = (L' + dL')C_{AL}(t_L + dt_L - t_0) - (G'_S\,dY')C_{AL}(t_i - t_0)$$
$$+ h_L a_H(t_i - t_L)\,dZ \qquad (7.41)$$

If Eq. (7.34) is substituted and the second-order differential $dY'\,dt_L$ ignored, this becomes

$$L'C_{AL}\,dt_L = (G'_S C_{AL}\,dY' - h_L a_H\,dZ)(t_i - t_L) \qquad (7.42)$$

Envelope III

$$\text{Rate enthalpy in} = G'_S H' + (L' + dL')C_{AL}(t_L + dt_L - t_0)$$

$$\text{Rate enthalpy out} = L'C_{AL}(t_L - t_0) + G'_S(H' + dH')$$

$$\text{Rate in} = \text{rate out (adiabatic operation)}$$

$$G'_S H' + (L' + dL')C_{AL}(t_L + dt_L - t_0) = L'C_{AL}(t_L - t_0) + G'_S(H' + dH') \quad (7.43)$$

Substitutions of Eq. (7.34) and the differential of Eq. (7.13) for dH' are made, and the term $dH'\,dt_L$ is ignored, whereupon this becomes

$$L'C_{AL}\,dt_L = G'_S\{C_S\,dt_G + [C_A(t_G - t_0) - C_{AL}(t_L - t_0) + \lambda_0]\,dY'\} \quad (7.44)$$

These will now be applied to the adiabatic operations.

Water cooling with air

This is without question the most important of the operations. Water, warmed by passage through heat exchangers, condensers, and the like, is cooled by contact with atmospheric air for reuse. The latent heat of water is so large that only a small amount of evaporation produces large cooling effects. Since the rate of mass transfer is usually small, the temperature level is generally fairly low, and the Lewis relation applies reasonably well for the air–water system, the relationships of the previous section may be greatly simplified by making reasonable approximations.

Thus, if the sensible heat terms of Eq. (7.44) are ignored in comparison with the latent heat, we have

$$L'C_{AL}\,dt_L = G'_S C_S\,dt_G + G'_S \lambda_0\,dY' \doteq G'_S\,dH \qquad (7.45)$$

Here the last term on the right ignores the Y' which appears in the definition of C_S. Integrating, on the further assumption that L' is essentially constant (little evaporation),

$$L'C_{AL}(t_{L2} - t_{L1}) = G'_S(H'_2 - H'_1) \qquad (7.46)$$

This enthalpy balance may be represented graphically by plotting the gas enthalpy H' against t_L, as in Fig. 7.12. The line ON on the chart represents Eq. (7.46), and it passes through the points representing the terminal conditions for the two fluids. Insofar as $L'_2 - L'_1$ is small in comparison with L', the line is straight and of slope $L'C_{AL}/G'_S$. The equilibrium curve in the figure is plotted for conditions of the gas at the gas-liquid interface, i.e., the enthalpy of saturated gas at each temperature.

If the mass-transfer rate is small, as it usually is, Eq. (7.36) may be written as

$$G'_S \, dY' = k_Y a_M(Y'_i - Y') \, dZ \qquad (7.47)$$

and Eq. (7.40) as

$$G'_S C_S \, dt_G = h_G a_H(t_i - t_G) \, dZ \qquad (7.48)$$

Ignoring the sensible heat of the transferred vapor, Eq. (7.42) becomes

$$L'C_{AL} \, dt_L = h_L a_H(t_L - t_i) \, dZ \qquad (7.49)$$

Substituting Eqs. (7.47) and (7.48) into (7.45):

$$G'_S \, dH' = h_G a_H(t_i - t_G) \, dZ + \lambda_0 k_Y a_M(Y'_i - Y') \, dZ \qquad (7.50)$$

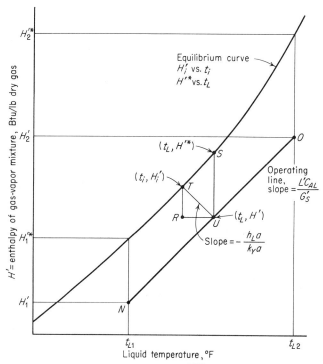

Fig. 7.12 Operating diagram for a water cooler.

If $h_G a_H / C_S k_Y a_M = r$, this becomes

$$G'_S \, dH' = k_Y a_M [(C_S r t_i + \lambda_0 Y'_i) - (C_S r t_G + \lambda_0 Y')] \, dZ \qquad (7.51)$$

For the special case where r = 1,[11,12] the terms in parentheses are gas enthalpies. The restriction that $r = 1$ requires Le $= 1$ (air–water), and $a_M = a_H = a$ (the latter will be true only for thoroughly irrigated tower filling; even for air–water contacting, values of r as high as 2 have been observed with low liquid rates[6]). With these understood, Eq. (7.51) is

$$G'_S \, dH' = k_Y a (H'_i - H') \, dZ \qquad (7.52)$$

which is remarkable in that the mass-transfer coefficient is used with an enthalpy driving force. Combining Eqs. (7.45), (7.49), and (7.52) then provides

$$G'_S \, dH' = k_Y a (H'_i - H') \, dZ = h_L a (t_L - t_i) \, dZ \qquad (7.53)$$

At a position in the apparatus corresponding to point U on the operating line (Fig. 7.12), point T represents the interface conditions and the distance TR the enthalpy driving force $H'_i - H'$ within the gas phase. By making constructions like the triangle RTU at several places along the operating line, corresponding H'_i and H' values may be obtained. Equation (7.53) then provides, assuming $k_Y a$ is constant,

$$\int_{H'_1}^{H'_2} \frac{dH'}{H'_i - H'} = \frac{k_Y a}{G'_S} \int_0^Z dZ = \frac{k_Y a Z}{G'_S} \qquad (7.54)$$

The integral may be evaluated graphically and the packed height Z computed. The enthalpy integral of Eq. (7.54) is sometimes given another interpretation. Thus,

$$\int_{H'_1}^{H'_2} \frac{dH'}{H'_i - H'} = \frac{H'_2 - H'_1}{(H'_i - H')_{\mathrm{av}}} = N_{tG} \qquad (7.55)$$

where the middle part of the equation is the number of times the average driving force divides into the enthalpy change. This is a measure of the difficulty of enthalpy transfer, called the *number of gas-enthalpy transfer units* N_{tG}. Consequently,

$$Z = H_{tG} N_{tG} \qquad (7.56)$$

where the height of a gas-enthalpy transfer unit $= H_{tG} = G'_S / k_Y a$. H_{tG} is frequently preferred over $k_Y a$ as a measure of packing performance since it is less dependent upon rates of flow and has the simple dimension of length.

As discussed in Chap. 5, an overall driving force representing the enthalpy difference for the bulk phases but expressed in terms of H' may be used, such as the vertical distance SU (Fig. 7.12). This requires a corresponding overall coefficient and leads to overall numbers and heights of transfer units:†

$$N_{tOG} = \int_{H'_1}^{H'_2} \frac{dH'}{H'^* - H'} = \frac{K_Y a Z}{G'_S} = \frac{Z}{H_{tOG}} \qquad (7.57)$$

† The water-cooling-tower industry frequently uses Eq. (7.57) in another form:

$$\frac{K_Y a Z}{L'} = \int_{t_{L1}}^{t_{L2}} \frac{dt_L}{H'^* - H'}$$

which results from combining Eqs. (7.45) and (7.57) and setting C_{AL} for water $= 1$.

The use of Eq. (7.56) is satisfactory (see Chap. 5) only if the equilibrium enthalpy curve of Fig. 7.12 is straight, which is not strictly so, or if $h_L a$ is infinite, so that the interface temperature equals the bulk-liquid temperature. Although the few data available indicate that $h_L a$ is usually quite large (see, for example, Illustration 6.5), there are uncertainties owing to the fact that many have been taken under conditions such that $h_G a_H / C_S k_Y a_M = r$ was *not* unity even though assumed to be so. In any case, it frequently happens that, for cooling-tower packings, only $K_Y a$ or H_{tOG}, and not the individual phase coefficients, are available.

Just as with concentrations (Chap. 5), an operating line on the enthalpy co-ordinates of Fig. 7.12 which anywhere touches the equilibrium curve results in a zero driving force and consequently an infinite interfacial surface, or infinite height Z, to accomplish a given temperature change in the liquid. This condition would then represent the limiting ratio of L'/G_S' permissible. It is also clear that point N, for example, will be below the equilibrium curve so long as the entering-air enthalpy H_1' is less than the saturation enthalpy $H_1'^*$ for air at t_{L1}. Since the enthalpy H' is for most practical purposes only a function of the adiabatic-saturation temperature (or, for air–water, the wet-bulb temperature), the entering-air wet-bulb temperature must be below t_{L1} *but its dry-bulb temperature need not be.* For this reason, it is perfectly possible to cool water to a value of t_{L1} less than the entering-air dry-bulb temperature t_{G1}. It is also possible to operate a cooler with entering air saturated, so long as its temperature is less than t_{L1}. The difference between the exit-liquid temperature and the entering-air wet-bulb temperature, $t_{L1} - t_{w1}$, called the "wet-bulb temperature approach," is then a measure of the driving force available for diffusion at the lower end of the equipment. In the design of cooling towers, this is ordinarily specified to be from 5 to 10°F, with t_{w1} set at the "5 percent wet-bulb temperature" (the wet-bulb temperature which is exceeded only 5 percent of the time on the average during the summer months). "Makeup" fresh water in recirculating water systems must be added to replace losses from entrainment, evaporation losses, and "blowdown." If makeup water introduces dissolved salts ("hardness") which will otherwise accumulate, a small amount of the water is deliberately discarded (blow-down) to keep the salt concentration at some predetermined level. Many other practical details are available.[10,13] Some cooling towers use a cross flow of water and air, for which the methods of computation are also available.[1]

The use of overall mass-transfer coefficients does not distinguish between convective and evaporative cooling of the liquid and will not permit computation of the humidity or dry-bulb temperature of the exit air. The air will ordinarily be very nearly saturated, and for purposes of estimating makeup requirements it may be so assumed. The temperature-humidity history of the air as it passes through the tower may be estimated by a graphical method on the $H' t_L$ diagram (Fig. 7.12) if $h_L a$ and $k_Y a$ are known,[12] but approach of the gas to saturation is very critical to the computations, and it is recommended instead that these be done by the methods outlined later (see page 208) which make no assumptions. Cooling towers for systems other than air–water (Le $\neq$ 1), or when $a_M \neq a_H$, must also be treated by the general methods discussed later.

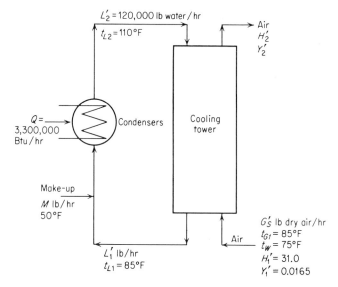

L'_2 = 120,000 lb water/hr

t_{L2} = 110°F

Air
H'_2
Y'_2

Q =
3,300,000
Btu/hr

Condensers

Cooling
tower

Make-up
M lb/hr
50°F

L'_1 lb/hr
t_{L1} = 85°F

Air

G'_S lb dry air/hr
t_{G1} = 85°F
t_W = 75°F
H'_1 = 31.0
Y'_1 = 0.0165

Fig. 7.13 *Flow sheet for Illustration 7.11.*

Illustration 7.11. A plant requires 2,000 lb/min of cooling water to flow through its distillation-equipment condensers, thereby removing 55,000 Btu/min from the condensers. The water will leave the condensers at 110°F. It is planned to cool it for reuse by contact with air in an induced-draft cooling tower. Makeup water will come from a well at 50°F. The design conditions chosen are entering air at 85°F dry-bulb, 75°F wet-bulb temperature; water cooled to within 10°F of the inlet-air wet-bulb temperature, i.e., to 85°F; an air/water ratio of 1.5 times the minimum. For the packing to be used, K_Ya is expected to be 200 lb/(hr)(cu ft)($\Delta Y'$), provided the liquid rate is at least 2,000 lb/(hr)(sq ft) and the gas rate 1,500 lb/(hr)(sq ft). Compute the required cross section and packed height of the cooling tower, and estimate the makeup water required.

Solution. Refer to Fig. 7.13, which represents the flow sheet of the operation. The entering-air humidity and enthalpy are taken from Fig. 7.5. The operating diagram (Fig. 7.14) contains the saturated air-enthalpy curve, and on this plot is point N representing the conditions at the bottom of the tower ($t_{L1} = 85°F$, $H'_1 = 31.0$). The operating line will pass through N and end at $t_{L2} = 110°F$. For the minimum value of G'_S, the operating line will have the least slope which causes it to touch the equilibrium curve and will consequently pass through point O', where $H'_2 = 84.7$ Btu/lb dry air. The slope of line $O'N$ is therefore

$$\frac{L'C_{AL}}{G'_{S,\min}} = \frac{120,000(1)}{G'_{S,\min}} = \frac{84.7 - 31.0}{110 - 85}$$

and $G'_{S,\min} = 55,900$ lb dry air/hr. For a gas rate of 1.5 times the minimum, $G'_S = 1.5(55,900) = 83,800$ lb dry air/hr. Therefore

$$\frac{H'_2 - 31.0}{110 - 85} = \frac{120,000(1)}{83,800}$$

and $H'_2 = 66.8$ Btu/lb dry air, plotted at point O. The operating line is therefore line ON. For a liquid rate of at least 2,000 lb/(hr)(sq ft), the tower cross section would be 120,000/2,000 = 60 sq ft. For a gas rate of at least 1,500 lb/(hr)(sq ft), the cross section will be 83,800/1,500 = 56 sq ft. The latter will therefore be used, since the liquid rate will then exceed the minimum to ensure $K_Ya = 200$.

Basis: 1 sq ft cross section. $G'_s = 1{,}500$ lb dry gas/hr. The driving force $H'^* - H'$ is computed at frequent intervals of t_L from Fig. 7.14 as listed below:

t_L, °F	H'^* (equilibrium curve)	H' (operating line)	$1/(H'^* - H')$
85	41.9	31.0	0.0917
90	48.2	38.3	0.1011
95	55.7	45.3	0.0980
100	64.0	52.5	0.0885
105	74.2	59.5	0.0680
110	84.7	66.8	0.0558

The data of the last two columns are plotted against each other, H' as abscissa, and the area under the curve is 3.18. From Eq. (7.57),

$$3.18 = \frac{K_Y a Z}{G'_s} = \frac{200Z}{1{,}500} \qquad Z = 23.8 \text{ ft of packed height}$$

(*Note:* For this case, $N_{tOG} = 3.18$, and $H_{tOG} = G'_s/K_Y a = 1{,}500/200 = 7.5$ ft.)

The makeup water requirement, M lb/hr, can only be estimated. Refer to Fig. 7.13. If the exit air is assumed to be saturated, its humidity Y'_2 must be that for saturated air at $H'_s = H'_2 = 66.8$, or $Y'_2 = 0.0453$. Since G'_s was calculated on the assumption that $L'_2 = L'_1$ (a straight operating line), thus not allowing for evaporation, it is best to eliminate G'_s in estimating M. An enthalpy balance for the entire plant,

$$3{,}300{,}000 + M(1)(50 - 32) + G'_s(31.0) = G'_s H'_2$$

A water balance,

$$M = G'_s(Y'_2 - 0.0165)$$

Eliminating G'_s, and substituting for H'_2 and Y'_2, $M = 2{,}690$ lb/hr. **Ans.**

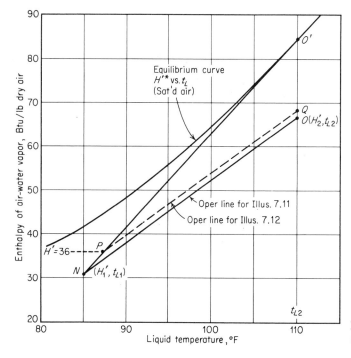

Fig. 7.14 *Solutions to Illustrations 7.11 and 7.12.*

Illustration 7.12. In the cooler of Illustration 7.11, to what temperature would the water be cooled if, after the tower was built and operated at the design L'/G'_S ratio, the entering air should enter at dry-bulb temperature $t_{G1} = 85°F$ and wet-bulb temperature $t_{w1} = 80°F$?

Solution. For the new conditions, $t_{L2} = 110°F$ and $H_1 = 36.0$ Btu/lb dry air, and the slope of the operating line is the same as that for Illustration 7.11. Refer to Fig. 7.14. The new operating line will be parallel to line ON and end at $H'_1 = 36.0$ and at $t_{L2} = 110°F$. Since the coefficient $K_Y a$ is unchanged, the line is located by trial and error so that the area under the curve of $1/(H'^* - H')$ vs. H' remains at 3.18, the value found previously. The line PQ (Fig. 7.14) is found to satisfy these conditions, and t_{L1} is read at point P as 87.4°F, the new outlet-water temperature.

Alternatively, it might have been assumed that the heat load of the tower, the same as the heat load of the plant which uses the circulating water, remains constant, so that

$$83,800(66.8 - 31.0) = 83,800(H'_2 - 36)$$

whence $H'_2 = 71.8$. This, by a procedure similar to that above, results in $t_{L1} = 86.0°F$ and $t_{L2} = 111°F$.

Dehumidification of air–water vapor

If a warm vapor-gas mixture is contacted with cold liquid so that the humidity of the gas is greater than that at the gas-liquid interface, vapor will diffuse toward the liquid, and the gas will be dehumidified. In addition, sensible heat may be transferred as a result of temperature differences within the system. For air–water vapor mixtures (Le = 1) contacted with cold water, the methods of water cooling apply with only obvious modification. The operating line on the gas enthalpy–liquid temperature graph will be above the equilibrium curve, the driving force is $H' - H'^*$, and Eq. (7.57) may be used with this driving force. For all other systems, for which Le $\neq 1$, the general methods below must be used.

Tray towers. Water cooling may be carried out in stagewise fashion in any of the tray towers discussed in Chap. 6, although it is not generally the custom to do so. The determination of the number of ideal trays, following the principles of Chap. 5, is done on the $H't_L$ diagram.

Recirculating liquid. Gas humidification-cooling

This is a special case where the liquid enters the equipment at the adiabatic-saturation temperature of the entering gas. This may be achieved by continuously reintroducing the exit liquid to the contactor immediately, without addition or removal of heat on the way, as in Fig. 7.15. The development which follows applies to any liquid-gas system, regardless of the Lewis number. In such a system, the temperature of the entire liquid will fall to, and remain at, the adiabatic-saturation temperature. The gas will be cooled and humidified, following along the path of the adiabatic-saturation curve on the psychrometric chart which passes through the entering-gas conditions. Depending upon the degree of contact, the gas will approach more or less closely equilibrium with the liquid, or its adiabatic-saturation conditions. This supposes that the makeup liquid enters at the adiabatic-saturation temperature also, but for most purposes the quantity of evaporation is so small relative to the total liquid circulation that minor deviations from this temperature for the makeup liquid may be ignored.

As has been shown previously, the enthalpy of the gas is practically a function only of its adiabatic-saturation temperature, which remains constant throughout the operation. The enthalpy of the liquid at constant temperature is also constant, so that an operating "line" on a plot such as Fig. 7.12 would be merely a single point on the equilibrium curve. This diagram cannot therefore be used for design purposes. The temperature and humidity changes, which lie entirely within the gas phase, can be used, however, and these are shown schematically in Fig. 7.15. If mass transfer is used as a basis for design, Eq. (7.47) becomes

$$G_S' \, dY = k_Y a (Y_{as}' - Y') \, dZ \tag{7.58}$$

$$\int_{Y_1'}^{Y_2'} \frac{dY'}{Y_{as}' - Y'} = \frac{k_Y a}{G_S} \int_0^Z dZ \tag{7.59}$$

and since Y_{as}' is constant,

$$\ln \frac{Y_{as}' - Y_1'}{Y_{as}' - Y_2'} = \frac{k_Y a Z}{G_S} \tag{7.60}$$

Equation (7.60) may be used directly, or it may be rearranged by solving for G_S' and multiplying each side by $Y_2' - Y_1'$ or its equivalent,

$$G_S'(Y_2' - Y_1') = \frac{k_Y a Z [(Y_{as}' - Y_1') - (Y_{as}' - Y_2')]}{\ln [(Y_{as}' - Y_1')/(Y_{as}' - Y_2')]} = k_Y a Z (\Delta Y')_{av} \tag{7.61}$$

where $(\Delta Y')_{av}$ is the logarithmic average of the humidity-difference driving forces a the ends of the equipment. Alternatively,

$$N_{tG} = \frac{Y_2' - Y_1'}{(\Delta Y')_{av}} = \ln \frac{Y_{as}' - Y_1'}{Y_{as}' - Y_2'} \tag{7.62}$$

and

$$H_{tG} = \frac{G_S'}{k_Y a} = \frac{Z}{N_{tG}} \tag{7.63}$$

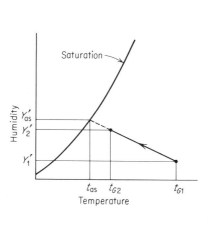

Fig. 7.15 *Recirculating liquid, gas humidification-cooling.*

where N_{tG} is the number of gas-phase transfer units and H_{tG} the corresponding height of a transfer unit.†

In contacting operations of this sort, where one phase approaches equilibrium with the other under conditions such that the characteristics of the latter do not change, the maximum change in the first phase corresponds to the operation of one theoretical stage (see Chap. 5). Since the humidity in adiabatic equilibrium with the liquid is Y'_{as}, the Murphree gas-phase stage efficiency is then

$$E_{MG} = \frac{Y'_2 - Y'_1}{Y'_{as} - Y'_1} = 1 - \frac{Y'_{as} - Y'_2}{Y'_{as} - Y'_1} = 1 - e^{-k_Y a Z/G'_S} = 1 - e^{-N_{tG}} \qquad (7.64)$$

If heat transfer is used as the basis for design, similar treatment of Eq. (7.48) leads to

$$G'_S C_{S1}(t_{G1} - t_{G2}) = \frac{h_G a Z[(t_{G1} - t_{as}) - (t_{G2} - t_{as})]}{\ln[(t_{G1} - t_{as})/(t_{G2} - t_{as})]} = h_G a Z(\Delta t)_{av} \qquad (7.65)$$

where $h_G a$ is the volumetric-heat-transfer coefficient of sensible-heat transfer between the bulk of the gas and the liquid surface.

Illustration 7.13. A horizontal spray chamber (Fig. 7.19) with recirculated water is to be used for the adiabatic humidification and cooling of air. The active part of the chamber is 5 ft long and has a cross section of 20 sq ft. With the nozzle arrangement provided, and when operated with the water-circulation rate recommended by the nozzle manufacturer, the coefficient of heat transfer is expected to be $h_G a = 85$ Btu/(hr)(cu ft)(°F). An amount 7,500 cu ft/min of air at 150°F, $Y' = 0.0170$ lb water/lb dry air, is to be blown through the spray.

    a. What exit temperature and humidity can be expected for the air?
    b. What makeup water will be needed?
    c. Express the performance in terms of $k_Y a$, N_{tG}, H_{tG}, and stage efficiency.
    d. If a duplicate spray chamber, operated in the same manner, were to be added in series with the first, what exit conditions would be expected for the air?

    Solution. a. From the psychrometric chart (Fig. 7.5), the initial air has a percentage humidity of 8.0%. The dry specific volume of air at 150°F = 15.38, and the saturated volume = 20.60 cu ft/lb dry air. The humid volume of the entering air is therefore

$$v_H = 15.38 + 0.08(20.60 - 15.38) = 15.80 \text{ cu ft humid air/lb dry air}$$

$$G'_S = \frac{7,500(60)}{15.80(20)} = 1,422 \text{ lb dry air/(hr)(sq ft)}$$

The initial humid heat = $C_{S1} = 0.24 + 0.45Y' = 0.24 + 0.45(0.017) = 0.248$ Btu/(lb dry air)(°F). $t_{G1} = 150$°F, and the air lies on the adiabatic-saturation line for $t_{as} = 90$°F. $Z = 5$ ft.

Eq. (7.65):
$$1,422(0.248)(150 - t_{G2}) = \frac{85(5)[(150 - 90) - (t_{G2} - 90)]}{\ln[(150 - 90)/(t_{G2} - 90)]}$$

$$= \frac{85(5)(150 - t_{G2})}{\ln[60/(t_{G2} - 90)]}$$

$$t_{G2} = 108°F$$

† To be entirely consistent with the definition of Chap. 8, Eq. (7.63) should read $H_{tG} = G'_S/k_Y a(1 - y_A)$. The value of $1 - y_A$ in the present application is, however, ordinarily very close to unity.

On the 90°F adiabatic-saturation curve, the humidity at this temperature is $Y_2' = 0.0268$ lb water/lb dry air.

  b. The makeup water,

$$G_S'(20)(Y_2' - Y_1') = 1,422(20)(0.0268 - 0.0170) = 278 \text{ lb/hr}$$

  c. Y_{as}' (at 90°F) = 0.0312 lb water/lb dry air.

Eq. (7.62):

$$N_{tG} = \ln \frac{Y_{as}' - Y_1'}{Y_{as}' - Y_2'} = \ln \frac{0.0312 - 0.0170}{0.0312 - 0.0268} = 1.15 \text{ transfer units}$$

Eq. (7.60):

$$k_Y a = \frac{G_S'}{Z} \ln \frac{Y_{as}' - Y_1'}{Y_{as}' - Y_2'} = \frac{1,422}{5} 1.15 = 327 \text{ lb water evapd/(hr)(cu ft)}(\Delta Y')$$

Eq. (7.63):

$$H_{tG} = \frac{Z}{N_{tG}} = \frac{5}{1.15} = 4.35 \text{ ft}$$

Eq. (7.64):

$$E_{MG} = 1 - e^{-N_{tG}} = 1 - \frac{1}{e^{1.15}} = 0.684, \text{ or } 68.4\%$$

  d. $Z = 10$ ft. At the same air rate and spray density, the coefficients are unchanged.

Eq. (7.65):

$$1,422(0.248)(150 - t_{G2}) = \frac{85(10)(150 - t_{G2})}{\ln [60/(t_{G2} - 90)]}$$

$$t_{G2} = 95.4°F$$

Y_2', read from the adiabatic-saturation curve as before, is 0.0298 lb water/lb dry air.

General methods

For all other countercurrent operations, and even for those discussed above when the approximations are not appropriate or when Le $\neq 1$, we must return to the equations on page 198. Equating the right-hand sides of Eqs. (7.42) and (7.44) provides

$$t_i = t_L + \frac{G_S'\{C_S(dt_G/dZ) + [C_A t_G - C_{AL} t_L + (C_{AL} - C_A)t_0 + \lambda_0](dY'/dZ)\}}{G_S' C_{AL}(dY'/dZ) - h_L a_H} \tag{7.66}$$

The humidity gradient in this expression is obtained from Eq. (7.36):

$$\frac{dY'}{dZ} = -\frac{M_A F_G a_M}{G_S'} \ln \frac{1 - P_{Ai}/P_t}{1 - p_{AG}/P_t} = -\frac{M_A F_G a_M}{G_S'} \ln \frac{Y' + M_A/M_B}{Y_i' + M_A/M_B} \tag{7.67}$$

$$\doteq -\frac{M_A k_G a_M}{G_S'} (p_{AG} - P_{Ai}) \doteq -\frac{k_Y a_M}{G_S'} (Y' - Y_i') \tag{7.67a}$$

where the approximations of Eq. (7.67a) are suitable for low vapor concentrations. The temperature gradient is taken from Eq. (7.40):

$$\frac{dt_G}{dZ} = -\frac{h_G' a_H(t_G - t_i)}{G_S' C_S} \doteq -\frac{h_G a_H(t_G - t_i)}{G_S' C_S} \tag{7.68}$$

where $h_G a_H$ rather than $h'_G a_H$ may be used at low transfer rates.   Unless a_H and a_M are separately known (which is not usual), there will be difficulty in evaluating h'_G exactly.   Here we must assume $a_H = a_M$:

$$h'_G a_H = \frac{N_A M_A C_A a_H}{1 - e^{-N_A M_A C_A a_H/h_G a_H}} \doteq \frac{N_A M_A C_A a_M}{1 - e^{-N_A M_A C_A a_M/h_G a_H}}$$

$$\doteq -\frac{G'_S C_A (dY'/dZ)}{1 - e^{G'_S C_A (dY'/dZ)/h_G a_H}}$$

(7.69)

The effect of the approximation is not normally important.

Equations (7.67) and (7.68) are integrated numerically, using a procedure outlined in Illustration 7.14.   Extensive trial and error is required, since t_i from Eq. (7.66) is necessary before P_{Ai} (or Y'_i) can be computed.   The t_i-P_{Ai} relationship is that of the vapor-pressure curve.   If at any point in the course of the calculations p_{AG} (or Y') at a given t_G calculates to be larger than the corresponding saturation vapor concentration, a fog will form in the gas phase, the entire analysis is invalid, and new conditions at the terminals of the tower must be chosen.

Illustration 7.14. A producer gas, 65% nitrogen, 35% carbon monoxide, 1 atm, 600°F, initially dry, is to be cooled to 80°F by countercurrent contact with water entering at 65°F.   A hurdle-packed tower will be used, with $G'_S = 500$ lb/(hr)(sq ft), $L'_2 = 1,000$ lb/(hr)(sq ft), for which the transfer coefficients (assumed constant) are

$$h_G a_H = 150 \text{ Btu/(hr)(cu ft)(°F)}$$

$$h_L a_H = 1000 \text{ Btu/(hr)(cu ft)(°F)}$$

$$F_G a_M = 21.8 \text{ lb moles/(hr)(cu ft)}$$

Compute the required height of the packed section.

Solution. For convenience, the base temperature will be taken as $t_0 = 65°F$.   The heat capacities will be assumed constant throughout: $C_{AL} = 1.0$, $C_A = 0.45$, $C_B(N_2 + CO) = 0.26$.   (*Note:* It is not necessary to assume these, or the transfer coefficients, to be constant.)   The given data provide $Y'_1 = 0$, $L'_2 = 1,000$, $G'_S = 500$, $t_{L2} = 65°F$, $t_{G1} = 600°F$, $t_{G2} = 80°F$, $C_{S1} = 0.26$, $\lambda_0 = 1,057.1$, $M_A = 18.02$, $M_B = 28.0$, $P_t = 1$ atm.

Calculations will be started at the bottom, for which L'_1 and t_{L1} must be known.   These will be determined by assuming an outlet gas humidity, to be checked at the end of the calculation.   Since the exit gas is likely to be nearly saturated ($Y'_s = 0.023$), estimate its humidity to be $Y'_2 = 0.02$, for which $C_{S2} = 0.26 + 0.02(0.45) = 0.269$.   An overall water balance [Eq. (7.33)]:

$$1,000 - L'_1 = 500(0.02 - 0)$$

$$L'_1 = 990 \text{ lb/(hr)(sq ft)}$$

An overall enthalpy balance [Eq. (7.35)]:

$$1,000(1)(65 - 65) + 500(0.26)(600 - 65) = 990(1)(t_{L1} - 65)$$

$$+ 500[0.269(80 - 65) + 0.02(1,057.1)]$$

$$t_{L1} = 122.5°F$$

At the bottom ($Z = 0$), t_i will be estimated by trial and error. After several trials, assume $t_i = 124.5°F$. $P_{Ai} = 0.1303$ atm.

Eq. (7.67): $$\frac{dY'}{dZ} = -\frac{18.02(21.8)}{500} \ln \frac{1 - 0.1303}{1 - 0} = 0.1705 \text{ lb } H_2O/(\text{lb dry gas})(\text{ft})$$

Eq. (7.69): $$h_G'a_H = -\frac{500(0.45)(0.1075)}{1 - e^{500(0.45)(0.1075)/150}} = 139 \text{ Btu}/(\text{hr})(\text{cu ft})(°F)$$

Eq. (7.68): $$\frac{dt_G}{dZ} = -\frac{139(600 - 124.5)}{500(0.26)} = -510°F/ft$$

For use in Eq. (7.66):

$$C_A t_G - C_{AL} t_L + (C_{AL} - C_A)t_0 + \lambda_0 = 0.45(600) - 1.0(122.5) + (1 - 0.45)65 + 1,057.1 = 1,240$$

Eq. (7.66): $$t_i = 122.5 + \frac{500[0.26(-510) + 1,240(0.1075)]}{500(1.0)(0.1075) - 1,000} = 124.5°F \quad \text{(check)}$$

$$\frac{dY'}{dt_G} = \frac{dY'/dZ}{dt_G/dZ} = \frac{0.1075}{-510} = -0.000211$$

A suitably small increment in gas temperature is now chosen, and with the computed gradient assumed constant over a small range, the conditions at the end of the increment are computed. In this case, take $\Delta t_G = -60°F$.

$$\Delta Z = \frac{\Delta t_G}{dt_G/dZ} = \frac{-60}{-510} = 0.1178 \text{ ft}$$

$$t_G = t_G \text{ (at } Z = 0) + \Delta t_G = 600 - 60 = 540°F$$

$$Y' = Y' \text{ (at } Z = 0) + \frac{dY'}{dt_G} \Delta t_G = 0 + (-0.000211)(-60) = 0.01266$$

$$p_{AG} = \frac{Y'}{Y' + M_A/M_B} = \frac{0.01266}{0.01266 + 18/28} = 0.0193 \text{ atm}$$

$$C_S = 0.26 + 0.45(0.01266) = 0.266$$

L' is calculated by a water balance [Eq. (7.33)] over the increment:

$$L' - 990 = 500(0.01266 - 0)$$
$$L' = 996.3$$

t_L is calculated by an enthalpy balance [Eq. (7.35)]:

$$996.3(1.0)(t_L - 65) + 500(0.26)(600 - 65) = 990(1)(122.5 - 65)$$
$$+ 500[0.266(540 - 65) + 1,057.1(0.01266)]$$

$$t_L = 122.3°F$$

New gradients dY'/dZ and dt_G/dZ at this level in the tower and another interval are then computed in exactly the same manner. The process is repeated until the gas temperature falls to 80°F. The intervals of Δt_G chosen must be small as the gas approaches saturation, and in this case they were ultimately reduced to $-10°F$. The computed t_G-Y' results are shown in Fig. 7.16 (the plotted points are those calculated at each interval) along with the saturation humidity curve. At $t_G = 80°F$, the sum of the ΔZ's $= Z = 6.7$ ft. However, Y_2' calculated to be 0.0222 and $t_{L2} = 66.2°F$, whereas

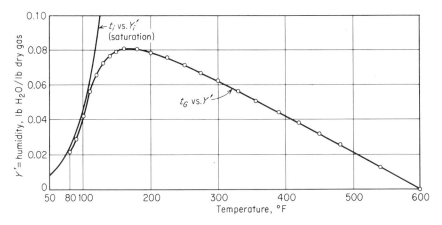

Fig. 7.16   *Gas temperatures and humidities for Illustration 7.14.*

the initially assumed Y'_2 was 0.02 (and $t_{L2} = 65°F$).   The result is therefore not exact, and the entire computation should be repeated with a new assumed Y'_2 until assumed and calculated values agree.

In this problem, the gas is initially humidified as it cools, but below 160°F it becomes dehumidified as it meets cold water.   The maximum bulk-liquid temperature is at the bottom, and the interface never rises above 125.4°F, despite the fact that the gas is initially very hot.

EQUIPMENT

Any of the gas-liquid contact devices described in Chap. ʹ6 are applicable to the operations described here, and conventional packed and tray towers are very effective in these services.   Air and water are low-cost materials, however, and when large volumes must be handled, as in many water-cooling operations, equipment of low initial cost and low operating cost is essential.   For this reason large-scale installations are more frequently of the type described below.

Water-cooling towers

The framework and internal packing is frequently redwood, a material which is very durable in continuous contact with water.   Impregnation of the wood with fungicides is common practice, and coating with neoprene for protection against fungus attack has also been done.   Siding for the towers is commonly redwood, asbestos cement, glass-reinforced polyester plastic, and the like.   Towers have been built entirely of plastic.   The internal packing ("fill") is usually a modified form of hurdle (see Chap. 6), horizontal slats arranged staggered or with alternate tiers at right angles.   A great many arrangements are used.[7,10]   Plastic packing may be molded in grid form.[4] The void space is very large, usually greater than 90 percent, in order that the gas pressure drop be as low as possible.   The air–water interfacial surface consequently includes not only that of the liquid films which wet the slats but also the surface of the droplets which fall as rain from each tier of slats to the next.

(a) Atmospheric

(b) Natural draft

(c) Forced draft

(d) Countercurrent induced draft

(e) Cross-flow induced draft

Fig. 7.17 *Cooling-tower arrangements.*

The common arrangements are shown schematically in Fig. 7.17.   Of the *natural-circulation* towers (Fig. 7.17*a* and *b*), the atmospheric towers depend on prevailing winds for air movement.   The natural-draft design ensures more positive air movement even in calm weather by depending upon the displacement of the warm air inside the tower by the cooler outside air.   Fairly tall chimneys are then required. Both these tower types must be relatively tall in order to operate at a small wet-bulb-temperature approach.   Natural-draft equipment is used commonly in the southwestern United States and in the Middle East, where the air humidity is usually low, and in parts of Europe where air temperatures are generally low.   In most of the United States, mechanical-draft equipment is commonly used.

Mechanical-draft towers may be of the forced-draft type (Fig. 7.17*c*), where the air is blown into the tower by a fan at the bottom.   These are particularly subject to recirculation of the hot, humid discharged air into the fan intake owing to the low discharge velocity, which materially reduces the tower effectiveness.   Induced draft, with the fan at the top, avoids this and also permits more uniform internal distribution of air.   The arrangements of Fig. 7.17*d* and *e* are most commonly used, and a more detailed drawing is shown in Fig. 7.18.   Liquid rates are ordinarily in the range 1 to 5

Fig. 7.18   *Induced-draft cooling tower.*   (*The Marley Co., Inc.*)

Fig. 7.19   *Schematic arrangement of a spray chamber.*

gal/(min)(sq ft)($L' = 500$ to 2,500), and superficial air velocities are of the order of 4 to 7 ft/sec ($G'_S = 1,200$ to 2,100), whereupon the air pressure drop is ordinarily less than 1 in. of water.   Entrainment, or "drift," eliminators at the top can maintain loss of water from this cause to less than 0.3 percent of the circulated water.

Spray chambers

These are essentially horizontal spray towers and may be arranged as in Fig. 7.19. They are frequently used for adiabatic humidification-cooling operations with recirculating liquid.   With large liquid drops, gas rates up to roughly 600 to 900 lb/(hr)(sq ft) are possible, but in any case entrainment eliminators are necessary.

Heat-transfer surfaces at the inlet and outlet provide for preheating and after-heating of the air, so that processes of the type shown in Fig. 7.20 may be carried out.

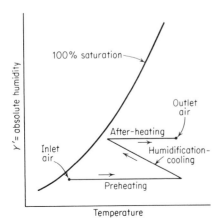

Fig. 7.20   *A simple conditioning process.*

If large humidity changes by this method are required, preheating of the air to unusually high temperatures is necessary, however. As an alternative, the spray water may be heated above the adiabatic-saturation temperature to which it will tend to come by direct injection of steam or by heating coils. Dehumidification may be practiced by cooling the water prior to spraying or by using refrigerating coils directly in the spray chamber. Operations of this sort cannot be followed with assurance on the enthalpy-temperature diagrams described earlier owing to the departure from strictly countercurrent-flow conditions which prevail. When an adequate spray density is maintained, it may be assumed that three banks of sprays in series will bring the gas to substantial equilibrium with the incoming spray liquid.

For comfort air conditioning, many compact devices are provided with a variety of these facilities, and automatic controls are available.

Spray ponds

These are sometimes used for water cooling where close approach to the air wet-bulb temperature is not required. Spray ponds are essentially fountains, where the water is sprayed upward into the air and allowed to fall back into a collection basin. They are subject to high windage losses of water.

Mass-transfer rates

The correlations of mass-transfer coefficients for the standard packings discussed in Chap. 6 are suitable for the operations discussed here (see particularly Illustration 6.5). Data for some of the special tower fillings usually used for water-cooling towers are available in texts specializing in this type of equipment,[10,13] and in some manufacturers' bulletins. Sieve and bubble-tray towers are very effective but are not commonly used in humidification, dehumidification, or gas-cooling operations for reasons of cost and relatively high gas pressure drop.

Dehumidification by other methods

Adsorption, such as those methods using activated silica gel or alumina as adsorbents (see Chap. 11), and washing gases with water solutions containing dissolved substances which appreciably lower the partial pressure of the water (see Chap. 8) are other commonly used dehumidifying processes, particularly when very dry gases are required.

NOTATION FOR CHAPTER 7

a = interfacial surface per unit volume of packing, sq ft/cu ft
a_H = interfacial surface for heat transfer, sq ft/cu ft
a_M = interfacial surface for mass transfer, sq ft/cu ft
c = concentration, lb moles/cu ft
C = heat capacity (of a gas or vapor unless otherwise indicated) at constant pressure, Btu/(lb)(°F)
C_L = heat capacity of a liquid at constant pressure, Btu/(lb)(°F)
C_S = humid heat, Btu (of a vapor-gas mixture)/(lb dry gas)(°F)
d = differential operator

D = diffusivity, sq ft/hr

e = 2.7183

E_D = eddy diffusivity of mass, sq ft/hr

E_H = eddy diffusivity of heat, sq ft/hr

$\mathbf{E}_{MG}$ = Murphree gas-phase stage efficiency, fractional

F = mass-transfer coefficient, lb moles/(hr)(sq ft)

G'_S = superficial mass velocity of gas, lb dry gas/(hr)(sq ft cross section)

h = convection heat-transfer coefficient, Btu/(hr)(sq ft)(°F)

h' = convection heat-transfer coefficient corrected for simultaneous mass transfer, Btu/(hr)(sq ft)(°F)

h_R = radiation heat-transfer coefficient in convection form, Btu/(hr)(sq ft)(°F)

H = enthalpy, Btu/lb

H' = enthalpy of a vapor-gas mixture, Btu/lb dry gas

H'^* = enthalpy of a saturated vapor-gas mixture in equilibrium with the bulk liquid, Btu/lb dry gas

H'_{as} = enthalpy of a saturated vapor-gas mixture at t_{as}, Btu/lb dry gas

H_{tG} = height of a gas-enthalpy transfer unit, ft

H_{tOG} = overall height of a gas-enthalpy transfer unit, ft

k = thermal conductivity, (Btu)(ft)/(hr)(sq ft)(°F)

k_c = mass-transfer coefficient, lb moles A transferred/(hr)(sq ft)(Δc)

k_G = mass-transfer coefficient, lb moles A transferred/(hr)(sq ft)(atm)

k_Y = mass-transfer coefficient, lb A transferred/(hr)(sq ft)($\Delta Y'$)

K_Y = overall mass-transfer coefficient, lb A transferred/(hr)(sq ft)($\Delta Y'$)

ln = natural logarithm

log = common logarithm

L' = superficial mass velocity of liquid, lb/(hr)(sq ft cross section)

Le = Lewis number = Sc/Pr

M = molecular weight, lb/lb mole

N = mass-transfer flux, lb moles/(hr)(sq ft)

N_{tG} = number of gas-enthalpy transfer units

N_{tOG} = number of overall gas-enthalpy transfer units

p = partial pressure, atm

p_{BM} = average partial pressure of component B, atm

P = vapor pressure of a pure substance, atm

P_t = total pressure, atm

Pr = Prandtl number = $C\mu/k$

Pv = product of pressure and specific volume, Btu/lb

q_s = heat-transfer flux for sensible heat, Btu/(hr)(sq ft)

Q = gain in enthalpy, Btu/lb

r = $h_G a_H / C_S k_Y a_M$

R = uhiversal gas constant, 0.729 (cu ft)(atm)/(lb mole)(°R)

S = interfacial surface, sq ft

Sc = Schmidt number = $\mu/\rho D$

t = temperature, °F

t_{as} = adiabatic-saturation temperature, °F

t_{DP} = dew-point temperature, °F

t_0 = reference temperature, °F

T = absolute temperature, °R

U = internal energy, Btu/lb

v = molal volume, cu ft/lb mole

v_H = humid volume, cu ft of vapor-gas mixture/lb dry gas

y = concentration in gas, mole fraction

Y = molal absolute humidity, lb moles vapor/lb mole dry gas

Y' = absolute humidity, lb vapor/lb dry gas

Y'_{as} = saturated absolute humidity at adiabatic-saturation temperature, lb vapor/lb dry gas

z = distance, ft

Z = length or height of active part of equipment, ft

α = thermal diffusivity, sq ft/hr

Δ = difference

λ = latent heat of vaporization, Btu/lb

λ' = molal latent heat of vaporization, (cu ft)(atm)/lb mole

λ_{as} = latent heat of vaporization at t_{as}, Btu/lb

λ_0 = latent heat of vaporization at t_0, Btu/lb

μ = viscosity, lb mass/(ft)(hr)

ρ = density, lb mass/cu ft

Subscripts:

1, 2 = positions 1, 2

as = adiabatic saturation

av   = average

A = substance A, the vapor

B = substance B, the gas

G = pertaining to the gas

i = interface

L = pertaining to the liquid

min = minimum

r = reference substance

s = saturated

w = at the wet-bulb temperature

0   = at the reference temperature

REFERENCES

1. Baker, D. R., and H. A. Skyrock: *J. Heat Transfer*, **83,** 339 (1961).
2. Bedingfield, C. H., and T. B. Drew: *Ind. Eng. Chem.*, **42,** 1164 (1950).
3. Dropkin, D.: *Cornell Univ. Eng. Expt. Sta. Bull.*, **23** (1936); **26** (1939).
4. Fuller, A. L., A. L. Kohl, and E. Butcher: *Chem. Eng. Progr.*, **53,** 501 (1957).
5. Grosvenor, W. M.: *Trans. AIChE*, **1,** 184 (1908).
6. Hensel, S. L., and R. E. Treybal: *Chem. Eng. Progr.*, **48,** 362 (1952).
7. Kelly, N. W., and L. K. Swenson: *Chem. Eng. Progr.*, **52,** 263 (1956).
8. Lynch, E. J., and C. R. Wilke: *AIChE J.*, **1,** 9 (1955).
9. McAdams, W. H.: "Heat Transmission," 3d ed., McGraw-Hill Book Company, New York, 1954.
10. McKelvey, K. K., and M. Brooke: "The Industrial Cooling Tower," D. Van Nostrand Company, Inc., Princeton, N.J., 1959.
11. Merkel, F.: *Ver. Deut. Forschungsarb.*, 275 (1925).
12. Mickley, H. S.: *Chem. Eng. Progr.*, **45,** 739 (1949).
13. Norman, W. S.: "Absorption, Distillation, and Cooling Towers," Longmans, Green & Co., Ltd., London, 1961.
14. Olander, D. R.: *AIChE J.*, **6,** 346 (1960); *Ind. Eng. Chem.*, **53,** 121 (1961).
15. Othmer, D. F., et al.: *Ind. Eng. Chem.*, **32,** 841 (1940); **34,** 952 (1942).
16. Parker, R. O.: Doctor of Engineering Science thesis, New York University, 1959; "The Psychrometric Ratio for the System Air–Water Vapor," *First Inter-Am. Congr. Chem. Eng.*, San Juan, Puerto Rico, October, 1961.
17. Parker, R. O., and R. E. Treybal: *Chem. Eng. Prog. Symp. Ser.*, **57**(32), 138 (1960).

PROBLEMS

7.1. Prepare a logarithmic reference-substance plot of the vapor pressure of acetone over a temperature range of 10°C to its critical temperature, 235°C, with water as reference substance. With the help of the plot, determine (*a*) the vapor pressure of acetone at 65°C, (*b*) the temperature at which acetone has a vapor pressure of 500 mm Hg, and (*c*) the latent heat of vaporization of acetone at 40°C (accepted value = 230.5 Btu/lb).

7.2. *a.* Compute the heat required to convert 5 lb acetone from a condition of saturated liquid at 10°C to superheated vapor at 500 mm Hg abs, and 100°C. The heat capacity of acetone as a liquid is 0.52, as a vapor 0.35 Btu/(lb)(°F).

b. Calculate the enthalpy of the acetone in the superheated condition of part *a* relative to liquid acetone at the same temperature, Btu/lb.

7.3. A mixture of nitrogen and acetone vapor at 800 mm Hg total pressure, 80°F, has a percentage saturation of 80%. Calculate (*a*) the absolute molal humidity, (*b*) the absolute humidity, lb acetone/lb nitrogen, (*c*) the partial pressure of acetone, (*d*) the relative humidity, (*e*) the volume percent acetone, and (*f*) the dew point.

7.4. In a plant for the recovery of acetone which has been used as a solvent, the acetone is evaporated into a stream of nitrogen gas. A mixture of acetone vapor and nitrogen is flowing through a duct, 12- by 12-in. cross section. The pressure and temperature at one point in the duct are 800 mm Hg, 100°F, and at this point the average velocity is 10 ft/sec. A wet-bulb thermometer (wick wet with acetone) indicates a wet-bulb temperature at this point of 80°F. Calculate lb acetone/hr carried by the duct. **Ans.**: 1,615.

7.5. An air–water vapor mixture, 1 atm, 350°F, flows in a duct (wall temperature = 350°F) at 10 ft/sec average velocity. A wet-bulb temperature, measured with an ordinary, unshielded thermometer covered with a wetted wick (⅜-in. outside diameter) and inserted in the duct at right angles to the duct axis, is 125°F. Under these conditions, the adiabatic-saturation curves of the psychrometric chart do not approximate wet-bulb lines, radiation to the wet bulb and the effect of mass transfer on heat transfer are not negligible, nor should k-type (rather than F) mass-transfer coefficients be used.

a. Make the best estimate you can of the humidity of the air, taking these matters into consideration.

b. Compute the humidity using the ordinary wet-bulb equation (7.26) with the usual h_G/k_Y, and compare.

7.6. Derive Eq. (7.28), the psychrometric ratio, from item 2, Table 3.2, using the heat- mass-transfer analogy.

7.7. Prepare a psychrometric chart of the mixture acetone-nitrogen at a pressure of 800 mm Hg over the ranges 0 to 140°F, $Y' = 0$ to 3 lb vapor/lb dry gas. Include the following curves, all plotted against temperature: (*a*) 100, 75, 50, and 25% humidity; (*b*) dry and saturated humid volumes; (*c*) enthalpy of dry and saturated mixtures expressed as Btu/lb dry gas, referred to liquid acetone and nitrogen gas at 0°F; (*d*) wet-bulb curve for $t_w = 80°F$; (*e*) adiabatic-saturation curves for $t_{as} = 80$ and 100°F.

7.8. A drier requires 3,000 cu ft/min of air at 150°F, 20% humidity. This is to be prepared from air at 80°F dry-bulb, 65° wet-bulb temperature by direct injection of steam into the air stream followed by passage of the air over steam-heated finned tubes. The available steam is saturated at 5 psig. Compute the lb of steam/hr required (*a*) for direct injection and (*b*) for the heat exchange.

7.9. Air in an amount 1,000 cu ft/min at 150°F, 20% humidity (condition 1), is passed over a refrigerated coil and thereby brought to 60°F, 90% humidity (condition 2), with the condensed moisture withdrawn at an average temperature of 55°F. The air is then reheated by means of a steam coil to 150°F (condition 3).

a. Tabulate the absolute humidity, wet-bulb temperature, dew point, enthalpy, and volume in cu ft/min for the moist air at each of the three conditions.

b. Compute the moisture removed, lb/min.

c. Compute the heat removed by the refrigerated coil, expressed as tons of refrigeration (1 ton of refrigeration = 200 Btu/min removed). **Ans.:** 18.

7.10. A recently installed induced-draft cooling tower was guaranteed by the manufacturer to cool 2,000 gal/min of water at 110°F to 85°F when the available air has a wet-bulb temperature of 75°F. A test on the tower, when operated at full fan capacity, provided the following data:

Inlet water, 2,000 gal/min, 115.0°F
Outlet water, 78.0°F
Inlet air 75°F dry-bulb, 60°F wet-bulb temperature
Outlet air, 99.8°F

a. What is the fan capacity, cu ft/min?

b. Can the tower be expected to meet the guarantee conditions?

7.11. *a.* Calculate the height of a 1-in.-ID wetted-wall tower required to bring dry air at 140°F to 90% saturation with water by adiabatic gas humidification-cooling with recirculated liquid. The air rate is to be 3,000 lb/(hr)(sq ft), and the thickness of the liquid film may be neglected. Use gas properties at the average conditions between bulk gas and interface.

b. Calculate the depth of 1-in. ceramic Raschig rings in a packed tower for the same humidification. L' will be set at 1,600 and G'_s at 500 lb/(hr)(sq ft). **Ans.:** 1.7 ft.

c. Compare the pressure drop, lb/sq ft, for the gas in both cases.

d. Compare the two devices by calculating $N_{tG}/\Delta P$ for each. What other factors should be considered in comparing the two?

7.12. It is desired to dehumidify 2,500 cu ft air/min, available at 100°F dry-bulb, 85°F wet-bulb temperature, to a wet-bulb temperature of 60°F in a countercurrent tower using water chilled to 50°F. The packing will be 2-in. ceramic Raschig rings. To keep entrainment at a minimum, G'_s will be 900 lb air/(hr)(sq ft), and a liquid rate of 1.5 times the minimum will be used. (*a*) Specify the cross section and height of the packed portion of the tower. (*b*) What will be the temperature of the outlet water? **Ans.:** (*a*) 3.9 ft.

7.13. Acetone is to be removed from a product in a continuous process by evaporation into a stream of inert (nonflammable) gas, essentially nitrogen. The resulting vapor-gas mixture, at 80°F, 1 atm total pressure, will have a partial pressure of acetone equal to 150 mm Hg. A scheme for recovering the acetone from the nitrogen involves washing the gas countercurrently with cold liquid acetone (entering at 10°F) in a packed tower. The vapor-gas mixture will enter the tower at a rate $G'_1 = 500$ lb total/(hr)(sq ft) and will leave with an acetone partial pressure of 40 mm Hg. This mixture will be returned to the evaporator. The cold acetone will enter at a rate $L'_2 = 1,500$ lb/(hr)(sq ft). Compute the depth of packing required. **Ans.:** 3 ft.

Data. For the packing, $k_G a_V p_{BM} = 0.038 G'^{0.6} L'^{0.4}$, where G' and L' are the mass velocities of *total* gas and liquid, respectively, and the coefficient will not be constant. The heat-transfer coefficient $h_G a$ will be estimated from this through the heat- mass-transfer analogy,

$$\text{St}_{\text{mass transfer}} \, \text{Sc}^{0.5} = \text{St}_{\text{heat transfer}} \, \text{Pr}^{0.5}$$

where St is the Stanton number. The Lewis number Sc/Pr = Le for nitrogen-acetone is 0.63. It will be assumed for lack of better information that $a_M = a_H = a$. The circumstances are such that the liquid-phase heat-transfer coefficient $h_L a$ is so large that it may be assumed infinite for calculation purposes ($t_i = t_L$). Use $t_0 = 10°$F, and $\lambda_0 = 244.5$ Btu/lb. The heat capacities may be taken as $C_{AL} = 0.514$, $C_A = 0.35$, $C_B = 0.26$ Btu/(lb)(°F).

CHAPTER EIGHT
GAS ABSORPTION

Gas absorption is an operation in which a gas mixture is contacted with a liquid for the purposes of preferentially dissolving one or more components of the gas and to provide a solution of these in the liquid. For example, the gas from by-product coke ovens is washed with water to remove ammonia and again with an oil to remove benzene and toluene vapors. Objectionable hydrogen sulfide is removed from such a gas or from naturally occurring hydrocarbon gases by washing with various alkaline solutions in which it is absorbed. Valuable solvent vapors carried by a gas stream may be recovered for reuse by washing the gas with an appropriate solvent for the vapors. Such operations require mass transfer of a substance from the gas stream to the liquid. When mass transfer occurs in the opposite direction, i.e., from the liquid to the gas, the operation is called desorption, or stripping. For example, the benzene and toluene are removed from the absorption oil mentioned above by contacting the liquid solution with steam, whereupon the vapors enter the gas stream and are carried away, and the absorption oil may be used again. The principles of both absorption and desorption are basically the same, and we may study both operations at the same time.

Ordinarily, these operations are used only for solute recovery or solute removal. Separation of solutes from each other to any important extent requires the fractionation techniques of distillation.

EQUILIBRIUM SOLUBILITY OF GASES IN LIQUIDS

The rate at which a gaseous constituent of a mixture will dissolve in an absorbent liquid depends upon the departure from equilibrium which is maintained, and therefore it is necessary to consider the equilibrium characteristics of gas-liquid systems. A very brief discussion of such matters was presented in Chap. 5, but some elaboration will be required here.

Two-component systems

If a quantity of a single gas and a relatively nonvolatile liquid are brought to equilibrium in the manner described in Chap. 5, the resulting concentration of dissolved gas in the liquid is said to be the gas solubility at the prevailing temperature and pressure. At fixed temperature, the solubility concentration will increase with pressure in the manner, for example, of curve A, Fig. 8.1, which shows the solubility of ammonia in water at 30°C.

Different gases and liquids yield separate solubility curves, which must ordinarily be determined experimentally for each system. If the equilibrium pressure of a gas at a given liquid concentration is high, as in the case of curve B (Fig. 8.1), the gas is

Fig. 8.1 *Solubilities of gases in water.*

said to be relatively insoluble in the liquid, while if it is low, as for curve C, the solubility is said to be high.   But these are relative matters only, for it is possible to produce any ultimate gas concentration in the liquid if sufficient pressure is applied, so long as the liquefied form of the gas is completely soluble in the liquid.

The solubility of any gas is influenced by the temperature, in a manner which is described by van't Hoff's law of mobile equilibrium: If the temperature of a system at equilibrium is raised, that change will occur which will absorb heat.   Usually, but not always, the solution of a gas results in an evolution of heat, and it follows that in most cases the solubility of a gas decreases with increasing temperature.   As an example, curve A (Fig. 8.1) for ammonia in water at 30°C lies above the corresponding curve for 10°C.   At the boiling point of the solvent, provided its vapor pressure is less than that of the gas or vapor solute, the gas solubility will be zero.

Multicomponent systems

If a mixture of gases is brought into contact with a liquid, under certain conditions the equilibrium solubilities of each gas will be independent of the others, provided, however, that the equilibrium is described in terms of the *partial pressures* in the gas mixture.   If all but one of the components of the gas are substantially insoluble, their concentrations in the liquid will be so small that they cannot influence the solubility of the relatively soluble component, and the generalization applies.   For example, curve A (Fig. 8.1) will also describe the solubility of ammonia in water when the ammonia is diluted with air, since air is so insoluble in water, provided that the ordinate of the plot be considered as the partial pressure of ammonia in the gas mixture.   This is most fortunate, since the amount of experimental work in gathering useful solubility data is thereby considerably reduced.   If several components of the mixture are appreciably soluble, the generalization will be applicable only provided that the solute gases are indifferent to the nature of the liquid, which will be the case only for ideal solutions.   For example, a mixture of propane and butane gases will dissolve in a nonvolatile paraffin oil independently since the solutions that result are substantially ideal.   On the other hand, the solubility of ammonia in water can be expected to be influenced by the presence of methylamine, since the resulting solutions of these gases are not ideal.   The solubility of a gas will also be influenced by the presence of a nonvolatile solute in the liquid, such as a salt in water solution, when such solutions are nonideal.

Ideal liquid solutions

When the liquid phase may be considered ideal, we may compute the equilibrium partial pressure of a gas from the solution without resort to experimental determination.

There are four significant characteristics of ideal solutions, all interrelated:

1. The average intermolecular forces of attraction and repulsion in the solution are unchanged on mixing the constituents.
2. The volume of the solution varies linearly with composition.

3. There is neither absorption nor evolution of heat in mixing of the constituents. In the case of gases dissolving in liquids, however, this criterion should not include the heat of condensation of the gas to the liquid state.

4. The total vapor pressure of the solution varies linearly with composition expressed as mole fractions.

In reality there are no ideal solutions, and actual mixtures only approach ideality as a limit.   Ideality would require that the molecules of the constituents be similar in size, structure, and chemical nature, and the nearest approach to such a condition is perhaps exemplified by solutions of optical isomers of organic compounds.   Practically, however, many solutions are so nearly ideal that for engineering purposes they may be so considered.   Adjacent or nearly adjacent members of a homologous series of organic compounds particularly fall in this category.   So, for example, solutions of benzene in toluene, of ethyl and propyl alcohols, or the paraffin hydrocarbon gases in paraffin oils may ordinarily be considered as ideal solutions.

When the gas mixture in equilibrium with an ideal liquid solution also follows the ideal-gas law, the partial pressure $p*$ of a solute gas A equals the product of its vapor pressure P at the same temperature and its mole fraction in the solution x. This is *Raoult's law*.

$$p* = Px \tag{8.1}$$

The nature of the solvent liquid does not enter into consideration except insofar as it establishes the ideality of the solution, and it follows that the solubility of a particular gas in ideal solution in any solvent is always the same.

Illustration 8.1. A gas mixture, after long contact with a hydrocarbon oil and establishment of equilibrium, has the following composition at 2 atm total pressure, 75°F: methane 60%, ethane 20%, propane 8%, n-butane 6%, n-pentane 6%. Calculate the composition of the equilibrium solution.

Solution. The equilibrium partial pressure $p*$ of each constituent in the gas is its volume fraction multiplied by the total pressure. These and the vapor pressures P of the constituents at 75°F are tabulated below. The prevailing temperature is above the critical value for methane, and at this low total pressure its solubility may be considered negligible. For each constituent its mole fraction in the liquid is calculated by Eq. (8.1), $x = p*/P$, and the last column of the table lists these as the answers to the problem. The remaining liquid, $1 - 0.264 = 0.736$ mole fraction, is the solvent oil.

Component	$p*$, equilibrium partial pressure, atm	P, vapor pressure at 75°F, atm	Mole fraction in the liquid, $x = \dfrac{p*}{P}$
Methane	$1.20 = 0.6(2.0)$		
Ethane	0.40	41.5	0.0097
Propane	0.16	8.84	0.018
n-Butane	0.12	2.33	0.052
n-Pentane	0.12	0.65	0.184
Total			0.264

For total pressures in excess of those for which the ideal-gas law applies, Raoult's law may frequently be used with fugacities substituted for the pressure terms.[13]

Nonideal liquid solutions

For liquid solutions which are not ideal, Eq. (8.1) will give highly incorrect results. Line D (Fig. 8.1), for example, is the calculated partial pressure of ammonia in equilibrium with water solutions at 10°C, assuming Raoult's law to be applicable, and it clearly does not represent the data. On the other hand, the straight line E is seen to represent the 10°C ammonia–water data very well up to mole fractions of 0.06 in the liquid. The equation of such a line is

$$y^* = \frac{p^*}{P_t} = mx \qquad (8.2)$$

where m is a constant. This is *Henry's law*,† and it is seen to be applicable with different values of m for each of the gases in the figure over at least a modest liquid-concentration range. Failure to follow Henry's law over wide concentration ranges may be the result of chemical interaction with the liquid or electrolytic dissociation, as is the case with ammonia–water, or nonideality in the gas phase. The less soluble gases, such as nitrogen or oxygen in water, can be expected to follow the law up to equilibrium partial pressures of 1 atm, and gases of the vapor type (which are below their critical temperature) will generally follow the law up to pressures of approximately 50 percent of the saturation value at the prevailing temperature provided no chemical action occurs in the liquid. In any case m must be established experimentally.

The advantages of straight-line plotting for interpolation and extrapolating experimental data are, of course, very great, and an empirical method of wide utility is an extension of the "reference-substance" vapor-pressure plot described in Chap. 7.[11] As an example of this, Fig. 8.2 shows the data for ammonia–water solutions, covering a wide range of concentrations and temperatures. The coordinates are logarithmic. The abscissa is marked with the vapor pressure of a convenient reference substance, in this case water, and the ordinate is the equilibrium partial pressure of the solute gas. Points are plotted where the corresponding temperatures for the vapor pressure of the reference substance and the partial pressure of solute are identical. For example, at 90°F the vapor pressure of water is 36 mm Hg, and the partial pressure of ammonia for a 10 mole percent solution is 130 mm Hg, and these pressures locate point A on the figure. The lines for constant liquid composition are straight with few exceptions. A temperature scale may later be substituted for the reference vapor-pressure scale, using the steam tables in the case of water as reference substance.

---

† For conditions under which Henry's law is inapplicable, Eq. (8.2) may be used in empirical fashion to describe experimental data, but the value of m (or $K = y^*/x$, which is sometimes used) will then be expected to vary with temperature, pressure, and concentration and must be listed as a function of these variables.

Fig. 8.2 *Reference-substance plot for gas solubility. The system ammonia–water, water as reference.*

Choice of solvent for absorption

If the principal purpose of the absorption operation is to produce a specific solution, as in the manufacture of hydrochloric acid, for example, the solvent is specified by the nature of the product. If the principal purpose is to remove some constituent from the gas, some choice is frequently possible. Water is, of course, the cheapest and most plentiful solvent, but the following properties are important considerations:

1. *Gas solubility.* The gas solubility should be high, thus increasing the rate of absorption and decreasing the quantity of solvent required. Generally solvents of a chemical nature similar to that of the solute to be absorbed will provide good solubility. Thus hydrocarbon oils, and not water, are used to remove benzene from coke-oven gas. For cases where the solutions formed are ideal, the solubility of the gas is the same in terms of mole fractions for all solvents. But it is greater in terms of weight fractions for solvents of low molecular weight, and smaller weights of such solvents, as measured in pounds, need to be used. Chemical reaction of solvent with the solute will frequently result in very high gas solubility, but if the solvent is to be recovered for reuse, the reaction must be reversible. For example, hydrogen sulfide may be removed from gas mixtures using ethanolamine solutions since the sulfide is readily absorbed at low temperatures and easily stripped at high temperatures.

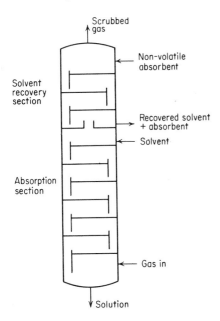

Scrubbed gas

Non-volatile absorbent

Solvent recovery section

Recovered solvent + absorbent

Solvent

Absorption section

Gas in

Solution

Fig. 8.3 *Tray absorber with volatile-solvent recovery section.*

Caustic soda absorbs hydrogen sulfide excellently but will not release it in a stripping operation.

2. *Volatility.* The solvent should have a low vapor pressure since the gas leaving an absorption operation is ordinarily saturated with the solvent and much may thereby be lost. If necessary, a second, less volatile liquid may be used to recover the evaporated portion of the first, as in Fig. 8.3. This is sometimes done, for example, in the case of hydrocarbon absorbers, where a relatively volatile solvent oil is used in the principal portion of the absorber because of the superior solubility characteristics and the volatilized solvent is recovered from the gas by a nonvolatile oil. Similarly, hydrogen sulfide may be absorbed by a water solution of sodium phenolate, but the desulfurized gas is further washed with water to recover the evaporated phenol.

3. *Corrosiveness.* The materials of construction required for the equipment should not be unusual or expensive.

4. *Cost.* The solvent should be inexpensive, so that losses are not costly, and should be readily available.

5. *Viscosity.* Low viscosity is preferred for reasons of rapid absorption rates, improved flooding characteristics in absorption towers, low pressure drops on pumping, and good heat-transfer characteristics.

6. *Miscellaneous.* The solvent if possible should be nontoxic, nonflammable, and chemically stable and should have a low freezing point.

MATERIAL BALANCES

The basic expressions for material balances and their graphical interpretation were presented for any mass-transfer operation in Chap. 5. Here they are adapted to the problems of gas absorption and stripping.

Countercurrent flow

Figure 8.4 shows a countercurrent tower which may be either a packed or spray tower, filled with bubble-cap trays, or of any internal construction to bring about liquid-gas contact.   The gas stream at any point in the tower consists of G total moles/(hr)(sq ft tower cross section), made up of diffusing solute A of mole fraction y, partial pressure p, or mole ratio Y, and nondiffusing, essentially insoluble gas G_S moles/(hr)(sq ft). The relationship among these are

$$Y = \frac{y}{1-y} = \frac{p}{P_t - p} \tag{8.3}$$

$$G_S = G(1-y) = \frac{G}{1+Y} \tag{8.4}$$

Similarly the liquid stream consists of L total moles/(hr)(sq ft), containing x mole fraction soluble gas, or mole ratio X, and essentially nonvolatile solvent L_S moles/(hr)(sq ft).

$$X = \frac{x}{1-x} \tag{8.5}$$

$$L_S = L(1-x) = \frac{L}{1+X} \tag{8.6}$$

Since the solvent gas and solvent liquid are essentially unchanged in quantity as they

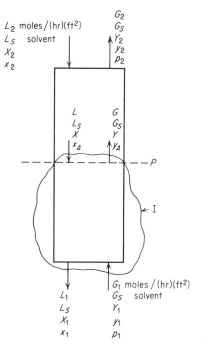

L_2 moles/(hr)(ft²)
L_S solvent
X_2
x_2

G_2
G_S
Y_2
y_2
p_2

L
L_S
X
x_A

G
G_S
Y
y_A

$-p$

$\leftarrow I$

L_1
L_S
X_1
x_1

G_1 moles /(hr)(ft²)
G_S solvent
Y_1
y_1
p_1

Fig. 8.4   *Flow quantities for an absorber or stripper.*

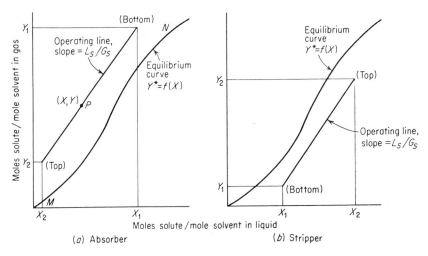

Fig. 8.5 *Operating lines for absorber and stripper.*

pass through the tower, it is convenient to express the material balance in terms of these. A solute balance about the lower part of the tower (envelope I) is†

$$G_S(Y_1 - Y) = L_S(X_1 - X) \qquad (8.7)$$

This is the equation of a straight line (the operating line) on X, Y coordinates, of slope L_S/G_S, which passes through (X_1, Y_1). Substitution of X_2 and Y_2 for X and Y shows the line to pass through (X_2, Y_2), as on Fig. 8.5a for an absorber. This line indicates the relation between the liquid and gas concentration at any level in the tower, as at point P.

The equilibrium-solubility data for the solute gas in the solvent liquid may also be plotted in terms of these concentration units on the same diagram, as curve MN, for example. Each point on this curve represents the gas concentration in equilibrium with the corresponding liquid at its local concentration and temperature. For an absorber (mass transfer from gas to liquid) the operating line always lies above the equilibrium-solubility curve, while for a stripper (mass transfer from liquid to gas) the line is always below, as in Fig. 8.5b.

The operating line is straight only when plotted in terms of the mole-ratio units. In terms of mole fractions or partial pressures the line is curved, as in Fig. 8.6 for an

† Equations (8.7) and (8.8) and the corresponding Figs. 8.4 to 8.8 are written as for packed towers, with 1 indicating the streams at the bottom and 2 those at the top. For tray towers, where tray numbers are used as subscripts, as in Fig. 8.12, the same equations apply, but changes in subscripts must be made. Thus Eq. (8.7) becomes, when applied to an entire tray tower,

$$G_S(Y_{N_p+1} - Y_1) = L_S(X_{N_p} - X_0)$$

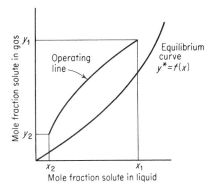

Fig. 8.6   *Operating line in mole fractions.*

absorber.   The equation of the line is then

$$G_S\!\left(\frac{y_1}{1-y_1}-\frac{y}{1-y}\right)=G_S\!\left(\frac{p_1}{P_t-p_1}-\frac{p}{P_t-p}\right)$$

$$=L_S\!\left(\frac{x_1}{1-x_1}-\frac{x}{1-x}\right) \qquad (8.8)$$

The total pressure P_t at any point may ordinarily be considered constant throughout the tower for this purpose.

Minimum liquid-gas ratio for absorbers

In the design of absorbers, the quantity of gas to be treated G or G_S, the terminal concentrations Y_1 and Y_2, and the composition of the entering liquid X_2 are ordinarily fixed by process requirements, but the quantity of liquid to be used is subject to choice. Refer to Fig. 8.7a.   The operating line must pass through point D and must end at the

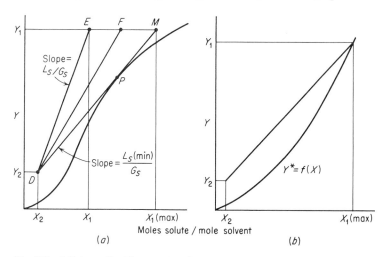

Fig. 8.7   *Minimum liquid-gas ratio, absorption.*

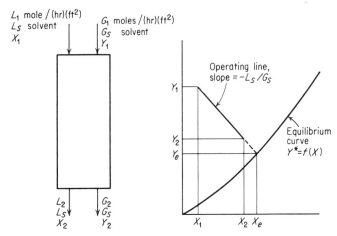

Fig. 8.8 *Cocurrent absorber.*

ordinate Y_1. If such a quantity of liquid is used to give operating line DE, the exit liquid will have the composition X_1. If less liquid is used, the exit-liquid composition will clearly be greater, as at point F, but since the driving forces for diffusion are less, the absorption is more difficult. The time of contact between gas and liquid must then be greater, and the absorber must be correspondingly taller. The minimum liquid which may be used corresponds to the operating line DM, which has the greatest slope for any line touching the equilibrium curve and is tangent to the curve at P. At P the diffusional driving force is zero, the required time of contact for the concentration change desired is infinite, and an infinitely tall tower results. This then represents the limiting liquid-gas ratio.

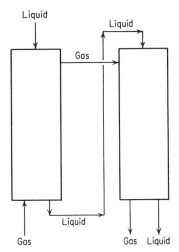

Fig. 8.9 *Countercurrent-cocurrent arrangement for very tall towers.*

The equilibrium curve is frequently concave upward, as in Fig. 8.7*b*, and the minimum liquid-gas ratio then corresponds to an exit-liquid concentration in equilibrium with the entering gas.

These principles also apply to strippers, where an operating line which anywhere touches the equilibrium curve represents a maximum ratio of liquid to gas and a maximum exit-gas concentration.

Cocurrent flow

When gas and liquid flow cocurrently, as in Fig. 8.8, the operating line has a negative slope $-L_S/G_S$. There is no limit on this ratio, but an infinitely tall tower would produce an exit liquid and gas in equilibrium, as at (X_e, Y_e). Cocurrent flow is used in the case where an exceptionally tall tower is built in two sections, as in Fig. 8.9, with the second section operated in cocurrent flow to save on the large-diameter gas pipe connecting the two. It may also be used if the gas to be dissolved in the liquid is a pure substance, where there is no advantage to countercurrent operation.

Illustration 8.2. A coal gas is to be freed of its light oil by scrubbing with wash oil as an absorbent and the light oil recovered by stripping the resulting solution with steam. The circumstances are:

a. Absorber. Gas in, 30,000 cu ft/hr at 800 mm Hg, 80°F, containing 2.0% by volume of light oil. The light oil will be assumed to be entirely benzene, and a 95% removal is required. The wash oil enters the absorber at 80°F, containing 0.005 mole fraction benzene, and has an average molecular weight of 260. An oil circulation rate of 1.5 times the minimum is to be used. Wash oil–benzene solutions are ideal. The temperature will be constant at 80°F.

b. Stripper. The solution from the absorber is heated to 250°F and enters the stripper at 1 atm pressure. Stripping steam is at atmospheric pressure, superheated to 250°F. The debenzolized oil, 0.005 mole fraction benzene, is cooled to 80°F and returned to the absorber. A steam rate of 1.5 times the minimum is to be used. The temperature will be constant at 250°F.

Compute the oil-circulation rate and the steam rate required.

Solution. a. Absorber. Basis: 1 hr. Define L, L_S, G, G_S in terms of moles/hr.

$$G_1 = 30,000 \frac{492}{460 + 80} \frac{800}{760} \frac{1}{359} = 80.8 \text{ moles gas in/hr}$$

$$y_1 = 0.02, \ Y_1 = \frac{0.02}{1 - 0.02} = 0.0204 \text{ mole benzene/mole dry gas}$$

$$G_S = 80.8(1 - 0.02) = 79.1 \text{ moles dry gas/hr}$$

For 95% removal of benzene,

$$Y_2 = 0.05(0.0204) = 0.00102 \text{ mole benzene/mole dry gas}$$

$$x_2 = 0.005, \ X_2 = \frac{0.005}{1 - 0.005} = 0.00502 \text{ mole benzene/mole oil}$$

At 80°F, the vapor pressure of benzene,

$$P = 100 \text{ mm Hg} = {}^{100}\!/_{760} = 0.1315 \text{ atm}$$

Eq. (8.1) for ideal solutions: $p^* = 0.1315x$

$$y^* = \frac{p^*}{P_t} \qquad P_t = \tfrac{800}{760} = 1.053 \text{ atm} \qquad Y^* = \frac{y^*}{1 - y^*} \qquad X = \frac{x}{1 - x}$$

Substitution in Eq. (8.1) yields

$$\frac{Y^*}{1 + Y^*} = \frac{0.1250X}{1 + X}$$

which is the equilibrium curve for the absorber, and it is plotted in Fig. 8.10. Operating lines originate at point D in this figure. For the minimum oil rate, line DE is drawn as the line of maximum slope which touches the equilibrium curve (tangent to the curve). At $Y_1 = 0.0204$, $X_1 = 0.176$ mole benzene/mole wash oil (point E).

$$\text{Min } L_S = \frac{G_S(Y_1 - Y_2)}{X_1 - X_2} = \frac{79.1(0.0204 - 0.00102)}{0.176 - 0.00502} = 8.95 \text{ moles oil/hr}$$

For 1.5 times the minimum, $L_S = 1.5(8.95) = 13.43$ moles oil/hr

$$X_1 = \frac{G_S(Y_1 - Y_2)}{L_S} + X_2 = \frac{79.1(0.0204 - 0.00102)}{13.43} + 0.00502 = 0.1192 \text{ mole benzene/mole oil}$$

The operating line is DF.

    b. Stripper. At 250°F the vapor pressure of benzene is 2,400 mm Hg, or 3.16 atm. The equilibrium curve for the stripper is therefore

$$\frac{Y^*}{1 + Y^*} = \frac{3.16X}{1 + X}$$

Fig. 8.10 *Solution to Illustration 8.2, absorption.*

Fig. 8.11 *Solution to Illustration 8.2, stripping.*

which is drawn in Fig. 8.11. For the stripper, $X_2 = 0.1192$, $X_1 = 0.00502$ mole benzene/mole oil. $Y_1 = 0$ mole benzene/mole steam. For the minimum steam rate, line MN is drawn tangent to the equilibrium curve, and at N the value of $Y_2 = 0.45$ mole benzene/mole steam.

$$\text{Min } G_S = \frac{L_S(X_2 - X_1)}{Y_2 - Y_1} = \frac{13.43(0.1192 - 0.00502)}{0.45 - 0} = 3.41 \text{ mole steam/hr}$$

For 1.5 times the minimum, the steam rate is $1.5(3.41) = 5.11$ moles steam/hr, corresponding to line MP.

COUNTERCURRENT MULTISTAGE OPERATION

Tray towers and similar devices bring about stepwise contact of the liquid and gas and are therefore countercurrent multistage cascades. On each tray of a bubble-cap tower, for example, the gas and liquid are brought into intimate contact and separated, somewhat in the manner of Fig. 5.14, and the tray thus constitutes a stage. Few of the tray devices described in Chap. 6 actually provide the parallel flow on each tray as shown in Fig. 5.14. Nevertheless it is convenient to use the latter as an arbitrary standard for design and for measurement of performance of actual trays regardless of their method of operation. For this purpose a *theoretical*, or *ideal*, tray is defined as one where the average composition of all the gas leaving the tray is in equilibrium with the average composition of all the liquid leaving the tray.

The number of ideal trays required to bring about a given change in composition

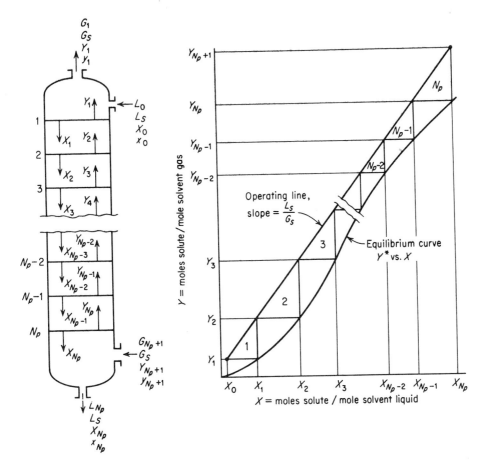

Fig. 8.12 *Tray absorber.*

of the liquid or the gas, for either absorbers or strippers, may then be determined graphically in the manner of Fig. 5.15. This is illustrated for an absorber in Fig. 8.12, where the liquid and gas compositions corresponding to each tray are marked on the operating diagram. Ideal tray 1, for example, brings about a change in liquid composition from X_0 to X_1 and of gas composition from Y_2 to Y_1. The step marked 1 on the operating diagram therefore represents this ideal tray. The nearer the operating line to the equilibrium curve, the more steps will be required, and should the two curves touch at any point corresponding to a minimum L_S/G_S ratio, the number of steps will be infinite. The steps may equally be constructed on diagrams plotted in terms of any concentration units, such as mole fractions or partial pressures. The construction for strippers is the same, with the exception, of course, that the operating line lies below the equilibrium curve.

It is usually convenient, for tray towers, to define the flow rates L and G simply as moles/hr, rather than to base them on unit tower cross section.

Dilute gas mixtures

For cases where both operating line and equilibrium curve may be considered straight, the number of ideal trays may be determined without recourse to graphical methods. This will frequently be the case for relatively dilute gas and liquid mixtures.   Henry's law [Eq. (8.2)] often applies to dilute solutions, for example.   If the quantity of gas absorbed is small, the total flow of liquid entering and leaving the absorber remains substantially constant, $L_0 \doteq L_{Np} \doteq L$ total moles/(hr)(sq ft), and similarly the total flow of gas is substantially constant at G total moles/(hr)(sq ft).   An operating line plotted in terms of mole fractions will then be substantially straight.   For such cases, the Kremser equations (5.50) to (5.57) and Fig. 5.16 apply.†   Small variations in A from one end of the tower to the other due to changing L/G as a result of absorption or stripping or to change in gas solubility with concentration or temperature may be roughly allowed for by use of the geometric average of the values of A at top and bottom.[7]   For large variations, either more elaborate corrections[5,9] for A, graphical computations, or tray-to-tray numerical calculations as developed below, must be used.

The absorption factor A

The absorption factor $A = L/mG$ is the ratio of the slope of the operating line to that of the equilibrium curve.   For values of A less than unity, corresponding to convergence of the operating line and equilibrium curve for the lower end of the absorber, Fig. 5.16 indicates clearly that the fractional absorption of solute is definitely limited, even for infinite theoretical trays.   On the other hand, for values of A greater than unity, any degree of absorption is possible if sufficient trays are provided.   For a fixed degree of absorption from a fixed amount of gas, as A increases beyond unity, the absorbed solute is dissolved in more and more liquid and becomes therefore less valuable.   At the same time, the number of trays decreases, so that the equipment cost

---

† These become, in terms of mole fractions,

Absorption:
$$\frac{y_{Np+1} - y_1}{y_{Np+1} - mx_0} = \frac{A^{Np+1} - A}{A^{Np+1} - 1}$$

$$N_p = \frac{\log \left[\dfrac{y_{Np+1} - mx_0}{y_1 - mx_0} \left(1 - \dfrac{1}{A} \right) + \dfrac{1}{A} \right]}{\log A}$$

Stripping:
$$\frac{x_0 - x_{Np}}{x_0 - y_{Np+1}/m} = \frac{S^{Np+1} - S}{S^{Np+1} - 1}$$

$$N_p = \frac{\log \left[\dfrac{x_0 - y_{Np+1}/m}{x_{Np} - y_{Np+1}/m} \left(1 - \dfrac{1}{S} \right) + \dfrac{1}{S} \right]}{\log S}$$

where $A = L/mG$, and $S = mG/L$.

decreases. From these opposing cost tendencies it follows that in all such cases, there will be a value of A, or of L/G, for which the most economical absorption results. This should be obtained generally by computing the total costs for several values of A and observing the minimum. As a rule of thumb for purposes of rapid estimates, it has been frequently found[3] that the most economical A will be in the range from 1.25 to 2.0.

The reciprocal of the absorption factor is called the stripping factor S.

Illustration 8.3. Determine the number of theoretical trays required for the absorber and the stripper of Illustration 8.2.

Solution. a. Absorber. Since the tower will be a tray device, the following notation changes will be made (compare Figs. 8.4 and 8.12):

L_1 is changed to L_{Np}		G_1 is changed to G_{Np+1}	
L_2	L_0	G_2	G_1
X_1	X_{Np}	Y_1	Y_{Np+1}
X_2	X_0	Y_2	Y_1
x_1	x_{Np}	y_1	y_{Np+1}
x_2	x_0	y_2	y_1

The operating diagram is established in Illustration 8.2, and is replotted in Fig. 8.13, where the theoretical trays are stepped off. Between 7 and 8 (approximately 7.6) theoretical trays are required.

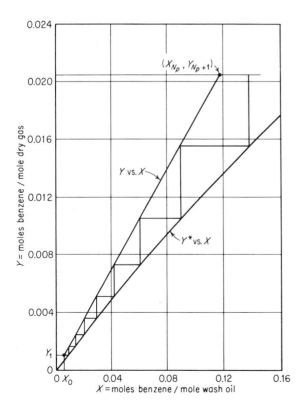

Fig. 8.13 *Illustration 8.3, the absorber.*

Alternatively, the number of theoretical trays may be computed analytically.

$$y_{Np+1} = 0.02 \qquad y_1 = \frac{0.00102}{1 + 0.00102} = 0.00102$$

$$x_0 = 0.005 \qquad m = \frac{y^*}{x} = 0.125$$

$$L_{Np} = L_s(1 + X_{Np}) = 13.43(1 + 0.1192) = 15.0 \text{ moles/hr}$$

$$A_{Np} = \frac{L_{Np}}{mG_{Np}} \doteq \frac{L_{Np}}{mG_{Np+1}} = \frac{15.0}{0.125(80.8)} = 1.485$$

$$L_0 = L_s(1 + X_0) = 13.43(1 + 0.005) = 13.5 \text{ moles/hr}$$

$$G_1 = G_s(1 + Y_1) = 79.1(1 + 0.00102) = 79.1 \text{ moles/hr}$$

$$A_1 = \frac{L_1}{mG_1} \doteq \frac{L_0}{mG_1} = \frac{13.5}{0.125(79.1)} = 1.368$$

$$\text{Av } A = [1.485(1.368)]^{0.5} = 1.425$$

$$\frac{y_1 - mx_0}{y_{Np+1} - mx_0} = \frac{0.00102 - 0.125(0.005)}{0.02 - 0.125(0.005)} = 0.0204$$

From Fig. 5.16 or Eq. (5.55), $N_p = 7.7$ theoretical trays.

b. Stripper. The trays were determined graphically in the same manner as for the absorber and found to be 6.7. Figure 5.16 for this case gave 6.0 trays owing to the relative nonconstancy of the stripping factor, $1/A_{Np} = S_{Np} = 1.197$, $1/A_1 = S_1 = 1.561$. The graphical method should be used.

Nonisothermal operation

Many absorbers and strippers deal with dilute gas mixtures and liquids, and it is frequently satisfactory in these cases to assume that the operation is isothermal. But actually absorption operations are usually exothermic, and when large quantities of solute gas are absorbed to form concentrated solutions, the temperature effects cannot be ignored. If by absorption the temperature of the liquid is raised to a considerable extent, the equilibrium solubility of the solute will be appreciably reduced and the capacity of the absorber decreased (or else much larger flow rates of liquid will be required). If the heat evolved is excessive, cooling coils may be installed in the absorber, or the liquid may be removed at intervals, cooled, and returned to the absorber. In the case of stripping, an endothermic action, the temperature tends to fall.

Consider the tray tower of Fig. 8.14. If Q_T Btu/hr is the heat removed from the entire tower by any means whatsoever, an enthalpy balance for the entire tower is

$$L_0 H_{L0} + G_{Np+1} H_{G,Np+1} = L_{Np} H_{L,Np} + G_1 H_{G1} + Q_T \qquad (8.9)$$

where H represents in each case the molal enthalpy of the stream at its particular concentration and condition. It is convenient to refer all enthalpies to the condition of pure liquid solvent, pure diluent (or solvent) gas, and pure solute at some base temperature t_o, with each substance assigned zero enthalpy for its normal state of aggregation at t_o and 1 atm pressure. Thus, the molal enthalpy of a liquid solution,

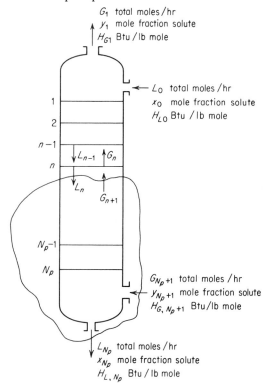

G_1 total moles/hr
y_1 mole fraction solute
H_{G1} Btu/lb mole

L_0 total moles/hr
x_0 mole fraction solute
H_{L0} Btu/lb mole

L_{n-1} G_n

L_n
G_{n+1}

G_{N_p+1} total moles/hr
y_{N_p+1} mole fraction solute
H_{G, N_p+1} Btu/lb mole

L_{N_p} total moles/hr
x_{N_p} mole fraction solute
H_{L, N_p} Btu/lb mole

Fig. 8.14   *Nonisothermal operation.*

temperature t_L, composition x mole fraction solute, is

$$H_L = C_L(t_L - t_o)M_{\mathrm{av}} + \Delta H_S \qquad (8.10)$$

where the first term on the right represents the sensible heat and the second the molal enthalpy of mixing, or integral heat of solution, at the prevailing concentration and at the base temperature t_o, *per mole of solution.*   If heat is evolved on mixing, ΔH_S will be a negative quantity.   If the absorbed solute is a gas at t_o, 1 atm, the gas enthalpy will include only sensible heat.   If the absorbed solute is a liquid at the reference conditions, as in the case of many vapors, the enthalpy of the gas stream must include also the latent heat of vaporization of the solute vapor (see Chap. 7).   For ideal solutions, ΔH_S for mixing liquids is zero, and the enthalpy of the solution is the sum of the enthalpies of the separate, unmixed constituents.   If the ideal liquid solution is formed from a gaseous solute, the heat evolved is the latent heat of condensation of the absorbed solute.

For *adiabatic* operation, Q_T of Eq. (8.9) is zero, and the temperature of the streams leaving an absorber will generally be higher than the entering temperatures owing to the heat of solution.   The rise in temperature causes a decrease in solute solubility, which in turn results in a larger minimum L/G, and a larger number of trays

than for isothermal absorption.   The design of such absorbers must be done numerically, calculating tray by tray from the bottom to the top.   The principle of an ideal
tray, that the effluent streams from the tray are in equilibrium both with respect to
composition and temperature, is utilized for each tray.   Thus, total and solute
balances up to tray n, envelope I, Fig. 8.14, are

$$L_n + G_{Np+1} = L_{Np} + G_{n+1} \tag{8.11}$$

$$L_n x_n + G_{Np+1} y_{Np+1} = L_{Np} x_{Np} + G_{n+1} y_{n+1} \tag{8.12}$$

from which L_n and x_n are computed.   An enthalpy balance is

$$L_n H_{L,n} + G_{Np+1} H_{G,Np+1} = L_{Np} H_{L,Np} + G_{n+1} H_{G,n+1} \tag{8.13}$$

from which the temperature of stream L_n may be obtained.   Stream G_n is then at the
same temperature as L_n and in composition equilibrium with it.   Equations (8.11) to
(8.13) are then applied to tray $n - 1$, and so forth.   To get started, since usually only
the temperatures of the entering streams L_0 and G_{Np+1} are known, it is usually necessary to estimate the temperature t_1 of the gas G_1 (which is the same as the top tray
temperature), and use Eq. (8.9) to compute the temperature of the liquid leaving at
the bottom of the tower.   The estimate is checked when the calculations reach the top
tray, and if necessary the entire computation is repeated.   The method is best illustrated by an example.

Illustration 8.4.   One lb mole per unit time of a gas consisting of 75% methane CH_4 and 25%
n-pentane vapor, n-C_5H_{12}, 80°F, 1 atm, is to be scrubbed with 2 lb moles/unit time of a nonvolatile
paraffin oil, mol wt 200, specific heat 0.45 Btu/(lb)(°F), entering the absorber free of pentane at 95°F.
Compute the number of theoretical trays for adiabatic absorption of 98% of the pentane.   Neglect
the solubility of CH_4 in the oil, and assume operation to be at 1 atm (neglect pressure drop for flow
through the trays).   The pentane forms ideal solutions with the paraffin oil.
  Solution.   Heat capacities over the temperature range 0 to 150°F are

$$CH_4: \quad 8.5 \text{ Btu/(lb mole)(°F)}$$

$$n\text{-}C_5H_{12}: \quad 28.6 \text{ Btu/(lb mole)(°F) as vapor}$$

$$42.4 \text{ Btu/(lb mole)(°F) as liquid}$$

The latent heat of vaporization of n-C_5H_{12} at 0°F = 12,550 Btu/lb mole.   Use a base temperature
$t_o = 0°F$.   Enthalpies referred to 0°F, liquid pentane, liquid paraffin oil, and gaseous methane, are
then

$$H_L = (1 - x)(0.45)(200)(t_L - 0) + x(42.4)(t_L - 0)$$
$$= t_L(90 - 47.6x) \text{ Btu/lb mole liquid solution}$$

$$H_G = (1 - y)(8.5)(t_G - 0) + y(28.6)(t_G - 0) + 12,550y$$
$$= t_G(8.5 + 20.1y) + 12,550y \text{ Btu/lb mole gas-vapor mixture}$$

For solutions which follow Raoult's law, combine Eqs. (8.1) and (8.2)

$$y^* = \frac{Px}{P_t} = mx$$

where P = vapor pressure of n-pentane. Thus, the vapor pressure of n-C_5H_{12} is 400 mm Hg at 65.8°F, whence $m = P/P_t = {}^{400}\!/_{760} = 0.53$. Similarly,

t, °F	70	80	90	100	110
m	0.60	0.73	0.87	1.05	1.25

It is convenient to prepare a graph of these.

Basis: unit time. From the given data,

$$G_{Np+1} = 1 \text{ lb mole} \qquad y_{Np+1} = 0.25$$

$$H_{G,Np+1} = 80[8.5 + 20.1(0.25)] + 12{,}550(0.25) = 4{,}220 \text{ Btu/lb mole}$$

$$L_0 = 2 \text{ lb moles} \qquad x_0 = 0$$

$$H_{L0} = 95(90) = 8{,}550 \text{ Btu/lb mole}$$

$$n\text{-}C_5H_{12} \text{ absorbed} = 0.98(0.25) = 0.245 \text{ lb mole}$$

$$n\text{-}C_5H_{12} \text{ in } G_1 = 0.25 - 0.245 = 0.005 \text{ lb mole}$$

$$G_1 = 0.75 + 0.005 = 0.755 \text{ lb mole}$$

$$\text{Required } y_1 = \frac{0.005}{0.755} = 0.00662$$

$$L_{Np} = 2 + 0.245 = 2.245 \text{ lb moles} \qquad x_{Np} = \frac{0.245}{2.245} = 0.1091$$

Assume $t_1 = 96°F$ (to be checked later).

$$H_{G1} = 96[8.5 + 20.1(0.00662)] + 12{,}550(0.00662) = 911.9 \text{ Btu/lb mole}$$

Eq. (8.9), with $Q_T = 0$:

$$2(8{,}550) + 4{,}220 = L_{Np}H_{L,Np} + 0.755(911.9)$$

$$L_{Np}H_{L,Np} = 20{,}632 \text{ Btu}$$

$$H_{L,Np} = \frac{20{,}632}{2.245} = t_{Np}[90 - 47.6(0.1091)]$$

$$t_{Np} = 108.5°F$$

$$\therefore \quad m_{Np} = 1.22 \quad \text{and} \quad y_{Np} = m_{Np}x_{Np} = 1.22(0.1091) = 0.1332$$

$$G_{Np} = \frac{0.75}{1 - 0.1332} = 0.865 \text{ lb mole}$$

$$H_{G,Np} = 108.5[8.5 + 20.1(0.1332)] + 12{,}550(0.1332) = 2{,}886 \text{ Btu/lb mole}$$

Eq. (8.11) with $n = N_p - 1$:

$$L_{Np-1} + G_{Np+1} = L_{Np} + G_{Np}$$

$$L_{Np-1} + 1 = 2.245 + 0.865$$

$$L_{Np-1} = 2.110 \text{ lb moles}$$

Eq. (8.12) with $n = N_p - 1$:

$$2.110x_{Np-1} + 0.25 = 0.245 + 0.865(0.1332)$$

$$x_{Np-1} = 0.0521$$

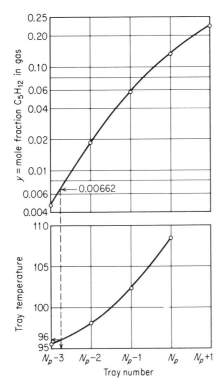

Fig. 8.15 *Solution to Illustration* 8.4.

Eq. (8.13) with $n = N_p - 1$:

$$2.110H_{L,Np-1} + 4,220 = 20,632 + 0.865(2,886)$$
$$H_{L,Np-1} = 8,960 \text{ Btu/lb mole}$$
$$8,960 = t_{Np-1}[90 - 47.6(0.0521)]$$
$$t_{Np-1} = 102.3°F$$

The computation is continued upward through the tower in this manner until the gas composition falls at least to $y = 0.00662$. The results are:

n = tray no.	t_n, °F	x_n	y_n
$N_p = 4$	108.5	0.1091	0.1332
$N_p - 1 = 3$	102.3	0.0521	0.0568
$N_p - 2 = 2$	98.2	0.0184	0.01875
$N_p - 3 = 1$	95.6	0.00463	0.00450

Figure 8.15 shows the calculated gas compositions and tray temperatures plotted against tray number. The required $y_1 = 0.00662$ occurs at 3.75 theoretical trays, and the temperature on the top tray is 96°F, as assumed initially. Had this temperature been other than 96°F, a new assumed value of t_1 and a new calculation would have been required. An integral number of trays will require a slightly greater (for $N_p = 3$) or less (for $N_p = 4$) liquid flow L_0, but since a tray efficiency must still be applied to obtain the number of real trays, the nonintegral number is ordinarily accepted.

When the temperature rise for the liquid is large, as with concentrated gases entering and small values of L/G, calculations of this sort become very tedious since the rate of convergence of the calculated and assumed t_1 is very slow. There may be a temperature maximum at some tray other than the bottom tray. If the number of trays is fixed, the outlet-gas composition and top-tray temperature must both be determined by trial and error.

Real trays and tray efficiency

Methods for estimating the Murphree tray efficiency corrected for entrainment $\mathbf{E}_{MGE}$ for sieve trays are discussed in detail in Chap. 6. For a given absorber or stripper, these permit estimation of the tray efficiency as a function of fluid compositions and temperature as they vary from one end of the tower to the other. Usually it is sufficient to make such computations at only three or four locations, and then proceed as in Fig. 8.16. The broken line is drawn between equilibrium curve and operating line at a fractional vertical distance from the operating line equal to the prevailing Murphree gas efficiency. Thus the value of $\mathbf{E}_{MGE}$ for the bottom tray is the ratio of the lengths of lines, AB/AC. Since the broken line then represents the real effluent compositions from the trays, it is used instead of the equilibrium curve to complete the tray construction, which now provides the number of real trays.

When the Murphree efficiency is constant for all trays, and under conditions such that the operating line and equilibrium curves are straight (Henry's law, isothermal operation, dilute solutions), then the overall tray efficiency can be computed, and the number of real trays may be determined analytically:

$$\mathbf{E}_O = \frac{\text{ideal trays}}{\text{real trays}} = \frac{\log\,[1 + \mathbf{E}_{MGE}(1/A - 1)]}{\log\,(1/A)} \tag{8.14}$$

For rough estimates, Fig. 6.15 is useful for bubble-cap trays.

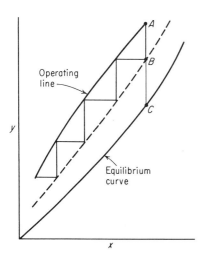

Fig. 8.16 *Use of Murphree efficiencies for an absorber.*

Illustration 8.5. A process for making small amounts of hydrogen by cracking ammonia is being considered, and it is desired to remove residual uncracked ammonia from the resulting gas. The gas will consist of H_2 and N_2 in the molar ratio of 3:1, containing 3 % NH_3 by volume, at 2 atm, 80°F.

There is available a sieve-tray tower, 30-in. diameter, containing 14 cross-flow trays at 18-in. tray spacing. On each tray, the downflow weir is 21 in. long and extends 2.0 in. above the tray floor. The perforations are $\frac{3}{16}$-in. diameter, arranged in triangular pitch on 0.5-in. centers, punched in sheet metal 0.078 in. thick. The total perforation area is 0.4 sq ft/tray. Estimate the capacity of the tower to remove ammonia from the gas by scrubbing with water. Assume isothermal operation at 80°F.

Solution. From the geometry of the tray arrangement, in the notation of Chap. 6, the following are calculated:

$$d = \text{tower diameter} = 30/12 = 2.50 \text{ ft}$$
$$A_t = \text{tower cross section} = 4.90 \text{ sq ft}$$
$$A_d = \text{downspout cross section} = 0.431 \text{ sq ft}$$
$$A_n = A_t - A_d = 4.47 \text{ sq ft} \qquad A_a = A_t - 2A_d = 4.04 \text{ sq ft}$$
$$A_h = 0.40 \text{ sq ft}$$
$$Z = \text{distance between downspouts} = 1.78 \text{ ft}$$
$$W = \text{weir length} = 2\tfrac{1}{12} = 1.75 \text{ ft}$$
$$h_W = \text{weir height} = 2.0 \text{ in.}$$
$$t = \text{tray spacing} = 18.0 \text{ in.}$$
$$z = \text{av flow width} = \frac{d + W}{2} = 2.12 \text{ ft}$$

Use a weir head $h_1 = 0.75$ in. $W/d = 21/30 = 0.7$, $h_1/d = 0.75/2.5 = 0.30$ in./ft. From Fig. 6.10, $(W/W_{\text{eff}})^{2/3} = 1.06$.

Eq. (6.5): $$0.75 = 5.38(1.06)\left(\frac{q}{W}\right)^{2/3} \qquad \frac{q}{W} = 0.0516 \text{ cu ft/(sec)(ft)}$$

$q = 0.0516(1.75) = 0.0905$ cu ft/sec liquid, or 5.15 lb/sec, or 0.286 lb mole/sec. This is a reasonable, but not the maximum possible, liquid flow rate.

$$\text{Liquid density} = \rho_L = 62.3 \text{ lb/cu ft}$$
$$\text{Av mol wt gas} = 0.03(17.03) + 0.97(0.25)(28.02) + 0.97(0.75)(2.02)$$
$$= 8.78 \text{ lb/lb mole}$$
$$\rho_G = \frac{8.78}{359} \frac{2}{1} \frac{492}{460 + 80} = 0.0466 \text{ lb/cu ft}$$

The flooding gas rate is found by simultaneous solution of Eqs. (6.1) and (6.3) by trial and error. Table 6.1: $a = 0.1535$, $b = 0.0935$. For these solutions, $\sigma' = 68$ dynes/cm surface tension. A gas rate of 1.82 lb/sec provides, through Eq. (6.3), $C_F = 0.366$; Eq. (6.1): $V_F = 13.40$ ft/sec at flooding. Using 65 % of the flood rate, $V = 0.65(13.40) = 8.75$ ft/sec, whence the gas rate $= V A_n \rho_G = 8.75(4.47)(0.0466) = 1.82$ lb/sec, or 0.207 lb moles/sec.

The methods of Chap. 6 then provide $h_D = 2.37$ in., $V_a = V A_n/A_a = 9.68$ ft/sec, $h_L = 0.77$ in., $h_R = 0.35$ in., $h_G = 3.47$ in., $h_2 = 0.2$ in., $h_3 = 3.67$ in.

$$h_W + h_1 + h_3 = 6.42 \text{ in.}$$

This is below $t/2 = 9.0$ in., flooding will not occur, and the flow rates are reasonable.

$$\frac{V}{V_F} = 0.65 \qquad \frac{L'}{G'}\left(\frac{\rho_G}{\rho_L}\right)^{0.5} = 0.078$$

and from Fig. 6.11, the fractional entrainment $E = 0.019$.

The methods of Chap. 2 provide D_G, the diffusivity of ammonia through the N_2–H_2 mixture, equal to 1.0 sq ft/hr. The gas viscosity $= 0.01125$ centipoise, whence $Sc_G = \mu_G/\rho_G D_G = 0.01125(2.42)/0.0466(1.0) = 0.585$.

The diffusivity of ammonia in the water solution $D_L = 9.38(10^{-5})$ sq ft/hr. For dilute solutions, NH_3–H_2O follows Henry's law, and at 80°F, the Henry-law constant $= m = y*/x = 0.707$. The absorption factor $= A = L/mG = 0.286/0.707(0.207) = 1.955$.

Eq. (6.31):	$N_{tG} = 0.817$	Eq. (6.34):	$\theta_L = 0.00074$ hr
Eq. (6.32):	$N_{tL} = 2.86$	Eq. (6.33):	$D_E = 236$ sq ft/hr
Eq. (6.23):	$N_{tOG} = 0.705$	Eq. (6.22):	$E_{OG} = 0.506$
Eq. (6.29):	Pe $= 18.1$	Eq. (6.28):	$\eta = 0.253$
Eq. (6.27):	$E_{MG} = 0.568$	Eq. (6.30):	$E_{MGE} = 0.566$

Since the quantity of gas absorbed is small relative to the total gas flow and the liquid solutions all dilute, the Murphree tray efficiency will be taken as constant for all trays. For the dilute solutions encountered here, the operating line is essentially straight. Consequently, Eq. (8.14):

$$E_O = \frac{\log\,[1 + 0.566(1/1.955 - 1)]}{\log\,(1/1.955)} = 0.482$$

(*Note:* for bubble-cap trays, Fig. 6.15 provides, as a rough estimate, $E_O = 0.55$.)

Eq. (8.14): $\qquad\qquad N_p = 14(0.482) = 6.75$ ideal trays

From Fig. 5.16,

$$\frac{y_1 - mx_0}{y_{Np+1} - mx_0} = \frac{y_1}{y_{Np+1}} = \frac{y_1}{0.03} = 0.0048$$

$y_1 = 0.000144$ mole fraction NH_3 in the effluent gas **Ans.**

CONTINUOUS-CONTACT EQUIPMENT

Countercurrent packed and spray towers operate in a different manner from plate towers in that the fluids are in contact continuously in their path through the tower, rather than intermittently. Thus, in a packed tower the liquid and gas compositions change continuously with height of packing. Every point on an operating line therefore represents conditions found somewhere in the tower, whereas for tray towers, only the isolated points on the operating line corresponding to trays have real significance.

Height equivalent to a theoretical plate

A simple method for designing packed towers, which was introduced many years ago, ignores the differences between stagewise and continuous contact. In this method the number of theoretical trays or plates required for a given change in concentration is computed by the methods of the previous section. This is then multiplied by a quantity, the height equivalent to a theoretical tray or plate (HETP) to give the required height of packing to do the same job. The HETP must be an experimentally determined quantity characteristic for each packing. Unfortunately it is found that the HETP varies, not only with the type and size of the packing but also very strongly with flow rates of each fluid and for every system with concentration as well, so that an enormous amount of experimental data would have to be accumulated to permit utilization of the method. The difficulty lies in the failure to account for the fundamentally different action of tray and packed towers, and the method has now largely been abandoned.

Absorption of one component

Consider a packed tower of unit cross section, as in Fig. 8.17. The total effective interfacial surface for mass transfer, as a result of spreading of the liquid in a film over the packing, is S sq ft/sq ft tower cross section. This is conveniently described as the product of a sq ft interfacial surface/cu ft packed volume by the packed volume, Z cu ft/sq ft tower cross section (the quantity a is the a_A of Chap. 6). In the differential volume dZ cu ft, the interface surface is

$$dS = a \, dZ \tag{8.15}$$

The quantity of solute A in the gas passing the differential section of the tower under consideration is Gy moles/(hr)(sq ft), and the rate of mass transfer is therefore $d(Gy)$ moles A/(hr)(differential volume). Since $N_B = 0$ and $N_A/(N_A + N_B) = 1.0$, application of Eq. (5.20) provides

$$N_A = \frac{\text{moles } A \text{ absorbed}}{\text{(hr)(interfacial surface)}} = \frac{d(Gy)}{a \, dZ} = F_G \ln \frac{1 - y_i}{1 - y} \tag{8.16}$$

Fig. 8.17 *Packed tower.*

Both G and y vary from one end of the tower to the other, but G_S, the solvent gas which is essentially insoluble, does not. Therefore,

$$d(Gy) = d\left(\frac{G_S y}{1-y}\right) = \frac{G_S\, dy}{(1-y)^2} = \frac{G\, dy}{1-y} \tag{8.17}$$

Substituting in Eq. (8.16), rearranging, and integrating,

$$Z = \int_0^Z dZ = \int_{y_2}^{y_1} \frac{G\, dy}{F_G a(1-y)\ln\left[(1-y_i)/(1-y)\right]} \tag{8.18}$$

The value of y_i may be found by the methods of Chap. 5, using Eq. (5.21) with $N_A/\Sigma N = 1$:

$$\frac{1-y_i}{1-y} = \left(\frac{1-x}{1-x_i}\right)^{F_L/F_G} = \left(\frac{1-x}{1-x_i}\right)^{F_{La}/F_{Ga}} \tag{8.19}$$

For any value of (x,y) on the operating curve plotted in terms of mole fractions, a curve of x_i vs. y_i from Eq. (8.19) is plotted to determine the intersection with the equilibrium curve. This provides the local y and y_i for use in Eq. (8.18).† Equation (8.18) may then be integrated graphically after plotting the integrand as ordinate vs. y as abscissa.

However, it is more customary to proceed as follows.[2] Since

$$y - y_i = (1 - y_i) - (1 - y) \tag{8.20}$$

the numerator and denominator of the integral of Eq. (8.18) may be multiplied respectively by the right- and left-hand sides of Eq. (8.20) to provide

$$Z = \int_{y_2}^{y_1} \frac{G(1-y)_{iM}\, dy}{F_G a(1-y)(y-y_i)} \tag{8.21}$$

where $(1-y)_{iM}$ is the logarithmic mean of $1-y_i$ and $1-y$. Defining a *height of a gas transfer unit* H_{tG} as

$$H_{tG} = \frac{G}{F_G a} = \frac{G}{k_y a(1-y)_{iM}} = \frac{G}{k_G a P_t (1-y)_{iM}} \tag{8.22}$$

Eq. (8.21) becomes

$$Z = \int_{y_2}^{y_1} H_{tG}\frac{(1-y)_{iM}\, dy}{(1-y)(y-y_i)} \doteq H_{tG}\int_{y_2}^{y_1}\frac{(1-y)_{iM}\, dy}{(1-y)(y-y_i)} \tag{8.23}$$

$$= H_{tG} N_{tG}$$

Here advantage is taken of the fact that the ratio $G/F_G a = H_{tG}$ is very much more constant than either G or $F_G a$, and in many cases may be considered constant within the accuracy of the available data. In the integral of Eq. (8.23) containing only the y terms, if we disregard the ratio $(1-y)_{iM}/(1-y)$, the remainder is seen to be the

---

† As demonstrated in Illustration 8.6, for moderately dilute solutions it is satisfactory to determine y_i by a line of slope $-k_x a/k_y a$ drawn from (x,y) on the operating line to intersection with the equilibrium curve, in accordance with Eq. (5.2).

number of times the average $y - y_i$ divides into the change of gas concentration $y_1 - y_2$. As in Chap. 7, this is a measure of the difficulty of the absorption, and the integral is called the *number of gas transfer units* N_{tG}. Equation (8.23) can be further simplified by substituting the arithmetic average for the logarithmic average $(1 - y)_{iM}$:[4]

$$(1 - y)_{iM} = \frac{(1 - y_i) - (1 - y)}{\ln [(1 - y_i)/(1 - y)]} \doteq \frac{(1 - y_i) + (1 - y)}{2} \tag{8.24}$$

which involves very little error. N_{tG} then becomes

$$N_{tG} = \int_{y_2}^{y_1} \frac{dy}{y - y_i} + \frac{1}{2} \ln \frac{1 - y_2}{1 - y_1} \tag{8.25}$$

which makes for simpler graphical integration.† For dilute solutions, the second term on the right of Eq. (8.25) is negligible, $F_G a \doteq k_y a$, and y_i may be obtained by plotting a line of slope $-k_x a/k_y a$ from points (x,y) on the operating line to intersection with the equilibrium curve.

The above relationships all have their counterparts in terms of liquid concentrations, derived in exactly the same way

$$Z = \int_{x_2}^{x_1} \frac{L \, dx}{F_L a(1 - x) \ln [(1 - x)/(1 - x_i)]} = \int_{x_2}^{x_1} \frac{L(1 - x)_{iM} \, dx}{F_L a(1 - x)(x_i - x)} \tag{8.26}$$

$$Z = \int_{x_2}^{x_1} H_{tL} \frac{(1 - x)_{iM} \, dx}{(1 - x)(x_i - x)} \doteq H_{tL} \int_{x_2}^{x_1} \frac{(1 - x)_{iM} \, dx}{(1 - x)(x_i - x)} = H_{tL} N_{tL} \tag{8.27}$$

$$H_{tL} = \frac{L}{F_L a} = \frac{L}{k_x a(1 - x)_{iM}} = \frac{L}{k_L ac(1 - x)_{iM}} \tag{8.28}$$

$$N_{tL} = \int_{x_2}^{x_1} \frac{dx}{x_i - x} + \frac{1}{2} \ln \frac{1 - x_1}{1 - x_2} \tag{8.29}$$

where H_{tL} = height of a liquid transfer unit
N_{tL} = number of liquid transfer units
$(1 - x)_{iM}$ = logarithmic mean of $1 - x$ and $1 - x_i$

Either set of equations leads to the same value of Z.

Strippers. The same relationships apply as for absorption. The "driving forces" $y - y_i$ and $x_i - x$ which appear in the above equations are then negative, but since for strippers $x_2 > x_1$, and $y_2 > y_1$, the result is a positive Z as before.

† In the graphical integration of Eq. (8.25), the plot of $1/(y - y_i)$ vs. y often covers awkwardly large ranges of the ordinate. This may be avoided[12] by replacing dy by its equal $y \, d \ln y$, so that

$$N_{tG} = 2.303 \int_{\log y_2}^{\log y_1} \frac{y}{y - y_i} d \log y + 1.152 \log \frac{1 - y_2}{1 - y_1} \tag{8.25a}$$

Illustration 8.6. The absorber of Illustrations 8.2 and 8.3 is to be a packed tower, 1.5 ft in diameter, filled with 1.5-in. Berl saddles.   The circumstances are:

Gas

Benzene content: in, $y_1 = 0.02$ mole fraction, $Y_1 = 0.0204$ mole/mole dry gas.
Out, $y_2 = 0.00102$ mole fraction, $Y_2 = 0.00102$ mole/mole dry gas.
Nonabsorbed gas: av mol wt $= 11.0$.
Rate in $= 80.8$ lb moles total/hr; 79.1 moles/hr nonbenzene.
Temperature $= 80°F$; pressure $= 800$ mm Hg.
Viscosity $= 0.01$ centipoise; $D_{AG} = 0.504$ sq ft/hr.

Liquid

Benzene content: in, $x_2 = 0.005$ mole fraction, $X_2 = 0.00502$ moles vapor/mole dry gas.
Out, $x_1 = 0.1065$ mole fraction, $X_1 = 0.1192$ mole vapor/mole gas.
Benzene-free oil: mol wt $= 260$, viscosity $= 2.0$ centipoises; sp gr 0.84; rate $= 13.43$ lb moles/hr.
Temp $= 80°F$; $D_{AL} = 1.85(10^{-5})$ sq ft/hr.
Surface tension $= 30$ dynes/cm; $m = y*/x = 0.1250$.

Compute the depth of packing required.

Solution. To plot the operating line, use Eq. (8.7) to calculate X and Y values (or read from Fig. 8.10), and convert to $x = X/(1 + X)$ and $y = Y/(1 + Y)$.   Thus,

$$79.1(0.0204 - Y) = 13.43(0.1192 - X)$$

X	x	Y	y
0.00502	0.00500	0.00102	0.00102
0.02	0.01961	0.00356	0.00355
0.04	0.0385	0.00695	0.00690
0.06	0.0566	0.01035	0.01024
0.08	0.0741	0.01374	0.01355
0.10	0.0909	0.01714	0.01685
0.1192	0.1065	0.0204	0.0200

Values of y and x (the operating line) are plotted along with the equilibrium line, $y = 0.1250x$, in Fig. 8.18.   Although the curvature in this case is not great, the operating line is not straight on mole-fraction coordinates.

The cross-sectional area of the absorber is $(1.5)^2\pi/4 = 1.77$ sq ft.   At the bottom,

$$L' = \frac{13.43(260) + 0.1192(13.43)(78)}{1.77} = 2,040 \text{ lb/(hr)(sq ft)}$$

Similarly at the top, $L' = 1,970$.   Av $L' = 2,005$ lb/(hr)(sq ft).   Also at the bottom

$$G' = \frac{80.8(0.98)(11) + 80.8(0.02)(78)}{1.77} = 563 \text{ lb/(hr)(sq ft)}$$

Similarly at the top, $G' = 493$.   Av $G' = 528$ lb/(hr)(sq ft).

The flow quantities change so little from one end of the tower to the other that the average values may be used to compute the mass-transfer coefficients, which may then be taken as constant. The circumstances are precisely those of Illustration 6.4, where it was found that

$$F_G a = 26.1 \text{ lb moles/(hr)(cu ft)} \qquad F_L a = 5.0 \text{ lb moles/(hr)(cu ft)}$$

For each plotted point on the operating line, Eq. (8.19) is then used to determine the interface compositions.   Thus, at $(x = 0.1065, y = 0.0200)$ on the operating line (point A, Fig. 8.18), Eq. (8.19) becomes

$$\frac{1 - y_i}{1 - 0.0200} = \left(\frac{1 - 0.1065}{1 - x_i}\right)^{5.0/26.1}$$

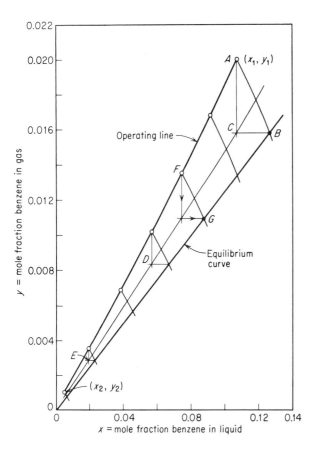

Fig. 8.18 *Solution to Illustration 8.6.*

This is plotted (y_i vs. x_i) as curve AB on Fig. 8.18, to intersect the equilibrium curve at B, where $y_i = 0.01580$.

Note: In this case, since the concentrations are low, an essentially correct value of y_i may be obtained by the following less tedious calculation. Table 3.1 shows

$$k_y a = \frac{F_G a}{p_{BM}/P_t} = \frac{F_G a}{(1-y)_{iM}} \qquad k_x a = \frac{F_L a}{(1-x)_{iM}}$$

At point A on the operating line, $1 - y = 1 - 0.02 = 0.98$, $1 - x = 1 - 0.1065 = 0.8935$. As an approximation, these may be taken as $(1-y)_{iM}$ and $(1-x)_{iM}$, respectively, whence

$$k_y a = \frac{26.1}{0.98} = 26.4 \text{ moles/(hr)(cu ft)(mole fraction)}$$

$$k_x a = \frac{5.0}{0.8935} = 5.60 \text{ moles/(hr)(cu ft)(mole fraction)}$$

In accordance with Eq. (5.2), $-k_x a/k_y a = -5.60/26.4 = -0.210$, and if a straight line of this slope is drawn from point A, it intersects the equilibrium curve at $y_i = 0.01585$. Curve AB, in other words, is nearly a straight line of slope -0.210. The error by this method becomes even less at lower solute concentrations. Where the F's must be used, it is sufficient to proceed as follows. On Fig. 8.18,

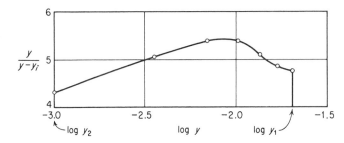

Fig. 8.19 *Graphical integration for Illustration 8.6.*

draw the vertical line AC to intersection with the horizontal line CB, thus locating the intersection C. Repeat the calculation at two other locations, such as at D and E, and draw the curve EDC. Interfacial concentrations G corresponding to any point F on the operating line may then be obtained by the construction shown on the figure leading to point G.

In a similar manner, the values of y_i tabulated below were determined, as shown on Fig. 8.18.

y	y_i	$\dfrac{y}{y - y_i}$	$\log y$
0.00102	0.000784	4.32	$-2.9999 = \log y_2$
0.00355	0.00285	5.03	-2.4498
0.00690	0.00562	5.39	-2.1612
0.01024	0.00830	5.39	-1.9897
0.01355	0.01090	5.11	-1.8681
0.01685	0.01337	4.84	-1.7734
0.0200	0.01580	4.76	$-1.6990 = \log y_1$

Since the mass-transfer coefficients are essentially constant, Eq. (8.25a) will be used to determine N_{tG}. From the data of the above tabulation, the curve for graphical integration of Eq. (8.25a) is plotted in Fig. 8.19. The area under the curve (to the zero ordinate) is 6.556. Then by Eq. (8.25a),

$$N_{tG} = 2.303(6.556) + 1.152 \log \frac{1 - 0.00102}{1 - 0.0200} = 15.11$$

The average gas rate is

$$G = \frac{80.8 + 79.1/(1 - 0.00102)}{2(1.77)} = 45.2 \text{ lb moles/(hr)(sq ft)}$$

Eq. (8.22): $$H_{tG} = \frac{G}{F_G a} = \frac{45.2}{26.1} = 1.735 \text{ ft}$$

$Z = H_{tG} N_{tG} = 1.735(15.11) = 26.0$ ft packed depth **Ans.**

Note: The circumstances are such that, for this problem, the simpler computations of Illustration 8.7 are entirely adequate. The method used above, however, is suitable for solutions of any concentration and where the equilibrium curve is not straight. If flow rates vary appreciably from top to bottom of the tower, so that mass-transfer coefficients vary, this is easily allowed for in determining values of y_i. In such cases, Eq. (8.18) would be used to compute Z.

Overall coefficients and transfer units ($m = dy_i/dx_i = $ const)

In cases where the equilibrium-distribution curve is straight and the ratio of-mass-transfer coefficients is constant, it was shown in Chap. 5 that overall mass-transfer coefficients are convenient.   The expressions for the height of packing may then be written

$$Z = N_{tOG}H_{tOG} \tag{8.30}$$

$$N_{tOG} = \int_{y_2}^{y_1} \frac{(1 - y)_{*M}\, dy}{(1 - y)(y - y^*)} \tag{8.31}$$

$$N_{tOG} = \int_{y_2}^{y_1} \frac{dy}{y - y^*} + \frac{1}{2}\ln\frac{1 - y_2}{1 - y_1} \tag{8.32}$$

$$N_{tOG} = \int_{Y_2}^{Y_1} \frac{dY}{Y - Y^*} + \frac{1}{2}\ln\frac{1 + Y_2}{1 + Y_1} \tag{8.33}$$

$$H_{tOG} = \frac{G}{F_{OG}a} = \frac{G}{K_y a(1 - y)_{*M}} = \frac{G}{K_G a P_t(1 - y)_{*M}} \tag{8.34}$$

Here y^* (or Y^*) is the solute concentration in the gas corresponding to equilibrium with the bulk liquid concentration x (or X), so that $y - y^*$ (or $Y - Y^*$) is simply the vertical distance between operating line and equilibrium curve. $(1 - y)_{*M}$ is the logarithmic average of $1 - y$ and $1 - y^*$.   These methods are convenient since interfacial concentrations need not be obtained, and Eq. (8.33) is especially convenient since the operating line on X, Y coordinates is straight. N_{tOG} is the *number of overall gas transfer units*, H_{tOG} the *height of an overall gas transfer unit*.

Equations (8.30) to (8.34) are usually used when the principal mass-transfer resistance resides within the gas.   For cases where the principal mass-transfer resistance lies within the liquid, it is more convenient to use

$$Z = N_{tOL}H_{tOL} \tag{8.35}$$

$$N_{tOL} = \int_{x_2}^{x_1} \frac{(1 - x)_{*M}\, dx}{(1 - x)(x^* - x)} \tag{8.36}$$

$$N_{tOL} = \int_{x_2}^{x_1} \frac{dx}{x^* - x} + \frac{1}{2}\ln\frac{1 - x_1}{1 - x_2} \tag{8.37}$$

$$N_{tOL} = \int_{X_2}^{X_1} \frac{dX}{X^* - X} + \frac{1}{2}\ln\frac{1 + X_1}{1 + X_2} \tag{8.38}$$

$$H_{tOL} = \frac{L}{F_{OL}a} = \frac{L}{K_x a(1 - x)_{*M}} = \frac{L}{K_L ac(1 - x)_{*M}} \tag{8.39}$$

Dilute solutions

The computation of the number of transfer units for dilute mixtures can be greatly simplified.   When the gas mixture is dilute, for example, the second term of the definition of N_{tOG} [Eq. (8.32)] becomes entirely negligible and may be discarded

$$N_{tOG} = \int_{y_2}^{y_1} \frac{dy}{y - y^*} \tag{8.40}$$

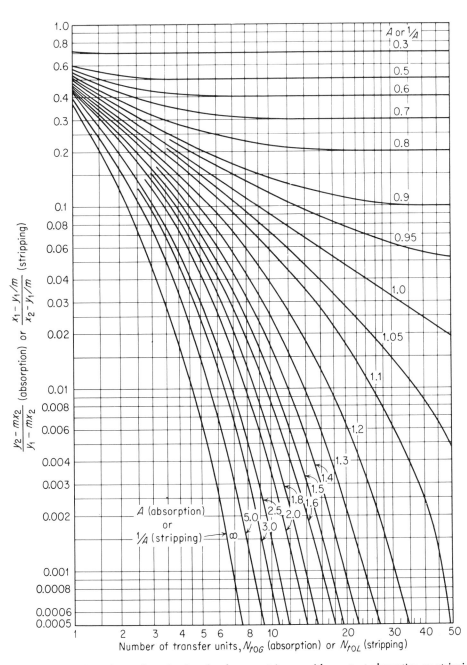

Fig. 8.20 *Number of transfer units for absorbers or strippers with constant absorption or stripping factor.*

If the equilibrium curve in terms of mole fractions is linear over the range of compositions x_1 to x_2, then

$$y^* = mx + r \tag{8.41}$$

If the solutions are dilute, the operating line may be considered as a straight line as well

$$y = \frac{L}{G}(x - x_2) + y_2 \tag{8.42}$$

so that the driving force $y - y^*$ is then linear in x

$$y - y^* = qx + s \tag{8.43}$$

where q, r, and s are constants.   Therefore Eq. (8.40) becomes

$$N_{tOG} = \frac{L}{G}\int_{x_2}^{x_1} \frac{dx}{qx + s} = \frac{L}{Gq}\ln\frac{(y - y^*)_1}{(y - y^*)_2} = \frac{y_1 - y_2}{\dfrac{(y - y^*)_1 - (y - y^*)_2}{\ln[(y - y^*)_1/(y - y^*)_2]}} \tag{8.44}$$

$$N_{tOG} = \frac{y_1 - y_2}{(y - y^*)_M} \tag{8.45}$$

where $(y - y^*)_M$ is the logarithmic average of the concentration differences at the ends of the tower.   This equation is sometimes used in the familiar rate form obtained by substituting the definition of N_{tOG}

$$G(y_1 - y_2) = K_G a Z P_t (y - y^*)_M \tag{8.46}$$

Dilute solutions, Henry's law

If Henry's law applies [r of Eq. (8.41) $= 0$], by elimination of x between Eqs. (8.41) and (8.42) and substitution of y^* in Eq. (8.40) there results for absorbers[4]

$$N_{tOG} = \frac{\ln\left[\left(\dfrac{y_1 - mx_2}{y_2 - mx_2}\right)\left(1 - \dfrac{1}{A}\right) + \dfrac{1}{A}\right]}{1 - 1/A} \tag{8.47}$$

where $A = L/mG$, as before.   For strippers, the corresponding expression in terms of N_{tOL} is similar

$$N_{tOL} = \frac{\ln\left[\left(\dfrac{x_2 - y_1/m}{x_1 - y_1/m}\right)(1 - A) + A\right]}{1 - A} \tag{8.48}$$

These are shown in convenient graphical form in Fig. 8.20.

Graphical construction for transfer units[1]

Equation (8.45) demonstrates that one overall gas transfer unit results when the change in gas composition equals the average overall driving force causing the change. Consider now the operating diagram of Fig. 8.21, where line KB has been drawn so as to be everywhere vertically halfway between the operating line and equilibrium

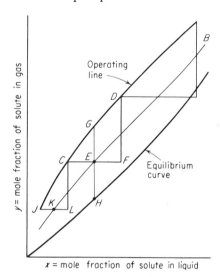

y = mole fraction of solute in gas

Operating line

Equilibrium curve

x = mole fraction of solute in liquid

Fig. 8.21 *Graphical determination of transfer units.*

curve. The step CFD, which corresponds to one transfer unit, has been constructed by drawing the horizontal line CEF so that line $CE = EF$ and continuing vertically to D. $y_G - y_H$ may be considered as the average driving force for the change in gas composition $y_D - y_F$ corresponding to this step. Since $GE = EH$, and if the operating line may be considered straight, $DF = 2(GE) = GH$, the step CFD corresponds to one transfer unit. In similar fashion the other transfer units were stepped off ($JK = KL$, etc.). For computing N_{tOL}, the line KB would be drawn horizontally halfway between equilibrium curve and operating line and would bisect the vertical portions of the steps.

Overall heights of transfer units

When overall numbers of transfer units are appropriate, the overall heights of transfer units may be synthesized from those for the individual phases through the relationships developed in Chap. 5. Thus, Eq. (5.25a), with $m' = m'' = m = $ const, may be written

$$\frac{G}{F_{OG}a} = \frac{G(1 - y)_{iM}}{F_G a(1 - y)_{*M}} + \frac{mG}{L} \frac{L}{F_L a} \frac{(1 - x)_{iM}}{(1 - y)_{*M}} \tag{8.49}$$

whence, by definition of the heights of transfer units,

$$H_{tOG} = H_{tG} \frac{(1 - y)_{iM}}{(1 - y)_{*M}} + \frac{mG}{L} H_{tL} \frac{(1 - x)_{iM}}{(1 - y)_{*M}} \tag{8.50}$$

If the mass-transfer resistance is essentially all in the gas, $y_i \doteq y^*$, and

$$H_{tOG} = H_{tG} + \frac{mG}{L} H_{tL} \frac{(1 - x)_{iM}}{(1 - y)_{*M}} \tag{8.51}$$

and, for dilute solutions, the concentration ratio of the last equation may be dropped. In similar fashion, Eq. (5.26a) yields

$$H_{tOL} = H_{tL} \frac{(1 - x)_{iM}}{(1 - x)_{*M}} + \frac{L}{mG} \grave{H}_{tG} \frac{(1 - y)_{iM}}{(1 - x)_{*M}} \tag{8.52}$$

and if the mass-transfer resistance is essentially all in the liquid,

$$H_{tOL} = H_{tL} + \frac{L}{mG} H_{tG} \frac{(1 - y)_{iM}}{(1 - x)_{*M}} \tag{8.53}$$

The concentration ratio of the last equation may be dropped for dilute solutions. Data for the individual phase coefficients are summarized for standard packings in Chap. 6.

Illustration 8.7. Repeat the computation of Illustration 8.6, using the simplified procedures for dilute mixtures.

Solution. Number of transfer units. *a.* Use Eq. (8.45). $y_1 = 0.02$, $x_1 = 0.1065$, $y_1^* = mx_1 = 0.125(0.1065) = 0.01331$, $(y - y^*)_1 = 0.02 - 0.01331 = 0.00669$. $y_2 = 0.00102$, $x_2 = 0.0050$, $y_2^* = mx_2 = 0.125(0.0050) = 0.000625$, $(y - y^*)_2 = 0.00102 - 0.000625 = 0.000395$.

$$(y - y^*)_M = \frac{0.00669 - 0.000395}{\ln (0.00669/0.000395)} = 0.00223$$

$$N_{tOG} = \frac{0.02 - 0.00102}{0.00223} = 8.55 \quad \textbf{Ans.}$$

b. Eq. (8.47) or Fig. 8.20. Av $A = 1.425$ (Illustration 8.3).

$$\frac{y_2 - mx_2}{y_1 - mx_2} = \frac{0.00102 - 0.125(0.005)}{0.02 - 0.125(0.005)} = 0.0204.$$

From either Eq. (8.47) or Fig. 8.20, $N_{tOG} = 8.8$. **Ans.**

c. The graphical construction for transfer units is shown in Fig. 8.22. The mole-ratio coordinates are satisfactory for dilute mixtures, and the operating line and equilibrium curve were redrawn from Fig. 8.10. The line *BD* was drawn everywhere vertically midway between operating line and equilibrium curve, and the transfer-unit steps constructed by making the horizontal-line segments such as *AB* and *BC* equal. The number of transfer units required is 8⅔. **Ans.**

d. Eq. (8.33). From Fig. 8.10, for each value of X, values of Y are read from the operating line *DF* and Y^* from the equilibrium curve (or these may be computed from the equations of these lines).

X	Y	Y^*	$\dfrac{1}{Y - Y^*}$
$X_2 = 0.00502$	0.00102	0.00062	2,500
0.02	0.00356	0.00245	901
0.04	0.00695	0.00483	462
0.06	0.01035	0.00712	310
0.08	0.01374	0.00935	228
0.10	0.01714	0.01150	177.5
$X_1 = 0.1192$	0.0204	0.01350	145.0

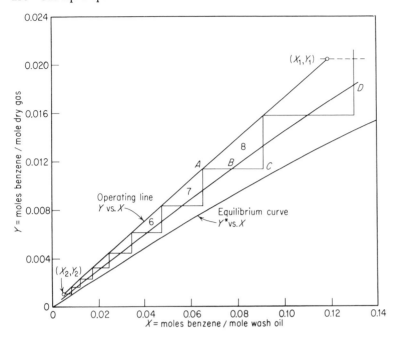

Fig. 8.22   *Solution to Illustration 8.7.*

The integral of Eq. (8.23) may be evaluated graphically from a plot of $1/(Y - Y^*)$ as ordinate vs. Y as abscissa, or, following the suggestion of Eq. (8.25a), from a plot of $Y/(Y - Y^*)$ as ordinate vs. log Y as abscissa.   The integral term is then 8.63.   Then

$$N_{tOG} = 8.63 + \frac{1}{2} \ln \frac{1 + 0.00102}{1 + 0.0204} = 8.62 \quad \textbf{Ans.}$$

Height of a transfer unit.   Since the solutions are dilute, Eq. (8.51) becomes

$$H_{tOG} = H_{tG} + \frac{mG}{L} H_{tL} = H_{tG} + \frac{H_{tL}}{A}$$

From Illustration 6.4, $F_G a = 26.1$, $F_L a = 5.0$ lb moles/(hr)(cu ft).   Av $G = 45.2$ lb moles/(hr)(sq ft) (Illustration 8.6).   Av $L = (15.0 + 13.5)/2(1.77) = 8.05$ lb moles/(hr)(sq ft).

Eq. (8.22): $$H_{tG} = \frac{G}{F_G a} = \frac{45.2}{26.1} = 1.735 \text{ ft}$$

Eq. (8.28): $$H_{tL} = \frac{L}{F_L a} = \frac{8.05}{5.00} = 1.61 \text{ ft}$$

$$H_{tOG} = 1.735 + \frac{1.61}{1.425} = 2.87 \text{ ft}$$

$$Z = H_{tOG} N_{tOG} = 2.87(8.8) = 25.3 \text{ ft} \quad \textbf{Ans.}$$

Nonisothermal operation

All the relationships above for packed towers are correct for either isothermal or non-isothermal operation. For the nonisothermal case, as in adiabatic tray absorbers, the only difficulty will be in the location of the equilibrium curve owing to the temperature rise. For packed towers, the differential equations for heat and mass transfer, together with mass and enthalpy balances, must be integrated numerically in a manner similar to that described for adiabatic contact of a pure liquid with a gas (Chap. 7). This is beyond the scope of this book but is described elsewhere.[13] For relatively dilute solutions, a conservative approximation can be made by assuming that all the heat evolved on absorption is taken up by the liquid, thus neglecting any temperature rise of the gas. This results in a higher liquid temperature than is likely, which will lead to a tower slightly taller than need be used. This method is used in the following example.

Illustration 8.8. In a plant for manufacturing ethyl alcohol by molasses fermentation, the carbon dioxide, CO_2, evolved during fermentation, which contains ethanol vapor, is presently discarded without attempt to recover the ethanol. The CO_2 issues from the fermenters at 1 atm, av temp 80°F, and may be assumed to be in equilibrium at this temperature with an alcohol-water solution containing 6.5 wt % ethanol. The gas volume is 15,000 cu ft/hr. The fermentation liquor (beer) is presently distilled to recover the ethanol, which has a value of $0.10 per pound in the dilute solution (before distillation).

It is proposed to recover the ethanol in the CO_2 by washing the gas with water at 80°F and to use the resultant dilute ethanol solution in making up the fresh fermentation liquor. The plant operates 350 days per year. Duct work presently used to lead the gas away from the fermenters will be adapted to the new absorber. Design the absorber.

Solution. Partial pressures of ethanol and water of aqueous ethanol solutions are shown, in the manner of Othmer and White,[11] in Fig. 8.23. The ethanol pressure from pure water is, of course,

Fig. 8.23 *Equilibrium partial pressure of ethanol-water solutions.*

zero.   The data are from "International Critical Tables," vol. III, p. 290.   Interpolating for 6.5 wt %
ethanol at 80°F (vapor pressure pure $H_2O = 26.3$ mm Hg), $p_{EtOH} = 7.5$ mm Hg, $p_{H_2O} = 25.5$ mm Hg.
For the gas entering the absorber, therefore, $y_1 = 7.5/760 = 0.00986$ mole fraction ethanol.

Gas in

$$15,000(49\%_{40})(\frac{1}{359}) = 38.1 \text{ moles/hr}$$

$$\text{Ethanol in} = 38.1(0.00986) = 0.376 \text{ mole/hr} = 17.3 \text{ lb/hr}$$

$$\text{Water vapor in} = 38.1(25.5/760) = 1.28 \text{ moles/hr} = 23.1 \text{ lb/hr}$$

$$CO_2 \text{ in} = 38.1 - 0.376 - 1.28 = 36.4 \text{ moles/hr} = 1,600 \text{ lb/hr}$$

$$\text{Total wt} = 1,640 \text{ lb/hr}$$

$$\text{Value of ethanol presently lost} = 17.3(350)(24)(0.10) = \$14,550 \text{ per year}$$

Gas out.   Assume temporarily that all ethanol is removed, that the pressure is 1 atm, and that
the gas leaving is saturated with water.   The CO_2 absorption will be negligible.

$$CO_2 \text{ out} = 36.4 \text{ moles/hr} = 1,600 \text{ lb/hr}$$

$$\text{Water vapor out} = \frac{36.4(26.3)}{760 - 26.3} = 1.305 \text{ moles/hr}$$

$$\text{Total gas out} = 36.4 + 1.305 = 37.7 \text{ moles/hr}$$

$$\text{Av gas rate} = \frac{38.1 + 37.7}{2} = 37.9 \text{ moles/hr}$$

Enthalpy, or heat, balance.   "International Critical Tables," vol. V, pp. 159–160, lists heats of
solution of ethanol in water.   For 80°F, expressed in engineering units, some of these are as follows:

x of ethanol	0.05	0.10	0.15	0.20	0.25
Ht of soln at 80°F, Btu/mole ethanol	−3350	−2750	−2020	−1463	−1075

The heats of solution are referred to liquid water and liquid ethanol at 80°F.   Use a base
temperature $t_o = 80°F$.   Rewrite Eq. (8.13) with packed-tower notation

$$H_L L - H_{L2} L_2 = H_G H - H_{G2} G_2 = G_S(H_G' - H_{G2}')$$

where H_G' is molal enthalpy gas/mole dry gas, CO_2.   The water content of the gas will be essentially
constant throughout the absorber, and, neglecting any sensible-heat change of the gas (gas temperature constant at 80°F), the enthalpy of the gas is only the latent heat of vaporization of the
ethanol content, 17,920 Btu/mole ethanol at 80°F. $Y = $ moles ethanol/mole CO_2.

$$G_S(H_G' - H_{G2}') = G_S(17,920)(Y - Y_2)$$

Ethanol balance: $\quad G_S(Y - Y_2) = L_S(X - X_2) = L_S X$

Since the entering liquid is pure water at 80°F, $H_{L2} = 0$.   The heat balance then becomes

$$H_L \frac{L}{L_S} = 17,920X$$

Let $X = 0.01$ mole ethanol/mole water.

$$\therefore \quad L/L_S = 1.01 \qquad x_{EtOH} = \frac{0.01}{1.01} = 0.00989$$

Fig. 8.24 *Adiabatic equilibrium curve, Illustration 8.8.*

From the preceding table, by extrapolation, the heat of solution is -3830 Btu/mole ethanol.   This is converted to Btu/mole solution by multiplying by moles ethanol/mole solution or $X/(1 + X)$.

$$\Delta H_S = -\frac{3,850(0.01)}{1 + 0.01} = -38.2 \text{ Btu/mole solution}$$

$$M_{av} = \frac{0.01(46.05) + 1(18.02)}{1.01} = 18.31 \text{ lb/mole}$$

$$C_L = 1.0 \text{ Btu/(lb)(°F)}$$

Eq. (8.10):
$$H_L = 1.0(t_L - 80)18.31 - 38.2$$

$$\therefore \quad [1.0(t_L - 80)18.31 - 38.2]1.01 = 17,920(0.01)$$

$$t_L = 91.9°F$$

From Fig. 8.23 at this temperature and concentration, the partial pressure of ethanol $= 5.0$ mm Hg. $y_{EtOH}^* = 5.0/760 = 0.00658$.   In similar fashion,

x_{EtOH}	0	0.00497	0.00989	0.01475
t_L, °F	80	86	91.9	97.4
y_{EtOH}^*	0	0.00302	0.00658	0.01316

This provides the equilibrium curve of Fig. 8.24.

   Diameter of absorber. Use 1-in. stoneware Berl saddles.   The average slope of the equilibrium curve is approximately 0.73.   For an economical liquid rate, take $A = L/mG = 1.6$.   Therefore

$L/G = 1.6(0.73) = 1.17$ moles water/mole gas. Therefore use $1.17(37.9) = 44.5$ moles water/hr $= 804$ lb/hr.

At the bottom of the tower, assuming all ethanol is absorbed, the liquid rate is $804 + 17.3 = 821$ lb/hr.

$$\rho_G = \frac{1,640}{15,000} = 0.1093 \text{ lb/cu ft} \qquad \rho_L = 62.0 \text{ lb/cu ft}$$

$$\frac{L'}{G'}\left(\frac{\rho_G}{\rho_L}\right)^{0.5} = \frac{821}{1,640}\left(\frac{0.1093}{62.0}\right)^{0.5} = 0.021$$

At flooding, the ordinate of Fig. 6.26 $= 0.2$. For 1-in. Berl saddles, $C_f = 110$ (Table 6.2). $\mu_L' = 0.95$ centipoise, $\rho_W/\rho_L \doteq 1$. With the notation of Fig. 6.26, at flooding,

$$G' = \left(\frac{0.2 g_c' \rho_G \rho_L}{C_f \mu_L'^{0.2}} \frac{\rho_L}{\rho_W}\right)^{0.5} = \left[\frac{0.2(4.17)(10^8)(0.1093)(62.0)}{110(0.95)^{0.2}}\right]^{0.5}$$

$$= 2,300 \text{ lb/(hr)(sq ft)}$$

To allow for future expansion of the process, use $G' = 800$ lb/(hr)(sq ft). Therefore $L' = 800(821)/1,640 = 400$ lb/(hr)(sq ft). Cross section of tower $= 1,640/800 = 2.05$ sq ft.

$$\text{Tower diam} = \left[\frac{4(2.05)}{\pi}\right]^{0.5} = 1.62 \text{ ft} = 19.5 \text{ in.}$$

Use 20-in. standard pipe.

Tower height. No value of the exit-gas concentration of ethanol y_2 is specified. This is typical, and y_2 must be established by the design engineer.

The greater the extent of absorption of ethanol (the lower the y_2), the taller (and more costly) will be the tower, yet the greater will be the savings from recovery of presently lost ethanol. Clearly there is a most economical value of y_2 which, if the value of lost ethanol is counted as a cost, will correspond to the minimum cost. Ordinarily to determine this, several values of y_2 must be assumed, the corresponding costs determined, and the y_2 for least cost determined from the resulting data. Here, since the solutions are dilute, an analytical expression can be developed for the cost in terms of y_2 which can then be treated formally for determining the economic optimum.

On Fig. 8.24, with y_2 anticipated to be very small, a typical operating line is drawn. The outlet concentration in the liquid is then in the neighborhood of 0.008 mole fraction. The great majority of the transfer units are clearly located at the dilute end of the tower, and the slope of the equilibrium curve at the dilute end (up to $x = 0.007$) is 0.607. Therefore, use the dilute-end absorption factor, $A = L_2/mG_2 = 44.5/0.607(37.7) = 1.94$ to determine the N_{tOG}.

Eq. (8.47):
$$N_{tOG} = \frac{\ln\left[(0.00986/y_2)(1 - 1/1.94) + 1/1.94\right]}{1 - 1/1.94}$$

$$= 2.06 \ln\left(\frac{0.00479}{y_2} + 0.515\right)$$

To determine the mass-transfer coefficients and H_{tOG}, the correlations of Chap. 6 will be used, for which diffusivities are needed. The average liquid temperature $= 85°F = 29.4°C$. "International Critical Tables," vol. V, p. 70, gives the diffusivity of ethanol in water at $x = 0.004$ and $10°C$ as $0.8(10^{-5})$ sq cm/sec. The viscosity of water at $10°C = 1.308$, at $29.4°C = 0.80$ centipoise. Refer to Chap. 2. $T/D_L\mu_L = $ const.

$$\therefore \quad D_L \text{ at } 29.4°C = \frac{29.4 + 273}{10 + 273} \frac{1.308}{0.80} 0.8(10^{-5})$$

$$= 1.4(10^{-5}) \text{ sq cm/sec, or } 5.34(10^{-5}) \text{ sq ft/hr}$$

$$Sc_L = \frac{\mu_L}{\rho_L D_L} = \frac{0.80(2.42)}{62.0(5.34)(10^{-5})} = 575$$

Similarly, by the methods of Chap. 2, $D_G = D_{\text{EtOH-CO}_2} = 0.304$ sq ft/hr.

$$\mu_G \text{ for } CO_2 = 0.015 \text{ centipoise at } 85°F$$

$$Sc_G = \frac{\mu_G}{\rho_G D_G} = \frac{0.015(2.42)}{0.1093(0.304)} = 1.092$$

Table 6.2: $\epsilon = 0.69$.   Table 6.4: $d_s = 0.1050$ ft.   Since the solutions are so dilute, their properties are essentially those of water.   Therefore

$$\beta = 0.965 d_s^{0.376} = 0.412$$

$$\phi_{tW} = \frac{2.50(10^{-5})(400)^{0.412}}{(0.1050)^2} = 0.0267$$

Eq. (6.40):

$$\epsilon_o = \epsilon - \phi_t = 0.69 - 0.0267 = 0.663$$

$$G = \frac{37.9 \text{ moles/hr}}{2.05 \text{ sq ft}} = 18.5 \text{ moles/(hr)(sq ft)}$$

Eq. (6.39):

$$\frac{F_G(1.092)^{\frac{2}{3}}}{18.5} = 1.195\left[\frac{0.1050(800)}{0.015(2.42)(1-0.663)}\right]^{-0.36}$$

$$F_G = 0.93 \text{ lb moles/(hr)(sq ft)}$$

Table 6.3:

$$a_{AW} = a = 15.89(800)^{0.686(10^{-4})(400)-0.1029}$$
$$= 9.48 \text{ sq ft/cu ft}$$

Eq. (8.22):

$$H_{tG} = \frac{G}{F_G a} = \frac{18.5}{0.93(9.48)} = 2.10 \text{ ft}$$

For the liquid, Eq. (6.41):

$$\frac{k_L(0.1050)}{5.34(10^{-5})} = 25.1\left[\frac{0.1050(400)}{0.80(2.42)}\right]^{0.45}(575)^{0.5}$$

$$k_L = 1.15 \text{ lb moles/(hr)(cu ft)(lb mole/cu ft)}$$

$$\text{Av } L = \frac{44.5 \text{ moles } H_2O/hr + 0.376/2 \text{ moles EtOH/hr}}{2.05} = 21.8 \text{ moles/(hr)(sq ft)}$$

$$c = \frac{62.0}{18.2} = 3.44 \text{ lb moles/cu ft}$$

For the dilute solutions used to determine k_L, $(1-x)_{iM} \doteq 1$

Eq. (8.28):

$$H_{tL} = \frac{L}{k_L ac(1-x)_{iM}} = \frac{21.8}{1.15(9.48)(3.44)} = 0.58 \text{ ft}$$

Eq. (8.51), neglecting the concentration ratio,

$$H_{tOG} = 2.10 + \frac{0.58}{1.94} = 2.40 \text{ ft}$$

$$Z = H_{tOG}N_{tOG} = 2.40(2.06) \ln\left(\frac{0.00479}{y_2} + 0.515\right) = 4.90 \ln\left(\frac{0.00479}{y_2} + 0.515\right)$$

Cost for power. For $G' = 800$, $L' = 400$ lb/(hr)(sq ft), the abscissa of Fig. 6.26 = 0.021, the ordinate = 0.0242.   Therefore $\Delta P/Z = (0.175$ in $H_2O/ft)(5.2) = 0.91$ lb/(sq ft)(ft).

$$\Delta P = 0.91Z$$

With an overall efficiency of blower and motor = 50%, the power required for gas flow is

$$\frac{0.91Z(15,000)}{3,600(550)(0.50)} = 0.0138Z \text{ hp}$$

The height of the shell = $Z + 4$ ft, allowing for gas and liquid inlets at the ends. Power for pumping liquid is essentially that to elevate it to the top of the tower, since pipe friction is negligible. For a motor-pump efficiency of 80%, the power for liquid flow is

$$\frac{(Z + 4)(804)}{3,600(550)(0.80)} = 0.000506(Z + 4) \text{ hp}$$

At $0.015 per kilowatt-hour the annual power cost is

$$[0.0138Z + 0.000506(Z + 4)](0.7457)(350)(24)(0.015) = 13.48Z + 1.90 \qquad \$/yr$$

Cost of equipment. This must be expressed as an annual cost to make it additive with the power cost.

$$\text{Cost of packing} = \$10/\text{cu ft or } 2.05Z(10) = \$20.5Z$$

Twenty-inch pipe weighs 123 lb/ft, and at $0.20 per pound, the tower shell cost is $123(0.20)(Z + 4) = \$24.6(Z + 4)$.

Allowing a factor of 100% for end closures, foundation, piping, and installation, the cost of the tower is

$$[20.5Z + 24.6(Z + 4)]2 = \$(90.2Z + 196.8)$$

If the cost of the installation is amortized over 3 years, and the maintenance cost is 5% annually, the annual cost of the tower is

$$\frac{90.2Z + 196.8}{3} + 0.05[20.5Z + 24.6(Z + 4)] = 32.3Z + 70.5 \qquad \$/yr$$

To this must be added the annual cost P of installed pump, blower, and motors. Since such equipment is available in incremental sizes, the choice will not depend on Z for substantial ranges of Z, and need not be evaluated now.

Cost of alcohol. The value of the lost alcohol (mol wt 46.05) in the scrubbed gas is

$$y_2(37.7)(46.05)(0.10)(350)(24) = 1,460,000 y_2 \qquad \$/yr$$

Total annual cost C

$$C = (32.3Z + 70.5 + P) + (13.48Z + 1.90) + 1,460,000 y_2 \qquad \$/yr$$

Substituting the value of Z, this becomes

$$C = 225 \ln \left(\frac{0.00479}{y_2} + 0.515 \right) + 72.4 + P + 1,460,000 y_2$$

To make this a minimum, dC/dy_2 is set equal to zero:

$$\frac{dC}{dy_2} = \frac{-225(0.00479)/y_2^2}{0.00479/y_2 + 0.515} + 1,460,000 = 0$$

Optimum $y_2 = 0.0001515$ mole fraction ethanol in the exit gas.

$$Z = 4.90 \ln (0.00479/0.0001515 + 0.515) = 17 \text{ ft packed height.}$$

The annual cost is then $C = 1,074 + P$ dollars per year. If the pump, blower, and motors cost $300, with 100% allowed for installation and 5% for maintenance, $P = 300(\frac{2}{3} + 0.05) = \$215$ per year, and the annual cost is $1,289, representing a savings over present practice of $14,550 - 1,289 = \$13,261$.

There are other economic balances which may be made for this design.   Thus, the absorption factor was chosen arbitrarily here, but it influences the cost.   Larger packing sizes cost less per cubic foot and offer less gas pressure drop per foot, but their H_{tOG} is greater, and therefore an optimum packing size exists.   Other packing types may be investigated.   If there is no concern about future expansion of the process, a closer approach to flooding will lead to lower H_{tOG} but higher gas pressure drop, and the gas mass velocity then is subject to economic balance.

MULTICOMPONENT SYSTEMS

The previous discussion has assumed that only one component of the gas stream has an appreciable solubility in the absorbent liquid.   When the gas contains more than one soluble component, or where the solvent gas itself has an appreciable solubility, some modifications are necessary.   The almost complete lack of solubility data for multicomponent systems, except where ideal solutions are formed in the liquid phase and the solubilities of the various components are therefore mutually independent, unfortunately makes estimates of even the ordinary cases very difficult.   However, some of the more important industrial applications fall in the ideal-solution category, e.g., the absorption of hydrocarbons from gas mixtures in nonvolatile hydrocarbon oils as in the recovery of natural gasoline.

In principle, the problem for tray towers should be capable of solution by the same tray-to-tray methods used in Illustration 8.4 for one component absorbed, through Eqs. (8.9) to (8.13).   These expressions are indeed valid.   If, as with one component absorbed, computations are to be started at the bottom of the tower, the outlet-liquid temperature and composition must be known.   This, as before, requires that the outlet-gas temperature be estimated, but in addition, in order to complete the enthalpy balance of Eq. (8.9), also requires that the complete outlet-gas composition with respect to each component be estimated at the start.   Herein lies the difficulty.

The quantities which are ordinarily fixed before an absorber design is started are the following:

1. Rate of flow, composition, and temperature of entering gas.
2. Composition and temperature of entering liquid (but not flow rate).
3. Pressure of operation.
4. Heat gain or loss (even if set at zero, as for adiabatic operation).

Under these circumstances it can be shown[10] that the principal variables still remaining are:

1. The liquid flow rate (or liquid/gas ratio).
2. The number of ideal trays.
3. The fractional absorption of any one component.

Any *two of these last, but not all three*, may be arbitrarily fixed for a given design. Having specified two, the third is automatically fixed, as is the extent of absorption of all substances not already specified and the outlet-stream temperatures.   For example, if the liquid rate and number of ideal trays are specified, the extent of absorption of each substance of the gas is automatically fixed and may not be arbitrarily chosen. Or, if the liquid rate and extent of absorption of one substance are specified, the number of ideal trays and the extent of absorption of all components are automatically fixed and may not be chosen arbitrarily.

As a result, for the tray-to-tray calculations suggested above, not only must the outlet-gas temperature be guessed, but also the complete outlet-gas composition, all to be checked at the end of the calculation.   This becomes so hopeless a trial-and-error procedure that it cannot be done practically without some guidance.   This is provided through an approximate procedure, either that offered by the Kremser equations, which apply only for constant absorption factor, or through some procedure allowing for variation of the absorption factor with tray number.   To establish the latter, we first need an exact expression for the absorber with varying absorption factor.   This was first derived by Horton and Franklin,[9] as outlined below.

Refer to Fig. 8.25, which shows a multitray absorber or stripper.   Since all components may transfer between gas and liquid, there may be no substance which passes through at constant rate in the gas, for example.   It is convenient, therefore, to define all gas compositions in terms of the entering gas, and similarly all liquid compositions in terms of the entering liquid.   Thus, for any component in the liquid leaving any tray n,

$$X'_n = \frac{\text{moles component in } L_n/\text{time}}{L_0} = \frac{x_n L_n}{L_0}$$

Fig. 8.25   *Multicomponent absorber or stripper.*

and for any component in the gas G_n,

$$Y'_n = \frac{\text{moles component in } G_n/\text{time}}{G_{Np+1}} = \frac{y_n G_n}{G_{Np+1}}$$

where x and y are the usual mole fractions.

The equations which follow may all be written separately for each component. Consider the tower of Fig. 8.25 to be an absorber. A material balance for any component about ideal tray n is

$$L_0(X'_n - X'_{n-1}) = G_{Np+1}(Y'_{n+1} - Y'_n) \tag{8.54}$$

The equilibrium relation for the ideal tray is†

$$y_n = m_n x_n \tag{8.55}$$

or, in terms of the new concentrations,

$$Y'_n \frac{G_{Np+1}}{G_n} = m_n X'_n \frac{L_0}{L_n} \tag{8.56}$$

Similarly, for tray $n - 1$,

$$Y'_{n-1} \frac{G_{Np+1}}{G_{n-1}} = m_{n-1} X'_{n-1} \frac{L_0}{L_{n-1}} \tag{8.57}$$

Solving Eqs. (8.56) and (8.57) for the X's, substituting in Eq. (8.54), and rearranging, we have

$$Y'_n = \frac{Y'_{n+1} + A_{n-1} Y'_{n-1}}{1 + A_n} \tag{8.58}$$

where $A_n = L_n/m_n G_n$ and $A_{n-1} = L_{n-1}/m_{n-1} G_{n-1}$ are the component absorption factors on the two trays.

If the absorber contained only one tray ($n = 1$), Eq. (8.58) would read

$$Y'_1 = \frac{Y'_2 + A_0 Y'_0}{1 + A_1} \tag{8.59}$$

From Eq. (8.57),

$$Y'_0 = m_0 X'_0 \frac{L_0}{L_0} \frac{G_0}{G_{Np+1}} = \frac{m_0 X'_0 G_0}{G_{Np+1}} \tag{8.60}$$

and

$$A_0 Y'_0 = \frac{L_0}{m_0 G_0} \frac{m_0 X'_0 G_0}{G_{Np+1}} = \frac{L_0 X'_0}{G_{Np+1}} \tag{8.61}$$

Substituting this into Eq. (8.59) provides

$$Y'_1 = \frac{Y'_2 + L_0 X'_0/G_{Np+1}}{1 + A_1} \tag{8.62}$$

If the absorber contained two trays, Eq. (8.58) with $n = 2$ would become

$$Y'_2 = \frac{Y'_3 + A_1 Y'_1}{1 + A_2} \tag{8.63}$$

Substituting Y'_1 from Eq. (8.62) and rearranging,

$$Y'_2 = \frac{(A_1 + 1) Y'_3 + A_1 L_0 X'_0/G_{Np+1}}{A_1 A_2 + A_2 + 1} \tag{8.64}$$

Similarly, for a three-tray absorber,

$$Y'_3 = \frac{(A_1 A_2 + A_2 + 1) Y'_4 + A_1 A_2 L_0 X'_0/G_{Np+1}}{A_1 A_2 A_3 + A_2 A_3 + A_3 + 1} \tag{8.65}$$

---

† The ratio y/x at equilibrium is usually written as K, but here we use m to distinguish this from the mass-transfer coefficients.

and for N_p trays,

Y'_{Np}

$$= \frac{(A_1A_2A_3 \cdots A_{Np-1} + A_2A_3 \cdots A_{Np-1} + \cdots + A_{Np-1} + 1)Y'_{Np+1} + A_1A_2 \cdots A_{Np-1}L_0X_0/G_{Np+1}}{A_1A_2A_3 \cdots A_{Np} + A_2A_3 \cdots A_{Np} + \cdots + A_{Np} + 1}$$

(8.66)

In order to eliminate Y'_{Np}, which is inside the absorber, a component material balance about the entire absorber,

$$L_0(X'_{Np} - X'_0) = G_{Np+1}(Y'_{Np+1} - Y'_1)$$

(8.67)

and Eq. (8.56) for $n = N_p$,

$$Y'_{Np} = m_{Np}X'_{Np}\frac{L_0}{L_{Np}}\frac{G_{Np}}{G_{Np+1}} = \frac{L_0X'_{Np}}{A_{Np}G_{Np+1}}$$

(8.68)

are solved simultaneously to eliminate X'_{Np}, the result substituted for Y'_{Np} in Eq. (8.68), whence rearrangement yields

$$\begin{aligned}\frac{Y'_{Np+1} - Y'_1}{Y'_{Np+1}} &= \frac{A_1A_2A_3 \cdots A_{Np} + A_2A_3 \cdots A_{Np} + \cdots + A_{Np}}{A_1A_2A_3 \cdots A_{Np} + A_2A_3 \cdots A_{Np} + \cdots + A_{Np} + 1} \\ &- \frac{L_0X'_0}{G_{Np+1}Y'_{Np+1}}\frac{A_2A_3A_4 \cdots A_{Np} + A_3A_4 \cdots A_{Np} + \cdots + A_{Np} + 1}{A_1A_2A_3 \cdots A_{Np} + A_2A_3 \cdots A_{Np} + \cdots + A_{Np} + 1}\end{aligned}$$

(8.69)

Equation (8.69) is an expression for the fractional absorption of any component, exact because it is based only upon material balances and the condition of equilibrium which defines an ideal tray.

A similar expression for strippers is

$$\begin{aligned}\frac{X'_0 - X'_{Np}}{X'_0} &= \frac{S_1S_2 \cdots S_{Np} + S_1S_2 \cdots S_{Np-1} + \cdots + S_1}{S_1S_2 \cdots S_{Np} + S_1S_2 \cdots S_{Np-1} + \cdots + S_1 + 1} \\ &- \frac{G_{Np+1}Y'_{Np+1}}{L_0X'_0}\frac{S_1S_2 \cdots S_{Np-1} + S_1S_2 \cdots S_{Np-2} + \cdots + S_1 + 1}{S_1S_2 \cdots S_{Np} + S_1S_2 \cdots S_{Np-1} + \cdots + S_1 + 1}\end{aligned}$$

(8.70)

In order to use Eqs. (8.69) or (8.70), the L/G ratio for each tray and the tray temperatures (which determine the m's) are required to compute the A's or the S's. If the liquids are not ideal, m for any component on any tray additionally depends upon the complete liquid composition on the tray. The same is true for the gas compositions under conditions for which the gas solutions are not ideal. The equations are practically useful, therefore, only for ideal solutions.

As an approximation,[9] the gas rate G_n for tray n of an absorber may be estimated on the assumption that the fractional absorption is the same for each tray:

$$\frac{G_n}{G_{n+1}} \doteq \left(\frac{G_1}{G_{Np+1}}\right)^{1/N_p}$$

(8.71)

or

$$G_n \doteq G_{Np+1}\left(\frac{G_1}{G_{Np+1}}\right)^{(N_p+1-n)/N_p}$$

(8.72)

The liquid rate L_n may then be obtained by material balance to the end of the tower. Similarly in strippers,

$$L_n \doteq L_0\left(\frac{L_{Np}}{L_0}\right)^{n/N_p}$$

(8.73)

where G_n is determined by material balance. If the molar latent heats and heat capacities are all alike for all components, and if no heat of solution is evolved, the temperature rise on absorption is roughly proportional to the amount of absorption, so that, approximately,

$$\frac{G_{Np+1} - G_{n+1}}{G_{Np+1} - G_1} \doteq \frac{t_{Np} - t_n}{t_{Np} - t_0} \tag{8.74}$$

and similarly for stripping,

$$\frac{L_0 - L_n}{L_0 - L_{Np}} \doteq \frac{t_0 - t_n}{t_0 - t_{Np}} \tag{8.75}$$

In order further to simplify the computations, Edmister[5] has writtten the Horton-Franklin equations in terms of average or "effective" absorption and stripping factors instead of the A's and S's for each tray. Thus, for absorption, Eq. (8.69) becomes

$$\frac{Y'_{Np+1} - Y'_1}{Y'_{Np+1}} = \left(1 - \frac{L_0 X'_0}{A' G_{Np+1} Y'_{Np+1}}\right) \frac{A_E^{Np+1} - A_E}{A_E^{Np+1} - 1} \tag{8.76}$$

For a two-tray absorber, it develops that

$$A' = \frac{A_{Np}(A_1 + 1)}{A_{Np} + 1} \tag{8.77}$$

and

$$A_E = [A_{Np}(A_1 + 1) + 0.25]^{0.5} - 0.5 \tag{8.78}$$

These are exact, but it is found that Eqs. (8.76) to (8.78) apply reasonably well for any number of trays, provided that unusual temperature profiles (such as a maximum temperature on an intermediate tray) do not develop. If $X'_0 = 0$, Eq. (8.76) is the Kremser equation. It is also convenient to note that $(A_E^{Np+1} - A_E)/(A_E^{Np+1} - 1)$ is the Kremser function [Eq. (5.54)], and the ordinate of Fig. 5.16 is 1 minus this function. Similarly for stripping,

$$\frac{X'_0 - X'_{Np}}{X'_0} = \left(1 - \frac{G_{Np+1} Y'_{Np+1}}{S' L_0 X'_0}\right) \frac{S_E^{Np+1} - S_E}{S_E^{Np+1} - 1} \tag{8.79}$$

with

$$S' = \frac{S_1(S_{Np} + 1)}{S_1 + 1} \tag{8.80}$$

and

$$S_E = [S_1(S_{Np} + 1) + 0.25]^{0.5} - 0.5 \tag{8.81}$$

Equation (8.79) becomes the Kremser equation if $Y'_{Np+1} = 0$.

Components present only in the entering gas will be absorbed, and those present only in the entering liquid will be stripped. If a component is present in both streams, the terms in the parentheses of the right-hand sides of Eqs. (8.76) and (8.79) are computed, and the equation is used which provides the positive quantity.

Equations (8.76) and (8.79) may be used to determine the number of ideal trays required to absorb or strip a component to a specified extent and to estimate the extent of absorption or stripping of all other components. This then provides a basis for using the exact equations of Horton and Franklin, Eqs. (8.69) and (8.70). These latter may be used only for an integral number of ideal trays. A change of L_0/G_{Np+1} may be necessary to meet the specifications exactly with such an integral number; alternatively the nearest larger integral number of trays may be accepted.

Illustration 8.9. A gas analyzing 70 mole % CH_4, 15% C_2H_6, 10% n-C_3H_8, and 5% n-C_4H_{10}, at 75°F, 2 atm, is to be scrubbed in an adiabatic tray absorber with a liquid containing 1 mole % n-C_4H_{10}, 99% nonvolatile hydrocarbon oil, at 75°F, using 3.5 moles liquid/mole entering gas. The pressure is to be 2 atm, and at least 70% of the C_3H_8 of the entering gas is to be absorbed. The solubility of CH_4 in the liquid will be considered negligible, and the other components form ideal solutions. Estimate the number of ideal trays required and the composition of the effluent streams.

Solution. In what follows, CH_4, C_2H_6, C_3H_8, and C_4H_{10} will be identified as C_1, C_2, C_3, and C_4, respectively. Physical properties are:

Component	Av sp ht, 0 to 100°F, Btu/(lb mole)(°F)		Latent heat of vaporization, 0°F, Btu/lb mole	$m = \dfrac{y^{*}\dagger}{x}$		
	Gas	Liquid		75°F	80°F	85°F
C_1	8.50					
C_2	12.71	25.10	5,100	13.1	13.5	14.0
C_3	18.16	27.8	7,600	4.00	4.25	4.50
C_4	24.45	33.1	10,100	1.15	1.25	1.35
Oil		90.0				

† Values of m from C. L. Depriester, *Chem. Eng. Progr. Symp. Ser.*, **49** (7), 1 (1953).

Basis: 1 lb mole entering gas; $t_o = 0$°F; enthalpies are referred to gaseous C_1 and other components liquid at 0°F. Gas in: $G_{Np+1} = 1.0$ lb mole, $t_{Np+1} = 75$°F.

Component	$Y'_{Np+1} = y_{Np+1}$	Enthalpy, Btu/lb mole	$H_{G,Np+1}y_{Np+1}$
C_1	0.70	$8.50(75 - 0) = 638$	$446 = 638(0.70)$
C_2	0.15	$12.71(75 - 0) + 5,100 = 6,055$	910
C_3	0.10	$18.16(75 - 0) + 7,600 = 8,960$	896
C_4	0.05	$24.45(75 - 0) + 10,000 = 11,930$	596
	1.00		$2,848 = H_{G,Np+1}$

Liquid in: $L_0 = 3.5$ lb moles, $t_0 = 75$°F.

Component	$X'_0 = x_0$	$L_0X'_0$	Enthalpy, Btu/lb mole	$H_{L0}L_0X'_0$
C_4	0.01	0.035	$33.1(75 - 0) = 2,480$	$86.9 = 2,480(0.035)$
Oil	0.99	3.465	$90.0(75 - 0) = 6,750$	23,400
	1.00	3.50		$23,487 = H_{L0}L_0$

Preliminary calculations. The total absorption is estimated to be 0.15 lb mole, and an average temperature 80°F is assumed.   A rough value of L/G at the top is then $3.5/(1 - 0.15) = 4.20$, and at the bottom $(3.5 + 0.15)/1.0 = 3.65$, with an average of 3.93.   The number of ideal trays is fixed by the C_3 absorption specified.   For C_3, m at 80°F $= 4.25$, rough $A = 3.93/4.25 = 0.925$.   Equation (8.76), with fractional absorption $= 0.7$ and $X_0' = 0$,

$$0.7 = \frac{0.925^{Np+1} - 0.925}{0.925^{Np+1} - 1}$$

This can be solved for N_p directly.   Alternatively, since Fig. 5.16 has as its ordinate $(1 -$ Kremser function$) = 0.3$, then with $A = 0.925$, $N_p = 2.8$.   Since the Horton-Franklin equations will be used later, an integral number of trays $N_p = 3$ is chosen.   Figure 5.16 with $N_p = 3$, $A = 0.925$, shows an ordinate of 0.28, or 0.72 fraction of C_3 absorbed.

$$\frac{Y'_{Np+1} - Y'_1}{Y'_{Np+1}} = \frac{0.10 - Y'_1}{0.10} = 0.72$$

$$Y'_1 = 0.028 \text{ lb mole } C_3 \text{ in } G_1$$

For C_2, $m = 13.5$ at 80°F, rough $A = 3.93/13.5 = 0.291$.   At low A's, Fig. 5.16 shows the ordinate to be $1 - A$, and the fractional absorption $= 0.291$.

$$\frac{Y'_{Np+1} - Y'_1}{Y'_{Np+1}} = \frac{0.15 - Y'_1}{0.15} = 0.291$$

$$Y'_1 = 0.1064 \text{ lb mole } C_2 \text{ in } G_1$$

C_4 is present in both entering liquid and gas.   At 80°F, $m = 1.25$, rough $A = 3.93/1.25 = 3.15$, rough $S = 1/3.15 = 0.317$.   Then

$$1 - \frac{L_0 X_0'}{A' G_{Np+1} Y'_{Np+1}} = 1 - \frac{3.5(0.01)}{3.15(1.0)(0.05)} = +0.778$$

$$1 - \frac{G_{Np+1} Y'_{Np+1}}{S' L_0 X_0'} = 1 - \frac{1(0.05)}{0.317(3.5)(0.01)} = -3.48$$

The C_4 will therefore be absorbed.   Equation (8.76):

$$\frac{0.05 - Y'_1}{0.05} = 0.778 \frac{3.15^4 - 3.15}{3.15^4 - 1}$$

At $N_p = 3$, $A = 3.15$, Fig. 5.16 provides an ordinate of 0.023.   Therefore

$$\frac{0.05 - Y'_1}{0.05} = 0.778(1 - 0.023)$$

$$Y'_1 = 0.0120 \text{ lb mole } C_4 \text{ in } G_1$$

Edmister method. Estimate the top-tray temperature $t_1 = 77$°F.   This is to be verified later. The results of the preliminary calculations then give the following approximate results:

G_1

Component	Y'_1	Enthalpy, Btu/lb mole	$H_{G1} Y'_1$
C_1	0.70	$8.5(77 - 0) = 655$	$459 = 655(0.70)$
C_2	0.1064	$12.71(77 - 0) + 5,100 = 6,080$	648
C_3	0.0280	$18.16(77 - 0) + 7,600 = 9,000$	252
C_4	0.0120	$24.4(77 - 0) + 10,000 = 11,982$	144
	$0.8464 = G_1$		$1,503 = H_{G1} G_1$

L_3

Component	Lb moles $= L_3 x_3$	Enthalpy	$H_{L3}L_3 x_3$
C_2	$0.15 - 0.1064 = 0.0436$	$25.0 t_3$	$1.093 t_3 = 0.0436(25.0) t_3$
C_3	$0.10 - 0.028 = 0.0720$	$27.8 t_3$	$2.00 t_3$
C_4	$0.035 + 0.05 - 0.012 = 0.0730$	$33.1 t_3$	$2.42 t_3$
Oil	3.465	$90.0 t_3$	$312 t_3$
	$L_3 = 3.654$		$317.5 t_3 = H_{L3}L_3$

Overall enthalpy balance, Eq. (8.9) with $Q_T = 0$, $G_{Np+1} = 1.0$, $N_p = 3$:

$$23,487 + 2,848 = 317.5 t_3 + 1,503$$
$$t_3 = 78.5°F$$

Equation (8.76) may now be used to obtain a second approximation of the effluent compositions.

Eq. (8.72) with $n = 2$: $G_2 = 1.0 \left(\dfrac{0.8464}{1.0} \right)^{(3+1-2)/3} = 0.894$

Eq. (8.11) with $n = 1$: $L_1 + 1.0 = 3.654 + 0.894$

$$L_1 = 3.548$$

$$\frac{L_1}{G_1} = \frac{3.548}{0.8464} = 4.195$$

Eq. (8.72) with $n = 3$: $G_3 = 1.0 \left(\dfrac{0.8464}{1.0} \right)^{(3+1-3)/3} = 0.947$

$$\frac{L_3}{G_3} = \frac{4.654}{0.947} = 3.86$$

For C_4: m at 77°F $= 1.19$ $A_1 = \dfrac{4.195}{1.19} = 3.51$

m at 78.5°F $= 1.22$ $A_3 = \dfrac{3.86}{1.22} = 3.16 = A_{Np}$

Eq. (8.77): $A' = 3.43$
Eq. (8.78): $A_E = 3.31$
Eq. (8.76): $Y_1' = 0.0110$ lb mole C_4 in G_1
C_4 in $L_3 = 0.035 + 0.05 - 0.0110 = 0.0740$ lb mole $= L_3 x_3$

In similar fashion, the Y_1''s for the other components, together with outlet gas and outlet liquid enthalpies, may be computed:

Component	Y_1'	$H_{G1}Y_1'$, 77°F	$L_3 x_3$	$H_{L3}L_3 x_3$
C_1	0.700	459	0	0
C_2	0.1064	645	0.044	$1.10 t_3$
C_3	0.0278	250	0.0722	$2.01 t_3$
C_4	0.0110	132	0.0740	$2.45 t_3$
Oil			3.465	$312 t_3$
	$0.8448 = G_1$	$1,486 = H_{G1}G_1$	$3.655 = L_3$	$317.6 t_3 = H_{L3}L_3$

Equation (8.9) again shows $t_3 = 78.5°F$. The results are sufficiently close to those of the first estimate that we may proceed with Eq. (8.69).

Horton-Franklin method. Equations (8.72) and (8.11), used as above with $G_1 = 0.8448$, now show

Tray n	G_n	L_n	$\dfrac{L_n}{G_n}$	t_n, °F
1	0.8448	3.548	4.20	77
2	0.893	3.583	4.01	77
3	0.928	3.655	3.94	78.5

t_2 is estimated through Eq. (8.74) with $n = 2$:

$$\frac{1 - 0.928}{1 - 0.8448} = \frac{78.5 - t_2}{78.5 - 75}$$

The temperatures permit tabulation of m's, and the L_n/G_n's permit calculation of A for each component on each tray. Equation (8.69) then gives Y_1' and a material balance the moles of each component in L_3:

Component	A_1	A_2	A_3	Y_1' [Eq. (8.69)]	L_3x_3
C_1				0.700	0
C_2	0.318	0.304	0.294	0.1062	0.0448
C_3	1.025	0.979	0.938	0.0263	0.0737
C_4	3.53	3.37	3.23	0.0108	0.0742
Oil					3.465
				$0.8433 = G_1$	$3.658 = L_3$

An enthalpy balance again shows $t_3 = 78.5°F$.

For most purposes, the preceding results will be reasonably satisfactory. But they are correct only if the A values for each component on each tray are correct. These may be checked by first verifying the L/G ratios. For the components found in both liquid and gas,

$$A_n = \frac{L_n}{m_n G_n} = \frac{L_n}{(y_n/x_n)G_n} \tag{8.82}$$

or

$$G_n y_n = \frac{L_n x_n}{A_n} \tag{8.83}$$

If there are G_S moles/time of nonabsorbed gas, then

$$G_n = G_S + \Sigma \frac{L_n x_n}{A_n} \tag{8.84}$$

and Eq. (8.11) will provide $L_n x_n$, whose sum is L_n.   The L_n/G_n ratios may then be compared with those used previously.

Illustration 8.9, continued. For tray 3, $G_s = 0.7$ lb mole C_1.   For C_2, $G_3 y_3 = 0.0448/0.294 = 0.1522$, and Eq. (8.11) with $n = 2$ provides $L_2 x_2 = 0.0448 + 0.1522 - 0.15 = 0.0470$.   Similarly,

Component	$G_3 y_3$	$L_2 x_2$
C_1	0.700	
C_2	0.1522	0.0470
C_3	0.0785	0.0522
C_4	0.0230	0.0472
Oil		3.465
	$0.9537 = G_3$	$3.6114 = L_2$

The value of $L_2 x_2$ is similarly used with the previous A_2's to obtain G_2, etc.   In this way it is found that

$$\frac{L_3}{G_3} = \frac{3.658}{0.9537} = 3.84 \qquad \frac{L_2}{G_2} = 3.82 \qquad \frac{L_1}{G_1} = 3.98$$

which are different from those used before.

The procedure then to be followed is to repeat the use of Eq. (8.69) with the new L/G ratios to provide A's, repeating the check of L/G and use of Eq. (8.69) until agreement is reached.   This still leaves the temperatures to be checked.   For an assumed top-tray temperature, an overall tower enthalpy balance provides t_{Np}.   With the compositions and flow rates for each stream as last determined, individual tray enthalpy balances provide the temperature of each tray.   These are repeated until the assumed t_1 agrees with that calculated.   New m's and A's are then used with Eq. (8.69), and the entire procedure repeated until a completely consistent set of L/G's and temperatures are obtained, at which time the problem is solved.   The procedure is very tedious, and methods for reducing the work, including the use of high-speed computers, have been given much study.[6,8,14]

Use of reflux—reboiled absorbers

Refer again to the preceding illustration.   Considering only the three substances absorbed, the wet gas contained these roughly in the proportions $C_2H_6 : C_3H_8 : C_4H_{10} = 50 : 33 : 17$.   The rich oil leaving the absorber contained the same substances in the approximate ratio $23 : 38 : 39$.   Despite its low solubility, the proportion of absorbed gas which is ethane is high, owing to the relatively high proportion of this substance in the original wet gas.   If it is desired to reduce the relative proportions of ethane in the rich oil, the oil just as it leaves the tower must be in contact with a gas relatively leaner in ethane and richer in propane and butane.   Such a gas can be

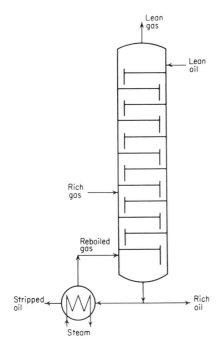

Fig. 8.26 *Reboiled absorber.*

obtained by heating a part of the rich oil, which will then evolve a gas of the required low ethane content. This evolved gas may then be returned to an extension of the absorber below the inlet of the wet gas, where in rising past the oil it will strip out the ethane (and also any methane which may have been absorbed as well). The ethane not absorbed will now, of course, leave with the lean gas. The heat exchanger where a portion of the rich oil is heated is called a *reboiler*, and the arrangement of Fig. 8.26 may be used.

A stream returned to a cascade of stages, as represented by the trays in the absorber, for the purposes of obtaining an enrichment beyond that obtained by counter-current contact with the feed to the cascade, is called *reflux*. This principle is used extensively in distillation, liquid extraction, and adsorption, but it is applicable to any countercurrent enrichment operation.

NOTATION FOR CHAPTER 8

a	= interfacial surface, sq ft/cu ft active volume
A	= absorption factor = L/mG, dimensionless
c	= concentration, lb moles/cu ft
C_L	= specific heat of the liquid, Btu/(lb)(°F)
d	= differential operator

D	= diffusivity, sq ft/hr
E_{MGE}	= Murphree gas tray efficiency, corrected for entrainment, fractional
E_o	= overall tray efficiency, fractional
F	= mass-transfer coefficient, lb moles/(hr)(sq ft)
F_o	= overall mass-transfer coefficient, lb moles/(hr)(sq ft)
G	= total gas rate, lb moles/hr for tray towers, lb moles/(hr)(sq ft) for packed towers
G'	= total gas rate, lb/(hr)(sq ft)
G_s	= rate of solvent gas, lb mole/hr for tray towers, lb moles/(hr)(sq ft) for packed towers
H_G	= gas enthalpy, Btu/lb mole
H'_G	= gas enthalpy, Btu for the gas/lb mole solvent gas
H_L	= liquid enthalpy, Btu/lb mole liquid
H_t	= height of a transfer unit, ft
H_{to}	= overall height of a transfer unit, ft
ΔH_S	= integral heat of solution, Btu/lb mole solution
k_G	= gas mass-transfer coefficient, lb moles/(hr)(sq ft)(atm)
k_L	= liquid mass-transfer coefficient, lb moles/(hr)(sq ft)(lb moles/cu ft)
k_x	= liquid mass-transfer coefficient, lb moles/(hr)(sq ft)(mole fraction)
k_y	= gas mass-transfer coefficient, lb moles/(hr)(sq ft)(mole fraction)
K	= overall mass-transfer coefficient (units indicated by subscript as for k's)
ln	= natural logarithm
log	= common logarithm
L	= total liquid rate, lb moles/hr for tray towers, lb moles/(hr)(sq ft) for packed towers
L'	= total liquid rate, lb moles/(hr)(sq ft)
L_S	= rate of solvent liquid, lb moles/hr for tray towers, lb moles/(hr)(sq ft) for packed towers
m	= slope of the equilibrium curve = dy^*/dx
M	= molecular weight, lb/lb mole
N_A	= mass-transfer flux of A, lb moles/(hr)(sq ft)
N_p	= number of ideal trays, plates, or stages
N_t	= number of transfer units
N_{to}	= overall number of transfer units
p	= partial pressure, atm
p^*	= partial pressure in equilibrium with a liquid solution, atm
P	= vapor pressure, atm
P_t	= total pressure, atm
q, r, s	= constants
S	= interfacial surface, sq ft/sq ft tower cross section
	= stripping factor, mG/L
t_L	= liquid temperature, °F
t_o	= base temperature for enthalpy, °F
x	= concentration in the bulk liquid, mole fraction
x^*	= concentration in equilibrium with the bulk gas, mole fraction
x_i	= concentration in the liquid at the interface, mole fraction
X	= concentration in the bulk liquid, lb moles solute/lb mole solvent
X^*	= concentration in equilibrium with bulk gas concentration, lb moles solute/lb mole solvent
X'	= concentration in the bulk liquid, lb moles/lb mole entering liquid
y	= concentration in the bulk gas, mole fraction
y^*	= concentration in the gas in equilibrium with the bulk liquid, mole fraction
y_i	= concentration in the gas at the interface, mole fraction
Y	= concentration in the bulk gas, lb moles solute/lb mole solvent gas
Y^*	= concentration in equilibrium with the bulk liquid, lb moles solute/lb mole solvent gas
Y'	= concentration in the bulk gas, lb moles/lb mole entering gas
Z	= height of packing

Subscripts

av   = average
G = gas
i = interface
L = liquid
M = logarithmic mean
n = effluent from tray n
$n + 1$ = effluent from tray $n + 1$
Np = effluent from tray N_p
$Np + 1$ = effluent from tray $N_p + 1$
O = overall (transfer units and mass-transfer coefficients)
0   = entering liquid (tray tower)
1   = bottom (of a packed tower); effluent from tray 1 (tray tower)
2   = top (of a packed tower); effluent from tray 2 (tray tower)

REFERENCES

   1. Baker, T. C.: *Ind. Eng. Chem.*, **27,** 977 (1935).
   2. Chilton, T. H., and A. P. Colburn: *Ind. Eng. Chem.*, **27,** 255 (1935).
   3. Colburn, A. P.: *Trans. AIChE*, **35,** 211 (1939).
   4. Colburn, A. P.: *Ind. Eng. Chem.*, **33,** 111 (1941).
   5. Edmister, W. C.: *Ind. Eng. Chem.*, **35,** 837 (1943).
   6. Friday, J. R., and B. D. Smith: *AIChE J.*, **10,** 698 (1964).
   7. Hachmuth, K. H.: *Chem. Eng. Progr.*, **45,** 716 (1949); **47,** 523, 621 (1951).
   8. Holland, C. D.: "Multicomponent Distillation," Prentice-Hall, Inc., Englewood Cliffs, N.J., 1963.
   9. Horton, G., and W. B. Franklin: *Ind. Eng. Chem.*, **32,** 1384 (1940).
   10. Kwauk, M.: *AIChE J.*, **2,** 240 (1956).
   11. Othmer, D. F., and R. E. White: *Ind. Eng. Chem.*, **34,** 952 (1942).
   12. Rackett, H. G.: *Chem. Eng.*, Dec. 21, 1964, p. 108.
   13. Sherwood, T. K., and R. L. Pigford: "Absorption and Extraction," 2d ed., McGraw-Hill Book Company, New York, 1952.
   14. Smith, B. D.: "Design of Equilibrium Stage Processes," McGraw-Hill Book Company, New York, 1963.

PROBLEMS

   8.1. A scheme for removal of hydrogen sulfide from a gas by scrubbing with water at 75°F is being considered.   The gas contains 2% H_2S and is to be scrubbed to a concentration of 0.1% H_2S.   The water is H_2S-free.   Henry's law describes the solubility, and $p^*/x = 545$ atm/mole fraction.

   a. For a countercurrent absorber, calculate the liquid/gas ratio, moles water/mole gas for 1.2 times the minimum, and the composition of the exit liquid, (1) if the pressure is 1 atm, and (2) if the pressure is 10 atm.

   b. The absorber for (*a*) would have to be excessively tall, and the various schemes in Fig. 8.27 are being considered as means of using two shorter absorbers.   Make freehand sketches of operating diagrams, one for each scheme, showing the relation between operating lines for the two absorbers and the equilibrium curve.   Mark the concentrations of Fig. 8.27 on each diagram, but do not compute the concentrations.

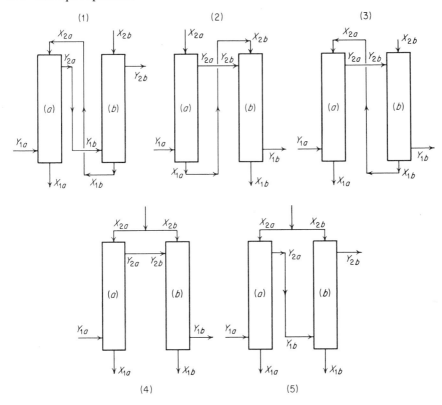

Fig. 8.27 *Absorber arrangement for Prob. 8.1.*

8.2. The equilibrium partial pressures of carbon dioxide over aqueous solutions of mono-ethanolamine (30 wt %) [Mason and Dodge, *Trans. AIChE,* **32,** 27 (1936)] are as follows:

Moles CO₂	Partial pressure CO₂, mm Hg		
Mole solution	77°F	122°F	167°F
0.050			65
0.052		7.5	93.5
0.054		13.6	142.6
0.056		25.0	245
0.058	5.6	47.1	600
0.060	12.8	96.0	
0.062	29.0	259	
0.064	56.0		
0.066	98.7		
0.068	155		
0.070	232		

A plant for manufacturing dry ice will burn coke in air to produce a flue gas, which when cleaned and cooled will contain 15% CO_2, 6% O_2, 79% N_2. The gas will be blown into a bubble-tray scrubber at 1.2 atm, 77°F, to be scrubbed with 30% ethanolamine solution entering at 77°F. The scrubbing liquid, which is recycled from a stripper, will contain 0.058 mole CO_2/mole solution. The gas leaving the scrubber is to contain 2% CO_2. Assume isothermal operation.

a. Determine the minimum liquid/gas ratio, moles/mole.

b. Determine the number of pounds of solution to enter the absorber per cubic foot of entering gas, for an L/G ratio of 1.2 times the minimum. **Ans.:** 1.165.

c. Determine the number of theoretical trays for the conditions of (*b*). **Ans.:** 2.5.

d. The viscosity of the solution is 6.0 centipoises; sp gr = 1.012. Estimate the average *m*, and the overall tray efficiency to be expected. How many real trays are required?

8.3. *a.* Determine the number of ideal trays for the absorption of Prob. 8.2, assuming adiabatic operation. Use 1.6 lb absorbent solution/cu ft gas in, which will be about 1.2 times the minimum. The heat of solution of CO_2 in the solution is 720 Btu evolved/lb CO_2 absorbed, referred to gaseous CO_2 and liquid solution. The specific heat of the solution is 0.82 Btu/(lb solution)(°F) at all CO_2 concentrations. **Ans.:** 2.6.

b. Suppose the absorber planned for isothermal operation (L/G and theoretical trays of Prob. 8.2) were operated adiabatically. What concentration of CO_2 in the exit gas could be expected? [Note that this normally requires trial-and-error determination of both the top-tray temperature and exit-gas concentration. However, study of the calculations of part (*a*) should indicate that, in this case, the top-tray temperature need not be determined by trial.]

8.4. Carbon disulfide, CS_2, used as a solvent in a chemical plant is evaporated from the product in a drier into an inert gas (essentially nitrogen, N_2) in order to avoid an explosion hazard. The vapor-nitrogen mixture is to be scrubbed with an absorbent hydrocarbon oil, which will be subsequently steam-stripped to recover the CS_2. The CS_2–N_2 mixture has a partial pressure of CS_2 equal to 50 mm Hg at 75°F and is to be blown into the absorber at essentially atmospheric pressure at the rate of 50,000 cu ft/hr. The vapor content of the gas is to be reduced to 0.5%. The absorption oil has an average molecular weight 180, viscosity 2 centipoises, and specific gravity 0.81 at 75°F. The oil enters the absorber essentially stripped of all CS_2, and solutions of oil and CS_2 are ideal. The vapor pressure of CS_2 at 75°F = 346 mm Hg. Assume isothermal operation.

a. Determine the minimum liquid/gas ratio.

b. For a liquid/gas ratio of 1.5 times the minimum, determine the pounds of oil per hour to enter the absorber.

c. Determine the number of theoretical trays required, both graphically and analytically.

d. For a conventional bubble-cap-tray tower, estimate the overall tray efficiency to be expected and the number of real trays required.

8.5. Design a suitable perforated tray for the absorber of Prob. 8.4, and compute its hydraulics. Determine the tray efficiency (which may be considered constant for all the trays) and the number of real trays required graphically, and also through Eq. (8.14). Take the surface tension as 30 dynes/cm.

8.6. Determine the number of ideal trays for the absorber of Prob. 8.4, assuming adiabatic operation. Use a liquid rate of 18,000 lb/hr, which is about 1.5 times the minimum. The specific heat of the oil = 86.5, of liquid CS_2 = 18.2, and of CS_2 vapor = 11.2, all Btu/(lb mole)(°F). The latent heat of CS_2 = 12,000 Btu/lb mole at 75°F. **Ans.:** 3.8.

8.7. Starting with Eq. (8.31), replace the *y*'s by equivalent *Y*'s and derive Eq. (8.33).

8.8. With the help of the Kremser equations and Eq. (8.47), derive the relation between N_p and N_{tOG} for constant absorption factor. Establish the conditions when $N_p = N_{tOG}$.

8.9. Design a tower packed with 2-in. ceramic Raschig rings for the carbon disulfide scrubber of Prob. 8.4. Assume isothermal operation, use a liquid/gas ratio of 1.5 times the minimum, and a gas pressure drop not exceeding 0.40 in water per foot of packing. Tower shells are available in diameter increments of 2 in. The liquid surface tension = 30 dynes/cm. A procedure follows:

a. Determine the diameter of the tower.

b. Using average (top and bottom) flow rates and fluid properties, compute the mass-transfer coefficients F_Ga and F_La and heights of transfer units H_{tG}, H_{tL}, and H_{toG}.

c. Compute N_{tG}, and with H_{tG}, the packing height. **Ans.:** 15.5 ft.

d. Compute N_{toG} through the following methods, and the corresponding packing height for each: Eq. (8.33), Eq. (8.45), and Fig. 8.20.

e. Compare the gas pressure drop for the full depth of packing with that for all the trays of Prob. 8.5. At a power cost of $0.015 per kilowatt-hour, and a blower-motor efficiency of 50%, calculate the annual (350 days) difference in power cost for the two towers.

8.10. It is desired to reduce the ammonia content of 6,000 cu ft/hr (80°F, 1 atm) of an ammonia-air mixture from 5.0 to 0.04% by volume by water scrubbing. There is available a 1-ft-diameter tower packed to a depth of 12 ft with 1-in. Berl saddles. Is the tower satisfactory, and if so, what water rate should be used? At 80°F, ammonia-water solutions follow Henry's law up to 5 mole % ammonia in the liquid, and $m = 1.414$.

8.11. A tower, 1-ft diameter, is packed with 1-in. Berl saddles to a depth of 12 ft. It is to be fed with 6,000 cu ft/hr (80°F, 1 atm) of an ammonia-air mixture containing 5% ammonia by volume, and with pure water at 80°F. In what follows, operation may be considered isothermal, and Henry's law applies up to 5 mole % ammonia in the liquid, with $m = 1.414$.

a. If the water rate is set at 400 lb/hr, calculate the concentration of ammonia in the effluents.

Since at the low water rate in part (*a*) the liquid mass-transfer coefficient and the interfacial area are both low, consideration is also being given to the following two schemes, each of which provides the same substantial increase in liquid irrigation rate. In each case, calculate the effluent compositions to be expected, and compare the rate of absorption with that of (*a*).

b. Fresh water is to be used at the rate of 3,500 lb/hr.

c. Fresh water is to be used at the rate of 400 lb/hr, but 3,100 lb/hr of the liquid will be continuously recycled from the bottom to the top of the tower.

8.12. As a result of an absorption process, there are two solutions which must be stripped of absorbed solute. The first, 25 moles/hr, is a solution of benzene in a nonvolatile oil, containing 0.10 mole fraction benzene. The second, 10 moles/hr, is a solution of benzene in oil of the same type, 0.05 mole fraction benzene. Each will be preheated to 250°F and will be stripped in the same tower at 1 atm abs, with superheated steam at 250°F. The liquid effluent from the stripper is to contain no more than 0.005 mole fraction benzene. Assume isothermal operation. Raoult's law applies, and at 250°F, the vapor pressure of benzene = 2,400 mm Hg.

a. The more concentrated solution will enter the top tray of the stripper, and the less concentrated will be fed to that tray where the benzene concentration most nearly matches its concentration. Determine the minimum steam rate, the number of ideal trays required for 1.25 times the minimum steam rate, and the ideal tray number for feeding the less-concentrated solution.

Ans.: Nine ideal trays.

b. How many ideal trays would be required if both liquids were fed to the top tray of the stripper, using the same steam rate as in part (*a*)?

c. Suppose, with the same steam rate as in part (*a*), the more dilute feed had to be introduced onto the fifth ideal tray from the top. What then would be the total number of ideal trays required?

8.13. A process is being considered which involves crystallizing a product from methanol and drying the wet crystals by evaporation of the methanol into air. The resulting air-methanol mixture, estimated as 25,000 cu ft/hr at 80°F, 1 atm, will contain 5% methanol by volume. This is to be recovered by countercurrent scrubbing in a packed tower with water, available at 80°F. The scrubbed gas will be returned to the driers, and its methanol content must be no greater than 0.1%. The methanol-water solution will be distilled to recover the methanol.

It is agreed that the absorber will be a tower packed with 1.5-in. ceramic Raschig rings, and will operate essentially adiabatically. Its cost, including the shell and packing, will be $25 per cubic foot.

It will be designed to operate at 70% of the flooding gas rate. Allow 150% of the tower cost for installation and piping, amortized over a 2-yr period. Allow 5% of the tower cost for annual maintenance. Fan and motor for moving the gas will operate at 50% overall efficiency, pump and motor for moving liquid at 80%. Power costs $0.015 per kilowatt-hour. Operation is expected for 350 twenty-four-hour days per year. The heat cost for distillation of the methanol solution is estimated to be $(7{,}500/x - 33{,}000)10^{-6}$ dollars per pound mole contained methanol, where x is the mole fraction methanol in the feed to the still (absorber effluent). The cost of fan, pump, motors, and distillation equipment is not expected to be dependent upon variations in absorber design covered in this problem.

Determine the most economical water rate for the absorber.

The following were interpolated from the listings in "International Critical Tables," vol. III, p. 290; vol. V, p. 159:

Mole % methanol in water solution	Equilibrium partial pressure of methanol, mm Hg		Heat of soln in water, 80°F, Btu/lb mole methanol
	39.9°C	59.4°C	
0	0	0	
5	25.0	50	−2715
10	46.0	102	−2370
15	66.5	151	−2030

The heat of solution is referred to liquid water and liquid methanol at 80°F. Extend the partial-pressure data by the methods of Fig. 8.2.

8.14. A gas containing 88% CH_4, 4% C_2H_6, 5% $n\text{-}C_3H_8$, and 3% $n\text{-}C_4H_{10}$ is to be scrubbed isothermally at 100°F, 5 atm pressure, in a tower containing the equivalent of eight ideal trays. It is desired to remove 80% of the C_3H_8. The lean oil will contain 0.5 mole % of C_4H_{10} but none of the other gaseous constituents. What quantity of lean oil, moles/mole wet gas, should be used, and what will be the composition of the rich oil and scrubbed gas? The Henry's law constants m are: CH_4, 32; C_2H_6, 6.7; $n\text{-}C_3H_8$, 2.4; $n\text{-}C_4H_{10}$, 0.74.

8.15. An absorber of four ideal trays, to operate adiabatically at 150 psia, is fed with 1 mole/time each of liquid and gas, each entering at 90°F, as follows:

Component	Liquid mole fraction	Gas mole fraction
CH_4		0.70
C_2H_6		0.12
$n\text{-}C_3H_8$		0.08
$n\text{-}C_4H_{10}$	0.02	0.06
$n\text{-}C_5H_{12}$	0.01	0.04
Nonvolatile oil	0.97	

Estimate the composition and rate (mole/time) of the exit gas. Necessary data follow.

Henry's law constants [Depriester: *Chem. Eng. Progr. Symp. Ser.*, **49** (7), 1 (1953)], enthalpies in Btu/lb mole at 90°F relative to saturated liquid at −200°F (Maxwell, "Data Book on Hydrocarbons," D. Van Nostrand Company, Inc., Princeton, N.J., 1950) and molar heat capacities are:

Component	90°F			100°F	110°F	C_p, Btu/(lb mole)(°F)	
	m	H_G	H_L	m	m	Gas	Liquid
CH_4	16.5	5,550	4,200	17.0	17.8	9.0	12.0
C_2H_6	3.40	9,700	6,700	3.80	4.03	15.0	20.0
$n\text{-}C_3H_8$	1.16	13,350	7,250	1.30	1.44	19.0	31.0
$n\text{-}C_4H_{10}$	0.35	17,650	8,900	0.41	0.47	23.0	38.0
$n\text{-}C_5H_{12}$	0.123	21,900	10,600	0.140	0.165	28.0	44.0
Oil							90.0

CHAPTER NINE
DISTILLATION

Distillation is a method of separating the components of a solution which depends upon the distribution of the substances between a gas and a liquid phase, applied to cases where all components are present in both phases. Instead of introducing a new substance into the mixture in order to provide the second phase, as is done in gas absorption or desorption, the new phase is created from the original solution by vaporization or condensation.

In order to make clear the distinction among distillation and the other operations, let us cite a few specific examples. In the separation of a solution of common salt and water, the water may be completely vaporized from the solution without removal of salt since the latter is for all practical purposes quite nonvolatile at the prevailing conditions. This is the operation of evaporation. Distillation, on the other hand, is concerned with the separation of solutions where all the components are appreciably volatile. In this category, consider the separation of the components of a liquid solution of ammonia and water. By contacting the ammonia-water solution with air, which is essentially insoluble in the liquid, the ammonia may be stripped or desorbed by processes which were discussed in Chap. 8, but the ammonia is then mixed with water vapor and air and is not obtained in pure form. On the other hand, by application of heat, we may partially vaporize the solution and thereby create a gas phase consisting of nothing but water and ammonia. And since the gas will be richer in ammonia than the residual liquid, a certain amount of separation will have resulted. By appropriate manipulation of the phases, or by repeated vaporizations and condensations, it is then ordinarily possible to make as complete a separation as may be desired, recovering both components of the mixture in as pure a state as we wish.

The advantages of such a separation method are clear. In distillation the new phase differs from the original by its heat content, but heat is readily added or removed without difficulty, although of course the cost of doing this must inevitably be considered. Absorption or desorption operations, on the other hand, which depend upon the introduction of a foreign substance, provide us with a new solution which in turn may have to be separated by one of the diffusional operations unless it happens that the new solution is useful directly.

There are in turn certain limitations to distillation as a separation process. In absorption or similar operations, where it has been agreed to introduce a foreign substance to provide a new phase for distribution purposes, we may ordinarily choose from a great variety of solvents in order to provide the greatest possible separation effect. For example, since water is ineffectual in absorbing hydrocarbon gases from a gas mixture, we choose instead a hydrocarbon oil which provides a high solubility. But in distillation there is no such choice. The gas which may be created from a liquid by application of heat inevitably consists only of the components comprising the liquid. Since the gas is therefore chemically very similar to the liquid, the change in composition resulting from the distribution of the components between the two phases is ordinarily not very great. Indeed, in some cases the change in composition is so small that the process becomes impractical; it may even happen that there is no change in composition whatsoever.

Nevertheless the direct separation which is ordinarily possible by distillation, into pure products requiring no further processing, has made this perhaps the most important of all the mass-transfer operations.

VAPOR-LIQUID EQUILIBRIA

The successful application of distillation methods depends greatly upon an understanding of the equilibria which exist between the vapor and liquid phases of the mixtures encountered. A brief review of these is therefore essential. The emphasis here will be on binary mixtures.

Pressure-temperature-concentration phase diagram

Let us first consider binary mixtures which we shall term "ordinary," by which is meant that the liquid components dissolve in all proportions to form homogeneous solutions which are not necessarily ideal and that no complications of maximum or minimum boiling points occur. We shall consider component A of the binary mixture A-B as the more volatile, i.e., the vapor pressure of pure A at any temperature is higher than the vapor pressure of pure B. The vapor-liquid equilibrium for each pure substance of the mixture is of course its vapor pressure–temperature relationship, as indicated in Fig. 7.1. For binary mixtures an additional variable, concentration, must

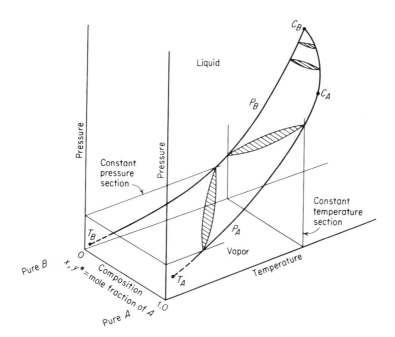

Fig. 9.1   *Binary vapor-liquid equilibria.*

likewise be considered.   Mole fractions are the most convenient concentration terms
to use, and throughout this discussion x will be the mole fraction of the more volatile
substance A in the liquid and y^* the corresponding equilibrium mole fraction of A
in the vapor.

Complete graphical representation of the equilibria requires a three-dimensional
diagram, as in Fig. 9.1.   The curve marked P_A is the vapor-pressure curve of A, lying
entirely in the nearest composition plane at $x = 1.0$.   The curve extends from its
critical point C_A to its triple point T_A, but the complications of the solid phase which
do not enter into distillation operations will not be considered.   Similarly curve P_B
is the vapor pressure of pure B, in the far plane at $x = 0$.   The liquid and vapor
regions at compositions between $x = 0$ and 1.0 are separated by a double surface
which extends smoothly from P_A to P_B.   The shape of this double surface is most
readily studied by considering sections at constant pressure and constant temperature,
examples of which are shown in the figure.

Constant-pressure equilibria

Consider first a typical section at constant pressure (Fig. 9.2*a*).   The intersection of
the double surface of Fig. 9.1 with the constant-pressure plane produces a looped curve
without maxima or minima extending from the boiling point of pure B to that of
pure A at the pressure in question.   The upper curve provides the temperature-vapor

composition $(t\text{-}y^*)$ relationship, the lower that of the temperature-liquid composition $(t\text{-}x)$. Liquid and vapor mixtures at equilibrium are at the same temperature and pressure throughout, so that horizontal *tie lines* such as line DF join equilibrium mixtures at D and F. There are an infinite number of such tie lines for this diagram. A mixture on the lower curve, as at point D, is a saturated liquid; a mixture on the upper curve, as at F, is a saturated vapor. A mixture at E is a two-phase mixture, consisting of a liquid phase of composition at D and a vapor phase of composition at F, in such proportions that the average composition of the entire mixture is represented by E. The relative amounts of the equilibrium phases are related to the segments of the tie line,

$$\frac{\text{Moles of } D}{\text{Moles of } F} = \frac{\text{line } EF}{\text{line } DE} \tag{9.1}$$

Consider a solution at G in a closed container which may be kept at constant pressure by moving a piston. The solution is entirely liquid. If it is heated, the first bubble of vapor forms at H and has the composition at J, richer in the more volatile substance, and hence the lower curve is called the bubble-point temperature curve. As more of the mixture is vaporized, more of the vapor forms at the expense of the liquid, giving rise, for example, to liquid L and its equilibrium vapor K, although the composition of the entire mass is still the original as at G. The last drop of liquid vaporizes at M and has the composition at N. Superheating the mixture follows the path MO. The mixture has vaporized over a temperature range from H to M, unlike the single vaporization temperature of a pure substance. Thus, the term *boiling point* for a solution ordinarily has no meaning since vaporization occurs over a temperature

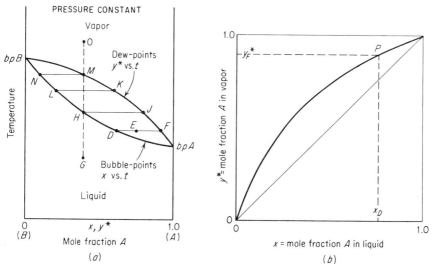

Fig. 9.2   *Constant-pressure vapor-liquid equilibria.*

range, i.e., from the bubble point to the dew point. If the mixture at O is cooled, all the phenomena reappear in reverse order. Condensation, for example, starts at M, whence the upper curve is termed the dew-point curve, and continues to H.

If a solution such as that at H is boiled in an open vessel, on the other hand, with the vapors escaping into the atmosphere, since the vapor is richer in the more volatile substance, the liquid residue must therefore become leaner. The temperature and composition of the saturated residual liquid therefore move along the lower curve toward N as the distillation proceeds.

The vapor-liquid equilibrium compositions may be shown also on a distribution diagram (x vs. y^*) as in Fig. 9.2b. Point P on the diagram represents the tie line DF, for example. Since the vapor is richer in the more volatile substance, the curve lies above the 45° diagonal line, which has been drawn in for comparison.

Relative volatility

The greater the distance between the equilibrium curve and the diagonal of Fig. 9.2b, the greater the difference in liquid and vapor compositions and the more readily is the separation by distillation made. One numerical measure of this is called the *separation factor*, or, particularly in the case of distillation, the *relative volatility* α. This is the ratio of the concentration ratio of A and B in one phase to that in the other and is a measure of the separability,

$$\alpha = \frac{y^*/(1-y^*)}{x/(1-x)} = \frac{y^*(1-x)}{x(1-y^*)} \tag{9.2}$$

The value of α will ordinarily change as x varies from 0 to 1.0. If $y^* = x$ (except at $x = 0$ or 1), $\alpha = 1.0$, and no separation is possible. The larger the value of α above unity, the greater the degree of separability.

Increased pressures

At higher pressures the sections at constant pressure will of course intersect the double surface of Fig. 9.1 at increased temperatures. The intersections may be projected onto a single plane, as in Fig. 9.3a. It should be noted that not only do the looped curves occur at higher temperatures, but also they usually become narrower. This is readily seen from the corresponding distribution curves of Fig. 9.3b. The relative volatilities, and hence the separability, therefore usually become less at higher pressures. As the critical pressure of one component is exceeded, there is no longer a distinction between vapor and liquid for that component, and for mixtures the looped curves are therefore shorter, as at pressures above P_{t3}, the critical for A in the figure. Distillation separations can be made only in the region where a looped curve exists.

For particular systems, the critical pressure of the less volatile substance may be reached before that of the more volatile, and it is also possible that the double surface of Fig. 9.1 will extend at intermediate compositions to a small extent beyond the critical pressures of either substance.

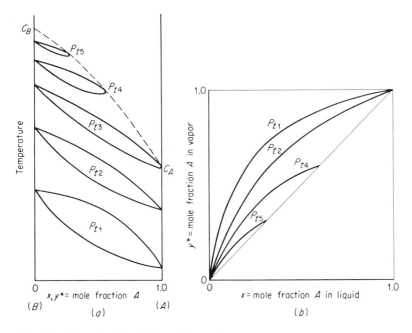

Fig. 9.3 *Vapor-liquid equilibria at increased pressure.*

Constant-temperature equilibria

A typical constant-temperature section of the three-dimensional phase diagram is shown in Fig. 9.4. The intersection of the constant-temperature plane with the double surface of Fig. 9.1 provides the two curves which extend without maxima or minima from the vapor pressure of pure B to that of pure A. As before, there are an infinite number of horizontal tie lines, such as TV, which join an equilibrium vapor as at V to its corresponding liquid at T. A solution in a closed container at W is entirely a liquid, and if the pressure is reduced at constant temperature, the first bubble of vapor forms at U, complete vaporization occurs at S, and further reduction in pressure results in a superheated vapor as at R.

Ideal solutions—Raoult's law

Before studying the characteristics of mixtures which deviate markedly from those just described, let us consider the equilibria for the limiting case of mixtures whose vapors and liquids are ideal. The nature of ideal solutions and the types of mixtures which approach ideality were discussed in Chap. 8.

For an ideal solution, the equilibrium partial pressure p^* of a constituent at a fixed temperature equals the product of its vapor pressure P when pure at this temperature and its mole fraction in the liquid. This is Raoult's law.

$$p_A^* = P_A x \qquad p_B^* = P_B(1 - x) \tag{9.3}$$

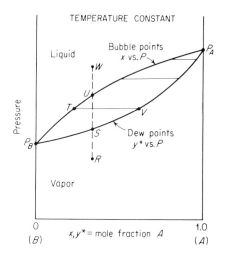

Fig. **9.4** *Constant-temperature vapor-liquid equilibria.*

If the vapor phase is also ideal,

$$P_t = p_A^* + p_B^* = P_A x + P_B(1 - x) \tag{9.4}$$

and the total as well as the partial pressures are linear in x at a fixed temperature. These relationships are shown graphically in Fig. 9.5. The equilibrium vapor composition may then be computed at this temperature. For example, the value of y^* at point D on the figure equals the ratio of the distances FG to EG,

$$y^* = \frac{p_A^*}{P_t} = \frac{P_A x}{P_t} \tag{9.5}$$

$$1 - y^* = \frac{p_B^*}{P_t} = \frac{P_B(1 - x)}{P_t} \tag{9.6}$$

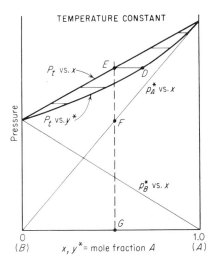

Fig. **9.5** *Ideal solutions.*

The relative volatility α is, by substitution in Eq. (9.2),

$$\alpha = \frac{P_A}{P_B} \tag{9.7}$$

For ideal solutions, it is possible then to compute the entire vapor-liquid equilibria from the vapor pressures of the pure substances. For all other mixtures, however, it is necessary to obtain the data experimentally.

Illustration 9.1. Compute the vapor-liquid equilibria at constant pressure of 1 atm for mixtures of n-heptane with n-octane, which may be expected to form ideal solutions.

Solution. The boiling points at 1 atm of the substances are n-heptane (A), 98.4°C; n-octane (B), 125.6°C. Computations are therefore made between these temperatures. For example, at 110°C, $P_A = 1,050$ mm Hg, $P_B = 484$ mm Hg, $P_t = 760$ mm Hg.

Eq. (9.4): $\qquad x = \dfrac{P_t - P_B}{P_A - P_B} = \dfrac{760 - 484}{1,050 - 484} = 0.487$ mole fraction heptane in liquid

Eq. (9.5): $\qquad y^* = \dfrac{P_A x}{P_t} = \dfrac{1,050(0.487)}{760} = 0.674$ mole fraction heptane in vapor

Eq. (9.7): $\qquad \alpha = \dfrac{P_A}{P_B} = \dfrac{1,050}{484} = 2.17$

In similar fashion, the data of the following table may be computed:

t, °C	P_A, mm Hg	P_B, mm Hg	x	y^*	α
98.4	760	333	1.0	1.0	2.28
105	940	417	0.655	0.810	2.25
110	1,050	484	0.487	0.674	2.17
115	1,200	561	0.312	0.492	2.14
120	1,350	650	0.1571	0.279	2.08
125.6	1,540	760	0	0	2.02

Curves of the type of Fig. 9.2 may now be plotted. Note that although the vapor pressures of the pure substances vary considerably with temperature, α for ideal solutions does not. In this case, an average of the computed α's is 2.16, and substituting this in Eq. (9.2), rearranged,

$$y^* = \frac{\alpha x}{1 + x(\alpha - 1)} = \frac{2.16x}{1 + 1.16x}$$

provides an expression which for many purposes is a satisfactory empirical relation between y^* and x for this system at 1 atm.

Positive deviations from ideality

A mixture whose total pressure is greater than that computed for ideality [Eq. (9.4)] is said to show positive deviations from Raoult's law. Most mixtures fall into this category. In these cases the partial pressures of each component are larger than the

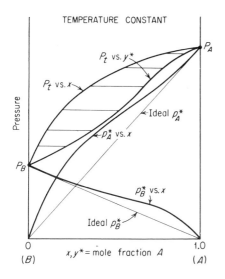

TEMPERATURE CONSTANT

P_t vs. y^*

P_t vs. x

Pressure

P_A

←Ideal p_A^*

←p_A^* vs. x

P_B

p_B^* vs. x

Ideal p_B^*

0

(B) $x, y^* =$ mole fraction A 1.0

(A)

Fig. 9.6 *Positive deviation from ideality.*

ideal, as shown in Fig. 9.6.† It should be noted that as the concentration for each component approaches unity mole fraction, the partial pressures for that substance approach ideality tangentially. Raoult's law, in other words, is nearly applicable to the substance present in very large concentrations. This is the case for all substances except where association within the vapor or electrolytic dissociation within the liquid occurs.

The distribution diagram (x vs. y^*) for systems of this type appears much the same as that of Fig. 9.2b.

Minimum-boiling mixtures—azeotropes. When the positive deviations from ideality are sufficiently large and the vapor pressures of the two components are not too far apart, the total-pressure curves at constant temperature may rise through a maximum at some concentration, as in Fig. 9.7a. Such a mixture is said to form an azeotrope, or constant-boiling mixture. The significance of this is more readily seen by study of the constant-pressure section (Fig. 9.7b or c). The liquid- and vapor-composition curves are tangent at point L, the point of azeotropism at this pressure, which represents the minimum-boiling temperature for this system. For all mixtures of composition less than L, such as those at C, the equilibrium vapor (E) is richer in the more volatile component than the liquid (D). For all mixtures richer than L, however, such as at F, the equilibrium vapor (G) is less rich in the more volatile substance than the liquid (H). A mixture of composition L gives rise to a vapor of composition identical with the liquid, and it consequently boils at constant temperature

† The ratio of the actual equilibrium partial pressure of a component p^* to the ideal value Px is the activity coefficient referred to the pure substance: $\gamma = p^*/Px$. Since γ is greater than unity in these cases and log γ is therefore positive, the deviations are termed *positive* deviations from ideality. A very extensive science of the treatment of nonideal solutions through activity coefficients has been developed by which, from a very small number of data, all the vapor-liquid equilibria of a system may be predicted.[4,12]

Fig. 9.7 *Minimum-boiling azeotropism in the system carbon disulfide–acetone. (a) At constant temperature; (b) and (c) at constant pressure.*

and without change in composition. If solutions either at D or H are boiled in an open vessel with continual escape of the vapors, the temperature and composition of the residual liquids in each case move along the lower curve away from point L (toward K for a liquid at H, and toward J for one at D).

Solutions such as these cannot be completely separated by ordinary distillation methods at this pressure, since at the azeotropic composition $y^* = x$ and $\alpha = 1.0$.† The azeotropic composition as well as its boiling point changes with pressure. In some cases, changing the pressure may eliminate azeotropism from the system.

Azeotropic mixtures of this sort are very common, and thousands have been recorded.[19,20] One of the most important is the ethanol-water azeotrope which at 1 atm occurs at 89.4 mole percent ethanol and 78.2°C. Azeotropism disappears in this system at pressures below 70 mm Hg.

Partial liquid miscibility. Some substances exhibit such large positive deviations from ideality that they do not dissolve completely in the liquid state, as in the case of isobutanol-water (Fig. 9.8). The curves through points C and E represent the solubility limits of the constituents at relatively low temperatures. Mixtures of composition and temperature represented by points within the central area, such as point D, form two liquid phases at equilibrium at C and E, and line CE is a liquid tie line. Mixtures in the regions on either side of the solubility limits such as at F are homogeneous liquids. The solubility ordinarily increases with increased temperature, and the central area consequently decreases in width. If the pressure were sufficiently high so that vaporization did not occur, the liquid-solubility curves would continue along the broken extensions as shown. At the prevailing pressure, however, vaporization occurs before this can happen, giving rise to the branched vapor-liquid equilibrium curves. For homogeneous liquids such as that at F, the vapor-liquid equilibrium phenomena are normal, and such a mixture boils initially at H to give the first bubble of vapor of composition J. The same is true of any solution richer than M, except that here the vapor is leaner in the more volatile component. Any two-phase liquid mixture within the composition range from K to M will boil at the temperature of the line KM, and all these give rise to the same vapor of composition L. A liquid mixture of average composition L, which produces a vapor of the same composition, is sometimes called a *heteroazeotrope*. The corresponding distribution diagram with the tie line HJ, solubility limits at the boiling point K and M, and the azeotropic point L, is shown in Fig. 9.8b.

In relatively few instances the azeotropic composition lies outside the limits of insolubility. One such case is the system methyl ethyl ketone–water.

Insoluble liquids; steam distillation. The mutual solubility of some liquids is so small that they may be considered substantially insoluble: points K and M (Fig. 9.8) are then for all practical purposes on the vertical axes of these diagrams. This is the case for a mixture such as a hydrocarbon and water, for example. If the liquids are

---

† For compositions to the right of L (Fig. 9.7) α as usually computed is less than unity, and the reciprocal of α is then ordinarily used.

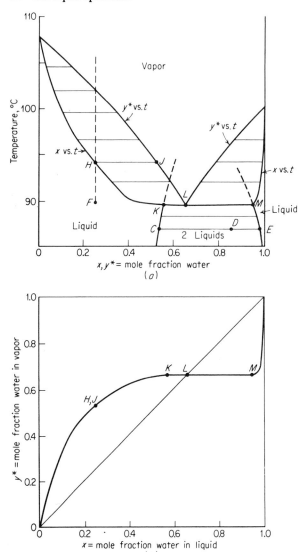

Fig. 9.8   *Isobutanol–water at 1 atm.*

completely insoluble, the vapor pressure of either component cannot be influenced by the presence of the other, and each exerts its true vapor pressure at the prevailing temperature.   When the sum of the separate vapor pressures equals the total pressure, the mixture boils, and the vapor composition is readily computed, assuming the applicability of the simple gas law,

$$P_A + P_B = P_t \tag{9.8}$$

$$y^* = \frac{P_A}{P_t} \tag{9.9}$$

So long as two liquid phases are present, the mixture will boil at the same temperature and produce a vapor of constant composition.

   Illustration 9.2. A mixture containing 50 g water and 50 g ethylaniline, which may be assumed to be essentially insoluble, is boiled at atmospheric pressure. Describe the phenomena that occur.
   Solution. Since the liquids are insoluble, each exerts its own vapor pressure, and when the sum of these equals 760 mm Hg, the mixture boils.

t, °C	P_A (water), mm Hg	P_B (ethylaniline), mm Hg	$P_t = P_A + P_B$, mm Hg
38.5	51.1	1	52.1
64.4	199.7	5	205
80.6	363.9	10	374
96.0	657.6	20	678
99.15	737.2	22.8	760
113.2	1,225	40	1,265
204		760	

   The mixture boils at 99.15°C.

$$y^* = \frac{P_A}{P_t} = \frac{737.2}{760} = 0.97 \text{ mole fraction water}$$

$$1 - y^* = \frac{P_B}{P_t} = \frac{22.8}{760} = 0.03 \text{ mole fraction ethylaniline}$$

The original mixture contained $50/18.02 = 2.78$ g moles water and $50/121.1 = 0.412$ g mole ethylaniline. The mixture will continue to boil at 99.15°C, with an equilibrium vapor of the indicated composition, until all the water has evaporated together with $2.78(0.03/0.97) = 0.086$ g mole of the ethylaniline. The temperature will then rise to 204°C, and the equilibrium vapor will be pure ethylaniline.

   Note that by this method of distillation with steam, so long as liquid water is present, the high-boiling organic liquid can be made to vaporize at a temperature much lower than its normal boiling point without the necessity of a vacuum-pump equipment operating at 22.8 mm Hg. If boiled at 204°C, this compound will undergo considerable decomposition. However, the heat requirements of the steam-distillation process are great since such a large amount of water must be evaporated simultaneously. Alternatives would be (1) to operate at a different total pressure in the presence of liquid water where the ratio of the vapor pressures of the substances may be more favorable and (2) to bubble superheated steam (or other insoluble gas) through the mixture in the absence of liquid water and to vaporize the ethylaniline by allowing it to saturate the steam.

Negative deviations from ideality

When the total pressure of a system at equilibrium is less than the ideal value, the system is said to deviate negatively from Raoult's law. Such a situation is shown in

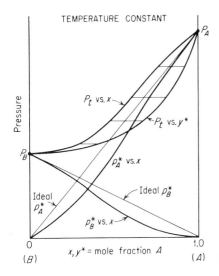

Fig. 9.9 *Negative deviations from ideality.*

Fig. 9.9 at constant temperature.   Note that in this case, as with positive deviations, where neither vapor association nor liquid dissociation occurs, the partial pressures of the constituents of the solution approach ideality as their concentrations approach 100 percent.   The constant-pressure diagram for such a case has the same general appearance as the diagrams shown in Fig. 9.2.

Maximum-boiling mixtures—azeotropes

When the difference in vapor pressures of the components is not too great and in addition the negative deviations are large, the curve for total pressure against composition may pass through a minimum, as in Fig. 9.10*a*.   This condition gives rise to a maximum in the boiling temperatures, as at point *L* (Fig. 9.10*b*), and a condition of azeotropism.   The equilibrium vapor is leaner in the more volatile substance for liquids whose *x* is less than the azeotropic composition and greater if *x* is larger. Solutions on either side of the azeotrope, if boiled in an open vessel with escape of the vapor, will ultimately leave a residual liquid of the azeotropic composition in the vessel.

Maximum-boiling azeotropes are less common than the minimum type.   One which is very well known is that of hydrochloric acid–water (11.1 mole % HCl, 110°C, at 1 atm), which may be prepared simply by boiling a solution of any strength of the acid in an open vessel.   This is one method of standardizing hydrochloric acid.

Enthalpy-concentration diagrams

Binary vapor-liquid equilibria may also be plotted on coordinates of enthalpy vs. concentration at constant pressure.   Liquid-solution enthalpies include both sensible heat and the heat of mixing the components

$$H_L = C_L(t_L - t_o)M_{\text{av}} + \Delta H_S \tag{9.10}$$

Fig. 9.10 *Maximum-boiling azeotropism in the system acetone–chloroform. (a) At constant temperature; (b) and (c) at constant pressure.*

where C_L is the heat capacity of the solution, Btu/(lb)(°F), and ΔH_S is the heat of solution at t_o and the prevailing concentration referred to the pure liquid components, Btu/lb mole *solution.* For saturated liquids, t_L is the bubble point corresponding to the liquid concentration at the prevailing pressure. Heat-of-solution data vary in form, and some adjustment of the units of tabulated data may be necessary. If heat is evolved on mixing, ΔH_S will be negative, and for ideal solutions it is zero. For ideal solutions, the heat capacity is the weighted average of those for the pure components.

For present purposes, saturated-vapor enthalpies may be calculated adequately by assuming that the unmixed liquids are heated separately as liquids to the gas temperature t_G (the dew point), each vaporized at this temperature, and the vapors mixed

$$H_G = y[C_{LA}M_A(t_G - t_o) + \lambda_A M_A] + (1 - y)[C_{LB}M_B(t_G - t_o) + \lambda_B M_B] \quad (9.11)$$

where λ_A, λ_B = latent heats of vaporization of pure substances at t_G, Btu/lb
    C_{LA}, C_{LB} = heat capacities of pure liquids, Btu/(lb)(°F)

In the upper part of Fig. 9.11, which represents a typical binary mixture, the enthalpies of saturated vapors at their dew points have been plotted vs. y and those of the saturated liquids at their bubble points vs. x. The vertical distances between the

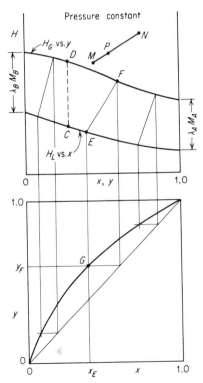

Fig. 9.11 *Enthalpy-concentration coordinates.*

two curves at $x = 0$ and 1 represent, respectively, the molar latent heats of B and A. The heat required for complete vaporization of solution C is $H_D - H_C$ Btu/lb mole solution.   Equilibrium liquids and vapors may be joined by tie lines, of which line EF is typical.   The relation between this equilibrium phase diagram and the xy plot is shown in the lower part of Fig. 9.11.   Here the point G represents the tie line EF, located on the lower plot in the manner shown.   Other tie lines, when projected to the xy plot, produce the complete equilibrium-distribution curve.

Characteristics of the Hxy and xy diagrams.[31]   Let point M on Fig. 9.11 represent M moles of a mixture of enthalpy H_M and concentration z_M, and similarly N is N moles of a mixture of properties H_N, z_N.   Adiabatic mixing of M and N will produce P moles of a mixture of enthalpy H_P and concentration z_P.   A total material balance is

$$M + N = P \tag{9.12}$$

and a balance for component A is

$$M z_M + N z_N = P z_P \tag{9.13}$$

An enthalpy balance is

$$M H_M + N H_N = P H_P \tag{9.14}$$

Elimination of P between Eqs. (9.12) and (9.13) and between (9.12) and (9.14) yields

$$\frac{M}{N} = \frac{z_N - z_P}{z_P - z_M} = \frac{H_N - H_P}{H_P - H_M} \tag{9.15}$$

This is the equation of a straight line on the enthalpy-concentration plot, passing through points (H_M, z_M), (H_N, z_N), and (H_P, z_P).   Point P is therefore on the straight line MN, located so that $M/N =$ line NP/line PM.   Similarly if mixture N were *removed* adiabatically from mixture P, the mixture M would result.

Consider now mixture C (H_C, z_C) on Fig. 9.12.   It will be useful to describe such a mixture in terms of saturated vapors and liquids, since distillation is mostly concerned with such mixtures. C may be considered the result of adiabatically removing saturated liquid D from saturated vapor E (DE is *not* a tie line), and x_D and y_E may be located on the lower diagram as shown.   But C may equally well be considered as having been produced by adiabatically subtracting F from G, or J from K, or indeed by such a combination of saturated liquids and vapors given by any line from C which intersects the saturated-enthalpy curves.   These, when projected to the lower diagram, form the curve shown there.   Thus any point C on the Hxy diagram may be represented by the difference between saturated vapors and liquids, and in turn also by a curve on the xy plot.   For the combination $E - D = C$, a material balance shows

$$\frac{D}{E} = \frac{z_C - y_E}{z_C - x_D} = \frac{\text{line } CE}{\text{line } CD} \tag{9.16}$$

This is the equation on the xy diagram of the chord of slope D/E drawn between point (y_E, x_D) and $y = x = z_C$ on the 45° line.   Similarly, the ratios F/G and J/K would be shown by the slopes of chords drawn from these points to $y = x = z_C$.

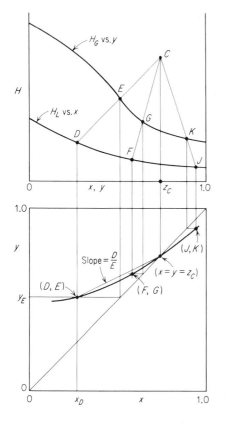

If C is on equilibrium vapor curve, the line is horizontal, on liquid eqo line it is vertical. If C is off at infinity, the line lies on the 45° line.

Fig. 9.12   *Relation between the diagrams.*

Consideration of the geometry of the diagram will readily show the following:

1. If the $H_G y$ and $H_L x$ curves are straight parallel lines (which will occur if the molar latent heats of A and B are equal, if the heat capacities are constant over the prevailing temperature range, and if there is no heat of solution), then $D/E = F/G = J/K$ for adiabatic subtraction, since the line-segment ratios are then equal, and the curve on xy representing C becomes a straight line.

2. If point C is moved upward, the curve on xy becomes more steep, ultimately coinciding with the 45° line when C is at infinite enthalpy.

3. If point C is on the $H_G y$ curve, the curve on xy becomes a horizontal straight line; if C is on the $H_L x$ curve, the curve on xy becomes a vertical straight line.

These concepts will be useful in understanding the applications of these diagrams.

Multicomponent systems

Nonideal systems of three components may be treated graphically, using triangular coordinates to express the compositions in the manner of Chap. 10, but for more than three components graphical treatment becomes very complicated.   Actually our knowledge of nonideal systems of this type is extremely limited, and very few data have been accumulated. It is generally unsafe to predict detailed behavior of a multicomponent system from considerations of the pure components alone, or even from a knowledge of the simple binary systems that may be formed from the components. For example, three-component systems sometimes form ternary azeotropes, whose equilibrium vapor and liquid phases have identical composition. But the fact that one, two, or three binary azeotropes are known among the components does not make the formation of a ternary azeotrope certain, and a ternary azeotrope need not necessarily coincide with the composition of minimum or maximum boiling temperature for the system at constant pressure.

Ideal systems. Many of the multicomponent systems of industrial importance may be considered nearly ideal in the liquid phase for all practical purposes. This is particularly true for hydrocarbon mixtures of the same homologous series, such as those of the paraffin series or the lower-boiling aromatic hydrocarbons.† In such cases Raoult's law may be applied. If the components are A, B, C, etc., then, at a fixed temperature,

$$p_A^* = P_A x_A \qquad p_B^* = P_B x_B \qquad p_C^* = P_C x_C \qquad p_J^* = P_J x_J \qquad (9.17)$$

and, for an ideal vapor,

$$P_t = p_A^* + p_B^* + p_C^* + \cdots = \Sigma p^* \qquad (9.18)$$

Since $y_A^* = p_A^*/P_t$, etc., then, for any component J,

$$y_J^* = \frac{p_J^*}{\Sigma p^*} = \frac{P_J x_J}{\Sigma P x} \qquad (9.19)$$

The relative volatility of two substances forming an ideal solution is the ratio of their vapor pressures [Eq. (9.7)], so that the relative volatility of substance J with respect to substance C, for example, is

$$\alpha_{JC} = \frac{P_J}{P_C} \qquad (9.20)$$

Dividing numerator and denominator of Eq. (9.19) by P_C, we obtain, since $\alpha_{CC} = 1$,

$$y_J^* = \frac{\alpha_{JC} x_J}{\alpha_{AC} x_A + \alpha_{BC} x_B + x_C + \alpha_{DC} x_D + \cdots} = \frac{\alpha_{JC} x_J}{\Sigma \alpha x} \qquad (9.21)$$

This form of the equation is sometimes more convenient for computing compositions than Eq. (9.19) since, as has been demonstrated, the relative volatilities change much more slowly with temperature than do vapor pressures.

---

† Hydrocarbons of different molecular structure, however, frequently form such nonideal solutions that azeotropism occurs, as, for example, in the binary systems hexane–methyl cyclopentane, hexane–benzene, and benzene–cyclohexane.

Illustration 9.3. A liquid contains 50 mole % benzene, 25 mole % toluene, and 25 mole % o-xylene. At 1 atm pressure, compute its bubble point and the composition of the equilibrium vapor. The solution may be considered ideal.

Solution. For a first estimate the temperature of initial boiling (bubble point) will be assumed to be 90°C. This will be the bubble point provided the sum of the partial pressures equals the prevailing total pressure, 760 mm Hg. The following table shows the sum to be only 652.5 mm Hg, and subsequent trials show 95°C to be the correct temperature. The vapor composition is then calculated with the final partial pressures.

Substance	x	Temp = 90°C		Temp = 95°C		y^*
		Vapor pressure P, mm Hg	$p^* = Px$, mm Hg	Vapor pressure P, mm Hg	$p^* = Px$, mm Hg	
Benzene	0.50	1,030	515 = 0.5(1,030)	1,200	600	0.789 = $^{600}/_{760}$
Toluene	0.25	410	102.5	475	118.5	0.156
o-Xylene	0.25	140	35.0	166	41.5	0.0545
			652.5 = Σp^*		760 = Σp^*	1.0 = Σy^*

Had it been desired to obtain the vapor composition only, the first estimate of the temperature would for many purposes have been satisfactory. As an alternative calculation, relative volatilities may be based on toluene (taken arbitrarily; any of the three substances would have served equally well) and y^* calculated by means of Eq. (9.21) as follows:

Substance	x	P, 90°C, mm Hg	α	αx	y^*
Benzene	0.50	1,030	2.51 = 1,030/410	1.255 = 2.51(0.5)	0.789 = 1.255/1.5905
Toluene	0.25	410	1.0	0.250	0.157
o-Xylene	0.25	140	0.342	0.0855	0.0537
				$\Sigma \alpha x$ = 1.5905	Σy^* = 1.0

Note that the y^*'s are practically the same as those computed at the correct temperature, 95°C.

For purposes of computing liquid compositions in equilibrium with a given vapor and the dew point, the Raoult's law equations may be written for any component J as

$$x_J = \frac{p_J^*}{P_J} = \frac{P_t y_J^*}{P_J} = \frac{y_J^*/\alpha_{JC}}{\Sigma(y^*/\alpha)} \qquad (9.22)$$

and

$$\Sigma x = 1.0 \qquad (9.23)$$

For cases where the ideal-gas law is inapplicable, fugacities may be used instead of vapor pressures and total pressures, and the ideal-solution law becomes at constant temperature†

$$y_J^* = m_J x_J \tag{9.24}$$

where m for a particular component changes with temperature and pressure, but not with composition.[4] In this case,

$$\alpha_{JC} = \frac{m_J}{m_C} \tag{9.25}$$

and the expressions for computing bubble points and dew points containing α may still be used. If in addition the liquid is nonideal, Eq. (9.24) may be used as an empirical relationship with m varying with temperature, pressure, and composition.

It must be emphasized that for all ordinary purposes the vapor-liquid equilibria should be experimentally determined. Very few systems can be considered sufficiently close to ideality to permit computation of the data from vapor pressures. The techniques for experimental determination have been reasonably well established, and methods of extending data, which depend on thermodynamic treatment, are also available.[4,12]

SINGLE-STAGE OPERATION—FLASH VAPORIZATION

Flash vaporization, or equilibrium distillation as it is sometimes called, is a single-stage operation wherein a liquid mixture is partially vaporized, the vapor allowed to come to equilibrium with the residual liquid, and the resulting vapor and liquid phases are separated and removed from the apparatus. It may be carried out batchwise or in continuous fashion.

A typical flow sheet is shown schematically in Fig. 9.13 for continuous operation. Here the liquid feed is heated in a conventional tubular heat exchanger or by passing it through the heated tubes of a fuel-fired furnace. The pressure is then reduced, vapor forms at the expense of the liquid adiabatically, and the mixture is introduced into a vapor-liquid separating vessel. The separator shown is of the cyclone type, where the feed is introduced tangentially into a covered annular space. The liquid portion of the mixture is thrown by centrifugal force to the outer wall and leaves at the bottom, while the vapor rises through the central chimney and leaves at the top. The vapor may then pass to a condenser, not shown in the figure. Particularly for flash vaporization of a volatile substance from a relatively nonvolatile one, operation in the separator may be carried out under reduced pressure, but not so low that ordinary cooling water will not condense the vapor product.

The product, D moles/hr, richer in the more volatile substance, is in this case entirely a vapor. The material and enthalpy balances are

$$F = D + W \tag{9.26}$$

$$Fz_F = Dy_D + Wx_W \tag{9.27}$$

$$FH_F + Q = DH_D + WH_W \tag{9.28}$$

---

† K rather than m is frequently used to denote the proportionality between y^* and x.

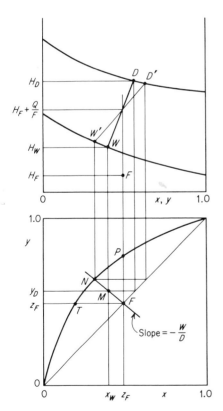

Fig. 9.13 *Continuous flash vaporization.*

Fig. 9.14 *Flash vaporization.*

These, when solved simultaneously, yield

$$-\frac{W}{D} = \frac{y_D - z_F}{x_W - z_F} = \frac{H_D - (H_F + Q/F)}{H_W - (H_F + Q/F)} \tag{9.29}$$

On the *Hxy* diagram, this represents a straight line through points of coordinates (H_D, y_D) representing D, (H_W, x_W) representing W, and $(H_F + Q/F, z_F)$ representing the feed mixture after it leaves the heat exchanger of Fig. 9.13. It is shown on the upper part of Fig. 9.14 as the line DW. The two left-hand members of Eq. (9.29) represent the usual single-stage operating line on distribution coordinates, of negative slope as for all single-stage (cocurrent) operations (see Chap. 5), passing through compositions representing the influent and effluent streams, points F and M on the lower figure. If the effluent streams were in equilibrium, the device would be an ideal stage, and the products D' and W' would be on a tie line in the upper figure and on the equilibrium curve at N on the lower figure. The richest vapor, but infinitesimal in amount, is that corresponding to P at the bubble point of the feed; and the leanest liquid, but also infinitesimal in amount, is that corresponding to T at the dew point of the feed. The compositions of the actual products will be between these limits, depending upon the extent of vaporization of the feed and the stage efficiency.

Partial condensation

All the equations apply equally well to the case where the feed is a vapor, and Q, the heat removed in the heat exchanger to produce incomplete condensation, is taken as negative. On the upper part of Fig. 9.14, point F is then either a saturated or super-heated vapor.

Illustration 9.4. A liquid mixture containing 50 mole % n-heptane (A), 50 mole % n-octane (B), at 80°F, is to be continuously flash-vaporized at 1 atm pressure to vaporize 60 mole % of the feed. What will be the composition of the vapor and liquid and the temperature in the separator for an ideal stage?

Solution. Basis: $F = 100$ moles feed, $z_F = 0.50$. $D = 60$ moles, $W = 40$ moles, $-W/D = -40/60 = -0.667$.

The equilibrium data were determined in Illustration 9.1 and are plotted in Fig. 9.15. The point representing the feed composition is plotted at P, and the operating line is drawn with a slope -0.667 to intersect the equilibrium curve at T, where $y_D^* = 0.575$ mole fraction heptane and $x_W = 0.387$ mole fraction heptane. The temperature at T is 113°C (235.4°F $= t_L = t_G$).

Multicomponent systems—ideal solutions

For mixtures which form ideal liquid solutions containing components A, B, C, etc., the equilibrium relation for any component J may be written as

$$y_{JD}^* = m_J x_{JW} \tag{9.30}$$

Equation (9.29) also applies for each of the components, and when combined with Eq. (9.30) for any component J, for an ideal stage

$$\frac{W}{D} = \frac{m_J x_{JW} - z_{JF}}{z_{JF} - x_{JW}} = \frac{y_{JD}^* - z_{JF}}{z_{JF} - y_{JD}^*/m_J} \tag{9.31}$$

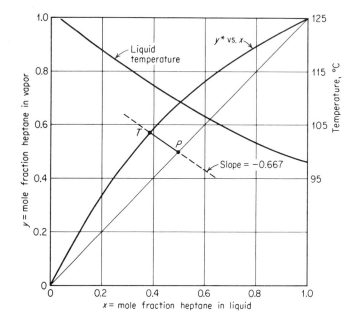

Fig. 9.15   *Solution to Illustration 9.4.*

This provides the following, useful for equilibrium vaporization,

$$y_{JD}^* = \frac{z_{JF}(W/D + 1)}{1 + W/Dm_J} \tag{9.32}$$

$$\Sigma y_D^* = 1.0 \tag{9.33}$$

and for condensation,

$$x_{JW} = \frac{z_{JF}(W/D + 1)}{m_J + W/D} \tag{9.34}$$

$$\Sigma x_W = 1.0 \tag{9.35}$$

Thus Eq. (9.32) may be used for each of the components with appropriate values of m and z_F, and the sum of the y_D^*'s so calculated must equal unity if the correct conditions of W/D, temperature, and pressure have been chosen.   A similar interpretation is used for Eqs. (9.34) and (9.35).   These expressions reduce in the limit to the dew-point and bubble-point equations (9.22) and (9.21), respectively.

Illustration 9.5.   A liquid containing 50 mole $\%$ benzene (A), 25 mole $\%$ toluene (B), and 25 mole $\%$ o-xylene (C) is flash-vaporized at 1 atm pressure and 100°C.   Compute the amounts of liquid and vapor products and their compositions.   The solutions follow Raoult's law.
   Solution.   For Raoult's law, $y^* = Px/P_t = mx$, so that for each component $m = P/P_t$. $P_t = 760$ mm Hg.   In the following table, column 2 lists the vapor pressures P at 100°C for each substance and column 3 the corresponding value of m.   The feed composition is listed in column 4.   A value of W/D is arbitrarily chosen as 3.0 and Eq. (9.32) used to compute y_D^*'s in column 5.   Since the sum

of the y_D^*'s is not unity, a new value of W/D is chosen until finally (column 6) $W/D = 2.08$ is seen to be correct.

Basis: $F = 100$ moles.

$$100 = W + D \qquad \frac{W}{D} = 2.08$$

$$\therefore \quad D = 32.5 \text{ moles} \qquad W = 67.5 \text{ moles}$$

The composition of the residual liquid may be found by material balance or by equilibrium relation, as in column 7.

Substance	$P =$ vapor pressure, mm Hg	$m = \dfrac{P}{760}$	z_F	$\dfrac{W}{D} = 3.0$ $\dfrac{z_F(W/D + 1)}{1 + W/Dm} = y_D^*$	$\dfrac{W}{D} = 2.08$ y_D^*	$x_W = \dfrac{Fz_F - Dy_D^*}{W}$ $= \dfrac{y_D^*}{m}$
(1)	(2)	(3)	(4)	(5)	(6)	(7)
A	1,370	1.803	0.50	$\dfrac{0.5(3 + 1)}{1 + 3/1.803} = 0.750$	0.715	0.397
B	550	0.724	0.25	0.1940	0.1983	0.274
C	200	0.263	0.25	0.0805	0.0865	0.329
				$\Sigma = 1.0245$	0.9998	1.000

Successive flash vaporizations may be made on the residual liquids in a series of single-stage operations, whereupon the separation will be better than that obtained if the same amount of vapor were formed in a single operation. As the amount of vapor formed in each stage becomes smaller and the total number of vaporizations larger, the operation approaches differential distillation in the limit.

DIFFERENTIAL OR SIMPLE DISTILLATION

If during an infinite number of successive flash vaporizations of a liquid only an infinitesimal portion of the liquid were flashed each time, the net result would be equivalent to a differential or simple distillation.

In practice this can only be approximated. A batch of liquid is charged to a kettle or still fitted with some sort of heating device such as a steam jacket, as in Fig. 9.16. The charge is boiled slowly, and the vapors are withdrawn as rapidly as they form to a condenser, where they are liquefied, and the condensate (distillate) is collected in the receiver. The apparatus is essentially a large-scale replica of the ordinary laboratory distillation flask and condenser. The first portion of the distillate will be the richest in the more volatile substance, and as distillation proceeds, the vaporized product becomes leaner. The distillate may therefore be collected in several separate batches, called "cuts," to give a series of distilled products of various purities. Thus, for example, if a ternary mixture contained a small amount of a very

Fig. 9.16 *Batch still.*

volatile substance A, a majority of substance B of intermediate volatility, and a small amount of C of low volatility, the first cut, which would be small, would contain the majority of A.   A large second cut would contain the majority of B reasonably pure but nevertheless contaminated with A and C, and the residue left in the kettle would be largely C.   While all three cuts would contain all three substances, nevertheless some separation would have been obtained.

For such an operation to approach even approximately the theoretical characteristics of a differential distillation, it would have to proceed infinitely slowly so that the vapor issuing from the liquid would at all times be in equilibrium with the liquid. All entrainment would have to be eliminated, and there could be no cooling and condensation of the vapor prior to its entering the condenser.   Despite the fact that these conditions are substantially impossible to attain, it is nevertheless useful to study the limiting results which a differential distillation could produce as a standard for comparison.

Binary mixtures

The vapor issuing from a true differential distillation is at any time in equilibrium with the liquid from which it rises, but changes continuously in composition.   The mathematical approach must therefore be differential. Assume that at any time during the course of the distillation there are L moles of liquid in the still of composition x mole fraction A and that an amount dD moles of distillate is vaporized, of mole fraction y^* in equilibrium with the liquid. Then we have the following material balances:

	Total material	Component A
Moles in	0	0
Moles out	dD	$y^* dD$
Moles accumulated	dL	$d(Lx) = L\,dx + x\,dL$
In $-$ out $=$ accumulation	$0 - dD = dL$	$0 - y^*\,dD = L\,dx + x\,dL$

The last two equations become

$$y^*\,dL = L\,dx + x\,dL \tag{9.36}$$

$$\int_W^F \frac{dL}{L} = \ln\frac{F}{W} = \int_{x_W}^{x_F} \frac{dx}{y^* - x} \tag{9.37}$$

where F is the moles of charge of composition x_F and W the moles of residual liquid of composition x_W. This is known as the Rayleigh equation, after Lord Rayleigh, who first derived it. It may be used to determine F, W, x_F, or x_W when three of these are known. Integration of the right-hand side of Eq. (9.37), unless an algebraic equilibrium relationship between y^* and x is available, is done graphically by plotting $1/(y^* - x)$ as ordinate against x as abscissa and determining the area under the curve between the indicated limits. The data for this are taken from the vapor-liquid equilibrium relationship. The *composited* distillate composition $y_{D,\text{av}}$ can be determined by a simple material balance,

$$Fx_F = Dy_{D,\text{av}} + Wx_W \tag{9.38}$$

Differential condensation

This is a similar operation where a vapor feed is slowly condensed under equilibrium conditions and the condensate withdrawn as rapidly as it forms. As in the case of distillation, the results can only be approximated in practice. A derivation similar to that above leads to

$$\ln\frac{F}{D} = \int_{y_F}^{y_D} \frac{dy}{y - x^*} \tag{9.39}$$

where F is the moles of feed vapor of composition y_F and D the vaporous residue of composition y_D.

The heat requirements of such processes may be worked out on enthalpy-concentration diagrams.[4]

Constant relative volatility

If Eq. (9.2) can describe the equilibrium relation at constant pressure by use of some average relative volatility α over the concentration range involved, this may be substituted in Eq. (9.37) to yield

$$\ln \frac{F}{W} = \frac{1}{\alpha - 1} \ln \frac{x_F(1 - x_W)}{x_W(1 - x_F)} + \ln \frac{1 - x_W}{1 - x_F} \qquad (9.40)$$

and graphical integration can be avoided.   This may be rearranged to another useful form,

$$\log \frac{Fx_F}{Wx_W} = \alpha \log \frac{F(1 - x_F)}{W(1 - x_W)} \qquad (9.41)$$

which relates the number of moles of A remaining in the residue, Wx_W, to that of B remaining, $W(1 - x_W)$.   These expressions are most likely to be valid for ideal mixtures, for which α is most nearly constant.

Illustration 9.6. Suppose the liquid of Illustration 9.4 [50 mole % n-heptane (A), 50 mole % n-octane (B)] were subjected to a differential distillation at atmospheric pressure, with 60 mole % of the liquid distilled.   Compute the composition of the composited distillate and the residue.
    Solution. Basis: F = 100 moles. $x_F = 0.50$, $D = 60$ moles, $W = 40$ moles.

Eq. (9.37):

$$\ln \frac{100}{40} = 0.916 = \int_{x_W}^{0.50} \frac{dx}{y^* - x}$$

The equilibrium data are given in Illustrations 9.1 and 9.4.   From these, the following are calculated:

x	0.50	0.46	0.42	0.38	0.34	0.32
y^*	0.689	0.648	0.608	0.567	0.523	0.497
$1/(y^* - x)$	5.29	5.32	5.32	5.35	5.50	5.65

x as abscissa is plotted against $1/(y^* - x)$ as ordinate, and the area under the curve obtained beginning at $x_F = 0.50$.   When the area equals 0.916, integration is stopped, and this occurs at $x_W = 0.33$ mole fraction heptane in the residue.   The composited distillate composition is obtained through Eq. (9.38),

$$100(0.50) = 60y_{D,av} + 40(0.33)$$

$$y_{D,av} = 0.614 \text{ mole fraction heptane}$$

Note that, for the same percentage vaporization, the separation in this case is better than that obtained by flash vaporization, i.e., each product is purer in its majority component.
    Alternatively, since for this system the average $\alpha = 2.16$ at 1 atm (Illustration 9.1),

Eq. (9.41):

$$\log \frac{100(0.5)}{40x_W} = 2.16 \log \frac{100(1 - 0.5)}{40(1 - x_W)}$$

from which by trial and error $x_W = 0.33$.

Distillation **309**

Multicomponent systems—ideal solutions

For multicomponent systems forming ideal liquid solutions, Eq. (9.41) can be written for any two components. Ordinarily one component is chosen on which to base the relative volatilities, whereupon Eq. (9.41) is written once for each of the others. For example, for substance J, with relative volatility based on substance B,

$$\log \frac{Fx_{JF}}{Wx_{JW}} = \alpha_{JB} \log \frac{Fx_{BF}}{Wx_{BW}} \tag{9.42}$$

and

$$\Sigma x_W = 1.0 \tag{9.43}$$

where x_{JF} is the mole fraction of J in the feed, x_{JW} that in the residue.

Illustration 9.7. A liquid containing 50 mole % benzene (A), 25 mole % toluene (B), and 25 mole % o-xylene (C) is differentially distilled at 1 atm, with vaporization of 32.5 mole % of the charge. Raoult's law applies. Compute the distillate and residue compositions. Note that this is the same degree of vaporization as in Illustration 9.5.

Solution. The average temperature will be somewhat higher than the bubble point of the feed (see Illustration 9.3) but is unknown. It will be taken as 100°C. Corrections can later be made by computing the bubble point of the residue and repeating the work, but α's vary little with moderate changes in temperature. The vapor pressures at 100°C are tabulated and α's calculated relative to toluene, as follows:

Substance	P = vapor pressure, 100°C, mm Hg	α	x_F
A	1,370	1,370/550 = 2.49	0.50
B	550	1.0	0.25
C	200	0.364	0.25

Basis: $F = 100$ moles, $D = 32.5$ moles, $W = 67.5$ moles.

Eq. (9.42):
$$\text{For } A, \log \frac{100(0.50)}{67.5x_{AW}} = 2.49 \log \frac{100(0.25)}{67.5x_{BW}}$$

$$\text{For } C, \log \frac{100(0.25)}{67.5x_{CW}} = 0.364 \log \frac{100(0.25)}{67.5x_{BW}}$$

Eq. (9.43):
$$x_{AW} + x_{BW} + x_{CW} = 1.0$$

Solving simultaneously by assuming values of x_{BW}, computing x_{AW} and x_{CW}, and checking their sum until it equals unity, there is obtained $x_{AW} = 0.385$, $x_{BW} = 0.285$, $x_{CW} = 0.335$. The sum is 1.005, which is taken as satisfactory.

The composited distillate composition is computed by material balances.

$$\text{For } A, 100(0.50) = 32.5y_{AD,av} + 67.5(0.385) \qquad y_{AD,av} = 0.742$$

Similarly,

$$y_{BD,av} = 0.178 \quad \text{and} \quad y_{CD,av} = 0.075$$

Note the improved separation over that obtained by flash vaporization (Illustration 9.5).

CONTINUOUS RECTIFICATION—BINARY SYSTEMS

Continuous rectification, or fractionation, is a multistage countercurrent distillation operation.   For a binary solution, with certain exceptions it is ordinarily possible by this method to separate the solution into its components, recovering each in any state of purity that is desired.

The fractionation operation

In order to understand how such an operation is carried out, recall the discussion of reboiled absorbers in Chap. 8 and Fig. 8.26.   There, because the liquid leaving the bottom of an absorber is at best in equilibrium with the feed and may therefore contain substantial concentrations of volatile component, trays installed below the feed point were provided with vapor generated by a reboiler to strip out the volatile component from the liquid.   This component then entered the vapor and left the tower at the top.   The upper section of the tower served to wash the gas free of less volatile component, which entered the liquid to leave at the bottom.

So, too, with distillation.   Refer to Fig. 9.17.   Here the feed is introduced more or less centrally into a vertical cascade of stages.   Vapor rising in the section above the feed (called the *absorption, enriching,* or *rectifying* section) is washed with liquid to remove or absorb the less volatile component.   Since no extraneous material is added, as in the case of absorption, the washing liquid in this case is provided by condensing the vapor issuing from the top, which is rich in more volatile component.   The liquid returned to the top of the tower is called *reflux,* and the material permanently removed is the *distillate,* which may be a vapor or a liquid, rich in more volatile component. In the section below the feed (*stripping* or *exhausting* section), the liquid is stripped of volatile component by vapor produced at the bottom by partial vaporization of the bottom liquid in the reboiler.   The liquid removed, rich in less volatile component, is the *residue,* or *bottoms.*   Inside the tower, the liquids and vapors are always at their bubble points and dew points, respectively, so that the highest temperatures are at the bottom, the lowest at the top.   The entire device is called a *fractionator.*

The purities obtained for the two withdrawn products will depend upon the liquid/gas ratios used and the number of ideal stages provided in the two sections of the tower, and the interrelation of these must now be established.   The cross-sectional area of the tower, however, is governed entirely by the quantities of materials handled, in accordance with the principles of Chap. 6.

Overall enthalpy balances

In Fig. 9.17, the ideal trays are numbered from the top down, and subscripts generally indicate the tray from which a stream originates: for example, L_n is moles liquid/hr falling from the nth tray.   A bar over the quantity indicates that it applies to the section of the column below the point of introduction of the feed.   The distillate product may be liquid, vapor, or a mixture.   The reflux, however, must be liquid. The molar ratio of reflux to withdrawn distillate is the *reflux ratio,* sometimes called

Fig. 9.17 *Material and enthalpy balance of a fractionator.*

the *external* reflux ratio,

$$R = \frac{L_0}{D} \qquad (9.44)$$

which is specified in accordance with principles to be established later.

Consider the condenser, envelope I (Fig. 9.17). A total material balance is

$$G_1 = D + L_0 \qquad (9.45)$$

or

$$G_1 = D + RD = D(R + 1) \qquad (9.46)$$

For substance A

$$G_1 y_1 = D z_D + L_0 x_0 \qquad (9.47)$$

Equations (9.45) to (9.47) establish the concentrations and quantities at the top of the tower. An enthalpy balance, envelope I,

$$G_1 H_{G1} = Q_C + L_0 H_{L0} + D H_D \tag{9.48}$$

$$Q_C = D[(R+1)H_{G1} - R H_{L0} - H_D] \tag{9.49}$$

provides the heat load of the condenser. The reboiler heat is then obtained by a complete enthalpy balance about the entire apparatus, envelope II,

$$Q_B = D H_D + W H_W + Q_C + Q_L - F H_F \tag{9.50}$$

where Q_L is the sum of all the heat losses. Heat economy is frequently obtained by heat exchange between the residue product, which issues from the column at its bubble point, and the feed for purposes of preheating the feed. Equation (9.50) still applies provided that any such exchanger is included inside envelope II.

Two methods will be used to develop the relationship among numbers of trays, liquid/vapor ratios, and product compositions. The first of these, the method of Ponchon and Savarit,[4,29,31,33] is rigorous and can handle all situations, but it requires detailed enthalpy data for its application. The second, the method of McCabe and Thiele,[26] a simplification requiring only concentration equilibria, is less rigorous yet nevertheless adequate for many purposes.†

MULTISTAGE (TRAY) TOWERS—THE METHOD OF PONCHON AND SAVARIT

The method will first be developed for the case of negligible heat losses.

The enriching section

Consider the enriching section through tray n, envelope III, Fig. 9.17. Tray n is any tray in this section. Material balances for the section are, for total material,

$$G_{n+1} = L_n + D \tag{9.51}$$

and for component A,

$$G_{n+1} y_{n+1} = L_n x_n + D z_D \tag{9.52}$$

$$G_{n+1} y_{n+1} - L_n x_n = D z_D \tag{9.53}$$

The left-hand side of Eq. (9.53) represents the difference in rate of flow of component A, up — down, or the net flow upward. Since for a given distillation the right-hand side is constant, it follows that the difference, or net rate of flow of A upward, is constant, independent of tray number in this section of the tower, and equal to that permanently withdrawn at the top. An enthalpy balance, envelope III, with *heat loss negligible*, is

$$G_{n+1} H_{G,n+1} = L_n H_{Ln} + Q_C + D H_D \tag{9.54}$$

---

† The treatment of the McCabe-Thiele method is complete in itself, and may be referred to directly, if desired.

Let Q' be the heat removed in the condenser and the permanently removed distillate, per mole of distillate. Then

$$Q' = \frac{Q_C + DH_D}{D} = \frac{Q_C}{D} + H_D \tag{9.55}$$

and

$$G_{n+1}H_{G,n+1} - L_n H_{Ln} = DQ' \tag{9.56}$$

The left-hand side of Eq. (9.56) represents the difference in rate of flow of heat, up — down, or the net flow upward. Since for a given set of circumstances the right-hand side is constant, then the difference, or net rate of flow upward, is constant, independent of tray number in this section of the tower, and equal to that permanently taken out at the top with the distillate and at the condenser.

Elimination of D between Eqs. (9.51) and (9.52) and between Eqs. (9.51) and (9.56) yields

$$\frac{L_n}{G_{n+1}} = \frac{z_D - y_{n+1}}{z_D - x_n} = \frac{Q' - H_{G,n+1}}{Q' - H_{Ln}} \tag{9.57}$$

L_n/G_{n+1} is called the *internal reflux ratio*.

On the *Hxy* diagram, Eq. (9.57) is the equation of a straight line through $(H_{G,n+1}, y_{n+1})$ at G_{n+1}, (H_{Ln}, x_n) at L_n, and (Q', z_D) at Δ_D. The last is called a *difference point*, since its coordinates represent differences in rates of flow:

$$\Delta_D \begin{cases} Q' = \dfrac{\text{difference in heat flow, up} - \text{down}}{\text{net moles total substance out}} = \dfrac{\text{net heat out}}{\text{net moles out}} \\[2ex] z_D = \dfrac{\text{difference in flow of component } A, \text{ up} - \text{down}}{\text{net moles total substance out}} = \dfrac{\text{net moles } A \text{ out}}{\text{net moles out}} \end{cases}$$

Δ_D then represents a fictitious stream, in amount equal to the net flow outward (in this case D) and of properties (Q', z_D) such that

$$G_{n+1} - L_n = \Delta_D \tag{9.58}$$

On the *xy* diagram, Eq. (9.57) is the equation of a straight line of slope L_n/G_{n+1}, through (y_{n+1}, x_n) and $y = x = z_D$. These are plotted on Fig. 9.18, where both diagrams are shown.

Figure 9.18 is drawn for the case of a total condenser. The distillate D and reflux L_0 then have identical coordinates and are plotted at point D. The location shown indicates that they are below the bubble point. If they were at the bubble point, D would be on the saturated-liquid curve. The saturated vapor G_1 from the top tray, when totally condensed, has the same composition as D and L_0. Liquid L_1 leaving ideal tray 1 is in equilibrium with G_1 and is located at the end of tie line 1. Since Eq. (9.57) applies to all trays in this section, G_2 can be located on the saturated-vapor curve by a line drawn from L_1 to Δ_D; tie line 2 through G_2 locates L_2, etc. Thus, alternate tie lines (each representing the effluents from an ideal tray) and construction lines through Δ_D provide the stepwise changes in concentration occurring

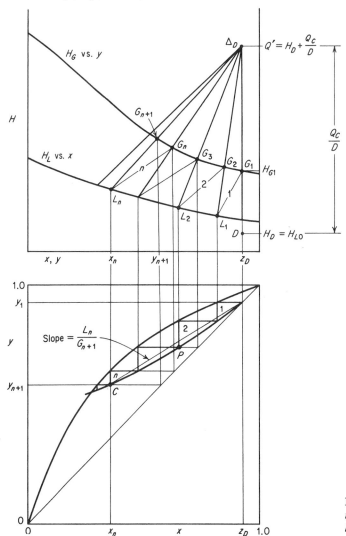

Fig. 9.18 *Enriching section, total condenser, reflux below the bubble point.*

in the enriching section.   Intersections of the lines radiating from Δ_D with the saturated-enthalpy curves, such as points G_3 and L_2, when projected to the lower diagram, produce points such as P.   These in turn produce the operating curve CP, which passes through $y = x = z_D$.   The tie lines, when projected downward, produce the equilibrium-distribution curve, and the stepwise nature of the concentration changes with tray number then becomes obvious.   The difference point Δ_D is used in this manner for all trays in the enriching section, working downward until the feed tray is reached.

Enriching trays may thus be located on the *Hxy* diagram alone by alternating construction lines to Δ_D and tie lines, each tie line representing an ideal tray.   As an alternative, random lines radiating from Δ_D may be drawn, their intersections with the $H_G y$ and $H_L x$ curves plotted on the xy diagram to produce the operating curve, and the trays determined by the step construction typical of such diagrams.

At any tray n (compare Fig. 9.12) the L_n/G_{n+1} ratio is given by the ratio of line lengths $\Delta_D G_{n+1}/\Delta_D L_n$ on the upper diagram of Fig. 9.18 or by the slope of the chord as shown on the lower diagram. Substituting Eq. (9.51) into Eq. (9.57) provides

$$\frac{L_n}{L_n + D} = \frac{H_{G,n+1} - Q'}{H_{Ln} - Q'} = \frac{y_{n+1} - z_D}{x_n - z_D} \qquad (9.59)$$

which can be arranged to

$$\frac{L_n}{D} = \frac{Q' - H_{G,n+1}}{H_{G,n+1} - H_{Ln}} = \frac{z_D - y_{n+1}}{y_{n+1} - x_n} \qquad (9.60)$$

Applying this to the top tray provides the external reflux ratio, which is usually the one specified:

$$R = \frac{L_0}{D} = \frac{Q' - H_{G1}}{H_{G1} - H_{L0}} = \frac{\text{line } \Delta_D G_1}{\text{line } G_1 L_0} = \frac{\text{line } \Delta_D G_1}{\text{line } G_1 D} \qquad (9.61)$$

For a given reflux ratio, the line-length ratio of Eq. (9.61) may be used to locate Δ_D vertically on Fig. 9.18, and the ordinate Q' may then be used to compute the condenser heat load.

In some cases a *partial condenser* is used, as in Fig. 9.19. Here a saturated vapor distillate D is withdrawn, and the condensate provides the reflux. This is frequently done when the pressure required for complete condensation of the vapor G_1, at reasonable condenser temperatures, would be too large. The Δ_D is plotted at an abscissa y_D corresponding to the composition of the withdrawn distillate. Assuming that an equilibrium condensation is realized, reflux L_0 is at the end of the tie line C. G_1 is located by the construction line $L_0\Delta_D$, etc. In the lower diagram, the line MN solves the equilibrium-condensation problem (compare Fig. 9.14). The reflux ratio $R = L_0/D = $ line $\Delta_D G_1/$line $G_1 L_0$, by application of Eq. (9.61). It is seen that the equilibrium partial condenser provides one ideal tray's worth of rectification. However, it is safest not to rely on such complete enrichment by the condenser and instead to provide trays in the tower equivalent to all the stages required.

The stripping section

Consider the envelope IV, Fig. 9.17, where tray m is any tray in the stripping section. A balance for total material is

$$\bar{L}_m = \bar{G}_{m+1} + W \qquad (9.62)$$

and, for component A,

$$\bar{L}_m x_m = \bar{G}_{m+1} y_{m+1} + W x_W \qquad (9.63)$$

$$\bar{L}_m x_m - \bar{G}_{m+1} y_{m+1} = W x_W \qquad (9.64)$$

The left-hand side of Eq. (9.64) represents the difference in rate of flow of component A, down − up, or the net flow downward. Since the right-hand side is a constant

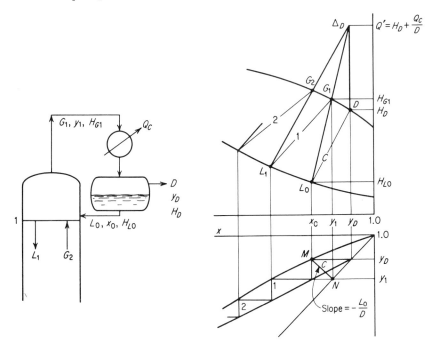

Fig. 9.19 *Partial condenser.*

for a given distillation, the difference is independent of tray number in this section of the tower and equal to the rate of permanent removal of A out the bottom. An enthalpy balance is

$$\bar{L}_m H_{Lm} + Q_B = \bar{G}_{m+1} H_{G,m+1} + W H_W \tag{9.65}$$

Define Q'' as the net flow of heat outward at the bottom, per mole of residue

$$Q'' = \frac{W H_W - W_B}{W} = H_W - \frac{Q_B}{W} \tag{9.66}$$

whence

$$\bar{L}_m H_{Lm} - \bar{G}_{m+1} H_{G,m+1} = W Q'' \tag{9.67}$$

The left-hand side of Eq. (9.67) is the difference in rate of flow of heat, down — up, which then equals the constant net rate of heat flow out the bottom for all trays in this section.

Elimination of W between Eqs. (9.62) and (9.63) and between Eqs. (9.62) and (9.67) provides

$$\frac{\bar{L}_m}{\bar{G}_{m+1}} = \frac{y_{m+1} - x_W}{x_m - x_W} = \frac{H_{G,m+1} - Q''}{H_{Lm} - Q''} \tag{9.68}$$

On the Hxy diagram, Eq. (9.68) is a straight line through $(H_{G,m+1}, y_{m+1})$ at $\bar{G}_{m+1}$, (H_{Lm}, x_m) at $\bar{L}_m$, and (Q'', x_W) at Δ_W. Δ_W is a *difference* point, whose coordinates mean

$$
\Delta_W \begin{cases} Q'' = \dfrac{\text{difference in heat flow, down } - \text{ up}}{\text{net moles of total substance out}} = \dfrac{\text{net heat out}}{\text{net moles out}} \\[2em] x_W = \dfrac{\text{difference in flow of component } A, \text{ down } - \text{ up}}{\text{net moles of total substance out}} = \dfrac{\text{moles } A \text{ out}}{\text{net moles out}} \end{cases}
$$

Thus, Δ_W is a fictitious stream, in amount equal to the net flow outward (in this case W), of properties (Q'', x_W),

$$
\bar{L}_m - \bar{G}_{m+1} = \Delta_W \tag{9.69}
$$

On the xy diagram, Eq. (9.68) is a straight line of slope $\bar{L}_m/\bar{G}_{m+1}$, through (y_{m+1}, x_m) and $y = x = x_W$. These straight lines are plotted on Fig. 9.20 for both diagrams.

Since Eq. (9.68) applies to all trays of the stripping section, the line on the Hxy plot of Fig. 9.20 from $\bar{G}_{N_p+1}$ (vapor leaving the reboiler and entering the bottom tray N_p of the tower) to Δ_W intersects the saturated-liquid–enthalpy curve at $\bar{L}_{N_p}$, the liquid leaving the bottom tray. Vapor $\bar{G}_{N_p}$ leaving the bottom tray is in equilibrium with liquid $\bar{L}_{N_p}$ and is located on the tie line N_p. Tie lines projected to the xy diagram produce points on the equilibrium curve, and lines through Δ_W provide points such as T on the operating curve. Substitution of Eq. (9.62) into Eq. (9.68) provides

$$
\frac{\bar{L}_m}{W} = \frac{H_{G,m+1} - Q''}{H_{G,m+1} - H_{Lm}} = \frac{y_{m+1} - x_W}{y_{m+1} - x_m} \tag{9.70}
$$

The diagrams have been drawn for the type of reboiler shown in Fig. 9.17, where the vapor leaving the reboiler is in equilibrium with the residue, the reboiler thus providing an ideal stage of enrichment (tie line B, Fig. 9.20). Other methods of applying heat at the bottom of the still are considered later.

Stripping-section trays may thus be determined entirely on the Hxy diagram by alternating construction lines to Δ_W and tie lines, each tie line accounting for an ideal stage. Alternatively, random lines radiating from Δ_W may be drawn, their intersections with curves $H_G y$ and $H_L x$ plotted on the xy diagram to produce the operating curve, and the stages determined by the usual step construction.

The complete fractionator

Envelope II of Fig. 9.17 may be used for material balances over the entire device

$$
F = D + W \tag{9.71}
$$

$$
F z_F = D z_D + W x_W \tag{9.72}
$$

Equation (9.50) is a complete enthalpy balance. If, in the absence of heat losses $(Q_L = 0)$, the definitions of Q' and Q'' are substituted into Eq. (9.50), it becomes

$$
F H_F = D Q' + W Q'' \tag{9.73}
$$

If F is eliminated from Eqs. (9.71) to (9.73), there results

$$
\frac{D}{W} = \frac{z_F - x_W}{z_D - z_F} = \frac{H_F - Q''}{Q' - H_F} \tag{9.74}
$$

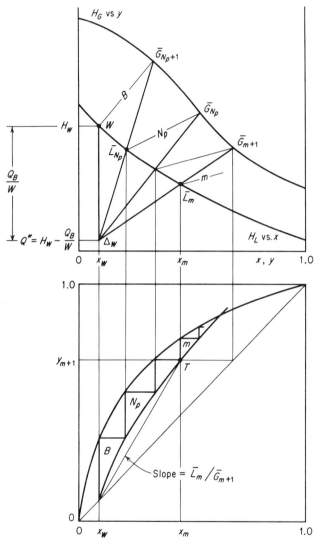

Fig. 9.20 *Stripping section.*

This is the equation of a straight line on the *Hxy* diagram, through (Q',z_D) at Δ_D, (H_F,z_F) at F, and (Q'',x_W) at Δ_W, as plotted in Fig. 9.21. In other words,

$$F = \Delta_D + \Delta_W \tag{9.75}$$

The location of F, representing the feed, on Fig. 9.21 shows the feed in this case to be a liquid below the bubble point. In other situations, F may be on the saturated-liquid or vapor curve, between them, or above the saturated-vapor curve. In any event, the two Δ points and F must lie on a single straight line.

The construction for trays is now clear. After locating F and the concentration

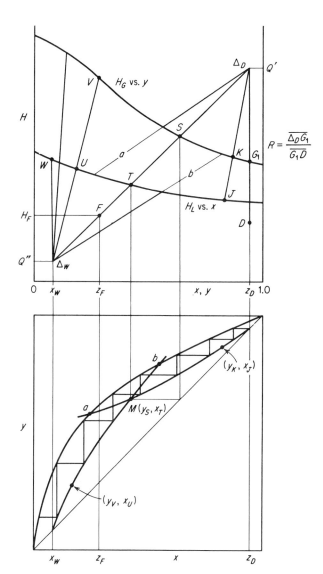

Fig. 9.21 *The entire fractionator.*
Feed below the bubble point and a
total condenser.

abscissas z_D and x_W corresponding to the products on the Hxy diagram, Δ_D is located vertically on line $x = z_D$ by computation of Q' or by the line-length ratio of Eq. (9.61) using the specified reflux ratio R.   The line $\Delta_D F$ extended to $x = x_W$ locates Δ_W, whose ordinate may be used to compute Q_B.   Random lines such as $\Delta_D J$ are drawn from Δ_D to locate the enriching-section operating curve on the xy diagram, and random lines such as $\Delta_W V$ are used to locate the stripping-section operating curve on the lower diagram.   The operating curves intersect at M, related to the line $\Delta_D F \Delta_W$ in the manner shown.   They intersect the equilibrium curve at a and b, corresponding to the tie lines on the Hxy diagram which, when extended, pass through

(a)

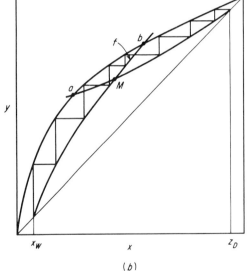

(b)

Fig. 9.22 *Delayed and early feed entries.*

Δ_D and Δ_W, respectively, as shown. Steps are drawn on the xy diagram between operating curves and equilibrium curve, beginning usually at $x = y = z_D$ (or at $x = y = x_W$ if desired), each step representing an ideal stage or tray. A change is made from the enriching to the stripping operating curve *at the tray on which the feed is introduced;* in the case shown the feed is to be introduced on the tray whose step straddles point M. The step construction is then continued to $x = y = x_W$.

Liquid and vapor flow rates may be computed throughout the fractionator from the line-length ratios [Eqs. (9.57), (9.60), (9.68), and (9.70)] on the Hxy diagram.

Feed-tray location

The material and enthalpy balances from which the operating curves are derived dictate that the stepwise construction of Fig. 9.21 must change operating lines at the tray where the feed is to be introduced. Refer to Fig. 9.22, where the equilibrium and operating curves of Fig. 9.21 are reproduced. In stepping down from the top of the fractionator, it is clear that, as shown in Fig. 9.22a, the enriching curve could have been used to a position as close to point a as desired. As point a is approached, however, the change in composition produced by each tray diminishes, and at a a *pinch* develops. As shown, tray f is the feed tray. Alternatively, the stripping operating curve could have been used at the first opportunity after passing point b, to provide the feed tray f of Fig. 9.22b (had the construction begun at x_W, introduction of feed might have been delayed to as near point b as desired, whereupon a pinch would develop at b).

In the design of a new fractionator, the smallest number of trays for the circumstances at hand is desired. This requires that the distance between operating and equilibrium curves be kept always as large as possible, which will occur if the feed tray is taken as that which straddles the operating-curve intersection at M, as in Fig. 9.21. The total number of trays for either Fig. 9.22a or b is of necessity larger. Delayed or early feed entry, as shown in these figures, is used only in cases where a separation is being adapted to an existing tower equipped with a feed-tray entry nozzle on a particular tray, which must then be used.

Consider again the feed tray of Fig. 9.21. It is understood that if the feed is all liquid, it is introduced above the tray in such a manner that it enters the tray along with the liquid from the tray above. Conversely, if the feed is all vapor, it is introduced underneath the feed tray. Should the feed be a mixed liquid and vapor, in principle it should be separated outside the column and the liquid portion introduced above, the vapor portion below, the feed tray. This is rarely done, and the mixed feed is usually introduced into the column without prior separation for reasons of economy. This will have only a small influence on the number of trays required.[3]

Increased reflux ratio

As the reflux ratio $R = L_0/D$ is increased, the Δ_D difference point on Fig. 9.21 must be located at higher values of Q'. Since Δ_D, F, and Δ_W are always on the same line, increasing the reflux ratio lowers the location of Δ_W. These changes result in larger values of L_n/G_{n+1} and smaller values of $\bar{L}_m/\bar{G}_{m+1}$, and the operating curves on the xy diagram move closer to the 45° diagonal. Fewer trays are then required, but Q_C, Q_W, L, $\bar{L}$, G, and $\bar{G}$ all increase; condenser and reboiler surfaces and tower cross section must be increased to accommodate the larger loads.

Total reflux

Ultimately, when $R = \infty$, $L_n/G_{n+1} = \bar{L}_m/\bar{G}_{m+1} = 1$, the operating curves both coincide with the 45° line on the xy plot, the Δ points are at infinity on the Hxy plot, and the number of trays required is the minimum value, N_m. This is shown on Fig. 9.23. The condition may be realized practically by returning all the distillate to the

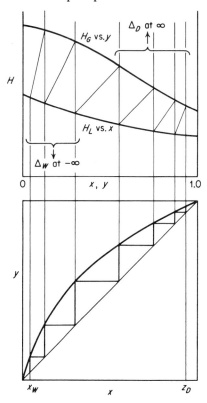

Fig. 9.23   *Total reflux and minimum stages.*

top tray as reflux and reboiling all the residue, whereupon the feed to the tower must be stopped.

Constant relative volatility

A useful analytical expression for the minimum number of theoretical stages can be obtained for cases where the relative volatility is reasonably constant.[9,39]   Applying Eq. (9.2) to the residue product,

$$\frac{y_W}{1 - y_W} = \alpha_W \frac{x_W}{1 - x_W} \tag{9.76}$$

where α_W is the relative volatility at the reboiler.   At total reflux the operating line coincides with the 45° diagonal so that $y_W = x_{Nm}$.   Therefore

$$\frac{x_{Nm}}{1 - x_{Nm}} = \alpha_W \frac{x_W}{1 - x_W} \tag{9.77}$$

Similarly for the last tray of the column, where α_{Nm} pertains,

$$\frac{y_{Nm}}{1 - y_{Nm}} = \alpha_{Nm} \frac{x_{Nm}}{1 - x_{Nm}} = \alpha_{Nm}\alpha_W \frac{x_W}{1 - x_W} \tag{9.78}$$

This procedure may be continued up the column until ultimately

$$\frac{y_1}{1-y_1} = \frac{x_D}{1-x_D} = \alpha_1 \alpha_2 \cdots \alpha_{Nm} \alpha_W \frac{x_W}{1-x_W} \tag{9.79}$$

If some average relative volatility α_{av} can be used,

$$\frac{x_D}{1-x_D} = \alpha_{av}^{N_m+1} \frac{x_W}{1-x_W} \tag{9.80}$$

or

$$N_m + 1 = \frac{\log \dfrac{x_D}{1-x_D}\dfrac{1-x_W}{x_W}}{\log \alpha_{av}} \tag{9.81}$$

which is known as Fenske's equation. The total minimum number of theoretical stages to produce products x_D and x_W is $N_m + 1$, which then includes the reboiler. For small variations in α, α_{av} may be taken as the geometric average of the values for the overhead and bottom products, $\sqrt{\alpha_1 \alpha_W}$. The expression may be used only with nearly ideal mixtures, for which α is nearly constant.

Minimum reflux ratio

The minimum reflux ratio R_m is the maximum ratio which will require an infinite number of trays for the separation desired, and it corresponds to the minimum reboiler heat load and condenser cooling load for the separation.

Refer to Fig. 9.24a, where the lightly drawn lines are tie lines which have been extended to intersect lines $x = z_D$ and $x = x_W$. It is clear that if Δ_D were located at point K, alternate tie lines and construction lines to Δ_D at the tie line k would coincide, and an infinite number of stages would be required to reach tie line k from the top of the tower. The same is true if Δ_W is located at point J. Since as Δ_D is moved upward and Δ_W downward the reflux ratio increases, the definition of minimum reflux ratio requires Δ_{Dm} and Δ_{Wm} for the minimum reflux ratio to be located as shown, with Δ_{Dm} at the highest tie-line intersection and Δ_{Wm} at the lowest tie-line intersection. In this case, it is the tie line which, when extended, passes through F, the feed, that determines both, and this is always the case when the xy equilibrium distribution curve is everywhere concave downward.

For some positively deviating mixtures with a tendency to form an azeotrope, an enriching-section tie line m in Fig. 9.24b gives the highest intersection with $x = z_D$, not that which passes through F. Similarly, as in Fig. 9.24c for some negatively deviating mixtures, a stripping-section tie line p gives the lowest intersection with $x = x_W$. These then govern the location of Δ_{Dm} as shown. For the minimum reflux ratio, either Δ_{Dm} is located at the highest intersection of an enriching-section tie line with $x = z_D$, or Δ_{Wm} is at the lowest intersection of a stripping-section tie line with $x = x_W$, consistent with the requirements that Δ_{Dm}, Δ_{Wm}, and F all be on the same straight line and Δ_{Dm} be at the highest position resulting in a pinch.

Once Q'_m is determined, the minimum reflux ratio may be computed through Eq. (9.61). Some larger reflux ratio must obviously be used for practical separations, whereupon Δ_D is located above Δ_{Dm}.

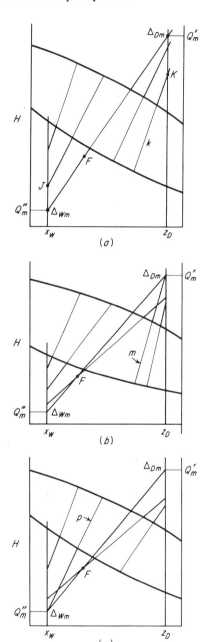

Fig. 9.24 *Minimum reflux ratio.*

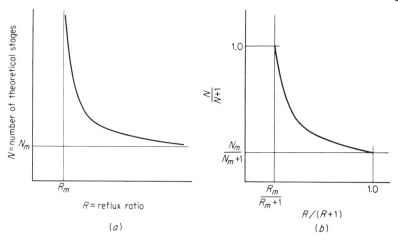

Fig. 9.25 *Reflux ratio–stage relation.*

Optimum reflux ratio

Any reflux ratio between the minimum and infinity will provide the desired separation, with the corresponding number of theoretical trays required varying from infinity to the minimum number, as in Fig. 9.25a.   Determination of the number of trays at several values of R, together with the limiting values of N_m and R_m, will usually permit plotting the entire curve with sufficient accuracy for most purposes.   The coordinate system of Fig. 9.25b[11] will permit locating the ends of the curve readily by avoiding the awkward asymptotes.   There have been several attempts at generalizing the curves of Fig. 9.25,[2,7,11,13] but the resulting charts yield only approximate results.

The reflux ratio which should be used for a new design should be the optimum, or the most economical, reflux ratio, for which the costs will be the least.   Refer to Fig. 9.26.   At the minimum reflux ratio the column requires an infinite number of

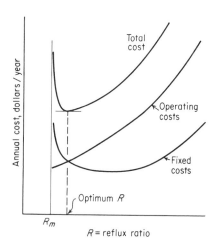

Fig. 9.26 *Most economical (optimum) reflux ratio.*

trays, and consequently the fixed cost is infinite, but the operating costs (heat for the reboiler, condenser cooling water, power for reflux pump) are least.   As R increases, the number of trays rapidly decreases, but the column diameter increases owing to the larger quantities of recycled liquid and vapor per unit quantity of feed.   The condenser, reflux pump, and reboiler must also be larger.   The fixed costs therefore fall through a minimum and rise to infinity again at total reflux.   The heat and cooling requirements increase almost directly with reflux ratio, as shown.   The total cost, which is the sum of operating and fixed costs, must therefore pass through a minimum at the optimum reflux ratio.   This will frequently but not always occur at a reflux ratio near the minimum value $(1.2R_m$ to $1.5R_m)$.

Illustration 9.8. Five thousand pounds per hour of a methanol (A)–water (B) solution containing 50 wt % methanol at 80°F is to be continuously rectified at 1 atm pressure to provide a distillate containing 95% methanol and a residue containing 1.0% methanol (by weight).   The feed is to be preheated by heat exchange with the residue, which will leave the system at 100°F.   The distillate is to be totally condensed to a liquid and the reflux returned at the bubble point.   The withdrawn distillate will be separately cooled before storage.   A reflux ratio of 1.5 times the minimum will be used.   Determine (a) quantity of the products; (b) enthalpy of feed and of products; (c) minimum reflux ratio; (d) minimum number of theoretical trays; (e) condenser and reboiler heat loads for specified reflux ratio; (f) number of theoretical trays for specified reflux ratio, and liquid and vapor quantities inside the tower.

Solution. a.   Mol wt methanol $= 32.04$, mol wt water $= 18.02$.   *Basis:* 1 hr.   Define quantities in terms of moles/hr.

$$F = \frac{5,000(0.50)}{32.04} + \frac{5,000(0.50)}{18.02} = 78.0 + 138.8 = 216.8 \text{ moles/hr}$$

$$z_F = \frac{78}{216.8} = 0.360 \text{ mole fraction methanol}$$

$$M_{av} \text{ for feed} = \frac{5,000}{216.8} = 23.1 \text{ lb/mole}$$

$$x_D = \frac{95/32.04}{95/32.04 + 5/18.02} = \frac{2.94}{3.217} = 0.915 \text{ mole fraction methanol}$$

$$M_{av} \text{ for distillate} = \frac{100}{3.217} = 31.1 \text{ lb/mole}$$

$$x_W = \frac{1/32.04}{1/32.04 + 99/18.02} = \frac{0.0312}{5.53} = 0.00565 \text{ mole fraction methanol}$$

$$M_{av} \text{ for residue} = \frac{100}{5.53} = 18.08 \text{ lb/mole}$$

Eq. (9.71): $216.8 = D + W$

Eq. (9.72): $216.8(0.360) = D(0.915) + W(0.00565)$

Solving simultaneously,

$$D = 84.4 \text{ moles/hr, or } 84.4(31.1) = 2,620 \text{ lb/hr}$$

$$W = 132.4 \text{ moles/hr, or } 132.4(18.08) = 2,380 \text{ lb/hr}$$

b. The vapor-liquid equilibria at 1 atm pressure are given in "The Chemical Engineers' Handbook," 4th ed., p. 13-5, specific heats of liquid solutions on p. 3-133, and latent heats of vaporization of methanol on p. 3-114. Heats of solution are available in "International Critical Tables," vol. V, p. 159, at $19.69°C = 67.5°F$, which will be used as t_o, the base temperature for computing enthalpies.

To compute enthalpies of saturated liquids, consider the case of $x = 0.3$ mole fraction methanol, $M_{av} = 22.2$. The bubble point $= 172.4°F$, specific heat $= 0.92$ Btu/lb°F, and the heat of solution is listed as 3.055 kilojoules evolved per gram mole methanol.

$$\Delta H_S = -3.055(238.9)(0.3)(1.8) = -394 \text{ Btu/lb mole solution}$$

where 238.9 converts from kilojoules to calories, 0.3 converts g moles methanol to g moles solution, and 1.8 to Btu/lb mole. Therefore, Eq. (9.10):

$$H_L = 0.92(172.4 - 67.5)22.2 - 394 = 1,746 \text{ Btu/lb mole}$$

To compute the enthalpy of saturated vapors, consider the case of $y = 0.665$ mole fraction methanol. The dew point is $172.4°F$. At this temperature, the latent heat of methanol is 450 Btu/lb, that of water is 994.9 Btu/lb. The specific heat of methanol is 0.617, of water 0.999 Btu/lb°F. Equation (9.11):

$$H_G = 0.665[0.617(32.04)(172.4 - 67.5) + 450(32.04)]$$
$$+ (1 - 0.665)[0.999(18.02)(172.4 - 67.5) + 994.9(18.02)]$$
$$= 17,600 \text{ Btu/lb mole}$$

The enthalpy data of Fig. 9.27 were computed in this manner.

From the vapor-liquid equilibria, the bubble point of the residue is $210°F$. Specific heat of residue is 0.998; of feed, 0.920. Enthalpy balance for feed preheat exchanger:

$$5,000(0.92)(t_F - 80) = 2,380(0.998)(210 - 100)$$
$$t_F = 136°F, \text{ temp at which feed enters tower}$$

(*Note:* The bubble point of the feed is $169°F$. Had t_F as computed above been higher than the bubble point, the above enthalpy balance would have been discarded and made in accordance with flash-vaporization methods.) For the feed, $\Delta H_S = -388$ Btu/lb mole. Enthalpy of feed at $136°F$ is

$$H_F = 0.92(136 - 67.5)(23.1) - 388 = 1,070 \text{ Btu/lb mole}$$

From Fig. 9.27, $H_D = H_{L0} = 1,565$, $H_W = 2,580$ Btu/lb mole.

c. Since the xy diagram (Fig. 9.28) is everywhere concave downward, the minimum reflux ratio is established by the tie line on Fig. 9.27 ($x = 0.37$, $y = 0.71$) which, when extended, passes through F, the feed. At Δ_{Dm}, $Q_m = 26,900$ Btu/lb mole. $H_{G1} = 16,600$ Btu/lb mole. Eq. (9.61):

$$R_m = \frac{26,900 - 16,600}{16,600 - 1,565} = 0.685$$

d. The minimum number of trays was determined on the xy diagram in the manner of the lower part of Fig. 9.23; and 4.9 ideal stages, including the reboiler, were obtained. $N_m = 4.9 - 1 = 3.9$.

e. For $R = 1.5(0.685) = 1.029$, Eq. (9.61) becomes

$$1.029 = \frac{Q' - 16,600}{16,600 - 1,565}$$

$$Q' = 32,070 = H_D + \frac{Q_\sigma}{D} = 1,565 + \frac{Q_\sigma}{84.4}$$

$$Q_\sigma = 2,575,000 \text{ Btu/hr condenser heat load}$$

Eq. (9.73): $$216.8(1,070) = 84.4(32,070) + 132.4Q''$$

$$Q'' = -18,690 = H_W - \frac{Q_B}{W} = 2,580 - \frac{Q_B}{132.4}$$

$$Q_B = 2,816,000 \text{ Btu/hr reboiler heat load}$$

f. On Fig. 9.27, Δ_D at ($x_D = 0.915$, $Q' = 32,070$) and Δ_W at ($x_W = 0.00565$, $Q'' = -18,690$) are plotted. Random lines from the Δ points, as shown, intersect the saturated-vapor and saturated-liquid curves at values of y and x, respectively, corresponding to points on the operating curve (note that for accurate results a large-scale graph and a sharp pencil are needed). These are plotted on Fig. 9.28 to provide the operating curves, which are nearly, but not exactly, straight. A total of nine ideal stages including the reboiler, or eight ideal trays in the tower, are required when the feed tray is the optimum (No. 5) as shown.

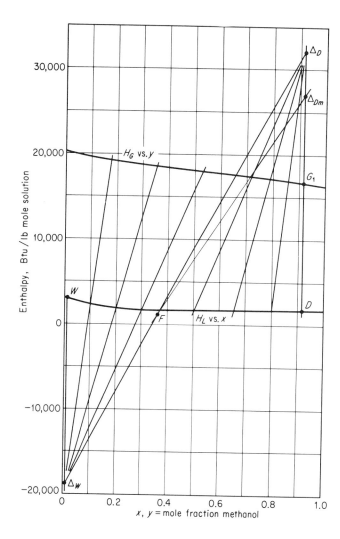

Fig. 9.27 *Enthalpy-concentration diagram for Illustration 9.8.*

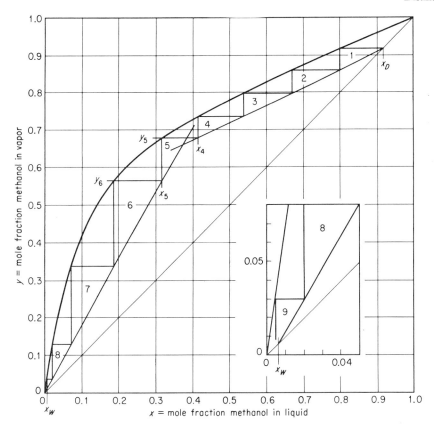

Fig. 9.28 *xy diagram for Illustration 9.8.*

At the top of the tower, $G_1 = D(R + 1) = 84.4(1.029 + 1) = 171.3$ lb moles/hr.

$$L_0 = DR = 84.4(1.029) = 86.7 \text{ lb moles/hr}$$

At the feed tray, $x_4 = 0.415$, $y_5 = 0.676$, $x_5 = 0.318$, $y_6 = 0.554$ (Fig. 9.28).

Eq. (9.60):
$$\frac{L_4}{D} = \frac{L_4}{84.4} = \frac{0.915 - 0.676}{0.676 - 0.415}$$

$$L_4 = 77.2 \text{ lb moles/hr}$$

Eq. (9.57):
$$\frac{L_4}{G_5} = \frac{77.2}{G_5} = \frac{0.915 - 0.676}{0.915 - 0.415}$$

$$G_5 = 161.5 \text{ lb moles/hr}$$

Eq. (9.70):
$$\frac{\bar{L}_5}{W} = \frac{\bar{L}_5}{132.4} = \frac{0.554 - 0.00565}{0.554 - 0.318}$$

$$\bar{L}_5 = 308 \text{ lb moles/hr}$$

Eq. (9.68):
$$\frac{L_5}{\bar{G}_6} = \frac{308}{\bar{G}_6} = \frac{0.554 - 0.00565}{0.318 - 0.00565}$$

$$\bar{G}_6 = 175.7 \text{ lb moles/hr}$$

At the bottom of the tower, Eq. (9.62): $L_{Np} = \bar{G}_W + W$

$$L_8 = \bar{G}_W + 132.4$$

Further, $y_W = 0.035$, $x_8 = 0.02$ (Fig. 9.28).

Eq. (9.68):
$$\frac{L_8}{\bar{G}_W} = \frac{0.035 - 0.00565}{0.02 - 0.00565}$$

Solving simultaneously, $\bar{G}_W = 127.6$, $L_8 = 260$ lb moles/hr.

Reboilers

The heat-exchanger arrangements to provide the necessary heat and vapor return at the bottom of the fractionator may take several forms.   Small fractionators used for pilot-plant work may merely require a jacketed kettle, as shown schematically in Fig. 9.29*a*, but the heat-transfer surface and the corresponding vapor capacity will necessarily be small.   The tubular heat exchanger built into the bottom of the tower (Fig. 9.29*b*) is a variation which provides larger surface, but cleaning requires shutdown of the distillation operation.   This type may also be built with an internal floating head.   Both of these provide a vapor entering the bottom tray essentially in equilibrium with the residue product, so that the last stage of the previous computations represents the enrichment owing to the reboiler.

External reboilers of several varieties are commonly used for large installations, and these may be arranged with spares for cleaning.   The kettle reboiler (Fig. 9.29*c*), with heating medium inside the tubes, provides a vapor to the tower essentially in equilibrium with the residue product and then behaves like an ideal stage.   The vertical thermosiphon reboiler of Fig. 9.29*d*, with the heating medium outside the tubes, may be operated so as to vaporize all the liquid entering it to produce a vapor of the same composition as the residue product, in which case there is no enrichment provided.   However, owing to fouling of the tubes, which may occur with this type of operation, it is more customary to provide for only partial vaporization, the mixture issuing from the reboiler comprising both liquid and vapor.   The reboiler of Fig. 9.29*e* receives liquid from the trapout of the bottom tray, which it partially vaporizes. Other arrangements are discussed by Hengstebeck,[14] and Fair[8] reviews their design. It is safest not to assume that an ideal stage's worth of fractionation will occur with thermosiphon reboilers but instead to provide the necessary stages in the tower itself. In Fig. 9.29, the reservoir at the foot of the tower customarily holds a 5- to 10-min flow of liquid to provide for reasonably steady operation of the reboiler.

Reboilers may be heated by steam, heat-transfer oil, or other hot fluids.   For some high-boiling liquids, the reboiler may be a fuel-fired furnace.

Use of open steam

When a water solution in which the nonaqueous component is the more volatile is fractionated, so that the water is removed as the residue product, the heat required may

(a) Jacketed kettle

Steam

Bottoms

(b) Internal reboiler

Steam

Bottoms

(c) Kettle-type reboiler

Vapor

Steam

Bottoms

(d) Thermo-syphon reboiler

Steam

Bottoms

(e) Thermo-syphon reboiler

Steam

Bottoms

Fig. 9.29   *Reboiler arrangements.*

be provided by admission of steam directly to the bottom of the tower. The reboiler is then dispensed with. For a given reflux ratio and distillate composition, more trays will usually be required in the tower, but these are usually cheaper than the replaced reboiler and its cleaning costs.

Refer to Fig. 9.30. While the enriching section of the tower is unaffected by the use of open steam and is not shown, nevertheless the overall material and enthalpy balances are influenced. Thus, in the absence of important heat loss,

$$F + \bar{G}_{Np+1} = D + W \tag{9.82}$$

$$Fz_F = Dz_D + Wx_W \tag{9.83}$$

$$FH_F + \bar{G}_{Np+1}H_{G,Np+1} = WH_W + DH_D + Q_C \tag{9.84}$$

where $\bar{G}_{Np+1}$ is the molar rate of introducing steam. On the Hxy diagram, the Δ_D difference point is located in the usual manner. For the stripping section, Δ_W has its usual meaning, a fictitious stream of size equal to the net flow outward

$$\Delta_W = \bar{L}_m - \bar{G}_{m+1} = W - \bar{G}_{Np+1} \tag{9.85}$$

of coordinates

$$\Delta_W \begin{cases} x_{\Delta W} = \dfrac{\text{net moles } A \text{ out}}{\text{net moles out}} = \dfrac{Wx_W}{W - \bar{G}_{Np+1}} \\[3mm] Q'' = \dfrac{\text{net heat out}}{\text{net moles out}} = \dfrac{WH_W - \bar{G}_{Np+1}H_{G,Np+1}}{W - \bar{G}_{Np+1}} \end{cases}$$

where $H_{G,Np+1}$ is the enthalpy of the steam. The point is shown on Fig. 9.31. Thus,

$$\bar{L}_m x_m - \bar{G}_{m+1}y_{m+1} = \Delta_W x_W \tag{9.86}$$

$$\bar{L}_m H_{Lm} - \bar{G}_{m+1}H_{G,m+1} = \Delta_W Q'' \tag{9.87}$$

and

$$\frac{\bar{L}_m}{\bar{G}_{m+1}} = \frac{y_{m+1} - x_{\Delta W}}{x_m - x_{\Delta W}} = \frac{H_{G,m+1} - Q''}{H_{Lm} - Q''} \tag{9.88}$$

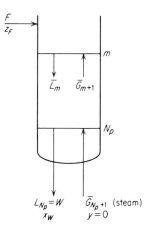

Fig. 9.30 *Use of open steam.*

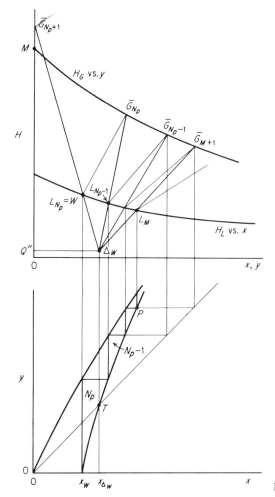

Fig. 9.31   *Use of open steam.*

The construction is shown on Fig. 9.31.   Equation (9.88) is the slope of a chord (not shown) between points P and T.   Here, the steam introduced is shown slightly superheated ($H_{G,Np+1} >$ saturated enthalpy); had saturated steam been used, $\bar{G}_{Np+1}$ would be located at point M.   Note that the operating curve on the x, y diagram passes through the 45° diagonal at T ($x = x_{\Delta W}$) and through the point ($x_W, y = 0$) corresponding to the fluids passing each other at the bottom of the tower.

Illustration 9.9.   Open steam, initially saturated at 10 psig pressure, will be used for the methanol fractionator of Illustration 9.8, with the same distillate rate and composition and the same reflux ratio.   Assuming that the feed enters the tower at the same enthalpy as in Illustration 9.8, determine the steam rate, bottoms composition, and the number of ideal trays.

   Solution.   From Illustration 9.8, $F = 216.8$, $z_F = 0.360$, $H_F = 1,070$, $D = 84.4$, $z_D = 0.915$, $H_D = 1,565$, and $Q_C = 2,575,000$, each in the usual units.   From the steam tables, the enthalpy of saturated steam at 10 psig $= 1,160.4$ Btu/lb referred to liquid water at 32°F. On expanding adiabatically through a control valve to the tower pressure, it will be superheated with the same enthalpy. The enthalpy of liquid water at 67.5°F (t_o for Illustration 9.8) $= 35.55$ Btu/lb referred to 32°F. Therefore $H_{G,Np+1} = (1,160.4 - 35.55)(18.02) = 20,280$ Btu/lb mole.

Eq. (9.82): $$216.8 + \bar{G}_{Np+1} = 84.4 + W$$

Eq. (9.83): $$216.8(0.360) = 84.4(0.915) + Wx_W$$

Eq. (9.84): $$216.8(1,070) + 20,280\bar{G}_{Np+1} = WH_W + 84.4(1,565) + 2,575,000$$

Since the bottoms will be essentially pure water, H_W is tentatively estimated as the enthalpy of saturated water (Fig. 9.28), 2,620 Btu/lb mole. Solving the equations simultaneously with this value for H_W, the steam rate is $\bar{G}_{Np+1} = 159.4$ and $W = 291.8$ lb moles/hr, with $x_W = 0.00281$. The enthalpy of this solution at the bubble point is 2,600 Btu/lb mole, sufficiently close to the assumed 2,620 to be acceptable. (Note that had the same interchange of heat between bottoms and feed been used as in Illustration 9.8, with bottoms discharged at 100°F, the feed enthalpy would no longer be 1,070 Btu/lb mole.) For Δ_W,

$$x_{\Delta W} = \frac{Wx_W}{W - \bar{G}_{Np+1}} = \frac{291.8(0.00281)}{291.8 - 159.4} = 0.0062$$

$$Q'' = \frac{WH_W - \bar{G}_{Np+1}H_{G,Np+1}}{W - \bar{G}_{Np+1}}$$

$$= \frac{291.8(2,600) - 159.4(20,280)}{291.8 - 159.4} = -18,650$$

The Hxy and xy diagrams for the enriching section are the same as in Illustration 9.8. For the stripping section, they resemble Fig. 9.31. The number of ideal stages is $N_p = 9.5$, and these must now all be included in the tower.

Multiple feeds

There are occasions when two or more feeds composed of the same substances but of different concentrations require distillation to give the same distillate and residue products. A single fractionator will then suffice for all.

Consider the two-feed fractionator of Fig. 9.32. The construction on the Hxy diagram for the sections of the column above F_1 and below F_2 are the same as for a single-feed column, with the Δ_D and Δ_W points located in the usual manner. For the middle section between the feeds, the difference point Δ_M may be located by consideration of material and enthalpy balances either toward the top, as indicated by the envelope shown on Fig. 9.32, or toward the bottom; the net result will be the same. Consider the envelope shown in the figure, with Δ_M representing a fictitious stream of quantity equal to the net flow upward and out

$$G'_{r+1} - L'_r = D - F_1 = \Delta_M \tag{9.89}$$

whose coordinates are

$$\Delta_M \begin{cases} x_{\Delta M} = \dfrac{\text{net moles } A \text{ out}}{\text{net moles out}} = \dfrac{Dz_D - F_1 z_{F1}}{D - F_1} \\[2ex] Q_M = \dfrac{\text{net heat out}}{\text{net moles out}} = \dfrac{Q_C + DH_D - F_1 H_{F1}}{D - F_1} \end{cases}$$

Δ_M may be either a positive or negative quantity.

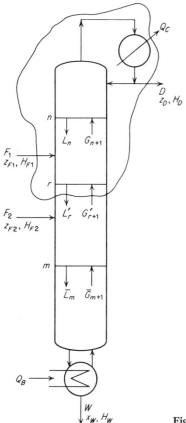

Fig. 9.32   *Fractionator with two feeds.*

Equation (9.89) may be used as a basis for component-A and enthalpy balances

$$G'_{r+1}y_{r+1} - L'_r x_r = \Delta_M x_{\Delta M} \qquad (9.90)$$

$$G'_{r+1}H_{G,r+1} - L_r H_{Lr} = \Delta_M Q_M \qquad (9.91)$$

whence

$$\frac{L'_r}{G'_{r+1}} = \frac{y_{r+1} - x_{\Delta M}}{x_r - x_{\Delta M}} = \frac{H_{G,r+1} - Q_M}{H_{Lr} - Q_M} \qquad (9.92)$$

Since

$$F_1 + F_2 = D + W = \Delta_D + \Delta_W \qquad (9.93)$$

then

$$\Delta_M = F_2 - W \qquad (9.94)$$

The construction (both feeds liquid) is shown on Fig. 9.33, where Δ_M lies on the line $\Delta_D F_1$ [Eq. (9.89)] and on the line $\Delta_W F_2$ [Eq. (9.94)].   A solution representing

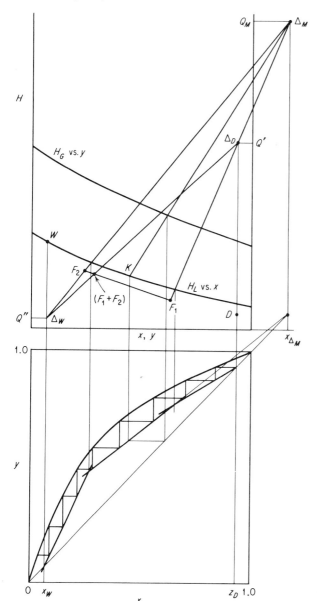

Fig. 9.33 *Construction for two feeds.*

the composited feed, with

$$z_{F,\text{av}} = \frac{F_1 z_{F_1} + F_2 z_{F_2}}{F_1 + F_2}, \qquad H_{F,\text{av}} = \frac{F_1 H_{F_1} + F_2 H_{F_2}}{F_1 + F_2}$$

must lie on the line $\Delta_D \Delta_W$ [Eq. (9.93)]. It is also possible for Δ_M to lie below and to the left of Δ_W. The operating curve for the middle section on the xy diagram is located by lines such as $\Delta_M K$, as shown. Trays are best drawn in the usual step fashion on the xy diagram, and for optimum location, the feed trays straddle the intersections of the operating curves, as shown.

Side streams

Side streams are products of intermediate composition withdrawn from the intermediate trays of the column. They are used frequently in the distillation of petroleum products, where intermediate properties not obtainable merely by mixing distillate or bottoms with feed are desired. They are used only infrequently in the case of binary mixtures, and are not treated here (see Prob. 9.17).

Heat losses

Most fractionators operate above ambient temperature, and heat losses along the column are inevitable since insulating materials have a finite thermal conductivity. The importance of the heat losses and their influence on fractionators need now to be considered.

Consider the fractionator of Fig. 9.17. A heat balance for the top n trays of the enriching section (envelope III) which includes the heat loss is[4]

$$G_{n+1} H_{G,n+1} = Q_C + D H_D + L_n H_{Ln} + Q_{Ln} \tag{9.95}$$

where Q_{Ln} is the heat loss for trays 1 through n. Defining

$$Q'_L = \frac{Q_C + D H_D + Q_{Ln}}{D} = Q' + \frac{Q_{Ln}}{D} \tag{9.96}$$

we have

$$G_{n+1} H_{G,n+1} - L_n H_{Ln} = D Q'_L \tag{9.97}$$

Q'_L is a variable since it depends upon how many trays are included in the heat balance. If only the top tray ($n = 1$) is included, the heat loss is small, and Q'_L is nearly equal to Q'. As more trays are included, Q_{Ln} and Q'_L increase, ultimately reaching their largest values when all enriching-section trays are included. Separate difference points are therefore needed for each tray.

For the stripping section up to tray m (envelope IV, Fig. 9.17),

$$\bar{L}_m H_{Lm} + Q_B = W H_W + \bar{G}_{m+1} H_{G,m+1} + \bar{Q}_{Lm} \tag{9.98}$$

Letting

$$Q''_L = \frac{W H_W - Q_B + \bar{Q}_{Lm}}{W} = Q'' + \frac{\bar{Q}_{Lm}}{W} \tag{9.99}$$

there results

$$\bar{L}_m H_{Lm} - \bar{G}_{m+1} H_{G,m+1} = W Q''_L \tag{9.100}$$

If the heat balance includes only the bottom tray, the heat loss is small, and Q_L'' nearly equals Q''. As more trays are included, $\bar{Q}_{Lm}$ and therefore Q_L'' increase, reaching their largest values when the balance is made over the entire stripping section. Separate difference points are needed for each tray.

The construction on the Hxy diagram is shown on Fig. 9.34 for a six-tray column and reboiler, liquid feed on to the fourth tray, and distillate at the bubble point. The procedure for design is one of trial and error. For example, as a first trial, heat losses might be neglected and trays calculated with fixed difference points, and after the size of the resulting column is determined, the first estimate of the heat losses for the two column sections may be made by the usual methods of heat-transfer

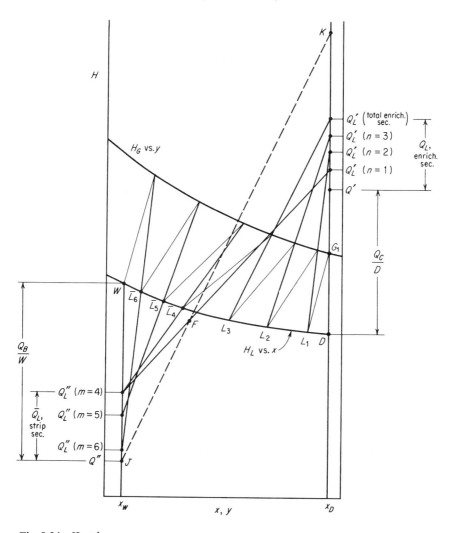

Fig. 9.34 *Heat losses.*

calculations. The heat losses may then be apportioned among the trays and the number of trays redetermined with the appropriate difference points. This leads to a second approximation of the heat loss, and so forth.

As Fig. 9.34 shows, heat losses increase the internal-reflux ratio, and *for a given condenser heat load*, fewer trays for a given separation are required (recall that the higher the enriching-section difference point and the lower the stripping-section difference point, the fewer the trays). However, the reboiler must provide not only the heat removed in the condenser but also the heat losses. Consequently, for the same reboiler heat load as shown on Fig. 9.34 but with complete insulation against heat loss, all the heat would be removed in the condenser, all the stripping trays would use point *J*, and all the enriching trays would use point *K* as their respective difference points. It therefore follows that, *for a given reboiler heat load or heat expenditure*, fewer trays are required for a given separation if heat losses are eliminated. For this reason, fractionators are usually well insulated.

High-purity products and tray efficiencies

Methods of dealing with these problems are considered following the McCabe-Thiele method and are equally applicable to Ponchon-Savarit calculations.

MULTISTAGE (TRAY) TOWERS—METHOD OF McCABE AND THIELE

This method, although less rigorous than that of Ponchon and Savarit, is nevertheless most useful since it does not require detailed enthalpy data. If such data must be approximated from fragmentary information, much of the exactness of the Ponchon-Savarit method is lost in any case. Except where heat losses or heats of solution are unusually large, the McCabe-Thiele method will be found adequate for most purposes. It hinges upon the fact that, as an approximation, the operating lines on the xy diagram may be considered straight for each section of a fractionator between points of addition or withdrawal of streams.

Equimolal overflow and vaporization

Consider the enriching section of the fractionator of Fig. 9.17. In the absence of heat losses, which can be (and usually are) made very small by thermal insulation for reasons of economy if for no other, Eq. (9.56) may be written

$$\frac{L_n}{G_{n+1}} = 1 - \frac{H_{G,n+1} - H_{Ln}}{Q' - H_{Ln}} \tag{9.101}$$

where Q' includes the condenser heat load and the enthalpy of the distillate, per mole of distillate. The liquid enthalpy H_{Ln} is ordinarily small in comparison with Q' since the condenser heat load must include the latent heat of condensation of at least the reflux liquid. If then $H_{G,n+1} - H_{Ln}$ is substantially constant, L_n/G_{n+1} will be constant also for a given fractionation.[32] From Eq. (9.11),

$$H_{G,n+1} = [y_{n+1}C_{LA}M_A + (1 - y_{n+1})C_{LB}M_B](t_{n+1} - t_o) + y_{n+1}\lambda_A M_A + (1 - y_{n+1})\lambda_B M_B \tag{9.102}$$

where t_{n+1} is the temperature of the vapor from tray $n + 1$ and the λ's are the latent heats of vaporization at this temperature. If the deviation from ideality of liquid solutions is not great, the first term in brackets of Eq. (9.102) is

$$y_{n+1}C_{LA}M_A + (1 - y_{n+1})C_{LB}M_B \doteq C_L M_{av} \tag{9.103}$$

From Eq. (9.10),

$$H_{Ln} = C_L(t_n - t_o)M_{av} + \Delta H_S \tag{9.104}$$

and

$$H_{G,n+1} - H_{Ln} = C_L M_{av}(t_{n+1} - t_n) + y_{n+1}\lambda_A M_A + (1 - y_{n+1})\lambda_B M_B - \Delta H_S \tag{9.105}$$

For all but unusual cases, the only important terms of Eq. (9.105) are those containing the latent heats. The temperature change between adjacent trays is usually small, so that the sensible-heat term is insignificant. The heat of solution can in most cases be measured in terms of hundreds of Btu/lb mole of solution, whereas the latent heats at ordinary pressures are usually of the order of 10,000 to 20,000 Btu/mole. Therefore, for all practical purposes,

$$H_{G,n+1} - H_{Ln} = (\lambda M)_{av} \tag{9.106}$$

where the last term is the weighted average of the molal latent heats. For many pairs of substances, the molal latent heats are nearly identical, so that averaging is unnecessary. If their inequality is the only barrier to application of these simplifying assumptions, it is possible to assign a fictitious molecular weight to one of the components so that the molal latent heats are then forced to be the same (if this is done, the entire computation must be made with the fictitious molecular weight, including operating lines and equilibrium data). This is, however, rarely necessary.

If it is sufficiently important, therefore, one can be persuaded that, for all but exceptional cases, the ratio L/G in the enriching section of the fractionator is essentially constant. The same reasoning can be applied to any section of a fractionator between points of addition or withdrawal of streams, although each section will have its own ratio.

Consider next two adjacent trays n and r, between which neither addition nor withdrawal of material from the tower occurs. A material balance provides

$$L_{r-1} + G_{n+1} = L_n + G_r \tag{9.107}$$

Since $L_{r-1}/G_r = L_n/G_{n+1}$, it follows that $L_n = L_{r-1}$ and $G_{n+1} = G_r$, which is the "principle of equimolal overflow and vaporization." The rate of liquid flow from each tray in a section of the tower is constant on a molar basis, but since the average molecular weight changes with tray number, the weight rates of flow are different.

It should be noted that, as shown in the discussion of Fig. 9.12, if the H_Gy and H_Lx lines on the Hxy diagram are straight and parallel, then in the absence of heat loss the L/G ratio for a given tower section will be constant regardless of the relative size of H_{Ln} and Q' in Eq. (9.101).

The general assumptions involved in the foregoing are customarily called the "usual simplifying assumptions."

Enriching section; total condenser—reflux at the bubble point

Consider a section of the fractionator entirely above the point of introduction of feed, shown schematically in Fig. 9.35a. The condenser removes all the latent heat from the overhead vapor but does not cool the resulting liquid further. The reflux and distillate product are therefore liquids at the bubble point, and $y_1 = x_D = x_0$. Since the liquid, L moles/hr, falling from each tray and the vapor, G moles/hr, rising from each tray are each constant if the usual simplifying assumptions pertain, subscripts are not needed to identify the source of these streams. The compositions, however, change. The trays shown are theoretical trays, so that the composition y_n of the vapor from the nth tray is in equilibrium with the liquid of composition x_n leaving

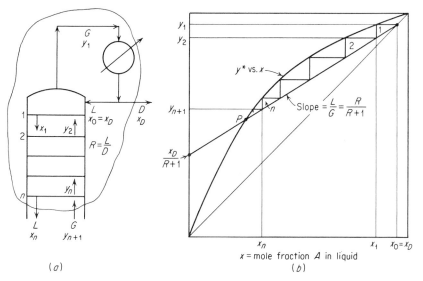

Fig. 9.35 *Enriching section.*

the same tray. The point (x_n, y_n), on x, y coordinates, therefore falls on the equilibrium curve.

A total material balance for the envelope in the figure is

$$G = L + D = D(R + 1) \tag{9.108}$$

For component A,

$$Gy_{n+1} = Lx_n + Dx_D \tag{9.109}$$

from which the enriching-section operating line is

$$y_{n+1} = \frac{L}{G} x_n + \frac{D}{G} x_D \tag{9.110}$$

$$y_{n+1} = \frac{R}{R + 1} x_n + \frac{x_D}{R + 1} \tag{9.111}$$

This is the equation of a straight line on x, y coordinates (Fig. 9.35b) of slope $L/G = R/(R + 1)$, and with a y intercept of $x_D/(R + 1)$. Setting $x_n = x_D$ shows $y_{n+1} = x_D$, so that the line passes through the point $y = x = x_D$ on the 45° diagonal. This point and the y intercept permit easy construction of the line. The concentration of liquids and vapors for each tray is shown in accordance with the principles of Chap. 5, and the usual "staircase" construction between operating line and equilibrium curve is seen to provide the theoretical tray-concentration variation. The construction obviously cannot be carried farther than point P.

In plotting the equilibrium curve of the figure, it is generally assumed that the pressure is constant throughout the tower. If necessary, the variation in pressure from tray to tray may be allowed for after determining the number of real trays, but this will require a trial-and-error procedure. It is ordinarily unnecessary except for operation under very low pressures.

Exhausting section; reboiled vapor in equilibrium with residue

Consider next a section of the fractionator below the point of introducing the feed, shown schematically in Fig. 9.36a. The trays are again theoretical trays. The rates of flow $\bar{L}$ and $\bar{G}$ are each constant from tray to tray, but not necessarily equal to the values for the enriching section. A total material balance,

$$\bar{L} = \bar{G} + W \tag{9.112}$$

and, for component A,

$$\bar{L}x_m = \bar{G}y_{m+1} + Wx_W \tag{9.113}$$

These provide the equation of the exhausting-section operating line,

$$y_{m+1} = \frac{\bar{L}}{\bar{G}} x_m - \frac{W}{\bar{G}} x_W \tag{9.114}$$

$$y_{m+1} = \frac{\bar{L}}{\bar{L} - W} x_m - \frac{W}{\bar{L} - W} x_W \tag{9.115}$$

This is a straight line of slope $\bar{L}/\bar{G} = \bar{L}(\bar{L} - W)$, and since when $x_m = x_W$, $y_{m+1} = x_W$, it passes through $x = y = x_W$ on the 45° diagonal (Fig. 9.36b). If the reboiled vapor y_W is in equilibrium with the residue x_W, the first step of the staircase construction represents the reboiler. The steps can be carried no farther than point T.

Fig. 9.36 Exhausting section.

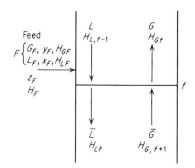

Fig. 9.37 *Introduction of feed.*

Introduction of feed

It is convenient before proceeding further to establish how the introduction of the feed influences the change in slope of the operating lines as we pass from the enriching to the exhausting sections of the fractionator.

Consider the section of the column at the tray where the feed is introduced (Fig. 9.37). The quantities of the liquid and vapor streams change abruptly at this tray, since the feed may consist of liquid, vapor, or a mixture of both. If, for example, the feed is a saturated liquid, $\bar{L}$ will exceed L by the amount of the added feed liquid. To establish the general relationship, an overall material balance about this section is

$$F + L + \bar{G} = G + \bar{L} \qquad (9.116)$$

and an enthalpy balance,

$$FH_F + LH_{L,f-1} + \bar{G}H_{G,f+1} = GH_{Gf} + \bar{L}H_{Lf} \qquad (9.117)$$

The vapors and liquids inside the tower are all saturated, and the molal enthalpies of all saturated vapors at this section are essentially identical since the temperature and composition changes over one tray are small. The same is true of the molal enthalpies of the saturated liquids, so that $H_{Gf} = H_{G,f+1}$ and $H_{L,f-1} = H_{Lf}$. Equation (9.117) then becomes

$$(\bar{L} - L)H_L = (\bar{G} - G)H_G + FH_F \qquad (9.118)$$

Combining this with Eq. (9.116),

$$\frac{\bar{L} - L}{F} = \frac{H_G - H_F}{H_G - H_L} = q \qquad (9.119)$$

The quantity q is thus seen to be the heat required to convert 1 mole of feed from its condition H_F to a saturated vapor, divided by the molal latent heat $H_G - H_L$. The feed may be introduced under any of a variety of thermal conditions ranging from a liquid well below its bubble point to a superheated vapor, for each of which the value of q will be different. Typical circumstances are listed in Table 9.1, with the corresponding range of values of q. Combining Eqs. (9.116) and (9.119),

$$\bar{G} - G = F(q - 1) \qquad (9.120)$$

which provides a convenient method for determining $\bar{G}$.

Table 9.1. Thermal conditions for the feed

Feed condition	G_F, moles/(hr)(sq ft)	L_F, moles/(hr)(sq ft)	H_{GF}, Btu/mole	H_{LF}, Btu/mole	H_F, Btu/mole	$q = \dfrac{H_G - H_F}{H_G - H_L}$	$\dfrac{q}{q-1}$
Liquid below bubble point	0	F		H_F	$H_F < H_L$	>1.0	>1.0
Saturated liquid	0	F		H_F	H_L	1.0	∞
Mixture of liquid and vapor†	G_F $F = G_F + L_F$	L_F	H_G	H_L	$H_G > H_F > H_L$	$\dfrac{L_F}{F}$ $1.0 > q > 0$	$\dfrac{L_F}{L_F - F}$
Saturated vapor	F	0	H_F		H_G	0	0
Superheated vapor	F	0	H_F		$H_F > H_G$	<0	$1.0 > \dfrac{q}{q-1} > 0$

† In this case the intersection of the q line with the equilibrium curve gives the compositions of the equilibrium liquid and vapor which comprise the feed. The q line is the flash-vaporization operating line for the feed.

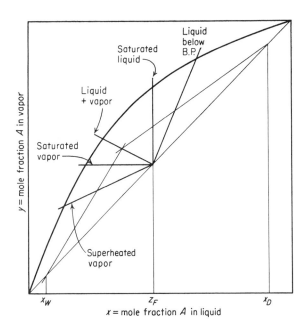

Fig. 9.38 *Location of q line for typical feed conditions.*

The point of intersection of the two operating lines will help locate the exhausting-section operating line. This may be established as follows. Rewriting Eqs. (9.110) and (9.114) without the tray subscripts,

$$yG = Lx + Dx_D \tag{9.121}$$

$$y\bar{G} = \bar{L}x - Wx_W \tag{9.122}$$

Subtracting,

$$(\bar{G} - G)y = (\bar{L} - L)x - (Wx_W + Dx_D) \tag{9.123}$$

Further, by an overall material balance,

$$Fz_F = Dx_D + Wx_W \tag{9.72}$$

Substituting this and Eqs. (9.119) and (9.120) in (9.123)

$$y = \frac{q}{q - 1}x - \frac{z_F}{q - 1} \tag{9.124}$$

This, the locus of intersection of operating lines (the q line), is a straight line of slope $q/(q - 1)$, and since $y = z_F$ when $x = z_F$, it passes through the point $x = y = z_F$ on the 45° diagonal. The range of the values of the slope $q/(q - 1)$ is listed in Table 9.1, and the graphical interpretation for typical cases is shown in Fig. 9.38. Here the operating-line intersection is shown for a particular case of feed as a mixture of liquid and vapor. It is clear that, for a given feed condition, fixing the reflux ratio at the top of the column automatically establishes the liquid/vapor ratio in the exhausting section and the reboiler heat load as well.

Location of the feed tray

The q line is useful in simplifying the graphical location of the exhausting line, but the point of intersection of the two operating lines does not necessarily establish the demarcation between the enriching and exhausting sections of the tower. Rather it is the introduction of feed which governs the change from one operating line to the other and establishes the demarcation, and at least in the design of a new column some latitude in the introduction of the feed is available.

Consider the separation shown partially in Fig. 9.39, for example. For a given feed, z_F and the q line are fixed. For particular overhead and residue products, x_D and x_W are fixed. If the reflux ratio is specified, the location of the enriching line DG is fixed, and the exhausting line KC must pass through the q line at E. If the feed is introduced upon the seventh tray from the top (Fig. 9.39a), line DG is used for trays 1 through 6, and, beginning with the seventh tray, the line KC must be used. If, on the other hand, the feed is introduced upon the fourth from the top (Fig. 9.39b), line KC is used for all trays below the fourth. Clearly a transition from one operating line to the other must be made somewhere between points C and D, but anywhere within these limits will serve. The least total number of trays will result if the steps on the diagram are kept as large as possible, or if the transition is made at the first opportunity after passing the operating-line intersection, as shown in Fig. 9.39c. In the design of a new column, this is the practice to be followed.

In the adaptation of an existing column to a new separation, the point of introducing the feed is limited to the location of existing nozzles in the column wall. The

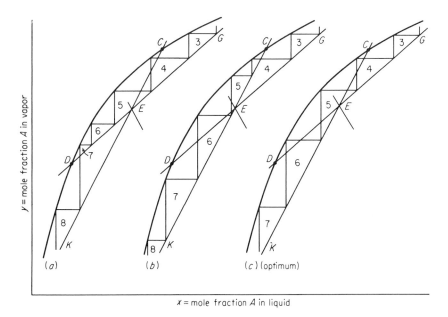

Fig. 9.39 *Location of feed tray.*

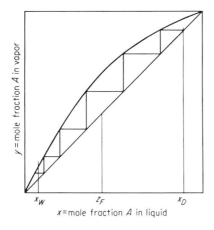

y = mole fraction A in vapor

x_W z_F x_D

x = mole fraction A in liquid

Fig. 9.40 *Total reflux and minimum trays.*

slope of the operating lines (or reflux ratio) and the product compositions to be realized must then be determined by trial and error, in order to obtain numbers of theoretical trays in the two sections of the column consistent with the number of real trays in each section and the expected tray efficiency.

Total reflux, or infinite reflux ratio

As the reflux ratio $R = L/D$ is increased, the ratio L/G increases, until ultimately, when $R = \infty$, $L/G = 1$ and the operating lines of both sections of the column coincide with the 45° diagonal as in Fig. 9.40. In practice this can be realized by returning all the overhead product back to the column as reflux (total reflux) and reboiling all the residue product, whereupon the forward flow of fresh feed must be reduced to zero. Alternatively such a condition may be interpreted as requiring infinite reboiler heat and condenser cooling capacity for a given rate of feed.

As the operating lines move farther away from the equilibrium curve with increased reflux ratio, the number of theoretical trays required to produce a given separation becomes less, until at total reflux the number of trays is the minimum N_m.

If the relative volatility is constant or nearly so, the analytical expression of Fenske, Eq. (9.81), may be used.

Minimum reflux ratio

The minimum reflux ratio R_m is the maximum ratio which will require an infinite number of trays for the separation desired, and it corresponds to the minimum reboiler heat and condenser cooling capacity for the separation. Refer to Fig. 9.41a. As the reflux ratio is decreased, the slope of the enriching operating line becomes less, and the number of trays required increases. Operating line MN, which passes through the point of intersection of the q line and the equilibrium curve, corresponds to the minimum reflux ratio, and an infinite number of trays would be required to reach point N from either end of the tower. In some cases, as in Fig. 9.41b, the minimum-reflux operating line will be tangent to the equilibrium curve in

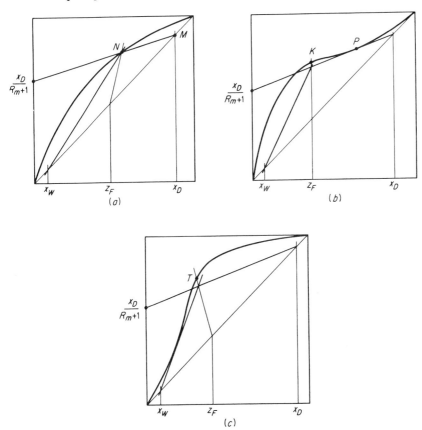

Fig. 9.41 *Minimum reflux ratio and infinite stages.*

the enriching section as at point P, while a line through K would clearly represent too small a reflux ratio. Owing to the interdependence of the liquid/vapor ratios in the two sections of the column, a tangent operating line in the exhausting section may also set the minimum reflux ratio, as in Fig. 9.41*c*.

For cases when the equilibrium curve is always concave downward, the minimum reflux ratio may be conveniently calculated analytically.[39] The required relationship may be developed by solving Eqs. (9.111) and (9.124) simultaneously to obtain the coordinates (x_a, y_a) of the point of intersection of the enriching operating line and the q line. Dropping the tray-number designation in Eq. (9.111), these are

$$x_a = \frac{x_D(q-1) + z_F(R+1)}{R+q} \qquad y_a = \frac{Rz_F + qx_D}{R+q}$$

At the minimum reflux ratio R_m, these coordinates are equilibrium values since they occur on the equilibrium curve. Substituting them into the definition of α, Eq. (9.2),

$$\frac{R_m z_F + qx_D}{R_m(1 - z_F) + q(1 - x_D)} = \frac{\alpha[x_D(q-1) + z_F(R_m+1)]}{(R_m+1)(1 - z_F) + (q-1)(1 - x_D)} \qquad (9.125)$$

This may be conveniently solved for R_m for any value of q.   Thus, for example, $q = 1$ (*feed liquid at the bubble point*)

$$R_m = \frac{1}{\alpha - 1}\left[\frac{x_D}{x_F} - \frac{\alpha(1 - x_D)}{1 - x_F}\right]$$

(9.126)

$q = 0$ (*feed vapor at the dew point*)

$$R_m = \frac{1}{\alpha - 1}\left(\frac{\alpha x_D}{y_F} - \frac{1 - x_D}{1 - y_F}\right) - 1$$

(9.127)

In each case, the α is that prevailing at the intersection of the q line and the equilibrium curve.

Optimum reflux ratio

The discussion given under the Ponchon-Savarit method applies.

Illustration 9.10.   Redesign the methanol-water fractionator of Illustration 9.8, using the simplifying assumptions of the McCabe-Thiele method.   The circumstances are:

Feed: 5,000 lb/hr, 216.8 lb moles/hr, $x_F = 0.360$ mole fraction methanol, av mol wt $= 23.1$, temperature entering the fractionator $= 136°F$.

Distillate: 2,620 lb/hr, 84.4 lb moles/hr, $x_D = 0.915$ mole fraction methanol, liquid at the bubble point.

Residue: 2,380 lb/hr, 132.4 lb moles/hr, $x_W = 0.00565$ mole fraction methanol.

Reflux ratio: 1.5 times the minimum.

Solution.   Refer to Fig. 9.42.   From the *txy* diagram, the bubble point of the feed at 0.360 mole fraction methanol is 169°F, and its dew point is 193°F.   The latent heats of vaporization at 193°F are $\lambda_A = 450$ Btu/lb for methanol, $\lambda_B = 982$ Btu/lb for water.   Specific heat of liquid methanol $= 0.65$, of liquid water $= 1.0$, of feed solution $= 0.92$.   Ignoring heats of solution, as is customary with the McCabe-Thiele method, the enthalpy of the feed at 169°F (the bubble point) referred to 136°F (the feed temperature) is

$$0.92(23.1)(169 - 136) = 702 \text{ Btu/lb mole}$$

The enthalpy of the saturated vapor at 193°F referred to liquids at 136°F is

$$0.36[0.65(32.04)(193 - 136) + 450(32.04)]$$
$$+ (1 - 0.36)[1(18.02)(193 - 136) + 982(18.02)] = 17,110 \text{ Btu/lb mole}$$

$$q = \frac{\text{heat to convert to a saturated vapor}}{\text{heat of vaporization}} = \frac{17,110 - 0}{17,110 - 702} = 1.04$$

(The same value, within slide-rule precision, is obtained if the heat of solution is considered.)

$$\frac{q}{q - 1} = \frac{1.04}{1.04 - 1} = 26$$

On Fig. 9.42, x_D, x_W, and z_F are located on the 45° diagonal, and the q line is drawn with slope $= 26$.   The operating line for minimum reflux ratio in this case passes through the intersection of the q line and equilibrium curve, as shown.

$$\frac{x_D}{R_m + 1} = \frac{0.915}{R_m + 1} = 0.57$$

$$R_m = 0.605 \text{ mole reflux/mole } D$$

The minimum number of ideal trays is determined using the 45° diagonal as operating lines (Fig. 9.42).   Theoretical stages to the number of 4.9, including the reboiler, are determined.

For $R = 1.5R_m = 1.5(0.605) = 0.908$ mole reflux/mole D, and for equimolal overflow and vaporization,

Eq. (9.44):
$$L = L_0 = RD = 0.908(84.4) = 76.5 \text{ lb moles/hr}$$

Eq. (9.108):
$$G = D(R + 1) = 85.4(0.908 + 1) = 160.9 \text{ lb moles/hr}$$

Eq. (9.119):
$$\bar{L} = qF + L = 1.04(216.8) + 76.5 = 302.5 \text{ lb moles/hr}$$

Eq. (9.120):
$$\bar{G} = F(q - 1) + G = 216.8(1.04 - 1) + 160.9 = 169.7 \text{ lb moles/hr}$$

$$\frac{x_D}{R + 1} = \frac{0.915}{0.908 + 1} = 0.480$$

Fig. 9.42 *Solution to Illustration 9.10. Minimum reflux ratio and minimum trays.*

Fig. 9.43 *Solution to Illustration 9.10.* $R = 0.908$ *mole reflux/mole distillate product.*

Refer to Fig. 9.43. The y intercept 0.480 and enriching and exhausting operating lines are plotted. Steps are drawn to determine the number of ideal trays, as shown. The exhausting operating line is used immediately after crossing the operating-line intersection, and the feed is therefore to be introduced on the fifth ideal tray from the top. A total of 8.8 ideal trays, including the reboiler, is required, and the tower must therefore contain 7.8 ideal trays. An integral number can be obtained by very slight adjustment of the reflux ratio, but since a tray efficiency must still be applied to obtain the number of real trays, this need not be done.

For cases where the residue composition is very small, it will be necessary to enlarge the scale of the lower left-hand part of the diagram in order to obtain the number of trays. In some cases the graphical determination may still be difficult because of the closeness of the exhausting line and the equilibrium curve. Logarithmic coordinates may then be used to maintain a satisfactory separation of the lines, as in the insert of Fig. 9.43. On such a graph, for very low values of x, the equilibrium curve will be substantially given by $y^* = \alpha x$, which is a straight line of unit slope. The exhausting operating line will, however, be curved and must be plotted from its equation. In this example, the equation is [Eq. (9.114)]

$$ y = \frac{302.5}{169.7}\, x - \frac{132.4}{169.7}\, 0.00565 = 1.785x - 0.0044 $$

The steps representing the ideal stages are made in the usual manner on these coordinates, continued down from the last made on the arithmetic coordinates (see also page 358).

The diameter of the tower and the tray design are established through the methods of Chap. 6. Note the substantially different liquid loads in the enriching and exhausting sections. A column of constant diameter for all sections is usually desired for reasons of simplicity in construction and lower cost. If, however, the discrepancy between liquid or vapor quantities in the two sections is considerable, and particularly if expensive alloy or nonferrous metal is used, different diameters for the two sections may be warranted.

Computations for other reflux ratios are easily and quickly made once the diagram and equations have been set up for one value of R. These provide data for determining the most economical R. The following table lists the important quantities for this separation at various values of R:

R	L	G	L	$\bar{G}$	No. ideal stages
$R_m = 0.605$	51.0	135.4	277	144.1	∞
0.70	59.0	143.4	285	152.1	11.5
0.80	67.5	151.9	294	160.6	10
0.908	76.5	160.9	303	169.7	8.8
1.029	86.7	171.3	313	180	8.3
2.0	168.8	253	395	262	6.5
4.0	338	422	564	431	5.5
∞	∞	∞	∞	∞	$4.9 = N_m + 1$

Included in the table are the data for the McCabe-Thiele method at $R = 1.029$, the reflux ratio used in Illustration 9.8 for the exact Ponchon-Savarit calculation. Illustration 9.8 showed nine ideal stages. It is noteworthy that for either method each at 1.5 times its respective value of R_m, the number of stages is essentially the same, and the maximum flow rates which would be used to set the mechanical design of the tower are sufficiently similar for the same final design to result.

Use of open steam

Ordinarily, heat is applied at the base of the tower by means of a heat exchanger (see page 330). When, however, a water solution is fractionated to give the nonaqueous solute as the distillate and the water is removed as the residue product, the heat required may be provided by the use of open steam at the bottom of the tower. The reboiler is then dispensed with. For a given reflux ratio and overhead composition, however, more trays will be required in the tower.

Refer to Fig. 9.44. Overall material balances for both components and for the more volatile substance are

$$F + \bar{G} = D + W \tag{9.128}$$

$$F z_F = D x_D + W x_W \tag{9.129}$$

where $\bar{G}$ is moles/hr of steam used, assumed saturated at the tower pressure. The enriching operating line is located as usual, and the slope of the exhausting line $\bar{L}/\bar{G}$ is related to L/G and the feed conditions in the same manner as before. A material balance for the more volatile substance below tray m in the exhausting

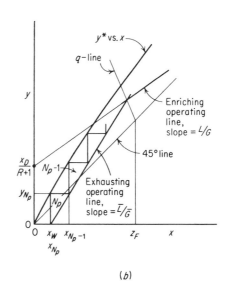

Fig. 9.44 *Use of open steam.*

section is

$$\bar{L}x_m + \bar{G}(0) = \bar{G}y_{m+1} + Wx_W \qquad (9.130)$$

and since $\bar{L} = W$ in this case,

$$\frac{\bar{L}}{\bar{G}} = \frac{y_{m+1}}{x_m - x_W} \qquad (9.131)$$

The exhausting line therefore passes through the point $(y = 0, x = x_W)$ as shown in Fig. 9.44b. The graphical tray construction must therefore be continued to the x axis of the diagram.

If the steam entering the tower, $\bar{G}_{Np+1}$, is superheated, it will vaporize liquid on tray N_p to the extent necessary to bring it to saturation, $\bar{G}_{Np+1}(H_{G,Np+1} - H_{G,sat})/\lambda M$, where $H_{G,sat}$ is the enthalpy of saturated steam and λM the molar latent heat at the tower pressure.

$$\bar{G} = \bar{G}_{Np+1}\left(1 + \frac{H_{G,Np+1} - H_{G,sat}}{\lambda M}\right) \qquad (9.132)$$

and

$$\bar{L} = \bar{G} - \bar{G}_{Np+1} + L_{Np} \qquad (9.133)$$

from which the internal $\bar{L}/\bar{G}$ ratio may be computed.

Condensers

Condensers are usually conventional tubular heat exchangers, arranged horizontally with the coolant inside the tubes. The condenser may be placed above the tower for gravity flow of the condensed reflux to the top tray. But it is usually more convenient for purposes of construction and cleaning to place the condenser nearer the ground and to return the reflux from an accumulator drum to the top tray by pumping. This procedure also provides more pressure drop for operation of control valves on the reflux line.

The condenser coolant is most frequently water. The pressure of the distillation must then be sufficiently high so that the available cooling water can condense the overhead vapor with an adequate temperature difference to provide reasonably rapid heat-transfer rates. The cost of the fractionator will, however, increase with increased pressure of operation, and in the case of very volatile distillates some low-temperature refrigerant may be used as a coolant.

If the condensate is cooled only to the bubble point, the withdrawn distillate is then usually further cooled in a separate heat exchanger to avoid vaporization loss on storage.

Partial condensers

It is occasionally desired to withdraw a distillate product in the vapor state, especially when the low boiling point of the distillate makes complete condensation difficult. In this case the overhead vapor is cooled sufficiently to condense the necessary liquid reflux and the residual vapor provides the product, as in Fig. 9.45.

A partial condenser may produce any of several results. (1) If time of contact between vapor product and liquid reflux is sufficient, the two will be in equilibrium with each other and the condenser provides an equilibrium condensation. (2) If the condensate is removed as rapidly as it forms, a differential condensation may

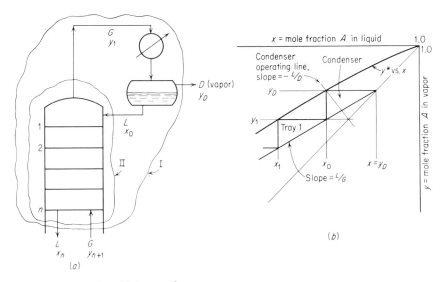

Fig. 9.45 *Partial equilibrium condenser.*

occur. (3) If cooling is very rapid, little mass transfer between vapor and condensate results, and the two will have essentially the same composition.

In case the first pertains, the condenser acts as one theoretical stage for the separation. The compositions y_D and x_0 may be computed by the methods of equilibrium condensation, as shown in Fig. 9.45b. The enriching operating line is then given as usual by material balances.

Envelope I

$$G = L + D \tag{9.134}$$

$$Gy_{n+1} = Lx_n + Dy_D \tag{9.135}$$

Envelope II

$$Gy_{n+1} + Lx_0 = Gy_1 + Lx_n \tag{9.136}$$

In the design of new equipment it is safer to ignore the enrichment which may be obtained by a partial condenser and to include the additional theoretical tray in the column, since it is difficult to ensure that equilibrium condensation will occur.

Cold reflux

If the overhead vapor is condensed and cooled below its bubble point so that the reflux liquid is cold, vapor G_1 rising from the top tray will be less in quantity than that for the rest of the enriching section since some will be required to condense and heat the reflux to its bubble point. External reflux L_0 will require $L_0 C_{L0} M_{\mathrm{av}}(t_{bpR} - t_R)$ Btu/hr, where t_{bpR} and t_R are the reflux bubble point and actual temperatures, respectively. An amount of vapor, $L_0 C_{L0} M_{\mathrm{av}}(t_{bpR} - t_R)/(\lambda M)_{\mathrm{av}}$ will condense to provide the heat, and the condensed vapor adds to L_0 to provide L, the liquid flow rate below the top tray. Therefore

$$L = L_0 + \frac{L_0 C_{L0} M_{\mathrm{av}}(t_{bpR} - t_R)}{(\lambda M)_{\mathrm{av}}} = RD\left[1 + \frac{C_{L0} M_{\mathrm{av}}(t_{bpR} - t_R)}{(\lambda M)_{\mathrm{av}}}\right] \tag{9.137}$$

where R is the usual external reflux ratio, L_0/D. Defining an *apparent* reflux ratio R' by

$$R' = \frac{L}{D} = \frac{L}{G - L} \tag{9.138}$$

gives

$$R' = R\left[1 + \frac{C_{L0} M_{\mathrm{av}}(t_{bpR} - t_R)}{(\lambda M)_{\mathrm{av}}}\right] \tag{9.139}$$

The enriching operating line becomes

$$y_{n+1} = \frac{R'}{R' + 1} x_n + \frac{x_D}{R' + 1} \tag{9.140}$$

and it is plotted through $y = x = x_D$, with a y intercept at $x_D/(R' + 1)$ and a slope $R'/(R' + 1)$.

Rectification of azeotropic mixtures

Minimum- and maximum-boiling azeotropic mixtures of the type shown in Figs. 9.7 and 9.10 may be treated by the methods already described, except that it will be impossible to obtain two products of compositions which fall on opposite sides of the azeotropic composition. In the rectification of a minimum-boiling azeotrope (Fig. 9.7), for example, the distillate product may be as close to the azeotropic composition as desired. But the residue product will be either rich in A or rich in B depending upon whether the feed is richer or leaner in A than the azeotropic mixture. In the case of maximum-boiling mixtures (Fig. 9.10) the residue product will always approach the azeotropic composition. These mixtures may sometimes be separated completely by addition of a third substance, as described later.

Insoluble mixtures which form two-liquid-phase azeotropes may, however, be readily separated completely, provided two fractionators are used. This depends upon the fact that the condensed distillate forms two liquid solutions on opposite sides of the azeotropic composition. Consider the separation of the mixture whose vapor-liquid equilibrium diagram is shown in Fig. 9.46, where the feed has the composition z_F and the solubility limits are x_{RI} and x_{RII} at the boiling point. If the feed is introduced into fractionator I of Fig. 9.47, it is evident that the residue product of composition x_{WI} may be as nearly pure B as desired. The enriching section may contain sufficient trays to produce an overhead vapor approaching the azeotropic composition M, such as vapor y_{DI}. This vapor, when totally condensed to mixture K at its boiling point, will form two insoluble liquids of composition x_{RI} and x_{RII}, which may be decanted as shown. The layer which is richer in B is returned to the

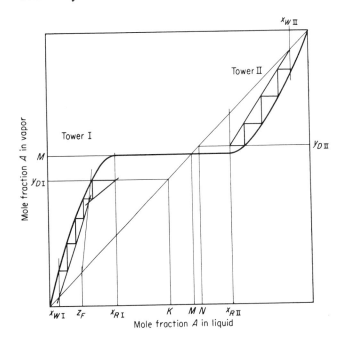

Fig. 9.46 *Fractionation of partially miscible mixtures.*

Fig. 9.47 *Two-tower system for partially miscible mixtures.*

top tray of column I as reflux. The enriching operating line for column I then passes through the point ($y = y_{DI}$, $x = x_{RI}$), as shown in Fig. 9.46, and its slope will be the liquid/vapor ratio in the enriching section.

The A-rich layer from the decanter (Fig. 9.47) is sent to the top tray of fractionator II, which contains only a stripping or exhausting section. It is clear from Fig. 9.46 that the residue product composition x_{WII} may be as nearly pure A as desired (turn the figure upside down to give it its usual appearance). The overhead vapor from tower II will be of composition y_{DII}, which, when totally condensed as mixture N, produces the same two insoluble liquids as the first distillate. Consequently a common condenser may be used for both towers.

In practice it will be desirable to cool the distillate below its bubble point to prevent excessive loss of vapor from the vent of the decanter. This changes the compositions x_{RI} and x_{RII} slightly and provides somewhat larger internal reflux ratios. If the feed itself consists of two insoluble liquids, it may be fed to the decanter, whereupon both fractionators then consist of exhausting sections only. When it is desired to remove the last traces of water from a substance such as a hydrocarbon, it is common practice to use only one tower from which the dry hydrocarbon is removed as the residue product. The hydrocarbon-rich layer from the decanter is returned as reflux, but the water layer, which contains very little hydrocarbon, is normally discarded.

The Ponchon-Savarit method may also be used,[31] but the necessary enthalpy data are rarely available for these systems.

Multiple feeds

If two solutions of different concentrations are to be fractionated to give the same products, both may be handled in the same fractionator. The McCabe-Thiele diagram for a two-feed column will resemble the lower part of Fig. 9.33, with operating lines straight. Each feed is considered separately (as if neither "knew" of the other's presence). The upper operating line is located as usual. The intermediate operating line, for the section of the column between feeds, intersects the enriching line at the q line for the richer feed and has a slope given by the L and G quantities computed through Eqs. (9.119) and (9.120). The lowermost operating line intersects the intermediate one at the q line for the less rich feed. For the least number of stages at a given reflux ratio, the feeds are each introduced at the stage whose construction on the diagram straddles their respective q line.

High-purity products

In Illustration 9.10 it was shown that for very low concentrations of more volatile substance in the residue, the graphical construction for stripping-section trays can be completed on logarithmic coordinates. This is readily done, since at very low concentrations the equilibrium curve is essentially linear, given by $y^* = \alpha x$. This plots as a straight 45° line on logarithmic coordinates, and α is taken for very low concentrations. The operating line is curved on such a graph, however, and must be plotted from its equation, (9.114). For very pure distillates a similar logarithmic graph can be constructed by turning the graph paper upside down and re-marking the coordinates as $(1 - \text{printed marking})$.[21] Thus, the printed 0.0001 is marked as 0.9999, etc. On such a graph the equilibrium curve is also straight at 45° for high concentrations, but the operating line is curved and must be plotted from its equation, (9.111). Specially drawn graph paper can be used for the complete diagram.[24]

As an alternative to these methods, calculations may be made analytically using the Kremser equations (5.50) to (5.57) or Fig. 5.16, since even for systems where the McCabe-Thiele assumptions are not generally applicable, the operating lines are straight at the extreme concentrations now under consideration. The *exhausting section* is considered as a stripper for the more volatile component, whence, for a kettle-type reboiler,

$$N_p - m + 1 = \frac{\log\left[\dfrac{(x_m - x_W/\alpha)}{(x_W - x_W/\alpha)}(1 - \bar{A}) + \bar{A}\right]}{\log(1/\bar{A})} \tag{9.141}$$

where x_m is the composition of the liquid leaving tray m, the last ideal tray obtained by graphical work, and $\bar{A} = L/\alpha G$. For a thermosiphon reboiler which totally vaporizes the liquid, the left-hand side of Eq. (9.141) is $N_p - m$. For open steam, the left-hand side is $N_p - m$, and x_W/α is omitted ($y_{Np+1} = 0$). The *enriching section* is considered as an absorber for the less volatile component

$$n - 1 = \frac{\log\left[\dfrac{(1 - y_n) - (1 - x_0)/\alpha}{(1 - y_1) - (1 - x_0)/\alpha}\left(1 - \dfrac{1}{A}\right) + \dfrac{1}{A}\right]}{\log A} \tag{9.142}$$

where y_n is the vapor leaving tray n, the last ideal tray obtained by graphical construction upward from the feed, x_0 is the reflux composition, and $A = \alpha L/G$.

For many ideal liquids, where α is nearly constant for all concentrations, the analytical calculation of Smoker[36] applies to the entire fractionator.

Tray efficiencies

Methods for estimating tray efficiencies are discussed in Chap. 6. Murphree vapor efficiencies are most simply used graphically on the *xy* diagram, whether this is derived from the exact Ponchon-Savarit calculation or with the simplifying assumptions, as shown in Illustration 9.11. Overall efficiencies E_O strictly have meaning only when the Murphree efficiency of all trays is the same and when the equilibrium and operating lines are both straight over the concentrations considered. The latter requirement can be met only over limited concentration ranges in distillation, but nevertheless the empirical correlation of Fig. 6.16 is useful for rough estimates, if not for final designs, with the exception that values of E_O for aqueous solutions are usually higher than the correlation shows.

Illustration 9.11. In the development of a new process, it will be necessary to fractionate 2,000 lb/hr of an ethanol-water solution containing 0.3 mole fraction ethanol, available at the bubble point.   It is desired to produce a distillate containing 0.80 mole fraction ethanol, with a substantially negligible loss of ethanol in the residue.

There is available a tower containing 20 identical cross-flow sieve trays, 30-in. diameter, with provision for introducing the feed only on the twelfth tray from the top.   The tower is suitable for use at 1-atm pressure.   The tray spacing is 18 in., the weir on each tray is 21 in. long, extending 2.25 in. above the tray floor, and the area of perforations is 0.5 sq ft/tray.

Determine a suitable reflux ratio for use with this tower, and estimate the corresponding alcohol loss, assuming that open steam at 10 psig will be used for heating and that adequate condenser capacity will be supplied.

Solution. The McCabe-Thiele method will be used.   Mol wt ethanol $= 46.05$, of water $= 18.02$. $z_F = 0.30$.

Basis: 100 lb moles feed.   Ethanol $= 30$ lb moles $= 1,383$ lb; water $= 70$ lb moles $= 1,263$ lb. Total feed $= 2,646$ lb.

Basis: 1 hr.   Feed contains $2,000(30/2,646) = 22.7$ lb moles ethanol and $2,000(70/2,646) = 52.9$ lb moles water, total $= 75.6$ lb moles.   If essentially all the ethanol is removed from the residue, the distillate $D = 22.7/0.80 = 28.4$ lb moles/hr, or $1,172$ lb/hr.   Vapor-liquid equilibrium data are available in "The Chemical Engineers' Handbook," 4th ed., p. 13-5.

Preliminary calculations indicate that the capacity of the tower is governed by the top vapor rate. At tray 1, av mol wt vapor $= 0.8(46.05) + 0.2(18.02) = 40.5$ lb/lb mole, temp $= 78.2°C$.   Using Chap. 6 notation,

$$\rho_G = \frac{40.5}{359}\frac{273}{273 + 78.2} = 0.0876 \text{ lb/cu ft}$$

$$\rho_L = 46.5 \text{ lb/cu ft} \qquad \sigma' \text{ (estd)} = 21 \text{ dynes/cm}$$

Table 6.1: for $t = 18$ in., $a = 0.1503$, $b = 0.0955$. The tower cross-sectional area $= A_t = \pi(30)^2/4(144) = 4.90$ sq ft, and for a 21-in. weir, $A_d = 0.088A_t = 0.43$ sq ft. The active area $A_a = 4.90 - 2(0.43) = 4.04$ sq ft. With $A_h = 0.5$ sq ft, and tentatively taking $(L'/G')(\rho_G/\rho_L)^{0.5} = 0.1$, Eq. (6.3) provides $C_F = 0.278$, and Eq. (6.1) shows $V_F = 6.40$ ft/sec as the flooding gas velocity based on $A_t - A_a = 4.90 - 0.43 = 4.47$ sq ft.

Calculations will be made for a reflux ratio $R = 3.0$, corresponding to $G = D(R + 1) = 28.4(3 + 1) = 113.6$ lb moles/hr vapor at the top, or

$$\frac{113.6(359)}{3,600} \frac{273 + 78.2}{273} = 14.6 \text{ cu ft/sec}$$

The vapor velocity is then $14.6/4.47 = 3.26$ ft/sec, or 51% of the flooding value (amply safe). $L = 3(28.4) = 85.2$ lb moles/hr, or 3,518 lb/hr. Therefore

$$\frac{L'}{G'}\left(\frac{\rho_G}{\rho_L}\right)^{0.5} = \frac{3,518}{14.6(3,600)(0.0876)}\left(\frac{0.0876}{46.5}\right)^{0.5} = 0.0332$$

Since for values of this quantity less than 0.1, Eq. (6.3) nevertheless uses 0.1, the calculated C_F is correct.

Since the feed is at the bubble point, $q = 1$, and Eq. (9.119):

$$L = L + qF = 85.2 + 1(79.6) = 160.8 \text{ lb moles/hr}$$

Eq. (9.120):

$$\bar{G} = G + F(q - 1) = G = 113.6 \text{ lb moles/hr}$$

The enthalpy of saturated steam (referred to 32°F) at 10 psig gage $= 1160.4$ Btu/lb, and this will be its enthalpy as it enters the tower if expanded to the tower pressure adiabatically. The enthalpy of saturated steam at 1 atm (neglecting tower pressure drop) $= 1150.4$ Btu/lb, and the latent heat $= 970.3$ Btu/lb.

Eq. (9.132):

$$113.6 = \bar{G}_{Np+1}\left[1 + \frac{(1160.4 - 1150.4)18.02}{970.3(18.02)}\right]$$

$$\bar{G}_{Np+1} = 112.0 \text{ lb moles steam/hr}$$

Eq. (9.133):

$$160.8 = 113.6 - 112.0 + L_{Np}$$

$$L_{Np} = W = 158.2 \text{ lb moles residue/hr}$$

Tray Efficiencies. Consider the situation at $x = 0.5$, $y^* = 0.654$, $t = 79.8°C$, which is in the enriching section. Here (Chap. 6 notation) $\rho_L = 49.4$, $\rho_G = 0.0780$ lb/cu ft, m (from equilibrium data) $= 0.42$, and by the methods of Chap. 2, $Sc_G = 0.930$, $D_L = 8(10^{-5})$ sq ft/hr. For $L = 85.2$ lb moles/hr, $q = 0.0154$ cu ft/sec, and for $G = 113.6$ lb moles/hr, $V_a = 3.63$ ft/sec. From the tray dimensions, $z = 2.12$ ft, $Z = 2.14$ ft, and $h_W = 2.25$ in.

Eq. (6.31): $N_{tG} = 1.275$ Eq. (6.9): $h_L = 1.838$

Eq. (6.34): $\theta_L = 0.01252$ Eq. (6.32): $N_{tL} = 34$

Eq. (6.23): $N_{toG} = 1.250$ Eq. (6.22): $\mathbf{E}_{OG} = 0.714$

Eq. (6.33): $D_E = 49$ Eq. (6.29): Pe $= 748$

Eq. (6.27): $\mathbf{E}_{MG} = 0.82$

Entrainment is negligible. Similarly,

x	0	0.1	0.3	0.5	0.7
$\mathbf{E}_{MG}$	0.65	0.70	0.82	0.82	0.82

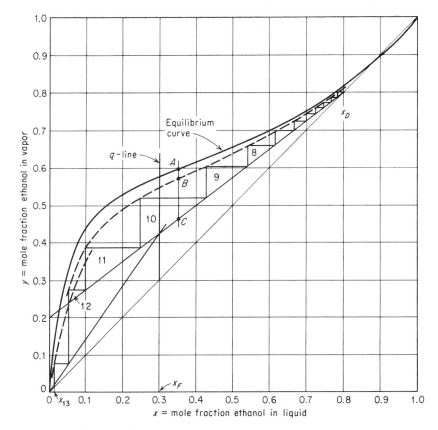

Fig. 9.48 *Solution to Illustration 9.11.*

Tray calculations. The operating-line intercept $= x_D/(R + 1) = 0.8/(3 + 1) = 0.2, q/(q - 1) = \infty$. The operating line for the enriching section and the q line are located as usual (Fig. 9.48). The exhausting-section operating line, on this scale of plot, passes through the origin for all practical purposes. The broken curve is located so that at each concentration, vertical distances corresponding to line BC and line AC are in the ratio E_{MG}. The curve is used instead of the equilibrium curve to locate real trays, as shown. The feed tray is the twelfth.

Below tray 13, calculations can be made on logarithmic coordinates as in Illustration 9.10, but this will necessitate trial-and-error location of the operating line since x_W is unknown. It is easier to proceed as follows.

From Fig. 9.48, $x_{13} = 0.0150$, and from this concentration down, the equilibrium curve is essentially straight ($\alpha = m = 8.95$), $E_{MG} = 0.65 = $ const, $\bar{A} = L/\alpha\bar{G} = 160.8/8.95(113.6) = 0.1582$. Equation (8.14) then provides the overall tray efficiency

$$E_O = \frac{\log\,[1 + 0.65(1/0.1582 - 1)]}{\log\,(1/0.1582)} = 0.897$$

There are 7 real or $7(0.897) = 6.28$ ideal trays to the bottom of the tower, whence Eq. (9.141) provides, for open steam,

$$6.28 = \frac{\log \left[(0.0150/x_W)(1 - 0.1582) + 0.1582 \right]}{\log \left(1/0.1582 \right)}$$

$x_W = 12(10^{-8})$ mole fraction ethanol in the residue.

This corresponds to an ethanol loss of approximately 0.02 lb/day. Larger reflux ratios would reduce this further, but the cost of additional steam will likely make them not worthwhile. Smaller values of R, with corresponding reduced steam cost but larger ethanol loss, should be considered, but care should be taken to ensure gas velocities above the weeping velocity [Eq. (6.17)].

CONTINUOUS-CONTACT EQUIPMENT (PACKED TOWERS)

Towers filled with the various types of packings described in Chap. 6 are frequently competitive in cost with trays, and they are particularly useful in cases where pressure drop must be low, as in low-pressure distillations, and where liquid holdup must be small, as in distillation of heat-sensitive materials whose exposure to high temperatures must be minimized. There are also available extremely effective packings for use in bench-scale work, capable of producing the equivalent of many stages in packed heights of only a few feet.[28]

The transfer unit

As in the case of packed absorbers, the changes in concentration with height produced by these towers are continuous rather than stepwise as for tray towers, and the computation procedure must take this into consideration. Figure 9.49*a* shows a schematic drawing of a packed-tower fractionator. As in the case of tray towers, it must be provided with a reboiler at the bottom (or open steam may be used if an aqueous residue is produced), a condenser, means of returning reflux and reboiled vapor, as well as means for introducing feed. The last may be accomplished by providing a short unpacked section at the feed entry, with adequate distribution of liquid over the top of the exhausting section (see Chap. 6).

The operating diagram, Fig. 9.49*b*, is determined in exactly the same fashion as for tray towers, using either the Ponchon-Savarit method, or, where applicable, the McCabe-Thiele simplifying assumptions. Equations for operating lines and enthalpy balances previously derived for trays are all directly applicable, with the exception that tray-number subscripts may be omitted. The operating lines are then simply the relation between x and y, the bulk liquid and gas compositions, prevailing at each horizontal section of the tower. As before, the change from enriching- to exhausting-section operating lines is made at the point where the feed is actually introduced, and for new designs a shorter column results, for a given reflux ratio, if this is done at the intersection of the operating lines. In what follows, this practice is assumed.

For packed towers, rates of flow are based on unit tower cross-sectional area, lb moles/(hr)(sq ft). As for absorbers, in the differential volume dZ cu ft, Fig. 9.49*a*, the interface surface is $a\,dZ$ sq ft, where a is the a_A of Chap. 6. The quantity of substance A in the vapor passing through the differential section is Gy moles/(hr)(sq ft), and the rate of mass transfer is $d(Gy)$ moles A/(hr)(differential volume).

Fig. 9.49   *Fractionation in a packed tower.*

Similarly, the rate of mass transfer is $d(Lx)$.   Even in those cases where the usual simplifying assumptions are not strictly applicable, G and L are, within a section of the column, each sufficiently constant so that equimolar counterdiffusion between phases is practically true: $N_A = -N_B$.   Consequently (see Table 3.1), $F_G = k_y'$, $F_L = k_x'$, and the mass-transfer flux is

$$N_A = \frac{d(Gy)}{a\,dZ} = k_y'(y_i - y) = \frac{d(Lx)}{a\,dZ} = k_x'(x - x_i) \qquad (9.143)$$

Therefore

$$Z_e = \int_0^{Z_e} dZ = \int_{(Gy)_a}^{(Gy)_2} \frac{d(Gy)}{k_y'a(y_i - y)} = \int_{(Lx)_a}^{(Lx)_2} \frac{d(Lx)}{k_x'a(x - x_i)} \qquad (9.144)$$

A similar expression, with appropriate integration limits, applies to the stripping section.

For any point (x,y) on the operating line, the corresponding point (x_i,y_i) on the equilibrium curve is obtained at the intersection with a line of slope $-k_x'/k_y' = -k_x'a/k_y'a$ drawn from (x,y), as shown in Fig. 9.49b.   For $k_x' > k_y'$, so that the principal mass-transfer resistance lies within the vapor, $y_i - y$ is more accurately read than $x - x_i$. The middle integral of Eq. (9.144) is then best used, evaluated graphically as the area under a curve of $1/k_y'a(y_i - y)$ as ordinate, Gy as abscissa, within the appropriate limits. For $k_x' < k_y'$, it is better to use the last integral. In this manner, variations in G, L, the coefficients, and the interfacial area with location on the operating lines are readily dealt with.

For cases where the usual simplifying assumptions apply, G and L within any section of the tower are each constant, and the heights of transfer units

$$H_{tG} = \frac{G}{k_y'a} \qquad H_{tL} = \frac{L}{k_x'a} \tag{9.145}$$

are sometimes sufficiently constant (or else average values for the section may be used) so that Eq. (9.144) may be written

$$Z_e = H_{tG} \int_{y_a}^{y_2} \frac{dy}{y_i - y} = H_{tG}N_{tG} \tag{9.146}$$

$$Z_e = H_{tL} \int_{x_a}^{x_2} \frac{dx}{x - x_i} = H_{tL}N_{tL} \tag{9.147}$$

with similar expressions for Z_s. The number of transfer units N_{tG} and N_{tL} are given by the integrals of Eqs. (9.146) and (9.147). It should be kept in mind, however, that the interfacial area a and the mass-transfer coefficients depend upon the mass rates of flow, which, because of changing average molecular weights with concentration, may vary considerably even if the molar rates of flow are constant. The constancy of H_{tG} and H_{tL} should therefore not be assumed without check.

Ordinarily the equilibrium curve for any section of the tower varies in slope sufficiently that overall mass-transfer coefficients and heights of transfer units cannot be used. If, however, the curve is essentially straight, we may write

$$Z_e = H_{tOG} \int_{y_a}^{y_2} \frac{dy}{y^* - y} = H_{tOG}N_{tOG} \tag{9.148}$$

$$Z_e = H_{tOL} \int_{x_a}^{x_2} \frac{dx}{x - x^*} = H_{tOL}N_{tOL} \tag{9.149}$$

where

$$H_{tOG} = \frac{G}{K_y'a} \qquad H_{tOL} = \frac{L}{K_x'a} \tag{9.150}$$

Here, $y^* - y$ is an overall "driving force" in terms of vapor compositions, and $x - x^*$ is a similar one for the liquid (see Fig. 9.49b). For such cases, Eqs. (8.45), (8.47), and (8.48) may be used to determine the number of overall transfer units without graphical integration. As shown in Chap. 5, with F's equal to the corresponding k'''s,

$$\frac{1}{K'_y} = \frac{1}{k'_y} + \frac{m}{k'_x} \tag{9.151}$$

$$\frac{1}{K'_x} = \frac{1}{mk'_y} + \frac{1}{k'_x} \tag{9.152}$$

$$H_{tOG} = H_{tG} + \frac{mG}{L} H_{tL} \tag{9.153}$$

$$H_{tOL} = H_{tL} + \frac{L}{mG} H_{tG} \tag{9.154}$$

where, in Eqs. (5.27) and (5.28), $m = m' = m'' =$ slope of a straight equilibrium curve.

Although practically all the meaningful data on mass-transfer coefficients in packings were obtained at relatively low temperatures, the limited evidence is that they may be used for distillation as well, where the temperatures are normally relatively high. Reviews of data specifically for distillation are available;[5,37] research in this area is badly needed.

Illustration 9.12. Determine suitable dimensions of packed sections of a tower for the methanol-water separation of Illustration 9.8, using 1.5-in. Raschig rings.

Solution. Vapor and liquid quantities throughout the tower, calculated in the manner of Illustration 9.8, with Eqs. (9.57), (9.60), (9.68), and (9.70) are:

Enriching section

x	t_L, °F	y	t_G, °F	Vapor		Liquid	
				moles/hr	lb/hr	moles/hr	lb/hr
0.915	150	0.915	154	171.3	5,303	86.7	2,723
0.600	160	0.762	165.5	164.0	4,684	79.6	2,104
0.370	169	0.656	173	160.9	4,378	76.5	1,779

Stripping section

x	t_L, °F	y	t_G, °F	Vapor		Liquid	
				moles/hr	lb/hr	moles/hr	lb/hr
0.370	169	0.656	173	168.6	4,585	301	7,000
0.200	179	0.360	193	161.6	3,721	294	6,138
0.100	189	0.178	203	160.6	3,296	293	5,690
0.02	206	0.032	210.5	127.6	2,360	260	4,767

The x and y values are those on the operating line (Fig. 9.28). The temperatures are bubble and dew points for the liquids and vapors, respectively. The operating lines intersect at $x = 0.370$, the dividing point between enriching and stripping sections.

The tower diameter will be set by the conditions at the top of the stripping section because of the large liquid flow at this point. Here (Chap. 6 notation),

$$\rho_G = \frac{4{,}585}{168.6(359)}\frac{492}{460 + 173} = 0.059 \text{ lb/cu ft}$$

$$\rho_L = 56.5 \text{ lb/cu ft}$$

and

$$\frac{L'}{G'}\left(\frac{\rho_G}{\rho_L}\right)^{0.5} = \frac{7{,}000}{4{,}185}\left(\frac{0.059}{56.5}\right)^{0.5} = 0.0495$$

Figure 6.26: loading (0.5 in H_2O/ft) provides an ordinate of 0.055. Since C_f (Table 6.2) = 95, $\mu'_L = 0.45$ centipoise, and $\rho_W = 60.7$ lb/cu ft,

$$G' \text{ at loading} = \left[\frac{0.055 g'_c \rho_G \rho_L}{C_f \mu'^{0.2}_L (\rho_W/\rho_L)}\right]^{0.5} = 940 \text{ lb/(hr)(sq ft)}$$

Choose a tower diameter of 2.5 ft (cross section = 4.90 sq ft), for which $G' = 4{,}585/4.90 = 932$ lb/(hr)(sq ft), $L' = 7{,}000/4.90 = 1{,}430$ lb/(hr)(sq ft), which are satisfactory.

Mass-transfer coefficients will be computed for this same location.

Table 6.3: $m = 1.82$, $n = -0.0048$, $p = 0.274$. Use $G' = 932(0.075/0.059)^{0.5} = 1{,}043$, whence $a_{AW} = 12.85$ sq ft/cu ft.

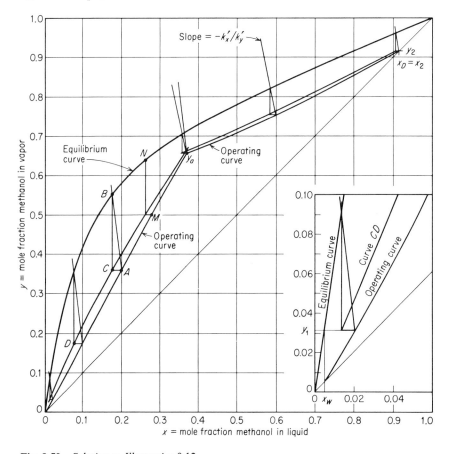

Fig. 9.50 *Solution to Illustration 9.12.*

Table 6.4: $d_s = 0.1740$ ft, $\beta = 0.499$, $\phi_{sW} = 0.0086$, $\phi_{tW} = 0.0279$, $\phi_{oW} = 0.0193$, $\phi_s = 0.00362$ (with $\mu'_L = 0.45$ centipoise, $\sigma' \doteq 29$ dynes/cm), $H = 0.90$, $\phi_o = 0.0174$, $\phi_t = 0.0210$.

Equation (6.42): $a_A = a = 12.85(0.0174/0.0193) = 11.55$ sq ft/cu ft. Table 6.2: $\epsilon = 0.71$; Eq. (6.40) $\epsilon_o = 0.71 - 0.0210 = 0.689$. By the methods of Chap. 2, $Sc_G = 1.0$. $G = 168.6/4.90 = 34.4$ lb moles/(hr)(sq ft), $\mu''_G = 0.0296$ lb/(ft)(hr), and by Eq. (6.39), $F_G = k'_y = 1.210$ lb moles/(hr)(sq ft)(mole fraction).

$$D_L = 18.6(10^{-5}) \text{ sq ft/hr}$$

$$Sc_L = 103.5$$

and by Eq. (6.41), $\qquad k_L = 3.12$ lb moles/(hr)(sq ft)(lb mole/cu ft)

Since the molar density of water at 169°F is 3.36 lb moles/cu ft, $F_L = k'_x = 3.12(3.36) = 10.5$ lb moles/(hr)(sq ft)(mole fraction). Similarly, values were calculated at each of the entries of the above table.

x	G	a	k'_y	k'_x
0.915	35.0	6.15	1.125	7.75
0.600	33.5	6.57	1.138	6.35
0.370	32.8	6.68	1.140	5.70
0.370	34.4	11.58	1.210	10.50
0.200	33.0	10.00	1.248	10.95
0.100	32.7	9.75	1.303	10.75
0.02	26.0	6.78	1.170	11.05

Figure 9.50 shows the equilibrium curve and operating curves as determined in Illustration 9.8. At $x = 0.2$, $y = 0.36$, on the operating curve, line AB was drawn with slope $= -k'_x/k'_y = -10.95/1.248 = -8.77$. Point B then provides the value of y_i for $y = 0.36$. Similarly the lines are erected at each of the x values of the table. Points such as C and D are joined by the curve CD. Then, at any point M, the corresponding y_i at N is easily located. The enlarged inset of the figure shows y_1 for the vapor entering the packed section to be in equilibrium with the reboiler liquid x_W. Since $k'_x > k'_y$, the middle integral of Eq. (9.144) will be used. The following values of y_i were determined in the manner described, with values of G, k'_y, and a obtained from a plot of these against y.

y	y_i	$\dfrac{1}{k'_y a(y_i - y)}$	Gy
$y_2 = 0.915$	0.960	2.82	$32.0 = (Gy)_2$
0.85	0.906	2.37	29.1
0.80	0.862	2.14	27.0
0.70	0.760	2.22	23.2
$y_a = 0.656$	0.702	3.50	$21.6 = (Gy)_a$
$y_a = 0.656$	0.707	1.40	$22.6 = (Gy)_a$
0.50	0.639	0.554	16.65
0.40	0.580	0.443	13.20
0.30	0.500	0.396	9.90
0.20	0.390	0.412	6.56
0.10	0.230	0.687	3.07
$y_1 = 0.032$	0.091	2.14	$0.83 = (Gy)_1$

Graphical integration (not shown) according to Eq. (9.144) provides $Z_e = 24.7$ ft for the enriching section, $Z_s = 14.9$ ft for the stripping section.

Berl saddles of the 1.5-in. size, because they provide substantially larger interfacial areas, lead to packed depths equal to roughly six-tenths of the above values, with approximately a 30% reduction of the gas pressure drop per foot, at the same mass velocities (although in this instance pressure drop is not important). A choice between such packings then revolves about their relative costs.

In the above example, H_{tG} for the stripping section varies from $34.4/1.210(11.58) = 2.46$ ft at the top to 3.27 ft at the bottom. Using Eq. (9.146) with an average $H_{tG} = 2.9$ yields $Z_s = 15.3$ rather than 14.9 ft as first computed. The equilibrium-curve slope varies so greatly that the use of H_{tOG} here is not recommended.

MULTICOMPONENT SYSTEMS

Many of the distillations of industry involve more than two components. While the principles established for binary solutions generally apply to such distillations, new problems of design are introduced which require special consideration.

Consider the continuous separation of a ternary solution consisting of components A, B, and C whose relative volatilities are in that order (A most volatile). In order to obtain the three substances in substantially pure form, either of the schemes of Fig. 9.51 may be used. According to scheme (a), the first column is used to separate C as a residue from the rest of the solution. The residue is necessarily contaminated with a small amount of B and with an even smaller amount of A, although if relative volatilities are reasonably large, the amount of the latter may be

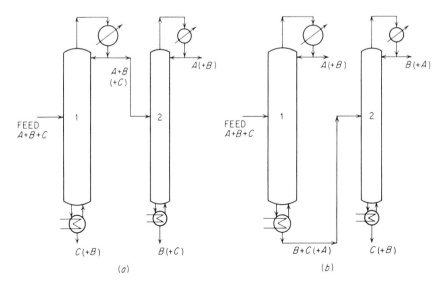

Fig. 9.51 *Separation of a ternary system.*

exceedingly small. The distillate, which is necessarily contaminated with at least a small amount of C, is then fractionated in a second column to provide nearly pure A and B. According to scheme (b), the first tower provides nearly pure A directly, and the residue is separated in the second. Which of the two schemes would be used depends upon the relative difficulty of the separation according to the two methods, but generally scheme (b) will be the more economical since it requires only one vaporization of substance A.

An important principle to be emphasized is that a single fractionator cannot separate more than one component in reasonably pure form from a multicomponent solution and that a total of $n - 1$ fractionators will be required for complete separation of a system of n components. It might at first be thought, for example, that the component of intermediate volatility B would tend to concentrate in reasonably pure form in the central parts of the first tower, from which it might be withdrawn as a *side stream*, thus allowing pure A and pure C to be withdrawn as distillate and residue, respectively. But this cannot occur. The feed tray of column 1, scheme (a), for example, will necessarily contain all three components in proportions not far from those prevailing in the feed itself. Trays immediately above the feed will therefore also contain appreciable quantities of all three substances, with the proportion of C gradually diminishing as we go higher in the enriching section. Similarly, trays immediately below the feed necessarily contain large proportions of all substances, with decreasing amounts of A and B as we penetrate more deeply into the exhausting section. While side streams are indeed sometimes withdrawn from fractionating towers, these streams must be further processed if they are to provide pure products.

The general principles of design of multicomponent fractionators are the same in many respects as those for binary systems, but the dearth of adequate vapor-liquid equilibrium data imposes severe restrictions on their application. These are especially needed for liquids which are not ideal, and the danger of attempting new designs without adequate equilibrium data or pilot-plant study for such solutions cannot be overemphasized. Inadequate methods of dealing with tray efficiencies for multicomponents represent another serious problem still to be solved.

Since the design calculations involve extensive trial and error, high-speed computers are frequently used. Except in extraordinary cases, it is not impossible to carry them out by hand, however, and this may be necessary when only a few designs are to be made. In what follows, hand calculations are assumed, and these will in any case provide an introduction to the computer methods. The most reliable design procedure is that of Thiele and Geddes.[38] This, or modifications of it, is the basis for many of the computer procedures. The method assumes that, for a given feed, the number of trays, position of the feed tray, and the liquid/vapor ratio and temperature for each tray are all known at the start, and it proceeds to compute the resulting distillate and residue products. In most cases, of course, at the beginning of a computation the necessary quantities are ordinarily unknown. The scheme outlined here begins by developing, with a minimum of trials, information necessary to use the Thiele-Geddes method, which then provides the final design.

Specification limitations

It will be assumed at the beginning that at least the following are established:

1. Temperature, pressure, composition, and rate of flow of the feed.

2. Pressure of the distillation (frequently fixed by the temperature of the available cooling water, which must be able to condense the distillate vapor to provide reflux).

3. Feed to be introduced on that tray which will result in the least total number of trays (optimum feed-tray location).

4. Heat losses (even if assumed to be zero).

Under these circumstances it has been shown[22] that there are left to the designer only three additional items which he may specify. Having chosen the three, all other characteristics of the fractionator are fixed. The designer may only calculate what they will be, and may arbitrarily assign values to them only temporarily for purposes of trial calculations and later verification. The three may be chosen from the following list, each item counting one:

1. Total number of trays.

2. Reflux ratio.

3. Reboil ratio, i.e., ratio of vapor produced by the reboiler to residue withdrawn.

4. Concentration of one component in one product (a maximum of two may be chosen).

5. Ratio of flow of one component in the distillate to the flow of the same component in the residue, or "split" of the component (a maximum of two may be chosen).

6. Ratio of total distillate to total residue.

In what follows, it will be assumed that the reflux ratio and splits of two components are specified. Modifications of the procedures are readily made for other cases. It is clear that, with more than two components in the feed, neither the complete compositions nor the rates of flow of either product are then known.

Key components

It is convenient first to list the feed components in order of their relative volatility. The more volatile components are called "light," the less volatile are "heavy." There will frequently be one component, the *light key component*, which is present in the residue in important amounts while components lighter than the light key are present in only very small amounts. If all components are present in the residue at important concentrations, then the most volatile is the light key. Similarly there will usually be one component, the *heavy key component*, present in the distillate in important amounts while components heavier than the heavy key are present only in small amounts. If all components are found in the distillate at important concentrations, then the least volatile is the heavy key.

The difficulty of the separation, as measured by the number of trays required for a given reflux ratio, is fixed by the key-component concentrations in the products. It is therefore important to establish which are the keys, and these may or may not be those whose splits have been specified.

Relative volatilities will be computed always with respect to the heavy key

$$\alpha_J = \frac{m_J}{m_{hk}} \qquad (9.155)$$

where J represents any component and hk the heavy key. Thus, $\alpha_{hk} = 1$, α's for components lighter than the heavy key are greater than 1, and those for heavier components are less than 1.

Minimum reflux ratio

This is the largest reflux ratio requiring an infinite number of trays to separate the key components.

With an infinite number of trays, it is possible to exclude from the distillate all components heavier than the heavy key. Since all components are present at the feed tray, and since it requires several enriching trays to reduce these heavy components to negligible concentrations, the "pinch" for these components, above which their concentration is zero, lies somewhere above the feed tray. Similarly an infinite number of trays permits exclusion from the residue of all components lighter than the light key, and there is a "pinch" for these several trays below the feed tray. The situation is therefore different from that for binary distillation, where at minimum reflux ratio there is only one pinch, usually at the feed tray.

Because of the possibility of excluding components from the products, computations at minimum reflux ratio help decide which are the key components. Components between the keys in volatility are found importantly in both products, and they are said to "distribute." Shiras et al.[34] show that at minimum reflux ratio, approximately

$$\frac{x_{JD}D}{z_{JF}F} = \frac{\alpha_J - 1}{\alpha_{lk} - 1} \frac{x_{lkD}D}{z_{lkF}F} + \frac{\alpha_{lk} - \alpha_J}{\alpha_{lk} - 1} \frac{x_{hkD}D}{z_{hkF}F} \qquad (9.156)$$

For $x_{JD}D/z_{JF}F$ less than -0.01 or greater than 1.01, component J will probably not distribute. For $x_{JD}D/z_{JF}F$ between 0.01 and 0.99, component J will undoubtedly distribute. The computations are made with first estimates of what the keys are, to be corrected as necessary.

Many methods of estimating the minimum reflux ratio R_m have been proposed, most of which are tedious to use and not necessarily very accurate. Since the only purpose of obtaining R_m is to estimate the product compositions at R_m and to ensure that the specified R is reasonable, an exact value is not required. Underwood's method,[40] which uses constant average α's and assumes constant L/G, is not exact but provides reasonable values without great effort; it is recommended (refer to the original papers for a derivation, which is lengthy). Two equations must be solved:

$$\Sigma \frac{\alpha_J z_{JF} F}{\alpha_J - \phi} = F(1 - q) \tag{9.157}$$

and

$$\Sigma \frac{\alpha_J x_{JD} D}{\alpha_J - \phi} = D(R_m + 1) \tag{9.158}$$

The first of these is written for all J components of the feed and solved for the necessary values of ϕ. There are $J - 1$ real, positive values of ϕ which satisfy the expression, and each lies between the α's of the components. However, the equation need be solved for only enough values of ϕ to determine, through Eq. (9.158), R_m and $x_{JD}D$ for components whose distribution is unknown. We thus require one more value of ϕ than there are components between the keys, and these will lie between α_{lk} and $\alpha_{hk} = 1$. Equation (9.158) is then written once for each value of ϕ so obtained, including the heavy key and all lighter components in the summations. These are solved simultaneously for R_m and the unknown $x_{JD}D$'s. If $x_{JD}D$ computes to be negative or greater than $z_{JF}F$, component J will not distribute, and the keys have been incorrectly chosen.

The α's are all computed at the average of the distillate dew point and the residue bubble point, which may require a few trial estimates. It is useful to note that in making dew-point calculations through Eq. (9.22), $\Sigma y_J/\alpha_J = m_{hk}$, and for bubble-point calculations through Eq. (9.21), $\Sigma \alpha_J x_J = 1/m_{hk}$, which helps determine the temperature.

Illustration 9.13. The following feed, at 180°F, 150 psi, is to be fractionated at that pressure so that the vapor distillate contains 98% of the C_3H_8 but only 1% of the C_5H_{12}:

Component	CH_4	C_2H_6	$n\text{-}C_3H_8$	$n\text{-}C_4H_{10}$	$n\text{-}C_5H_{12}$	$n\text{-}C_6H_{14}$
z_F, mole fraction	0.03	0.07	0.15	0.33	0.30	0.12

Estimate the minimum reflux ratio and the corresponding products.

Solution. The components will be identified as C_1, C_2, etc. Subscript numerals on m's, α's, etc., are temperatures, °F, if larger than 100; otherwise they represent tray numbers. Liquid solutions are assumed to be ideal. Values of m are taken from Depriester, *Chem. Eng. Progr. Symp. Ser.*, **49** (7), 1 (1953). Values of H, all as Btu/lb mole referred to the saturated liquid at $-200°F$, are taken from Maxwell, "Data Book on Hydrocarbons," D. Van Nostrand Company, Inc., Princeton, N.J., 1950. In the case of H_G for temperatures below the dew point, the enthalpy is that of the saturated vapor. In the case of H_L for temperatures above the critical, the enthalpy is that of the gas in solution. Values of m are conveniently plotted as log m vs. t°F for interpolation. Enthalpy may be plotted vs. t on arithmetic coordinates.

	100°F	150°F	200°F	250°F
C_1:				
m	17.0	19.7	22.0	24.0
H_G	5,610	6,050	6,550	7,000
H_L	4,390	4,950	5,550	6,200
C_2:				
m	3.80	5.12	6.45	8.10
H_G	9,820	10,580	11,330	12,120
H_L	7,200	7,800	8,600	9,400
C_3:				
m	1.30	2.03	2.96	4.00
H_G	13,550	14,530	15,600	16,800
H_L	7,550	9,180	11,300	13,380
C_4:				
m	0.41	0.75	1.20	1.80
H_G	17,900	18,950	20,050	21,630
H_L	9,250	11,100	13,100	15,250
C_5:				
m	0.140	0.297	0.520	0.85
H_G	22,180	23,550	24,930	26,300
H_L	11,000	13,200	15,500	17,950
C_6:				
m	0.056	0.150	0.250	0.450
H_G	25,900	27,700	29,500	31,300
H_L	12,550	15,150	17,850	20,750

Basis: 1 lb mole feed throughout.

Flash vaporization of the feed. Use Eq. (9.32). After several trials, assume $G_F/F = 0.333$, $L_F/G_F = 0.667/0.333 = 2.0$.

Component	z_F	m_{180}	$y = \dfrac{z_F(2 + 1)}{1 + 2/m}$
C_1	0.03	21.0	0.0829
C_2	0.07	5.90	0.1578
C_3	0.15	2.56	0.2530
C_4	0.33	1.00	0.3300
C_5'	0.30	0.42	0.1559
C_6	0.12	0.19	0.0312
	1.00		1.0108

Σy is sufficiently close to 1.0. Therefore $q = L_F/F = 0.67$. Tentatively assume $C_3 =$ light key, $C_5 =$ heavy key. Therefore specifications require $x_{lkD}D = 0.98(0.15) = 0.1470$ lb mole, $x_{hkD}D = 0.01(0.30) = 0.0030$ lb mole. Estimate the average temperature to be 175°F (to be checked).

Component	$z_F F$	m_{175}	α_{175}
C_1	0.03	21.0	$53.2 = 21.0/0.395$
C_2	0.07	5.90	14.94
lk C_3	0.15	2.49	6.30
C_4	0.33	0.95	2.405
hk C_5	0.30	0.395	1.0
C_6	0.12	0.180	0.456

Equation (9.156) is to be used for C_1, C_2, and C_6; the others distribute at R_m. Use y_{JD} instead of x_{JD} since distillate is a vapor.

C_1:
$$\frac{y_D D}{z_F F} = \left(\frac{53.2 - 1}{6.30 - 1}\right)\frac{0.1470}{0.15} + \left(\frac{6.30 - 53.2}{6.30 - 1}\right)\frac{0.0030}{0.30} = 9.761$$

Similarly, for C_2 and C_6 the values are 2.744 and -0.0892, respectively. None of these components will distribute at R_m, and the chosen keys are correct. The distillate contains 0.03 lb mole C_1, 0.07 lb mole C_2, and no C_6. The distribution of only C_4 to the products is unknown. Equation (9.157):

$$\frac{53.2(0.03)}{53.2 - \phi} + \frac{14.94(0.07)}{14.94 - \phi} + \frac{6.30(0.15)}{6.30 - \phi} + \frac{2.405(0.33)}{2.405 - \phi}$$

$$+ \frac{1.0(0.30)}{1.0 - \phi} + \frac{0.456(0.12)}{0.456 - \phi} = 1(1 - 0.67)$$

This is to be solved for the two values of ϕ lying between α_{C_3} and α_{C_4}, and α_{C_4} and α_{C_5}. Therefore, $\phi = 4.7760$ and 1.4177. Equation (9.158) is then written for each value of ϕ and for components C_1 through C_5. For $\phi = 4.776$,

$$\frac{53.2(0.03)}{53.2 - 4.776} + \frac{14.94(0.07)}{14.94 - 4.776} + \frac{6.30(0.1470)}{6.30 - 4.776} + \frac{2.405(y_{C_4 D}D)}{2.405 - 4.776} + \frac{1.0(0.0030)}{1.0 - 4.776} = D(R_m + 1)$$

This is repeated with $\phi = 1.4177$, and the two solved simultaneously. $y_{C_4 D}D = 0.1306$ lb mole C_4 in the distillate, $D(R_m + 1) = 0.6099$. For the distillate, try a dew point $= 115°F$:

Component	$y_D D$	y_D	m_{115}	α_{115}	$\dfrac{y_D}{\alpha_{115}}$
C_1	0.03	0.0789	18.0	100	0.000789
C_2	0.07	0.1840	4.2	23.3	0.00789
lk C_3	0.1470	0.3861	1.50	8.34	0.0463
C_4	0.1306	0.3431	0.500	2.78	0.1234
hk C_5	0.0030	0.0079	0.180	1.0	0.0079
	$D = 0.3806$	1.0000			0.1863

$m_{hk} = m_{C_5} = 0.1863$ at 116°F, and the assumed 115° was close enough. For the residue, try a bubble point = 235°F. The amount of residue is obtained from $x_{JW}W = z_{JF}F - y_{JD}D$:

Component	$x_W W$	x_W	m_{235}	α_{235}	$\alpha_{235} x_W$
lk C$_3$	0.0030	0.00484	3.65	5.00	0.0242
C$_4$	0.1994	0.3219	1.60	2.19	0.7050
hk C$_5$	0.2970	0.4795	0.730	1.00	0.4800
C$_6$	0.1200	0.1937	0.380	0.521	0.1010
	$W = 0.6194$	1.0000			1.3102

$m_{hk} = m_{C_5} = 1/1.3102 = 0.763$ at 237°F, and the assumed 235°F was close enough.

Average temperature = $(237 + 116)/2 = 176.5$°F (assumed 175° is close enough). Therefore,

$$D(R_m + 1) = 0.3806(R_m + 1) = 0.6099$$

$$R_m = 0.58 \text{ mole reflux/mole distillate}$$

Total reflux

The product compositions change with reflux ratio, and computations at total reflux will help decide the ultimate compositions.

Fenske's equation (9.81) is not limited to binary mixtures, and it may be applied to the key components to determine the minimum number of trays,

$$N_m + 1 = \frac{\log[(x_{lkD}D/x_{hkD}D)(x_{hkW}W/x_{lkW}W)]}{\log \alpha_{lk,av}} \tag{9.159}$$

where $N_m + 1$ is the total number of ideal stages including the reboiler (and a partial condenser if credit is taken for its fractionating ability). The equation may then be applied to determine the distribution of other components at total reflux,

$$\frac{x_{JD}D}{x_{JW}W} = \alpha_{J,av}^{N_m+1} \frac{x_{hkD}D}{x_{hkW}W} \tag{9.160}$$

The average α is the geometric mean of the values at the distillate dew point and residue bubble point, which may require a few trials to estimate. Winn[42] suggests a method to reduce the number of trials required.

Having obtained N_m and R_m, reference may be made to any of the several empirical correlations mentioned earlier[2,7,11,13] for an estimate of the number of trays at reflux ratio R. These can be unreliable, however, particularly if the majority of the trays are in the exhausting section of the tower.

Illustration 9.13, continued. Compute the number of ideal trays at total reflux and the corresponding products.

Solution. Tentatively assume the same distillate and residue temperatures as obtained for the minimum reflux ratio.

Component	α_{115}	α_{235}	$\alpha_{av} = (\alpha_{115}\alpha_{235})^{0.5}$
C_1	100	31.9	56.4
C_2	23.3	10.43	15.6
lk C_3	8.34	5.00	6.45
C_4	2.78	2.19	2.465
hk C_5	1.0	1.0	1.0
C_6	0.415	0.521	0.465

Eq. (9.159):
$$N_m + 1 = \frac{\log\,[(0.147/0.003)(0.297/0.003)]}{\log 6.45} = 4.55$$

Eq. (9.160) for C_4:
$$\frac{y_{C_4D}D}{x_{C_4W}W} = (2.465)^{4.55}\frac{0.003}{0.297} = 0.611$$

A C_4 balance: $y_{C_4D}D + x_{C_4W}W = z_{C_4F}F = 0.33$

Solving simultaneously,
$$y_{C_4D}D = 0.1255 \text{ lb mole} \qquad x_{C_4W}W = 0.2045 \text{ lb mole}$$

Similarly,

C_1: $x_{C_1W}W \doteq 0 \qquad y_{C_1D}D = 0.03$

C_2: $x_{C_2W}W \doteq 0 \qquad y_{C_2D}D = 0.07$

C_6: $y_{C_6D}D = 0.00003$ (negligible; assume 0) $x_{C_6W}W = 0.12$

Therefore, at total reflux,

Component	$y_D D$	$x_W W$
C_1	0.03	Nil
C_2	0.07	Nil
C_3	0.1470	0.0030
C_4	0.1255	0.2045
C_5	0.0030	0.2970
C_6	Nil	0.12
	$0.3755 = D$	$0.6245 = W$

The distillate dew point computes to be 115.5°F and the residue bubble point 234°F.   The assumed 115 and 235 are close enough.

Product compositions

For components between the keys, a reasonable estimate of their distribution at reflux ratio R may be obtained by linear interpolation of $x_{JD}D$ between R_m and total reflux according to $R/(R + 1)$.   For components lighter than the light key and heavier than the heavy key, unless there is clear indication of important distribution at total reflux and unless R is to be very large, it is best at this time to assume they do not distribute.   Even very small amounts of light components in the residue or of heavy components in the distillate enormously disturb the computations to follow.

Illustration 9.13, continued. A reflux ratio $R = 0.8$ will be used.   Estimate the product compositions at this reflux ratio.

Solution. Since C_1 and C_2 do not enter the residue (nor C_6 the distillate) appreciably at either total reflux or minimum reflux ratio, it is assumed that they will not at $R = 0.8$. C_3 and C_5 distributions are fixed by the specifications.   Only that of C_4 remains to be estimated.

R	$\dfrac{R}{R+1}$	$y_{C_4D}D$
∞	1.0	0.1255
0.8	0.445	?
0.58	0.367	0.1306

Using a linear interpolation,

$$y_{C_4D}D = \frac{1 - 0.445}{1 - 0.367}(0.1306 - 0.1255) + 0.1255 = 0.1300$$

Therefore, for the distillate,

Component	$y_D D$	y_D	$\dfrac{y_D}{\alpha_{115}}$	$x_0 = \dfrac{y_D/\alpha}{\Sigma y_D/\alpha}$
C_1	0.03	0.0789	0.00079	0.00425
C_2	0.07	0.1842	0.0079	0.0425
lk C_3	0.1470	0.3870	0.0464	0.2495
C_4	0.1300	0.3420	0.1230	0.6612
hk C_5	0.0030	0.0079	0.0079	0.0425
	$D = 0.3800$	1.0000	0.1860	1.0000

$m_{C_5} = 0.1860$; $t = 115°F$ distillate dew point.   The last column of the table shows the liquid reflux in equilibrium with the distillate vapor [Eq. (9.22)].

For the residue,

Component	$x_W W$	x_W	$\alpha_{235} x_W$	$y_{Np+1} = \dfrac{\alpha x_W}{\Sigma \alpha x_W}$
lk C_3	0.003	0.00484	0.0242	0.01855
C_4	0.200	0.3226	0.7060	0.5411
hk C_5	0.2970	0.4790	0.4790	0.3671
C_6	0.1200	0.1935	0.0955	0.0732
	$W = 0.6200$	1.0000	1.3047	1.0000

$m_{C_5} = 1/1.3047 = 0.767$; $t = 236°F$, residue bubble point. The last column shows the reboiler vapor in equilibrium with the residue [Eq. (9.21)].

Feed-tray location

Just as with binary mixtures, the change from enriching to exhausting section should be made as soon as greater enrichment is thereby produced. This ultimately can be determined only by trial in the Thiele-Geddes calculation,[10] but in the meantime some guidance is required. The following assumes constant L/G, neglects interference of components other than the keys, and assumes that the optimum feed tray occurs at the intersection of operating lines of the key components.[32]

Equation (9.109), the operating line for the enriching section, omitting the tray-number designations, may be written for each key component

$$x_{lk} = y_{lk}\frac{G}{L} - \frac{D}{L}x_{lkD} \tag{9.161}$$

$$x_{hk} = y_{hk}\frac{G}{L} - \frac{D}{L}x_{hkD} \tag{9.162}$$

Elimination of L provides

$$y_{lk} = \frac{x_{lk}}{x_{hk}}\left(y_{hk} - \frac{D}{G}x_{hkD}\right) + \frac{D}{G}x_{lkD} \tag{9.163}$$

Similarly, Eq. (9.113) for the exhausting section yields

$$y_{lk} = \frac{x_{lk}}{x_{hk}}\left(y_{hk} + \frac{W}{\bar{G}}x_{hkW}\right) - \frac{W}{\bar{G}}x_{lkW} \tag{9.164}$$

At the operating-line intersection, y_{lk} from Eqs. (9.163) and (9.164) are the same, as are y_{hk} and x_{lk}/x_{hk}. Equating the right-hand sides of the two expressions then produces

$$\left(\frac{x_{lk}}{x_{hk}}\right)_{\text{intersection}} = \frac{Wx_{lkW}/\bar{G} + Dx_{lkD}/G}{Wx_{hkW}/\bar{G} + Dx_{hkD}/G} \tag{9.165}$$

Combining Eqs. (9.72) and (9.120) for the light key produces

$$\frac{W}{\bar{G}}x_{lkW} + \frac{D}{G}x_{lkD} = \frac{GFz_{lkF} - DF(1-q)x_{lkD}}{[G - F(1-q)]G} \tag{9.166}$$

and a similar result is obtained for the heavy key. Putting these into Eq. (9.165) then yields, with $G/D = R + 1$,

$$\left(\frac{x_{lk}}{x_{hk}}\right)_{\text{intersection}} = \frac{z_{lkF} - x_{lkD}(1-q)/(R+1)}{z_{hkF} - x_{hkD}(1-q)/(R+1)} \tag{9.167}$$

Recall from the treatment of binaries that the feed tray f is the uppermost step on the exhausting-section operating line and that it rarely happens that the feed step exactly coincides with the operating-line intersection.   The feed-tray location is then given by

$$\left(\frac{x_{lk}}{x_{hk}}\right)_{f-1} > \left(\frac{x_{lk}}{x_{hk}}\right)_{\text{intersection}} > \left(\frac{x_{lk}}{x_{hk}}\right)_{f} \qquad (9.168)$$

Ultimately, the best feed-tray location is obtained through the Thiele-Geddes calculation.

Lewis and Matheson calculation[23]

This establishes the first (and usually the final) estimate of the number of trays required.   Although it is possible to allow for variations in the L/G ratio with tray number by tray-to-tray enthalpy balances at the same time, since the products are not yet firmly established, it is best to omit this refinement.

With constant L/G, the McCabe-Thiele operating lines, which are merely material balances, are applicable to each component.   Thus, for the enriching section, Eq. (9.109) is

$$y_{J,n+1} = \frac{L}{G} x_{Jn} + \frac{D}{G} z_{JD} \qquad (9.169)$$

This is used alternately with dew-point (equilibrium) calculations to compute tray by tray for each component from the top down to the feed tray.   For components heavier than the heavy key, there will be no z_{JD} available, and these components cannot be included.

For the exhausting section, it is convenient to solve Eq. (9.113) for x:

$$x_{Jm} = y_{J,m+1} \frac{\bar{G}}{\bar{L}} + \frac{W}{\bar{L}} x_{JW} \qquad (9.170)$$

This is used alternately with bubble-point (equilibrium) calculations to compute tray by tray for each component from the bottom up to the feed tray.   There are no values of x_{JW} for components lighter than the light key, and these cannot be included.

If, in the first estimate of product compositions, it is found that one product contains all components (lk = most volatile or hk = least volatile component of the feed), the computation can be started with this product and continued past the feed tray to the other end of the column.   The operating-line equations appropriate to each section must of course be used.   This will avoid the composition corrections discussed later.

Illustration 9.13, continued. Determine the number of ideal trays and the location of the feed tray for $R = 0.8$.

Solution. For locating the feed tray, Eq. (9.167):

$$\left(\frac{x_{lk}}{x_{hk}}\right)_{\text{intersection}} = \frac{0.15 - 0.3870(1 - 0.67)/1.8}{0.30 - 0.0079(1 - 0.67)/1.8} = 0.264$$

Enriching section:

$$D = 0.3800, \quad L = RD = 0.8(0.3800) = 0.3040$$

$$G = L + D = 0.3040 + 0.3800 = 0.6840$$

$$\frac{L}{G} = \frac{0.3040}{0.6840} = 0.445 \qquad \frac{D}{G} = \frac{0.3800}{0.6840} = 0.555$$

Eq. (9.169):

C_1:
$$y_{n+1} = 0.445x_n + 0.555(0.0789) = 0.455x_n + 0.0438$$

Similarly,

C_2
$$y_{n+1} = 0.455x_n + 0.1022$$

C_3:
$$y_{n+1} = 0.445x_n + 0.2148$$

C_4:
$$y_{n+1} = 0.445x_n + 0.1898$$

C_5:
$$y_{n+1} = 0.445x_n + 0.0044$$

Estimate $t_1 = 135°F$.

Component	x_0	y_1 [Eq. (9.169), $n = 0$]	α_{135}	$\dfrac{y_1}{\alpha}$	$x_1 = \dfrac{y_1/\alpha}{\Sigma y_1/\alpha}$
C_1	0.00425	0.0457	79.1	0.00058	0.00226
C_2	0.0425	0.1211	19.6	0.00618	0.0241
lk C_3	0.2495	0.3259	7.50	0.0435	0.1698
C_4	0.6612	0.4840	2.66	0.1820	0.7104
hk C_5	0.0425	0.0233	1.00	0.0239	0.0933
	1.0000	1.0000		0.2562	1.0000

$m_{C_5} = 0.2562$, $t_1 = 138°F$. Liquid x_1's in equilibrium with y_1. $(x_{lk}/x_{hk})_1 = 0.1698/0.0933 = 1.82$. Tray 1 is not the feed tray. Estimate $t_2 = 145°F$.

Component	y_2 [Eq. (9.169), $n = 1$]	α_{145}	$\dfrac{y_2}{\alpha}$	$x_2 = \dfrac{y_2/\alpha}{\Sigma y_2/\alpha}$
C_1	0.0448	68.9	0.00065	0.00221
C_2	0.1129	17.85	0.00632	0.0214
lk C_3	0.2904	6.95	0.0418	0.1419
C_4	0.5060	2.53	0.2000	0.6787
hk C_5	0.0459	1.00	0.0459	0.1557
	1.0000		0.2947	1.0000

$m_{C_5} = 0.2947$, $t_2 = 149°F$. $(x_{lk}/x_{hk})_2 = 0.1419/0.1557 = 0.910$. The tray calculations are con-tinued downward in this manner. The results for trays 5 and 6 are:

Component	x_5	x_6
C_1	0.00210	0.00204
C_2	0.0195	0.0187
lk C_3	0.1125	0.1045
C_4	0.4800	0.4247
hk C_5	0.3859	0.4500
t, °F	168	174
x_{lk}/x_{hk}	0.292	0.232

Applying Eq. (9.168), it is seen that tray 6 is the feed tray. Exhausting section:

$$\bar{L} = L + qF = 0.3040 + 0.67(1) = 0.9740$$
$$\bar{G} = \bar{L} - W = 0.9740 - 0.6200 = 0.3540$$
$$\frac{\bar{G}}{\bar{L}} = \frac{0.3540}{0.9740} = 0.364 \qquad \frac{W}{\bar{L}} = \frac{0.6200}{0.9740} = 0.636$$

Eq. (9.170): C_3: $\qquad x_m = 0.364 y_{m+1} + 0.636(0.00484) = 0.364 y_{m+1} + 0.00308$
Similarly,
C_4: $\qquad x_m = 0.364 y_{m+1} + 0.2052$
C_5: $\qquad x_m = 0.364 y_{m+1} + 0.3046$
C_6: $\qquad x_m = 0.364 y_{m+1} + 0.1231$

Estimate $t_{Np} = 230$°F.

Component	y_{Np+1}	x_{Np} [Eq. (9.170), $m = N_p$]	α_{230}	αx_{Np}	$y_{Np} = \dfrac{\alpha x_{Np}}{\Sigma \alpha x_{Np}}$
lk C_3	0.01855	0.00983	5.00	0.0492	0.0340
C_4	0.5411	0.4023	2.20	0.885	0.6118
hk C_5	0.3671	0.4382	1.0	0.4382	0.3028
C_6	0.0732	0.1497	0.501	0.0750	0.0514
	1.0000	1.0000		1.4474	1.0000

$m_{C_5} = 1/1.447 = 0.691$, $t_{Np} = 227$°F. y_{Np} in equilibrium with x_{Np}. $(x_{lk}/x_{hk})_{Np} = 0.00983/$ $0.4382 = 0.0224$. N_p is not the feed tray. In like fashion, x_{Np-1} is obtained from y_{Np} with Eq. (9.170), and the computations continued up the tower. The results for trays $N_p - 7$ to $N_p - 9$ are:

Component	x_{Np-7}	x_{Np-8}	x_{Np-9}
lk C_3	0.0790	0.0915	0.1032
C_4	0.3994	0.3897	0.3812
hk C_5	0.3850	0.3826	0.3801
C_6	0.1366	0.1362	0.1355
t, °F	204	202	201
x_{lk}/x_{hk}	0.205	0.239	0.272

Application of Eq. (9.168) shows tray $N_p - 8$ as the feed tray.   The data for $N_p - 9$ are discarded.
Then $N_p - 8 = 6$, and $N_p = 14$ trays.

Composition corrections

The previous computations provide two feed-tray liquids, computed from opposite
directions, which do not agree.   In most cases, the number of trays will be satisfactory nevertheless, but in order to get suitable tray temperatures and L/G ratios for
subsequent calculations, it is best to try to patch up the discrepancies for trays near
the feed tray, at least.   The following, due to Underwood,[39] is reasonably satisfactory.

Starting with the feed-tray liquid as computed from the enriching section, which
shows no heavy components, the mole fractions are all reduced proportionately so
that their sum, plus the mole fractions of the missing components (as shown in the
feed-tray composition as computed from the exhausting section) is unity.   The
bubble point is then recalculated.   The justification for this somewhat arbitrary
procedure is that the *relative* concentrations of the light components in the vapor will
remain about the same so long as their relative concentrations in the liquid are
unchanged.

The concentrations of the missing heavy components on trays above the feed
tray are next estimated.   For these, z_{JD} should be very small, and Eq. (9.169) shows

$$\frac{y_{J,n+1}}{y_{hk,n+1}} = \frac{Lx_{Jn}/G + Dz_{JD}/G}{Lx_{hk,n}/G + Dz_{hkD}/G} \doteq \frac{x_{Jn}}{x_{hkn}} \tag{9.171}$$

Since

$$\frac{y_{J,n+1}}{y_{hk,n+1}} = \frac{m_{J,n+1}x_{J,n+1}}{m_{hk,n+1}x_{hk,n+1}} = \frac{\alpha_{J,n+1}x_{J,n+1}}{x_{hk,n+1}} \tag{9.172}$$

then

$$x_{Jn} = \frac{\alpha_{J,n+1}x_{J,n+1}x_{hkn}}{x_{hk,n+1}} \tag{9.173}$$

The liquid mole fractions on tray n as previously determined are then reduced proportionately to accommodate those of the heavy components, and a new bubble point
is calculated.   This is continued upward until the concentrations on upper trays as
previously computed are no longer changed importantly.

Missing light components are added to trays below the feed in much the same
manner.   Thus, Eq. (9.170) for these provides

$$\frac{y_{J,m+1}}{y_{lk,m+1}} = \frac{x_{Jm} - Wx_{JW}/\bar{L}}{x_{lkm} - Wx_{lkW}/\bar{L}} \doteq \frac{x_{Jm}}{x_{lkm}} \tag{9.174}$$

where advantage is taken of the fact that x_{JW} must be small for these components.
As before,

$$\frac{y_{J,m+1}}{y_{lk,m+1}} = \frac{m_{J,m+1}x_{J,m+1}}{m_{lk,m+1}x_{lk,m+1}} = \frac{\alpha_{J,m+1}x_{J,m+1}}{\alpha_{lk,m+1}x_{lk,m+1}} \doteq \frac{\alpha_{Jm}x_{J,m+1}}{\alpha_{lkm}x_{lk,m+1}} \tag{9.175}$$

The last approximation results from assuming that the ratio of α's stays reasonably constant with small temperature changes.   Then

$$x_{J,m+1} = \frac{x_{Jm}\alpha_{lkm}x_{lk,m+1}}{\alpha_{Jm}x_{lkm}} \tag{9.176}$$

The mole fractions of the components on the lower tray are then proportionately reduced to accommodate the light components, and the bubble point is recalculated.

Illustration 9.13, continued. Compositions at the feed tray as previously determined are listed in the first two columns.   The old x_6's are reduced to accommodate the C_6 from $N_p - 8$, and the new x_6's are determined.   The new bubble point is 188°F.

Component	x_{Np-8}	Old x_6	$x_6(1 - 0.1362)$	New x_6	α_{188}
C_1		0.00204	0.00176	0.00176	46.5
C_2		0.0187	0.0162	0.0162	13.5
lk C_3	0.0915	0.1045	0.0903	0.0903	5.87
C_4	0.3897	0.4247	0.3668	0.3668	2.39
hk C_5	0.3826	0.4500	0.3887	0.3887	1.00
C_6	0.1362			0.1362	0.467
	1.0000	1.0000	0.8638	1.0000	

For tray 5, x_{C_6} is estimated, through Eq. (9.173),

$$x_{C_6,5} = \frac{0.467(0.1362)(0.3859)}{0.3887} = 0.0631$$

where 0.3859 is the concentration of the heavy key on tray 5 as previously calculated.   The old x_5's are all reduced by multiplying them by $1 - 0.0631$, whence their new sum plus 0.0631 for $C_6 = 1$. The new tray 5 has a bubble point of 176°F, and its equilibrium vapor may be obtained from the bubble-point calculation, as usual.   In similar fashion, the calculations are continued upward. Results for the top trays and the distillate are:

Component	x_2	y_2	x_1	y_1	x_0	y_D
C_1	0.00221	0.0444	0.00226	0.0451	0.00425	0.0789
C_2	0.0214	0.1111	0.0241	0.1209	0.0425	0.1842
C_3	0.1418	0.2885	0.1697	0.3259	0.2495	0.3870
C_4	0.6786	0.5099	0.7100	0.4840	0.6611	0.3420
C_5	0.1553	0.0458	0.0932	0.0239	0.0425	0.0079
C_6	0.00262	0.00034	0.00079	0.00009	0.00015	0.00001
t, °F	150		138		115	

To correct tray $N_p - 7 =$ tray 7, use Eq. (9.176) to determine the concentrations of C_1 and C_2 on tray 7. $x_{lk,m+1}$ is taken from the old $N_p - 7$.

$$x_{C_1,7} = \frac{0.00176(5.87)(0.0790)}{46.5(0.0903)} = 0.000194$$

$$x_{C_2,7} = \frac{0.0162(5.87)(0.0790)}{13.5(0.0903)} = 0.00615$$

The old x_{N_p-7} must be reduced by multiplying by $1 - 0.000194 - 0.00615$. The adjusted values together with those above constitute the new x_7's. The new bubble point is 202°F.

The calculations are continued downward in the same fashion. The new tray 6 has $x_{C_1} = 0.000023$, $x_{C_2} = 0.00236$. It is clear that concentrations for these components are reducing so rapidly that there is no need to go further.

Liquid/vapor ratios

With the corrected temperatures and compositions, it is now possible to estimate the L/G ratios on the trays reasonably well.

For the enriching section, Eq. (9.54) may be solved simultaneously with Eq. (9.51) to provide

$$G_{n+1} = \frac{Q_C + D(H_D - H_{Ln})}{H_{G,n+1} - H_{Ln}} \tag{9.177}$$

Equation (9.51) then provides L_n; G_n is computed through another application of Eq. (9.177), and hence L_n/G_n is obtained. Similarly for the exhausting section, Eqs. (9.62) and (9.65) provide

$$\bar{G}_{m+1} = \frac{Q_B + W(H_{Lm} - H_W)}{H_{G,m+1} - H_{Lm}} \tag{9.178}$$

and Eq. (9.62) gives the liquid rate. Usually it is necessary to compute only a few such ratios in each section and interpolate the rest from a plot of L/G vs. tray number.

It must be remembered that if the enthalpies are computed from temperatures and concentrations taken from the Lewis-Matheson data, even though corrected in the manner previously shown, the L/G ratios will still be estimates only, since the data upon which they are based assume constant L/G in each section.

Illustration 9.13, continued. Compute the condenser and reboiler heat loads and the L/G ratios.
Solution. The condenser heat load is given by Eq. (9.49). Values of x_0, y_D, and y_1 are taken from the corrected concentrations previously obtained.

Component	H_D, vapor, 115°F	$y_D H_D$	H_{L0}, 115°F	$x_0 H_{L0}$	H_{G1}, 138°F	$y_1 H_{G1}$
C_1	5,800	458	4,500	19.1	6,000	270.5
C_2	10,050	1,851	7,400	314.5	10,400	1,258
C_3	13,800	5,340	8,000	1,996	14,300	4,660
C_4	18,200	6,220	9,800	6,490	18,700	9,050
C_5	22,600	178.5	11,650	495	23,200	555
C_6	26,430	0.3	13,350	2	27,300	4.1
		$14,048 = H_D$		$9,307 = H_{L0}$		$15,798 = H_{G1}$

Eq. (9.49):
$$Q_C = 0.3800[(0.8 + 1)(15,798) - 0.8(9,307) - 14,048]$$
$$= 2640 \text{ Btu/lb mole feed}$$

In similar fashion, $H_W = 16,863$, $H_F = 14,730$, and Q_B [Eq. (9.50)] = 3700 Btu/lb mole feed.
For tray $n = 1$, $G_1 = L_0 + D = D(R + 1) = 0.3800(0.8 + 1) = 0.684$ lb mole. With x_1 and y_2 from the corrected compositions,

Component	H_{G2}, 150°F	$H_{G2}y_2$	H_{L1}, 138°F	$H_{L1}x_1$
C_1	6,050	268.5	4,800	10.9
C_2	10,580	1,178	7,700	185.8
C_3	14,530	4,200	8,800	1,493
C_4	18,950	9,660	10,700	7,600
C_5	23,550	1,081	12,700	1,183
C_6	27,700	9.4	14,550	11.5
		$16,397 = H_{G2}$		$10,484 = H_{L1}$

Eq. (9.177):
$$G_2 = \frac{2,640 + 0.38(14,048 - 10,484)}{16,397 - 10,484} = 0.675 \text{ lb mole}$$

$$L_2 = G_2 - D = 0.675 - 0.380 = 0.295 \text{ lb mole}$$

$$\frac{L_2}{G_2} = \frac{0.295}{0.675} = 0.437$$

Similarly, the calculations may be made for other trays in the enriching section.
For tray $N_p = 14$,

Component	$H_{G,15}$, 236°F	$y_{15}H_{G,15}$	$H_{L,14}$, 227°F	$x_{14}H_{L,14}$
C_1		Nil		Nil
C_2		Nil		Nil
C_3	16,450	305	12,600	123.7
C_4	21,200	11,480	13,700	5,500
C_5	25,900	9,500	16,200	7,100
C_6	30,800	2,255	18,700	2,780
		$23,540 = H_{G,15}$		$15,504 = H_{L,14}$

Similarly, $H_{L,13} = 15,818$, and $H_{G,14} = 22,619$.

Eq. (9.178):
$$\bar{G}_{15} = \frac{3,700 + 0.62(15,504 - 16,863)}{23,540 - 15,504} = 0.358$$

$$L_{14} = W + \bar{G}_{15} = 0.620 + 0.358 = 0.978$$

$$\bar{G}_{14} = \frac{3,700 + 0.62(15,818 - 16,863)}{22,619 - 15,818} = 0.448$$

$$\frac{L_{14}}{\bar{G}_{14}} = \frac{0.978}{0.448} = 2.18$$

and similarly for other exhausting-section trays. Thus,

Tray no.	$\dfrac{L}{G}$ or $\dfrac{L}{\bar{G}}$	t, °F	Tray no.	$\dfrac{L}{\bar{G}}$	t, °F
Condenser	0.80	115	8	3.25	206
1	0.432	138	9	2.88	208
2	0.437	150	10	2.58	210
3	0.369	158	11	2.48	212
4	0.305	165	12	2.47	217
5	0.310	176	13	2.42	221
6	1.53	188	14	2.18	227
7	4.05	202	Reboiler	1.73	236

These values are not final. They scatter erratically because they are based on the temperatures and concentrations computed with the assumption of constant L/G.

Method of Thiele and Geddes

With number of trays, position of the feed tray, temperatures, and L/G ratios, the Thiele-Geddes method proceeds to compute the products which will result, thus ultimately permitting a check of all previous calculations. The following is Edmister's[6] variation of the original.[38]

All the equations which follow apply separately for each component, and component designations are omitted. For the enriching section, consider first the condenser.

$$G_1 y_1 = L_0 x_0 + D z_D \tag{9.179}$$

$$\frac{G_1 y_1}{D z_D} = \frac{L_0 x_0}{D z_D} + 1 \tag{9.180}$$

For a total condenser, $x_0 = z_D = x_D$, and $L_0/D = R$. Therefore

$$\frac{G_1 y_1}{D z_D} = R + 1 = A_0 + 1 \tag{9.181}$$

For a partial condenser behaving like an ideal stage, $z_D = y_D$, $z_D/x_0 = y_D/x_0 = m_0$, and

$$\frac{G_1 y_1}{D z_D} = \frac{R}{m_0} + 1 = A_0 + 1 \tag{9.182}$$

A_0 is therefore either R or R/m_0, depending upon the type of condenser. For tray 1,

$$\frac{L_1 x_1}{G_1 y_1} = \frac{L_1}{G_1 m_1} = A_1 \tag{9.183}$$

where A_1 is the absorption factor for tray 1. Then

$$L_1 x_1 = A_1 G_1 y_1 \tag{9.184}$$

For tray 2,

$$G_2 y_2 = L_1 x_1 + D z_D \tag{9.185}$$

$$\frac{G_2 y_2}{D z_D} = \frac{L_1 x_1}{D z_D} + 1 = \frac{A_1 G_1 y_1}{D z_D} + 1 = A_1(A_0 + 1) + 1 = A_0 A_1 + A_1 + 1 \tag{9.186}$$

Generally, for any tray,

$$\frac{G_n y_n}{D z_D} = \frac{A_{n-1} G_{n-1} y_{n-1}}{D z_D} + 1 = A_0 A_1 A_2 \cdots A_{n-1} + A_1 A_2 \cdots A_{n-1} + \cdots + A_{n-1} + 1 \quad (9.187)$$

and for the feed tray,

$$\frac{G_f y_f}{D z_D} = A_0 A_1 A_2 \cdots A_{f-1} + A_1 A_2 \cdots A_{f-1} + \cdots + A_{f-1} + 1 \quad (9.188)$$

Consider next the exhausting section. For a kettle-type reboiler,

$$\frac{\bar{G}_{Np+1} y_{Np+1}}{W x_W} = \frac{\bar{G}_{Np+1} m_W}{W} = S_W \quad (9.189)$$

where S_W is the reboiler stripping factor. Since

$$L_{Np} x_{Np} = \bar{G}_{Np+1} y_{Np+1} + W x_W \quad (9.190)$$

then

$$\frac{L_{Np} x_{Np}}{W x_W} = \frac{\bar{G}_{Np+1} y_{Np+1}}{W x_W} + 1 = S_W + 1 \quad (9.191)$$

For a thermosiphon reboiler, $y_{Np+1} = x_W$, and

$$S_W = \frac{\bar{G}_{Np+1}}{W} \quad (9.192)$$

S_W is therefore defined by either Eq. (9.189) or (9.192), depending upon the type of reboiler. For the bottom tray,

$$\frac{\bar{G}_{Np} y_{Np}}{L_{Np} x_{Np}} = \frac{\bar{G}_{Np} m_{Np}}{L_{Np}} = S_{Np} \quad (9.193)$$

$$\bar{G}_{Np} y_{Np} = S_{Np} L_{Np} x_{Np} \quad (9.194)$$

Then

$$L_{Np-1} x_{Np-1} = \bar{G}_{Np} y_{Np} + W x_W \quad (9.195)$$

and

$$\frac{L_{Np-1} x_{Np-1}}{W x_W} = \frac{\bar{G}_{Np} y_{Np}}{W x_W} + 1 = \frac{S_{Np} L_{Np} x_{Np}}{W x_W} + 1 = S_{Np}(S_W + 1) = S_{Np} S_W + S_{Np} + 1 \quad (9.196)$$

In general, for any tray,

$$\frac{L_m x_m}{W x_W} = \frac{S_{m+1} L_{m+1} x_{m+1}}{W x_W} + 1 = S_{m+1} \cdots S_{Np-1} S_{Np} S_W + S_{m+1} \cdots S_{Np-1} S_{Np}$$

$$+ S_{m+1} \cdots S_{Np-1} + \cdots + S_{m+1} + 1 \quad (9.197)$$

and at the feed tray,

$$\frac{L_f x_f}{W x_W} = S_{f+1} \cdots S_{Np} S_W + S_{f+1} \cdots S_{Np} + \cdots + S_{f+1} + 1 \quad (9.198)$$

Edmister[6] provides shortcut methods involving "effective" A's and S's for use in Eqs. (9.188) and (9.198), much as for gas absorption.

At the feed tray,

$$A_f = \frac{L_f}{G_f m_f} = \frac{L_f x_f}{G_f y_f} \quad (9.199)$$

and

$$\frac{W x_W}{D z_D} \equiv \frac{L_f x_f}{G_f y_f} \frac{G_f y_f / D z_D}{L_f x_f / W x_D} = A_f \left(\frac{G_f y_f / D z_D}{L_f x_f / W x_W} \right) \quad (9.200)$$

Since

$$Fz_D = Wx_W + Dz_D \tag{9.201}$$

$$Dz_D = \frac{Fz_F}{Wx_W/Dz_D + 1} \tag{9.202}$$

For each component, Eqs. (9.188) and (9.198) are then used to compute the numerator and denominator, respectively, of the term in parentheses of Eq. (9.200), whence Wx_W/Dz_D, or the split of the component, is found. Equation (9.202) then provides Dz_D and Eq. (9.201), Wx_W.

The products thus computed are completely consistent with the number of trays, feed-tray position, and reflux ratio used, provided the A's and S's (or L/G's and temperatures) are correct. For checking these, it is necessary to use the general equations (9.187) and (9.197) for each tray in the appropriate section of the tower. To check tray n in the enriching section,

$$\frac{G_n y_n}{Dz_D} \frac{Dz_D}{G_n} = y_n \tag{9.203}$$

and this may be obtained from the data already accumulated. If $\Sigma y_{Jn} = 1$, the temperature is satisfactory. If not, a new temperature is obtained by adjusting the y's proportionately until they add to unity and computing the corresponding dew point. To check a tray in the exhausting section,

$$\frac{\bar{L}_m x_m}{Wx_W} \frac{Wx_W}{\bar{L}_m} = x_m \tag{9.204}$$

which is obtainable from the data. If $\Sigma x_{Jm} = 1$, the temperature is correct. If not, the x's are adjusted to add to unity and the bubble point computed. The new temperatures and compositions permit new enthalpy balances to obtain corrected L/G's for each tray, and the Thiele-Geddes calculation may be redone. Problems of convergence of this trial-and-error procedure are considered by Holland,[18] Lyster et al.,[25] and Smith.[35]

The true optimum feed-tray location is obtained by trial, altering the location and observing which location produces the smallest number of trays for the desired products.

Illustration 9.13, concluded. Reestimate the products through the Thiele-Geddes method.

Solution. The temperature and L/G profiles as previously estimated will be used. Computations will be shown for only one component, C_4; all other components are treated in the same manner.

Using the tray temperatures to obtain m, $A = L/mG$ for the enriching trays and $S = m\bar{G}/L$ for the exhausting trays are computed. Since a partial condenser is used, $A_0 = R/m_0$. For the kettle-type reboiler, $S_W = \bar{G}_{15} m_W/W$. Then, for C_4,

Tray	Condenser	1	2	3	4	5	6 = f
m	0.50	0.66	0.75	0.81	0.86	0.95	1.07
A	1.600	0.655	0.584	0.455	0.355	0.326	1.431

Tray	7 = f + 1	8	9	10	11	12	13	14	Reboiler
m	1.22	1.27	1.29	1.30	1.32	1.40	1.45	1.51	1.65
S	0.301	0.390	0.447	0.503	0.532	0.566	0.599	0.693	0.954

With these data

Eq. (9.188):
$$\frac{G_f y_f}{Dz_D} = 1.5778$$

Eq. (9.198):
$$\frac{L_f x_f}{Wx_W} = 1.5306$$

Eq. (9.200):
$$\frac{Wx_W}{Dz_D} = 1.431 \frac{1.5778}{1.5306} = 1.475$$

Eq. (9.202):
$$Dy_D = \frac{0.33}{1.475 + 1} = 0.1335$$

Eq. (9.201):
$$Wx_W = 0.33 - 0.1335 = 0.1965$$

Similarly,

Component	$\dfrac{G_f y_f}{Dz_D}$	$\dfrac{L_f x_f}{Wx_W}$	$\dfrac{Wx_W}{Dy_D}$	Dy_D	Wx_W
C_1	1.0150	$254(10^6)$	$288(10^{-10})$	0.03	Nil
C_2	1.0567	8,750	$2.98(10^{-5})$	0.07	Nil
C_3	1.1440	17.241	0.0376	0.1447	0.0053
C_4	1.5778	1.5306	1.475	0.1335	0.1965
C_5	15.580	1.1595	45.7	0.00643	0.29357
C_6	1,080	1.0687	7,230	0.0000166	0.11998
				$0.3846 = D$	$0.6154 = W$

These show that $0.1447(100)/0.15 = 96.3\%$ of the C_3 and 2.14% of the C_5 are in the distillate. These do not quite meet the original specifications. The temperatures and L/G's must still be corrected, however. Thus for tray 2 and component C_4, Eq. (9.187) yields $G_2 y_2/Dz_D = 2.705$. From the enthalpy balances, $G_2 = 0.675$. Therefore, by Eq. (9.203),

$$y_2 = \frac{2.705(0.1335)}{0.675} = 0.5349$$

Similarly,

Component	$\dfrac{G_2 y_2}{Dz_D}$	y_2	Adjusted y_2
C_1	1.0235	0.0454	0.0419
C_2	1.1062	0.1147	0.1059
C_3	1.351	0.2896	0.2675
C_4	2.705	0.5349	0.4939
C_5	10.18	0.0970	0.0896
C_6	46.9	0.00115	0.00106
		1.0828	1.0000

Since Σy_2 does not equal 1, the original temperature is incorrect. After adjusting the y's to add to unity as shown, the dew point $= 160°F$ instead of the $150°F$ used. Similarly all tray compositions and temperatures must be corrected, new L/G's obtained by enthalpy balances with the new compositions, temperatures, and L/G's, and the Thiele-Geddes calculations repeated.

Multicomponent fractionation finds its most complex applications in the field of petroleum refining. Petroleum products such as gasoline, naphthas, kerosenes, gas oils, fuel oils, and lubricating oils are each mixtures of hundreds of hydrocarbons, so many that their identity and actual number cannot readily be established. Fortunately, it is not usually specific substances that are desired in these products, but rather *properties*, so that specifications may be made as to boiling range, specific gravity, viscosity, and the like. Fractionators for these products cannot be designed by the detailed methods just described but must instead be based upon laboratory studies in small-scale equipment. As an example which illustrates the complex nature of some of these separations, consider the schematic diagram of a topping plant for the initial distillation of a crude oil (Fig. 9.52). The crude oil, after preliminary heat exchange with several of the products from the plant, is passed through the tubes of a gas-fired furnace, the tube-still heater. Here a portion of the oil is vaporized, somewhat larger in amount than that ultimately to be taken as vaporized products. The mixture of liquid and vapor then enters the large tray tower. Open steam is introduced at the bottom to strip the last traces of volatile substances from the residue product, and this steam passes up the column, where it lowers the effective pressure

Fig. 9.52 *Schematic arrangement, petroleum topping plant.*

and hence the temperature of the distillation. The steam and most volatile substances (crude gasoline) leaving the top tray are condensed, the water separated, and the gasoline sent to storage. Reflux in the scheme shown here is provided by withdrawing a portion of the liquid from the top tray and returning it after it has been cooled. The cold liquid condenses some of the rising vapors to provide internal reflux. Several trays down from the top of the tower, a side stream may be withdrawn which will contain the hydrocarbons characteristic of a desired naphtha product. Since the components of the more volatile gasoline are also present at this point, the liquid is steam-stripped in a short auxiliary tray tower, the steam and vaporized gasoline being sent back to the main fractionator. The stripped naphtha is then withdrawn to storage. In similar fashion kerosene and gas oil cuts may be withdrawn, but each must be separately steam-stripped. The individual steam strippers are frequently built into a single shell, as shown, for reasons of economy, so that from the outside the multipurpose nature of the smaller tower is not readily evident. The withdrawn products must ordinarily be further processed before they are considered finished.

The design, method of operation, and number of products from topping units of this sort may vary considerably from refinery to refinery. Indeed, any individual unit will be built for maximum flexibility of operation, with, for example, multiple nozzles for introducing the feed at various trays and multiple side-stream withdrawal nozzles, to allow for variations in the nature of the feed and in the products to be made.

Azeotropic distillation

This is a special case of multicomponent distillation used for separation of binary mixtures which are either difficult or impossible to separate by ordinary fractionation. If the relative volatility of a binary mixture is very low, the continuous rectification of the mixture to give nearly pure products will require high reflux ratios and correspondingly high heat requirements, as well as towers of large cross section and numbers of trays. In other cases the formation of a binary azeotrope may make it impossible to produce nearly pure products by ordinary fractionation. Under these circumstances a third component, sometimes called an "entrainer," may be added to the binary mixture to form a new low-boiling azeotrope with one of the original constituents, whose volatility is such that it may be easily separated from the other original constituent.

As an example of such an operation, consider the flow sheet of Fig. 9.53 for the azeotropic separation of acetic acid–water solutions, using butyl acetate as entrainer.[27] Acetic acid may be separated from water by ordinary methods, but only at great expense owing to the low relative volatility of the constituents despite their fairly large difference in boiling points at atmospheric pressure (nbp acetic acid = 118.1°C, nbp water = 100°C). Butyl acetate is only slightly soluble in water and consequently forms a heteroazeotrope with it (bp = 90.2°C). Therefore if at least sufficient butyl acetate is added to the top of the distillation column (1) to form the azeotrope with all the water in the binary feed, the azeotrope may be readily distilled from the high-boiling acetic acid which leaves as a residue product. The heteroazeotrope on

Fig. 9.53 *Azeotropic distillation of acetic acid–water with butyl acetate.*

condensation forms two insoluble liquid layers, one nearly pure water but saturated with ester, the other nearly pure ester saturated with water. The latter is returned to the top of the column as reflux and is the source of the entrainer in the column. The former may be stripped of its small entrainer content in a second small column (2). The separation of the heteroazeotrope from acetic acid is readily done, so that relatively few trays are required in the principal tower. On the other hand, heat must be supplied, not only to vaporize the water in the overhead distillate, but to vaporize the entrainer as well. The operation may also be done batchwise, in which case sufficient entrainer is charged to the still kettle, together with the feed, to azeotrope the water. The azeotrope is then distilled overhead.

Sometimes the new azeotrope which is formed contains all three constituents. The dehydration of ethanol-water mixture with benzene as added substance is an example. Dilute ethanol-water solutions may be continuously rectified to give at best mixtures containing 89.4 mole percent ethanol at atmospheric pressure, since this is the composition of the minimum-boiling azeotrope in the binary system. By introducing benzene into the top of a column fed with an ethanol-water mixture, the ternary azeotrope containing benzene (53.9 mole %), water (23.3 mole %), ethanol (22.8 mole %), boiling at 64.9°C, is readily separated from the ethanol (bp = 78.4°C) which leaves as a residue product. In this case also the azeotropic overhead product separates into two liquid layers, one rich in benzene which is returned to the top of the column as reflux, the other rich in water which is withdrawn. Since the latter contains appreciable quantities of both benzene and ethanol, it must be separately rectified. The ternary azeotrope contains nearly equal molar proportions of ethanol and water, and consequently dilute ethanol-water solutions must be given a preliminary rectification to produce substantially the alcohol-rich binary azeotrope which is used as a feed.

In still other cases the new azeotrope which is formed does not separate into two insoluble liquids, and special means for separating it, such as liquid extraction, must be provided, but this is less desirable.

It is clear that the choice of entrainer is a most important consideration. The added substance should preferably form a low-boiling azeotrope with only one of the constituents of the binary mixture it is desired to separate, preferably the constituent present in the minority so as to reduce the heat requirements of the process. The new azeotrope must be of sufficient volatility to make it readily separable from the remaining constituent and so that inappreciable amounts of entrainer will appear in the residue product. It should preferably be lean in entrainer content, to reduce the amount of vaporization necessary in the distillation. It should preferably be of the heterogeneous-liquid type, which then simplifies greatly the recovery of the entrainer. In addition, a satisfactory entrainer must be (1) cheap and readily available, (2) chemically stable and inactive toward the solution to be separated, (3) noncorrosive toward common construction materials, (4) nontoxic, (5) of low latent heat of vaporization, (6) of low freezing point to facilitate storage and outdoor handling, and (7) of low viscosity to provide high tray efficiencies.

Extractive distillation

This is a multicomponent-rectification method similar in purpose to azeotropic distillation. To a binary mixture which is difficult or impossible to separate by ordinary means a third component, termed a "solvent," is added which alters the relative volatility of the original constituents, thus permitting the separation. The added solvent is, however, of low volatility and is itself not appreciably vaporized in the fractionator.

As an example of such an operation, consider the process of Fig. 9.54. The separation of toluene (bp = 110.8°C) from paraffin hydrocarbons of approximately the same molecular weight is either very difficult or impossible, owing to low relative volatility or azeotropism, yet such a separation is necessary in the recovery of toluene from certain petroleum hydrocarbon mixtures. Using isooctane (bp = 99.3°C) as an example of a paraffin hydrocarbon, Fig. 9.54a shows that isooctane in this mixture is the more volatile, but the separation is obviously difficult. In the presence of phenol (bp = 181.4°C), however, the isooctane relative volatility increases, so that, with as much as 83 mole percent phenol in the liquid, the separation from toluene is relatively easy. A flow sheet for accomplishing this is shown in Fig. 9.54b, where the binary mixture is introduced more or less centrally into the extractive distillation tower (1), and phenol as the solvent is introduced near the top so as to be present in high concentration upon most of the trays in the tower. Under these conditions isooctane is readily distilled as an overhead product, while toluene and phenol are removed as a residue. Although phenol is relatively high-boiling, its vapor pressure is nevertheless sufficient so that its appearance in the overhead product must be

Fig. 9.54 *Extractive distillation of toluene–isooctane with phenol.* [*Vapor-liquid equilibria from Drickamer, Brown, and White, Trans. AIChE,* **41,** 555 (1945).]

prevented. The solvent-recovery section of the tower, which may be relatively short, serves to separate the phenol from the isooctane. The residue from the tower must be rectified in the auxiliary tower (2) to separate toluene from the phenol which is recycled, but this is a relatively easy separation. In practice, the paraffin hydrocarbon is a mixture rather than the pure substance isooctane, but the principle of the operation remains the same.

Such a process depends upon the difference in departure from ideality between the solvent and the components of the binary mixture to be separated. In the example given, both toluene and isooctane separately form nonideal liquid solutions with phenol, but the extent of the nonideality with isooctane is greater than that with toluene. When all three substances are present, therefore, the toluene and isooctane themselves behave as a nonideal mixture, and their relative volatility becomes high. Considerations of this sort form the basis for the choice of an extractive-distillation solvent. If, for example, a mixture of acetone (bp = 56.4°C) and methanol (bp = 64.7°C), which form a binary azeotrope, were to be separated by extractive distillation, a suitable solvent could probably be chosen from the group of aliphatic alcohols. Butanol (bp = 117.8°C), since it is a member of the same homologous series but not far removed, forms substantially ideal solutions with methanol, which are themselves readily separated. It will form solutions of positive deviation from ideality with acetone, however, and the acetone-methanol vapor-liquid equilibria will therefore be substantially altered in ternary mixtures. If butanol forms no azeotrope with acetone, and if it alters the vapor-liquid equilibrium of acetone-methanol sufficiently to destroy the azeotrope in this system, it will serve as an extractive-distillation solvent.

When both substances of the binary mixture to be separated are themselves chemically very similar, a solvent of an entirely different chemical nature will be necessary. Acetone and furfural, for example, are useful as extractive-distillation solvents for separating the hydrocarbons butene-2 and *n*-butane.

Generally the requirements of a satisfactory extractive-distillation solvent are:

1. High selectivity, or ability to alter the vapor-liquid equilibria of the original mixture sufficiently to permit its easy separation, with, however, use of only small quantities of solvent.

2. High capacity, or ability to dissolve the components in the mixture to be separated. It frequently happens that substances which are incompletely miscible with the mixture are very selective; yet if sufficiently high concentrations of solvent cannot be obtained in the liquid phase, the separation ability cannot be fully developed.

3. Low volatility in order to prevent vaporization of the solvent with the overhead product and to maintain high concentration in the liquid phase.

4. Separability. The solvent must be readily separated from the mixture to which it is added, and particularly it must form no azeotropes with the original substances.

5. The same considerations of cost, toxicity, corrosive character, chemical stability, freezing point, and viscosity apply as for entrainers for azeotropic distillation.

Extractive distillation is usually more desirable a process than azeotropic distillation since no large quantities of solvent must be vaporized. Furthermore, a greater choice of added component is possible since the process is not dependent upon the accident of azeotropic formation. It cannot be conveniently carried out in batch operations, however.

Azeotropic and extractive-distillation equipment can be designed using the general methods for multicomponent distillation, and detailed discussion is available.[1,17,32,35]

LOW-PRESSURE DISTILLATION

Many organic substances cannot be heated to temperatures which even approach their normal boiling points without chemical decomposition. If such substances are to be separated by distillation, then the pressure and the corresponding temperature must be kept low. The time of exposure of the substances to the distillation temperature must also be kept to a minimum, since the extent of thermal decomposition will thereby be reduced. For distillation under absolute pressures of the order of several lb/sq in., packed towers may be used, bubble-cap and sieve trays can be designed with pressure drops approaching 0.05 psi (2.6 mm Hg), and other simpler designs, such as the shower tray of Fig. 6.18, for which the pressure drops are of the order of 0.015 psi (0.75 mm Hg) are possible. Mechanically stirred spray and wetted-wall columns provide even smaller pressure drops.[30]

In the distillation of many natural products, such as the separation of vitamins from animal and fish oils as well as the separation of many synthetic industrial products such as plasticizers, the temperature may not exceed perhaps 200 to 300°C, where the vapor pressures of the substances may be a fraction of a millimeter of mercury. The conventional equipment is, of course, wholly unsuitable for such separations, not only because the pressure drop would result in high temperatures at the bottom of columns, but also because of the long exposure time to the prevailing temperatures resulting from high holdup.

Molecular distillation

This is a form of very-low-pressure distillation, conducted at absolute pressures of the order of 0.003 mm Hg, suitable for the heat-sensitive substances described above.

The rate at which evaporation takes place from a liquid surface is given by the Langmuir equation,

$$N'_A = 1006 p_A \left(\frac{1}{2\pi M_A R'' T}\right)^{0.5}$$
(9.205)

where N'_A = g moles substance A evaporated/(sec)(sq cm)
$\quad p_A$ = partial pressure of A, atm
$\quad M_A$ = mol wt of A
$\quad R''$ = universal gas const, 82.07 (cu cm) (atm)/(g mole)(°K)
$\quad T$ = abs temp, °K

At ordinary pressures the net rate of evaporation is, however, very much less than this, owing to the fact that the evaporated molecules are reflected back to the liquid after collisions occurring in the vapor. By reducing the absolute pressure to values used in molecular distillation, the mean free path of the molecules becomes very large, of the order of 1 cm. If the condensing surface is then placed at a distance from the vaporizing liquid surface not exceeding a few centimeters, very few molecules will return to the liquid, and the net rate of evaporation of each substance of a binary mixture will approach that given by Eq. (9.205). The vapor composition, or the composition of the distillate, will now be different from that given by ordinary equilibrium vaporization, and the ratio of the constituents in the distillate will approach

$$\frac{N'_A}{N'_B} = \frac{\text{moles of } A}{\text{moles of } B} = \frac{p_A / M_A{}^{0.5}}{p_B / M_B{}^{0.5}}$$
(9.206)

If this ratio is to be maintained, however, the surface of the liquid must be rapidly renewed, since otherwise the ratio of constituents in the surface will change as evaporation proceeds. The vigorous agitation or boiling present during ordinary distillations is absent under conditions of molecular distillation, and in most devices the liquid is caused to flow in a thin film over a solid surface, thus continually renewing the surface but at the same time maintaining low holdup of liquid.

Figure 9.55 shows a device which is used industrially for accomplishing a molecular distillation.[15] The degassed liquid to be distilled is introduced continuously at the bottom of the inner surface of the rotor, a rotating conical-shaped surface. The rotor may be as large as 5 ft in diameter at the top and may revolve at speeds of 400 to 500 rpm. A thin layer of liquid to be distilled, 0.05 to 0.1 mm thick, then

Fig. 9.55 *Schematic section, centrifugal molecular still of Hickman.*[15]

spreads over the inner surface and travels rapidly to the upper periphery under the action of centrifugal force. Heat is supplied to the liquid through the rotor by radiant electrical heaters, and the vaporized material is condensed upon the water-cooled louver-shaped condenser. This is maintained at temperatures sufficiently low to prevent reevaporation or reflection of the vaporized molecules. The residue liquid is caught in the collection gutter at the top of the rotor, and the distillate is drained from the collection troughs on the condenser. Each product is pumped from the still body, which is evacuated to the low pressures necessary for molecular distillation, and the time of residence of the substances in the still may be as low as several seconds or less. Such a device is capable of handling 50 to 250 gal/hr of liquid to be distilled and gives a separation of 80 to 95% of that indicated by Eq. (9.206). Multiple distillations are necessary for multistage separation effects.

NOTATION FOR CHAPTER 9

a = interfacial surface, sq ft/cu ft of packed section
A = more volatile component of a binary mixture
 = absorption factor = L/mG, dimensionless
B = less volatile component of a binary mixture
C = heat capacity at constant pressure, Btu/(lb)(°F)
d = differential operator
D = distillate rate, lb moles/hr for tray towers, lb moles/(hr)(sq ft) for packed towers
E_O = overall tray efficiency, as a fraction
E_{MG} = Murphree vapor tray efficiency, as a fraction
F = feed rate, lb moles/hr for tray towers, lb moles/(hr)(sq ft) for packed towers
 = quantity of feed, lb moles (batch distillation)
 = (with subscript) mass-transfer coefficient, lb moles/(hr)(sq ft)
G = vapor rate, lb moles/hr for tray towers, lb moles/(hr)(sq ft) for packed towers
H = enthalpy, Btu/lb mole of solution

H_{tG} = height of a gas transfer unit, ft
H_{tL} = height of a liquid transfer unit, ft
H_{tOG} = height of an overall gas transfer unit, ft
H_{tOL} = height of an overall liquid transfer unit, ft
ΔH_S = integral heat of solution, Btu/lb mole solution
k_x' = liquid mass-transfer coefficient, lb moles/(hr)(sq ft)(mole fraction)
k_y' = gas mass-transfer coefficient, lb moles/(hr)(sq ft)(mole fraction)
K_x' = liquid overall mass-transfer coefficient, lb moles/(hr)(sq ft)(mole fraction)
K_y' = gas overall mass-transfer coefficient, lb moles/(hr)(sq ft)(mole fraction)
ln = natural logarithm
log = common logarithm
L = liquid rate, lb moles/hr for tray towers, lb moles/(hr)(sq ft) for packed towers
L_0 = external reflux rate, lb moles/hr for tray towers, lb moles/(hr)(sq ft) for packed towers
m = slope of the equilibrium curve, $dy*/dx$
M = molecular weight, lb/lb mole
N = mass-transfer flux, lb moles/(hr)(sq ft interface)
N' = mass-transfer flux, g moles/(sec)(sq cm interface)
N_m = minimum number of ideal trays
N_p = number of ideal trays
N_{tG} = number of gas transfer units
N_{tL} = number of liquid transfer units
N_{tOG} = number of overall gas transfer units
N_{tOL} = number of overall liquid transfer units
p = partial pressure, atm
P = vapor pressure, atm
P_t = total pressure, atm
q = quantity defined by Eq. (9.119)
Q = net heat added, Btu/hr
Q_B = heat added at reboiler, Btu/hr for tray towers, Btu/(hr)(sq ft) for packed towers
Q_C = heat removed at condenser, Btu/hr for tray towers, Btu/(hr)(sq ft) for packed towers
Q_L = heat loss, Btu/hr for tray towers, Btu/(hr)(sq ft) for packed towers
Q' = quantity defined by Eq. (9.55)
Q'' = quantity defined by Eq. (9.66)
R = external reflux ratio, lb moles reflux/lb mole distillate
R' = apparent reflux ratio, defined by Eq. (9.138)
R'' = universal gas constant, 82.07 (cu cm)(atm)/(g mole)(°K)
R_m = minimum reflux ratio, lb moles reflux/lb mole distillate
S = stripping factor = mG/L, dimensionless
t = temperature, °F
t_o = base temperature for enthalpy computations, °F
T = absolute temperature, °K
W = residue rate, lb moles/hr for tray towers, lb moles/(hr)(sq ft) for packed towers; quantity of residue for batch distillation
x = concentration in the liquid (of A in binaries), mole fraction
$x*$ = liquid concentration in equilibrium with y, mole fraction
y = concentration in the vapor (of A in binaries), mole fraction
$y*$ = vapor concentration in equilibrium with x, mole fraction
z = average concentration in a solution or mixture, mole fraction
Z = height of packing, ft
α = relative volatility, defined by Eq. (9.2), dimensionless
α_{JC} = relative volatility of component J with respect to component C
Δ = difference point, representing a fictitious stream
λ = latent heat of vaporization, Btu/lb

Σ = summation
ϕ = root of Eq. (9.157)

Subscripts:

a = operating-line intersection
av   = average
A, B = components A, B
D = distillate
e = enriching section
f = feed tray
F = feed
G = gas
hk = heavy key component
i = interface
lk = light key component
L = liquid
m = tray m; minimum
n = tray n
r = tray r
s = stripping section
W = residue
1   = bottom of packed tower; tray 1
2   = top of packed tower; tray 2

REFERENCES

1. Benedict, M., and L. C. Rubin: *Trans. AIChE,* **41,** 353 (1945).
2. Brown, G. G., and H. Z. Martin: *Trans. AIChE,* **35,** 679 (1939).
3. Cavers, S. D.: *Ind. Eng. Chem. Fundamentals,* **4,** 229 (1965).
4. Dodge, B. F.: "Chemical Engineering Thermodynamics," McGraw-Hill Book Company, New York, 1944.
5. Eckert, J. S.: *Chem. Eng. Progr.,* **59**(5), 76 (1963).
6. Edmister, W. C.: *AIChE J.,* **3,** 165 (1957).
7. Erbar, J. H., and R. N. Maddox: *Petr. Refiner,* **40**(5), 183 (1961).
8. Fair, J. R.: *Chem. Eng.,* **69,** July 8, 119; Aug. 5, 101 (1963).
9. Fenske, M. R.: *Ind. Eng. Chem.,* **24,** 482 (1931).
10. Floyd, R. B., and H. G. Higgins: *Ind. Eng. Chem.,* **55**(6), 34 (1963).
11. Gilliland, E. R.: *Ind. Eng. Chem.,* **32,** 1220 (1940).
12. Gilmont, R.: "Thermodynamic Principles for Chemical Engineers," Prentice-Hall, Inc., Englewood Cliffs, N.J., 1959.
13. Hachmuth, K. H.: *Chem. Eng. Progr.,* **48,** 523, 570, 617 (1952).
14. Hengstebeck, R. J.: "Distillation, Principles and Design Procedures," Reinhold Publishing Corporation, New York, 1961.
15. Hickman, K. C. D.: *Ind. Eng. Chem.,* **39,** 686 (1947).
16. Hickman, K. C. D.: sec. 17 in "The Chemical Engineers' Handbook," 4th ed., McGraw-Hill Book Company, New York, 1963.
17. Hoffman, E. J.: "Azeotropic and Extractive Distillation," Interscience Publishers, Inc., New York, 1964.
18. Holland, C. D.: "Multicomponent Distillation," Prentice-Hall, Inc., Englewood Cliffs, N.J., 1963.
19. Horsley, L. H.: "Azeotropic Data," *Advan. Chem. Ser.,* **6** (1952).
20. Horsley, L. H., and W. S. Tamplin: "Azeotropic Data II," *Advan. Chem. Ser.,* **35** (1963).

21.   Horvath, P. J., and R. F. Schubert: *Chem. Eng.*, **64**, Feb. 10, 129 (1958).

22.   Kwauk, M.: *AIChE J.*, **2**, 240 (1956).

23.   Lewis, W. K., and G. L. Matheson: *Ind. Eng. Chem.*, **24**, 494 (1932).

24.   Lowenstein, J. G.: *Ind. Eng. Chem.*, **54**(1), 61 (1962).

25.   Lyster, W. N., S. L. Sullivan, D. S. Billingsley, and C. D. Holland: *Petr. Refiner*, **38**(6), 221; (7), 151; (10), 139 (1959).

26.   McCabe, W. L., and E. W. Thiele: *Ind. Eng. Chem.*, **17**, 605 (1925).

27.   Othmer, D. F.: *Chem. Eng. Progr.*, **59**(6), 67 (1963).

28.   Perry, E. S., and A. Weissberger (eds.): "Distillation," Techniques of Organic Chemistry, vol. IV, Interscience Publishers, Inc., New York, 1965.

29.   Ponchon, M.: *Tech. Mod.*, **13**, 20, 55 (1921).

30.   Raichle, L., and R. Billet: *Ind. Eng. Chem.*, **57**(4), 52 (1965).

31.   Randall, M., and B. Longtin: *Ind. Eng. Chem.*, **30**, 1063, 1188, 1311 (1938); **31**, 908, 1295 (1939); **32**, 125 (1940).

32.   Robinson, C. S., and E. R. Gilliland: "Elements of Fractional Distillation," 4th ed., McGraw-Hill Book Company, New York, 1950.

33.   Savarit, R.: *Arts Métiers*, 1922, 65, 142, 178, 241, 266, 307.

34.   Shiras, R. N., D. N. Hanson, and C. H. Gibson: *Ind. Eng. Chem.*, **42**, 871 (1950).

35.   Smith, B. D.: "Design of Equilibrium Stage Processes," McGraw-Hill Book Company, New York, 1963.

36.   Smoker, E. H.: *Trans. AIChE*, **34**, 165 (1938).

37.   Teller, A. J., S. A. Miller, and E. G. Scheibel: sec. 18 in "The Chemical Engineers' Handbook," 4th ed., McGraw-Hill Book Company, New York, 1963.

38.   Thiele, E. W., and R. L. Geddes: *Ind. Eng. Chem.*, **25**, 289 (1933).

39.   Underwood, A. J. V.: *Trans. Inst. Chem. Engrs.* (London), **10**, 112 (1932).

40.   Underwood, A. J. V.: *Chem. Eng. Progr.*, **44**, 603 (1948); **45**, 609 (1949).

41.   Watt, P. Ridgeway: "Molecular Stills," Reinhold Publishing Corporation, New York, 1963.

42.   Winn, F. W.: *Petr. Refiner*, **37**, 216 (1950).

PROBLEMS

9.1. Solutions of methanol and ethanol are substantially ideal.

a. Compute the vapor-liquid equilibria for this system at 1 and at 5 atm abs pressure, and plot xy and txy diagrams at each pressure.

b. For each pressure compute relative volatilities, and determine an average value.

c. Using Eq. (9.2) with the average volatilities, compare the values of y^* at each value of x so obtained with those computed directly from the vapor pressures.

9.2. A 1,000-lb batch of nitrobenzene is to be steam-distilled from a very small amount of a nonvolatile impurity, insufficient to influence the vapor pressure of the nitrobenzene. The operation is to be carried out in a jacketed kettle fitted with a condenser and distillate receiver. Saturated steam at 5 psig is introduced into the kettle jacket for heating. The nitrobenzene is charged to the kettle at 80°F, and it is substantially insoluble in water.

Liquid water at 80°F is continuously introduced into the nitrobenzene in the kettle, so as always to maintain a liquid water level. The mixture is distilled at atmospheric pressure. (*a*) At what temperature does the distillation proceed? (*b*) How much water is vaporized? (*c*) How much steam must be condensed in the kettle jacket? Neglect the heat required to bring the still up to operating temperature. The heat capacity of nitrobenzene is 0.33 Btu/(lb)(°F), and its latent heat of vaporization may be determined by the methods of Chap. 7.

9.3. A mixture contains 40 mole % methanol, 35 mole % ethanol, and 25 mole % *n*-propanol. Liquid solutions of these substances are substantially ideal. Assuming the applicability of the perfect-gas law, for a total pressure of 1 atm abs compute:

    a. The bubble point and the equilibrium vapor composition.

    b. The dew point and the equilibrium liquid composition.

9.4. Vapor-liquid equilibrium data at 1 atm abs and heats of solution for the system acetone (*A*)–water (*B*), in addition to heat-capacity and latent-heat data for acetone, are as follows:

x mole fraction acetone in liquid	Integral ht soln at 59°F, Btu/lb mole soln	y^* equil mole fraction acetone in vapor	Vapor-liquid temp, °F	Ht capacity at 63°F, Btu/(lb soln)(°F)
0.00	0	0.00	212	1.00
0.01	_34.0	0.253	197.1	0.998
0.02	−81.0	0.425	187.8	0.994
0.05	−192.3	0.624	168.3	0.985
0.10	−287.5	0.755	151.9	0.96
0.15	−331	0.798	146.2	0.93
0.20	−338	0.815	143.9	0.91
0.30	−309	0.830	141.8	0.85
0.40	−219	0.839	140.8	0.80
0.50	−150.5	0.849	140.0	0.75
0.60	−108.6	0.859	139.1	0.70
0.70		0.874	138.1	0.66
0.80		0.898	136.8	0.61
0.90		0.935	135.5	0.57
0.95		0.963	134.6	0.55
1.00		1.000	133.7	

	68	100	150	200	212
t, °F					
Ht capacity acetone, Btu/(lb)(°F)	0.53	0.54	0.56	0.58	
Latent ht vaporization, Btu/lb	242	233	219	206	203

Compute the enthalpies of saturated liquids and vapors relative to pure acetone and water at 59°F, and plot the enthalpy-concentration diagram, for 1 atm abs. Retain for use in Probs. 9.5, 9.6, and 9.12.

9.5. A liquid mixture containing 60 mole % acetone, 40 mole % water, at 80°F, is to be continuously flash-vaporized at 1 atm pressure, to vaporize 30 mole % of the feed.

    a. What will be the composition of the products and the temperature in the separator, if equilibrium is established?

    b. How much heat, Btu/lb mole of feed, is required? **Ans.:** 5849.

    c. If the products are each cooled to 80°F, how much heat, Btu/lb mole of feed, must be removed from each?

9.6. A saturated vapor at 1 atm pressure, containing 50 mole % acetone and 50 mole % water, is subject to equilibrium condensation to yield 50 mole % of the feed as liquid. Compute the equilibrium vapor and liquid compositions, the equilibrium temperature, and the heat to be removed, Btu/lb mole of feed.

9.7. The liquid solution of Prob. 9.5 is differentially distilled at 1 atm pressure to vaporize 30 mole % of the feed. Compute the composition of the composited distillate and the residue. Compare with the results of Prob. 9.5. **Ans.:** $y_D = 0.857$.

9.8. The ideal mixture containing 40 mole % methanol, 35 mole % ethanol, 25 mole % *n*-propanol is flash-vaporized to vaporize 60 mole % of the feed. Determine the compositions of the liquid and vapor products and their equilibrium temperature for 1 atm pressure.

9.9. The ideal solution containing 10 mole % methanol, 80 mole % ethanol, and 10 mole % *n*-propanol is to be differentially distilled at 1 atm pressure. The first 20 mole % of vapor will be discarded, following which a "heart cut" of 60 mole % will be distilled and separately retained. The 20 mole % of residue will be discarded. Compute the yield of ethanol in the heart cut and the composition of this product. **Ans.**: 60.5% yield ethanol at 0.822 mole fraction.

9.10. A jacketed kettle is originally charged with 30 moles of a mixture containing 40 mole % benzene, 60 mole % toluene. The vapors from the kettle pass directly to a total condenser, and the condensate is withdrawn. Liquid of the same composition as the charge is continuously added to the kettle at the rate of 15 moles/hr. Heat to the kettle is regulated to generate 15 moles vapor/hr, so that the total molar content of the kettle remains constant. The mixture is ideal, and the average relative volatility is 2.51. The distillation is essentially differential.

a. How long will the still have to be operated before vapor containing 50 mole % benzene is produced, and what is the composition of the composited distillate? **Ans.**: 1.466 hr, 0.555 mole fraction benzene.

b. If the rate at which heat is supplied to the kettle is incorrectly regulated so that 18 moles/hr of vapor are generated, how long will it take until vapor containing 50 mole % benzene is produced? **Ans.**: 1.08 hr.

9.11. An open kettle contains 50 lb moles of a dilute aqueous solution of methanol, mole fraction methanol = 0.02, at the bubble point, into which steam is continuously sparged. The entering steam agitates the kettle contents so that they are always of uniform composition, and the vapor produced, always in equilibrium with the liquid, is led away. Operation is adiabatic. For the concentrations encountered it may be assumed that the enthalpy of the steam and evolved vapor are the same, the enthalpy of the liquid in the kettle is essentially constant, and the relative volatility is constant at 7.6. Compute the quantity of steam to be introduced in order to reduce the concentration of methanol in the kettle contents to 0.001 mole fraction. **Ans.**: 20.5 lb moles.

Continuous fractionation: Savarit-Ponchon method

9.12. Ten thousand pounds per hour of an acetone-water solution, containing 25 wt % acetone, is to be fractionated at 1 atm pressure. It is desired to recover 99.5% of the acetone in the distillate at a concentration of 99 wt %. The feed will be available at 80°F and will be preheated by heat exchange with the residue product from the fractionator, which in turn will be cooled to 125°F. The distilled vapors will be condensed and cooled to 100°F by cooling water entering at 80°F and leaving at 105°F. Reflux will be returned at 100°F, at a reflux ratio $L_0/D = 1.8$. Open steam, available at 10 psig, will be used at the base of the tower. The tower will be insulated to reduce heat losses to negligible values. Physical property data are given in Prob. 9.4. Determine:

a. The hourly rate and composition of distillate and reflux.

b. The hourly condenser heat load and cooling water rate.

c. The hourly rate of steam and residue and the composition of the residue.

d. The enthalpy of the feed as it enters the tower and its condition (express quantitatively).

e. The number of ideal trays required if the feed is introduced at the optimum location. Use large-size graph paper and a sharp pencil. **Ans.**: 13.1.

f. The rates of flow, lb/hr, of liquid and vapor at the top, at $x = 0.6$, 0.1, 0.025, and at the bottom tray. For a tower of uniform diameter, the conditions on which tray control the diameter, if the criterion is a 75% approach to flooding?

9.13. Design a suitable sieve-tray tower for the fractionator of Prob. 9.12, determine the tray efficiencies, and the number of real trays required. **Ans.**: There is no single answer. For a diameter of 2.5 ft, tray spacing 20 in., $A_h/A_a = 0.1$, the Murphree efficiencies vary from 0.60 at the top to 0.78 at the bottom, 25 trays are required, with the feed on to the twentieth.

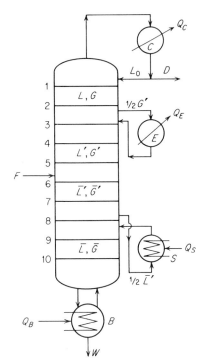

Fig. 9.56   *Arrangement for Prob.* 9.14.

9.14.   In a certain binary distillation, the overhead vapor condenser must be run at a temperature requiring mild refrigeration, and the available refrigeration capacity is very limited. The reboiler temperature is very high, and the available high-temperature heat supply is also limited. Consequently the scheme shown in Fig. 9.56 is adopted, where the intermediate condenser E and reboiler S operate at moderate temperatures. Condensers C and E are total condensers, delivering liquids at their bubble points. Reboiler S is a total vaporizer, delivering saturated vapor. Heat losses are negligible, $D = W$, the external reflux ratio $R = L_0/D = 1.0$, and other conditions are shown on the figure. The system is one which follows the McCabe-Thiele assumptions ($H_L x$ and $H_G y$ curves are straight and parallel). Feed is liquid at the bubble point.

a. Per mole of feed, compute the rates of flow of all streams, the relative size of the two condenser heat loads, and the relative size of the two vaporizer heat loads.

b. Establish the coordinates of all difference points. Sketch the Hxy diagram and locate the difference points, showing how they are related to the feed. Show the construction for trays.

c. Sketch the xy diagram, show all operating lines, and locate their intersections with the 45° diagonal. Show the construction for trays.

9.15.   A distillation column is operated at a temperature below that of the surroundings (as in the distillation of air). Owing to imperfect insulation, the entire enriching section is subject to a heat leak inward of Q_E Btu/hr, while the entire stripping section is subject to a heat leak inward of Q_S Btu/hr. Aside from the heat leaks, the system has all the characteristics which satisfy the McCabe-Thiele requirements.

a. Sketch the Hxy and the xy diagrams, labeling the coordinates of all significant points. Are the operating curves on the xy diagram concave upward or downward?

b. For a given condenser heat load, explain which is better: to design a new column with the inward heat leak minimized, or to take any possible advantage of a heat leak. Consider the reboiler heat load free, available from the surroundings.

c. Suppose the column with the inward heat leak is operated at full reboiler heat load, limited by the available heat-transfer surface. The column is then insulated thoroughly, essentially eliminating the heat leak, but without provision to alter the heat load of the reboiler or otherwise to alter the operation. Explain whether the separation obtained will be better than, worse than, or the same as, before the insulation was installed.

Continuous fractionation: McCabe-Thiele method

9.16. A solution of carbon tetrachloride and carbon disulfide containing 50 wt % each is to be continuously fractionated at atmospheric pressure at the rate of 4,000 lb/hr. The distillate product is to contain 95 wt % carbon disulfide, the residue 0.5%. The feed will be 30 mole % vaporized before it enters the tower. A total condenser will be used, and reflux will be returned at the bubble point. Equilibrium data are available in "The Chemical Engineers' Handbook," 4th ed., p. 13-5.

a. Determine the quantities of products, lb/hr and lb moles/hr.

b. Determine the minimum reflux ratio.

c. Determine the minimum number of ideal trays, graphically and by means of Eq. (9.81).

d. Determine the number of theoretical trays required at a reflux ratio equal to twice the minimum and the position of the feed tray. **Ans.:** 12.5 ideal stages.

e. Estimate the overall tray efficiency of a bubble-cap-tray tower of conventional design and the number of real trays.

f. Using the distillate temperature as the base temperature, determine the enthalpy of the feed, the products, and the vapor entering the condenser. Determine the heat loads of the condenser and reboiler. Latent and specific heats are available in "The Chemical Engineers' Handbook," 4th ed., pp. 3-113 and 3-126.

9.17. An acetone-water solution, 0.2 mole fraction acetone and at the bubble point, is to be fractionated at 1 atm pressure. No more than 0.1 % of the acetone content of the feed is to be lost to the residue. Two products other than the residue are required, each containing half of the recovered acetone: the first at 0.98, the second at 0.80 mole fraction acetone. Two schemes are being considered as outlined below. In both, open steam at 10 psig at the base of the tower and a total condenser delivering liquid at the bubble point will be used, with an external reflux ratio 1.5 times the minimum value. Equilibrium vapor-liquid data are given in Prob. 9.4. Use 100 lb moles of feed as a basis for computation.

a. The first scheme is to fractionate the entire feed, to remove the rich product as overhead distillate and the less rich product as a liquid side stream from an appropriate tray between the feed and the top tray.

1. Determine the quantities of distillate D and side stream S.

2. Determine the reflux ratio (use a large graph), and plot the enriching operating line.

3. For the section between side stream and feed, write the operating-line equation (make an acetone balance to the top, noting that for this section $G = G_1$ and $L = L_0 - S$), determine the point where $x = y$, the y intercept, and the point of intersection with the enriching line. $S =$ molar side-stream rate.

4. Determine the quantity of steam, x_W, and the total number of ideal trays required. **Ans.:** 18.2 ideal trays.

b. The second scheme will fractionate only part of the feed to produce the residue and a single distillate, $x_D = 0.98$. The product of $x = 0.8$ will be obtained by mixing the undistilled portion of the feed with part of the distillate. Total acetone loss to the residue is to be the same as in *a*. Determine the quantity of feed to be fractionated, the quantities of distillate, steam, residue, x_W, and the number of ideal trays. **Ans.:** 17.8 ideal trays.

c. Which scheme is to be preferred?

9.18. An aqueous solution of furfural contains 4 mole % furfural. It is to be continuously fractionated at 1 atm pressure to provide solutions containing 0.1 and 99.5 mole % furfural, respectively. Feed is liquid at the bubble point. Equilibrium data are available in "The Chemical Engineers' Handbook," 4th ed., p. 13-5.

a. Arrange a scheme for the separation using kettle-type reboilers, and determine the number of ideal trays required for a vapor boilup rate of 1.25 times the minimum for an infinite number of trays.

b. Repeat *a*, but use open steam at essentially atmospheric pressure for the tower delivering the water-rich product, with 1.25 times the minimum steam and vapor boilup rates.

c. Which scheme incurs the greater furfural loss to the water-rich product?

9.19. One thousand pounds per hour of an aniline-water solution containing 7 wt % aniline, at the bubble point, is to be steam-stripped in a tower packed with 1-in. Berl saddles with open steam to remove 99% of the aniline. The condensed overhead vapor will be decanted at 98.5°C, and the water-rich layer returned to the column. The aniline-rich layer will be withdrawn as distillate product. The steam rate will be 1.3 times the minimum. Design the tower so as not to exceed loading, and use standard pipe ("The Chemical Engineers" Handbook," 4th ed., p. 6-45) for the shell. *Note:* For concentrations where the equilibrium curve is nearly straight, it should be possible to use overall numbers and heights of transfer units. **Ans.:** 18.5 ft of packing.

Data. At 98.5°C, the solubility of aniline in water is 7.02 and 89.90 wt % aniline. The vapor-liquid equilibria at 745 mm Hg, at which pressure the tower will be operated, are [Griswold et al., *Ind. Eng. Chem.*, **32**, 878 (1940)]:

x = mole fraction aniline	0.002	0.004	0.006	0.008	0.010	0.012	Two liquid phases, 98.5°C
y^* = mole fraction aniline	0.01025	0.0185	0.0263	0.0338	0.03575	0.03585	0.0360

9.20. The following feed, liquid at the bubble point at 120 psia, is to be fractionated at 120 psia to provide no more than 7.45% of the n-C_5H_{12} in the distillate and no more than 7.6% of the n-C_4H_{10} in the bottoms, with a total condenser and reflux returned at the bubble point:

Component	x_F	150°F	200°F	250°F
n-C_3H_8	0.05			
m		2.50	3.7	5.2
H_G		14,700	15,700	16,850
H_L		9,200	11,300	13,400
i-C_4H_{10}	0.15			
m		1.31	1.91	2.96
H_G		17,600	19,100	20,600
H_L		10,700	12,600	14,950
n-C_4H_{10}	0.25			
m		0.90	1.50	2.50
H_G		19,000	20,200	21,700
H_L		11,100	13,100	15,200
i-C_5H_{12}	0.20			
m		0.44	0.76	1.31
H_G		22,500	23,900	25,600
H_L		12,900	15,100	17,500
n-C_5H_{12}	0.35			
m		0.35	0.65	1.16
H_G		23,550	25,000	26,300
H_L		13,200	15,500	18,000

The above table provides Henry's law constants and enthalpies as Btu/lb mole, from the same sources and with the same base as the data of Illustration 9.13.

Compute the minimum reflux ratio, the minimum number of ideal trays, and, for a reflux ratio $R = 2.58$, estimate the product analyses, condenser and reboiler heat loads, vapor and liquid rates per mole of feed throughout, and the number of ideal trays.   **Ans.:** 8 ideal trays + reboiler.

PART THREE
LIQUID-LIQUID
OPERATIONS

Liquid extraction, the only operation in this category, is basically very similar to the operations of gas-liquid contact described in the previous part. The creation of a new insoluble liquid phase by addition of a solvent to a mixture accomplishes in many respects the same result as the creation of a new phase by the addition of heat in distillation operations, for example, or by addition of gas in desorption operations. The separations produced by single stages, the use of countercurrent cascades and reflux to enhance the extent of separation—all have their liquid-extraction counterparts. The similarity among these will be exploited in explaining what liquid extraction can accomplish.

Certain differences in the operations nevertheless make it expedient to provide a separate treatment for liquid extraction. The considerably greater change in mutual solubility of the contacted liquid phases which may occur during passage through a cascade of stages requires somewhat different techniques of computation than are necessary for gas absorption or stripping. The considerably smaller differences in density of the contacted phases and their relatively low interfacial tension, as compared with the corresponding gas-liquid systems, require consideration in the design of apparatus. The larger number of variables which apparently influence the rate of mass transfer in countercurrent equipment makes the correlation of design data much more difficult. For these reasons separate treatment is desirable, at least for the present.

CHAPTER TEN
LIQUID EXTRACTION

Liquid extraction, sometimes called solvent extraction, is the separation of the constituents of a liquid solution by contact with another insoluble liquid. If the substances comprising the original solution distribute themselves differently between the two liquid phases, a certain degree of separation will result, and this may be enhanced by use of multiple contacts or their equivalent in the manner of gas absorption and distillation.

A simple example will indicate the scope of the operation and some of its characteristics. If a solution of acetic acid in water is agitated with a liquid such as ethyl acetate, some of the acid but relatively little water will enter the ester phase. Since at equilibrium the densities of the aqueous and ester layers are different, they will settle on cessation of agitation and may be decanted from each other. Since now the ratio of acid to water in the ester layer is different from that in the original solution and also different from that in the residual water solution, a certain degree of separation will have occurred. This is an example of stagewise contact, and it may be carried out either in batch or in continuous fashion. The residual water may be repeatedly extracted with more ester to reduce still further the acid content, or we may arrange a countercurrent cascade of stages. Another possibility is to use some sort of countercurrent continuous-contact device, where discrete stages are not involved. The use of reflux, as in distillation, may enhance still further the ultimate separation.

In all such operations, the solution which is to be extracted is called the *feed*, and the liquid with which the feed is contacted is the *solvent*. The solvent-rich product of the operation is called the *extract*, and the residual liquid from which solute has been removed is the *raffinate*.

More complicated processes may use two solvents to separate the components of a feed. For example, a mixture of *p*- and *o*-nitrobenzoic acids may be separated by distributing them between the insoluble liquids chloroform and water. The chloroform preferentially dissolves the para isomer and the water the ortho isomer. This is called *double-solvent*, or *fractional*, extraction.

Fields of usefulness

In distillation, where the vapor phase with which a liquid is contacted is created from the liquid by addition of heat, the vapor and liquid are necessarily of the same substances and are therefore chemically very similar. The separations produced depend on the vapor pressures of the substances. In the case of liquid extraction, on the other hand, the two phases are chemically quite different, and this leads to a separation of substances according to chemical type. There are therefore the following major fields of application for liquid extraction:

1. As a substitute for distillation or evaporation, particularly when the substances to be separated are chemically different. Here the relative costs are important, since extraction produces new solutions which must be separated, frequently by distillation or evaporation. Thus, for example, acetic acid may be separated from dilute solutions with water with difficulty by distillation, or with relative ease by extraction followed by distillation of the extract. For the more dilute solutions particularly, when much water must be vaporized in distillation, extraction is more economical, particularly since the heat of vaporization of most organic solvents is substantially less than that of water. Extraction may also be attractive as an alternative to distillation or evaporation when very low temperatures would be required to avoid thermal decomposition. For example, long-chain fatty acids may be separated from vegetable oils by high-vacuum distillation but more economically by extraction with liquid propane.

2. For separations not readily done by other methods. For example, aromatic and paraffinic hydrocarbons of nearly the same molecular weight can be separated readily by extraction with any of a number of solvents, e.g., sulfur dioxide, diethylene glycol, and sulfolane, but are impossible to separate by distillation since their vapor pressures are nearly the same. Many pharmaceutical products, e.g., penicillin, occur naturally in mixtures which are so complex that only liquid extraction is a feasible separation device. Many metal separations, particularly those which are expensive by chemical methods, such as uranium-vanadium, tantalum-columbium, and hafnium-zirconium, are economically done by extraction. Even low-cost inorganic chemicals such as phosphoric acid, boric acid, sodium hydroxide, and the like, can be economically purified by liquid-extraction means, despite the fact that the cost of solvent recovery must be included in the final reckoning.

EQUIPMENT

There are two major categories of equipment for liquid extraction:

1. Single-stage equipment, which provides one stage of contact in a single device or combination of devices. In such an apparatus, the liquids are mixed, extraction occurs, and the insoluble liquids are settled and separated. A countercurrent cascade of stages may be arranged for enhancement of the separation.

2. Multistage equipment, where the equivalent of many stages may be incorporated into a single device or apparatus.

SINGLE-STAGE EQUIPMENT

A single stage must provide facilities for mixing the insoluble liquids and for settling and decanting the emulsion or dispersion which results. In batch operation, mixing together with settling and decanting may take place in the same or in separate vessels. In continuous operation, different vessels are required, and the combination is called a *mixer-settler*.

Mixers

For efficient extraction, the mixing device must bring about intimate contact of the liquids. This usually requires that one liquid be dispersed in the form of small droplets into the other and that sufficient time of contact ("holding time") be provided to allow extraction to take place. The smaller the droplets and the larger their number, the greater will be the interfacial area produced, the more rapid will be the interphase mass transfer, and the less holding time will be required. It is, however, essential that the dispersion not be made so fine that subsequent settling is too slow.

To effect the dispersion requires the expenditure of mechanical work or power upon the system. The mere application of large amounts of power through some mixing device will not necessarily ensure adequate mixing, however. The mixing effectiveness, which may be loosely defined as the degree of dispersion produced per unit of power applied, depends greatly upon the design of the mixing device. As yet no really adequate measurements of this have been made, and we must rely instead on the stage efficiency as indication of the success of the mixing. This will include the influence of degree of dispersion, holding time, and rate of mass transfer upon the operation as a whole. It is known, however, that the degree of dispersion which results from the application of a fixed amount of power through a given mixer depends upon the properties of the liquids involved, including their densities, viscosities, and interfacial tension.

There are two major varieties of mixers, agitated vessels and flow mixers. The former are by far the more important.

Agitated vessels

These consist of a vessel to contain the liquids and a mechanical agitator to provide the mixing, as in Fig. 10.1. In such vessels strong vertical currents within the liquid

Baffle

Turbine

Fig. 10.1 *Agitated vessel for batch or continuous extraction.*

are necessary to ensure that the heavy liquid will not stratify at the bottom.   Radial rather than circular motion is desired, since the latter tends to stratify the liquids by centrifugal force, causing the heavy liquid to be flung to the side wall of the vessel. The circulation currents developed will depend upon the vessel shape, the presence of baffles, and the design, location, and speed of the agitation impeller.

The vessels are ordinarily vertical cylinders, circular rather than rectangular in cross section.   They may be fitted with internal baffles, which are necessary in cases where the liquid is in contact with air to prevent vortexing.   Four equally spaced vertical baffles, arranged radially as shown in the figure, of length equal to the liquid depth and width equal to one-tenth the tank diameter, are sufficient.   Baffles are customarily used also with full vessels, where there is no air-liquid interface, although the meager evidence is that in these cases the same extraction rates are given with less impeller power if baffles are omitted.[17]

Impellers of many designs are effective, and Fig. 10.2 shows several types.   The impeller diameter is usually one-third to one-half that of the vessel, and the shaft is best placed along the vessel axis.   Agitation power in the range 0.05 to 0.3 hp/cu ft vessel volume may be used, rarely more, depending upon how difficult it is to disperse the liquids: high interfacial tension and density difference make dispersion more difficult.   Impeller speeds for a given power may be estimated from standard correlations.[13,22,27]

For continuous operation, which is most common, the two liquids to be contacted usually flow upward through the vessel, and the dispersion produced is led from the top to a settling device.   Now the rate of extraction is proportional to an overall mass-transfer coefficient and the interfacial area, which should be as large as practical.   The area is governed by the size of the droplets produced (usually in the range 0.1 to 1 mm diameter, depending upon the liquid properties and the agitation power) and the volume fraction ϕ_D of dispersed phase in the vessel (dispersed-phase holdup). Drop-let diameters cannot be made too small, since difficulty in subsequent settling results, and consequently it is desirable to maintain a high value of ϕ_D. Ordinarily the liquid flowing at the smaller volume rate (the minority liquid) will be dispersed in the other, and at the agitator-power levels mentioned above, the value of ϕ_D will usually be the same as the volume fraction that the dispersed liquid represents of the total liquid entering the vessel. When the volume ratio of liquids to the vessel is small, say 0.1, for example, as may be the case when a particularly excellent solvent is used, only small values of ϕ_D will result. In this case, the interfacial area and hence the rate of mass transfer may be substantially increased by recycling part of the minority liquid flowing from the settler back to the mixer.[28] It is difficult, however, to main-tain ϕ_D at values much above 0.6 to 0.7,[19] and attempts to increase it beyond these values usually result in inversion of the dispersion.

Methods for estimating the droplet size, the interfacial area, and the mass-transfer coefficients, from which the stage efficiency may be computed, have been the subject of much study,[27] but many questions remain unanswered. Fortunately, stage effi-ciencies are usually very high. Particularly when extraction consists of diffusive mass transfer alone, a residence time within the mixing vessel (vessel volume/total volumetric rate of flow) of the order of 1 min or less is usually sufficient to produce fractional stage efficiencies greater than 0.9. Slow chemical reaction accompanying the extraction may increase the required time substantially.

Flow mixers

The power required for dispersion by flow mixers, or "line mixers," comes from pumping the liquids through the device. They have small volumes and consequently

(a)
Marine-type
propeller

(b)   (c)

Flat-bladed turbine impellers

Fig. 10.2 *Mixing impellers.*

(*a*) Elbow jet mixer (Courtesy, The Duriron Co.)

(*b*) Mixing nozzle (Courtesy,
The Duriron Co.)

(*c*) Orifice mixer

Fig. 10.3 *Flow mixers.*

provide little holding time.   They are especially useful for liquids of low viscosity and low interfacial tension, for which dispersion is not difficult.

Several types are shown in Fig. 10.3.   Jet mixers depend for their action upon impingement of one liquid, which is caused to flow through a small opening, upon the other when both are pumped into the mixer.   Mixing nozzles and orifices bring about mixing and dispersion by causing great turbulence when both liquids are pumped through the device.   Even ordinary globe valves may be used.   Each of these devices is effective and inexpensive to install but may incur high pressure drop and consequently may be expensive to operate.

Emulsions

The mixture of liquids issuing from any mixing device, an emulsion, consists of small droplets of one liquid dispersed throughout a continuum of the other.   The stability, or permanence, of the emulsion is of the utmost importance in liquid extraction, since it is necessary to separate the phases at each extraction stage.   Stable emulsions, those which do not settle and coalesce rapidly, must be avoided For an emulsion to "break," or separate into its phases in bulk, both sedimentation and coalescence of the dispersed phase must occur.

The rate of sedimentation of a quiescent emulsion is the more rapid if the size of the droplets and the density difference of the liquids are large and if the viscosity of the continuous phase is small. Stable emulsions, those which settle only over long periods of time, are usually formed when the diameter of the dispersed droplets is of the order of 1 to 1.5 μ, whereas dispersions of particle diameter 1 mm or larger usually sedimentate rapidly.

Coalescence of the settled droplets is the more rapid the higher the interfacial tension. Interfacial tension is ordinarily low for liquids of high mutual solubility and is lowered by the presence of emulsifying or wetting agents. In addition, high viscosity of the continuous phase hinders coalescence by reducing the rate at which the residual film between drops is removed. Dust particles, which usually accumulate at the interface between liquids, also hinder coalescence.

In the case of an unstable emulsion, after agitation has stopped, the mixture settles and coalesces rapidly into two liquid phases unless the viscosity is high. The appearance of a sharply defined interface between the phases (primary break) is usually very rapid, but one of the phases, ordinarily that in the majority, may remain clouded by a very fine fog or haze, a dispersion of the other phase. The cloud will eventually settle and leave the clouded phase clear (secondary break), but this may take a considerable time. The primary break of an unstable emulsion is usually so rapid that merely stopping agitation for a very short time, a matter of minutes, is sufficient to bring it about. In continuous multistage operation, it is usually impractical to hold the mixture between stages long enough to attain the secondary break.

Settlers

In continuous extraction, the dispersion from the mixer is allowed to flow through a vessel of sufficient size so that the time of residence is great enough to permit primary break. The cross section of such a device should be large so that turbulence is reduced to a minimum. An empty vessel may be employed, but baffles are often included, as in Fig. 10.4. Horizontal baffles reduce turbulence and also the distance through which the dispersed droplets must settle before coalescence. Other more elaborate devices are also in use.[27]

Neglecting the pressure drop for flow through the exit pipes, which should be kept to a minimum, the level of the interface within the settler (Fig. 10.4) will adjust itself so that

$$s\rho_H = t\rho_H + u\rho_L \tag{10.1}$$

For operation under pressure and with elimination of the siphon vents, a liquid-level controller activated by the interface position and operating a regulating valve in the exit pipe for the heavy liquid may be used.

Continuous centrifuges are sometimes used for decreasing the settling time, but they will not influence in any way the rate of coalescence of the settled dispersed phase.

Fig. 10.4 *Gravity settler.*

The latter may be assisted by causing the emulsion to flow through a bed of porous substance which is preferentially wetted by the dispersed phase. Glass fibers, steel wool, and coarse wire mesh have been successfully used as coalescers, and these should be placed upstream from the settling vessel.[23]

Multistage extraction

A continuous multistage extraction plant will consist of the required number of stages arranged according to the desired flow sheet. Each stage will consist of at least a mixer and a settler, as in the countercurrent plant of Fig. 10.5. The liquids will generally be pumped from one stage to the next, but occasionally gravity flow can be arranged if sufficient headroom is available. Many arrangements have been designed to reduce the amount of interstage piping and the corresponding cost.[27] Figure 10.6 is one such: the mixing vessels are immersed in the large circular settling tanks, heavy liquid flows by gravity, light liquid by air lift, and recycling of settled light liquid to the mixer is accomplished by overflow.

Fig. 10.5 *Flow sheet of three-stage countercurrent mixer-settler extraction cascade.*

Fig. 10.6   *Kerr-McGee uranium extractor.*

MULTISTAGE EQUIPMENT

When the liquids flow countercurrently through a single piece of equipment, the equivalent of as many ideal stages may be had as desired.   In such devices, the countercurrent flow is produced by virtue of the difference in densities of the liquids, and if the motivating force is the force of gravity, the extractor takes the form of a vertical tower, the light liquid entering at the bottom, the heavy liquid at the top.   As an alternative, a larger centrifugal force may be generated by rapidly rotating the extractor, in which case the counterflow is radial with respect to the axis of revolution.

There are several characteristics common to countercurrent extractors which have an important bearing upon their design and performance.   It is typical that only one of the liquids may be pumped through the device at any desired rate.   The maximum rate for the other will depend upon, among other things, the density difference of the liquids.   If an attempt is made to exceed this rate for the second liquid, the extractor will reject one of the liquids, and it is said to be *flooded*.   The same is true, of course, for gas-liquid contactors, but since the density difference is much smaller than for a gas and liquid, the flooding velocities of extractors are much lower.   For a given volumetric rate of liquids to be handled, the extractor cross section must be sufficiently large so that the flooding velocities are not reached.   The more open the cross section, the greater the flow rates before flooding occurs.   Internal structures, packing, mechanical agitators, and the like normally reduce the velocities at which flooding occurs.

Most of these devices are also subject to *axial mixing*, commonly called back mixing, which severely reduces the extraction rates.   Several phenomena are recognized to be involved.[31]   Because the velocity profile for a liquid across the tower cross section is not flat ("plug flow"), the dissolved solute is carried by the liquid at different rates in different locations in the cross section.   Where pockets of liquid within the extractor become mixed, the solute concentrations do not change regularly with axial distance.   Some liquid is caused to circulate in the wrong direction, movement which is induced by the flow of the other liquid.   The net result is a reduction in the concentration difference between the liquids, upon which the mass transfer depends.   The mathematical description of axial mixing has been fairly completely developed, but only recently has its importance been fully realized, and our quantitative knowledge of its effects is meager.

Spray towers

These, the simplest of the continuous-contact devices, consist merely of an empty vertical shell with provisions for introducing and removing the liquids.   Refer to Fig. 10.7a, where operation is shown with the light liquid dispersed.   Heavy liquid enters at the top, fills the tower completely (continuous phase), and flows out at the bottom.   Light liquid enters at the bottom through a distributor which disperses it into small droplets.   These rise through the downward-flowing heavy liquid and coalesce into a layer at the top.   The heavy liquid is shown leaving through a looped pipe A, and the head of heavy liquid at the bottom of the pipe (static pressure + friction resulting from flow) must balance the head of combined light and heavy liquids in the tower.   In this manner the interface B is maintained in the position shown.   The position of the interface may be regulated by the elevation of A, but it is more satisfactorily controlled in large-scale equipment by the valve C, which may be operated by a liquid-level controller actuated by the position of the interface itself.   The tap D is used periodically to withdraw scum and dust particles which accumulate at the interface and interfere with coalescence of the droplets of dispersed liquid.   The exit streams from this and other types of countercurrent towers are frequently passed through settlers of the sort shown in Fig. 10.4, to remove entrained droplets from the product liquids.

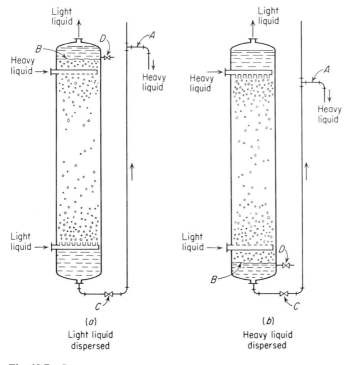

(*a*)
Light liquid
dispersed

(*b*)
Heavy liquid
dispersed

Fig. 10.7   *Spray tower.*

By reducing the height of pipe A or by opening the valve C the interface may be lowered to the position shown in Fig. 10.7b. The heavy liquid is now dispersed and the light liquid continuous. As an additional alternative the interface may be located more or less centrally in the tower.

The spray tower is inexpensive to build, easy to keep clean, and has a high flow capacity. The freedom with which the continuous phase can circulate leads to such severe axial-mixing effects and reduced extraction efficiency, however, that it is not normally used for industrial purposes. We have used it here principally to describe the methods of operating extraction towers generally.

Packed towers

Towers filled with the same random packings used for gas-liquid contact are also used for liquid extraction. The packing serves to reduce axial mixing and also to jostle and distort the droplets of dispersed phase, in this way improving somewhat the mass-transfer rates. A typical packed tower, arranged for light liquid dispersed, is shown schematically in Fig. 10.8. By lowering the interface (see page 417) it may be arranged for heavy liquid dispersed. The tower is usually straight-sided, as shown; some have been made with an expanded end section where the dispersed phase enters.[4]

The nature of the liquid flow in such towers requires that the choice of packing and arrangement of dispersed-phase distributor be given careful attention. If the dispersed liquid preferentially wets the packing, it will pass through in rivulets on the packing, not as droplets, and the interfacial area produced will be small. For this reason, the packing material should be preferentially wetted by the continuous phase. Usually, ceramics are preferentially wet by aqueous liquids, carbon and plastics by organic liquids. The packing should be sufficiently small, no greater than one-eighth the tower diameter, so that the packing density is fully developed yet larger than a certain critical size (see below). In cases where the material of the packing support is not wet by the dispersed droplets and where the distributor is placed outside the packing, the drops will have difficulty in entering the packing, and premature flooding results. For this reason it is always desirable to embed the dispersed-phase distributor in the packing, as in Fig. 10.8.

Dispersed-phase holdup[18]

For packing sizes d_F larger than a critical size d_{FC},

$$d_{FC} = 2.42 \left(\frac{\sigma g_c}{\Delta \rho g} \right)^{0.5} \tag{10.2}$$

there is a characteristic mean diameter of dispersed-phase droplet d_p which is nearly independent of packing size and shape. For smaller packings, the drop size is larger, and interfacial areas are smaller. Packings smaller than d_{FC} should not be used, and what follows is strictly for $d_F > d_{FC}$.

Flow rates are conveniently described as superficial velocities (volumetric rate/tower cross-sectional area), V_C and V_D ft/hr for the continuous and dispersed phases, respectively. Dispersed-phase holdup ϕ_D is an "operating" holdup, that which drains from the packing if liquid flow is stopped, and is expressed as a fraction of the void volume ϵ within the packed bed (see Table 6.2). At low

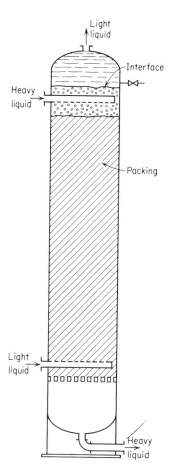

Light
liquid

Interface

Heavy
liquid

Packing

Light
liquid

Heavy
liquid

Fig. 10.8 *Packed extraction tower, light liquid dispersed.*

values of V_D, ϕ_D varies linearly with V_D up to a lower "transition point" reminiscent of loading in gas-liquid contact. With further increase in V_D, ϕ_D increases rapidly, the dispersed droplets tend to coalesce, and a second transition occurs. V_D can increase a small amount beyond this without marked increase in ϕ_D, but flooding ultimately results. Below the upper transition, the holdup is described by

$$\frac{V_D}{\epsilon\phi_D} + \frac{V_C}{\epsilon(1 - \phi_D)} = V_K(1 - \phi_D) \qquad (10.3)$$

Here, were it not for the additional permanent holdup, which is not included in ϕ_D, the left-hand side of Eq. (10.3) would represent a *slip* velocity, or superficial relative velocity. V_K is a "characteristic" velocity, a limiting mean drop velocity at $V_C = 0$ for low values of V_D, and is correlated from the experimental data by Fig. 10.9. For design purposes, it is recommended that ϕ_D be set in the range 0.10 to 0.20, the low value for V_D/V_C below 0.5, the flow rates being further checked for flooding.

The mean characteristic drop diameter d_p for liquids at equilibrium is given by

$$d_p = 0.92\left(\frac{\sigma g_c}{\Delta\rho\, g}\right)^{0.5} \frac{V_K\epsilon\phi_D}{V_D} \qquad (10.4)$$

For liquids which are not mutually saturated, or if extraction occurs from a dispersed organic to a continuous aqueous liquid, d_p will be larger to an extent which cannot be estimated. If extraction occurs in the reverse direction, d_p is evidently not altered. If the drops formed at the distributor nozzles are smaller than d_p, they grow very slowly by coalescence to the characteristic size, but premature flooding may result. It is best therefore to produce drops initially somewhat larger than those of Eq. (10.4), whereupon they are broken up within the packing to the characteristic size. In any case, the holes in the distributor should be at least sufficiently large (say ³⁄₁₆ to ¼ in. diameter) to avoid plugging.

Flooding

There have been a great many studies of flooding, and the results are not in good agreement. The studies were all made in the absence of mass transfer, and in view of the influence of mass transfer on d_p, it can be expected that there is an influence on flooding as well. The recommended work is that of Crawford and Wilke,[6] whose results are shown in Fig. 10.10. It is recommended that actual velocities be no larger than 50 to 60 percent of the flooding values in view of the uncertainties involved. Packing characteristics a_p and ϵ are given in Table 6.2.

Drop terminal velocities

Figure 10.9 contains the term V_t, the terminal velocity of a liquid drop in a liquid medium. This is the free-fall (or rise, depending on the relative density) velocity of a single isolated drop in the gravitational field. The terminal velocities of small drops, which are essentially spherical, are larger than those of solid spheres of the same diameter and density, owing to the mobility and internal circulation within the drop: the surface velocity is not zero, as it is for a solid. With increasing diameter, there occurs a transition drop size, beyond which the drop shape is no longer spherical (although it is nevertheless described with d_p as the diameter of a sphere of the same volume), and the drop oscillates and distorts. The terminal velocity of the transition size is a maximum, and for larger sizes the velocity falls slowly with increased diameter. Dimensional analysis shows Re = $f(C_D, We)$, where Re is the drop Reynolds number at terminal velocity, We is the drop Weber number, and C_D is the usual drag coefficient. For very pure liquids (no surface-active agents, no mass transfer),

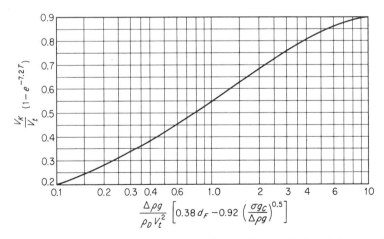

Fig. 10.9 *Characteristic drop velocities for packings.* [*Gaylor, Roberts, and Pratt: Trans. Inst. Chem. Engrs.* (*London*), **31**, 57 (1953).] *Not to be used for T < 0.25 ft or $d_F < d_{FC}$.*

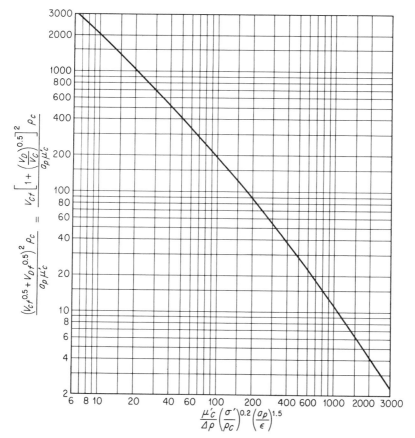

Fig. 10.10 *Flooding in packed towers.*[6]

and continuous phase viscosities less than 5 centipoises, the Hu-Kintner correlation[9] (Fig. 10.11) provides the functional relation. P is defined as

$$P = \frac{4\mathrm{Re}^4}{3C_D\,\mathrm{We}^3} = \frac{\rho_c^2(\sigma g_c)^3}{g\mu_c^4\,\Delta\rho} \tag{10.5}$$

and the transition maximum velocity occurs at an ordinate of Fig. 10.11 equal to approximately 70. For larger continuous phase viscosities, but not exceeding 30 centipoises, the ordinate of Fig. 10.11 should be multiplied by $(\mu_W/\mu_c)^{0.14}$, where μ_W is the viscosity of water.[11]   Minute amounts of impurities which are frequently present in practice can alter the terminal velocities profoundly (usually to lower values), and the effect of mass transfer is unknown.†

---

† The curve of Fig. 10.11 should not be extrapolated to lower values.   For values of the ordinate below 1.0, the equation of Klee and Treybal, *AIChE J.*, **2**, 444 (1956), will give more correct results:

$$V_t = \frac{53{,}000\Delta\rho^{0.58}\,d_p^{0.70}}{\rho_c^{0.45}\mu_c^{0.11}}$$

This equation will serve also for all drop sizes less than the transition size and continuous phase viscosity not exceeding 2 centipoises.

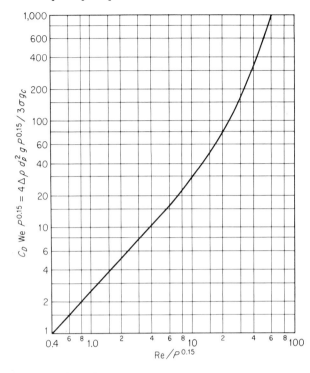

The y-axis is labeled $C_D \, \text{We} \, P^{0.15} = 4 \, \Delta\rho \, d_p^2 \, g \, P^{0.15} / 3 \sigma g_c$

The x-axis is labeled $\text{Re}/P^{0.15}$

Fig. 10.11 *Terminal settling velocities of single liquid drops in infinite liquid media.*[9]

Drop formation

A liquid may be dispersed into drops by passage through perforations in plates or pipes or by causing it to issue from a short open tube or nozzle. If the drop preferentially wets the material of the plate, the drop size is uncontrollably large, and it is best to use small nozzles which project from the surface. These may be punched in a flat plate in the manner of Fig. 10.12, with the burr left in place facing in the direction of drop formation.

In the absence of mass transfer, whose effect is not known, when the dispersed phase issues from a nozzle or perforated plate which is not preferentially wetted by the dispersed liquid, drop size will be uniform at a given velocity up to nozzle or perforation velocities of 0.3 ft/sec. At higher velocities jets or "streamers" of dispersed liquid issue from the openings, and these break up at some distance from the opening into relatively large drops of nonuniform size. For openings up to 0.31 in. diameter, Fig. 10.13 provides the uniform drop size d_p for nozzle velocities V_0' up to 0.3 ft/sec, and the diameter of the largest drop for $V_0' = 0.3$ to 1.0 ft/sec.[8] For velocities larger than this there is a tendency for the liquid to "atomize," and small but very nonuniform drops are produced.[12]

Despite the fact that packings reduce the axial mixing to much lower values than are found in spray towers, packed towers are still subject to it.[31] Packed towers are not very satisfactory when the ratio of flow rates to the tower is outside the range 0.5

Fig. 10.12 *Punched perforations for dispersed phase.*[15]

Fig. 10.13 *Drop diameters for dispersion of insoluble liquids through nozzles and perforations.*[8]

to 2.0, since then suitable dispersed phase holdup and interfacial area are difficult to establish and still avoid flooding.   Mass-transfer rates will generally be low except for systems of low interfacial tension.

Illustration 10.1. Isopropyl ether, 180 cu ft/hr, is to be used to extract acetic acid from a dilute solution in water, 120 cu ft/hr, in a tower packed with 1-in. Berl saddles.   The ether is to be dispersed. Physical properties are, for the aqueous phase, density = 63.0 lb/cu ft, viscosity = 3.1 centipoises; for the ether phase, density = 45.6 lb/cu ft; interfacial tension = 13 dynes/cm.   Determine the tower diameter to be used and the distributor characteristics.

Solution. $\sigma = $ (13 dynes/cm)(6.85)(10^{-5}) = 8.90(10^{-4}) lb/ft, $\Delta\rho = 63.0 - 45.6 = 17.4$ lb/cu ft, $g_c/g = 1$.   Equation (10.2):

$$d_{FC} = 2.42 \left[\frac{8.90(10^{-4})}{17.4} \right]^{0.5} = 0.0173 \text{ ft}$$

This corresponds to 0.21 in., so that the 1-in. Berl saddles are therefore satisfactory.   The saddles should be ceramic, preferably wet by the continuous aqueous phase.   Table 6.2: $\epsilon = 0.69$, $a_p = 76$.

Flooding. The abscissa of Fig. 10.10 is

$$\frac{\mu_C'}{\Delta\rho}\left(\frac{\sigma'}{\rho_C}\right)^{0.2}\left(\frac{a_p}{\epsilon}\right)^{1.5} = \frac{3.1}{17.4}\left(\frac{13}{63.0}\right)^{0.2}\left(\frac{76}{0.69}\right)^{1.5} = 149.3$$

and the corresponding ordinate is 125. Therefore

$$V_{Cf} = \frac{125 a_p \mu_C'}{[1 + (V_D/V_C)^{0.5}]^2 \rho_C} = \frac{125(76)(3.1)}{[1 + (^{180}\!/_{120})^{0.5}]^2 63.0} = 94.4 \text{ ft/hr}$$

$$V_{Df} = 94.4(^{180}\!/_{120}) = 141.5 \text{ ft/hr}$$

Tower diameter. Set $\phi_D = 0.20$. Equation (10.3), with $V_C = 120V_D/180$:

$$\frac{V_D}{0.69(0.20)} + \frac{120V_D/180}{0.69(1-0.20)} = V_K(1-0.20) \qquad \frac{V_K}{V_D} = 10.56$$

Eq. (10.4): $d_p = 0.92\left[\frac{8.90(10^{-4})}{17.4}\right]^{0.5} 10.56(0.69)(0.20) = 0.00958 \text{ ft}$

Eq. (10.5): $P = \dfrac{(63.0)^2[8.90(10^{-4})(4.18)(10^8)]^3}{4.18(10^8)[3.1(2.42)]^4(17.4)} = 885(10^4)$

and $P^{0.15} = 11.03$. The ordinate of Fig. 10.11 is, with $g/g_c = 1$,

$$\frac{4\Delta\rho\, d_p{}^2 g P^{0.15}}{3\sigma g_c} = \frac{4(17.4)(0.00958)^2(11.03)}{3(8.90)(10^{-4})} = 26.4$$

and therefore the abscissa $= 9$.

$$\frac{\text{Re}}{P^{0.15}} = \frac{d_p V_t \rho_C}{\mu_C P^{0.15}} = \frac{0.00958 V_t(63.0)}{3.1(2.42)(11.03)} = 9$$

$$V_t = 1,240 \text{ ft/hr, terminal drop velocity}$$

The abscissa of Fig. 10.9, with $d_F = \frac{1}{12} = 0.0833$ ft, is 2.6, and the corresponding ordinate is $0.725 = V_K/V_t$, since the exponential term will be negligible. Therefore $V_K = 0.725(1,240) = 900$ ft/hr.

$$V_D = \frac{V_K}{10.56} = \frac{900}{10.56} = 85.1 \text{ ft/hr}$$

This is 60% of the flooding velocity, and will be accepted. The tower cross section is therefore $180/85.1 = 2.11$ sq ft, corresponding to a diameter of 1.6 ft, say 1 ft, 8 in.

Dispersed-phase distributors. Since $d_p = 0.00958$ ft, the distributor nozzles should produce somewhat larger drops. For nozzle diameters of ¼ in., $d_o = 0.25/12 = 0.0208$ ft, and with a hole velocity $V_o' = 0.3$ ft/sec, the abscissa of Fig. 10.13 is 0.0651. The parameter is 0.236, whence d_p at the nozzle is 0.022 ft, which should be satisfactory. The volumetric rate through one hole is

$$(\pi/4)(0.0205)^2(0.3)(3,600) = 0.368 \text{ cu ft/hr}$$

so that $180/0.368 = 490$ holes are required.

Perforated-plate (sieve-plate) towers

These have proven very effective, both with respect to liquid-handling capacity and efficiency of extraction, particularly for systems of low interfacial tension. This is

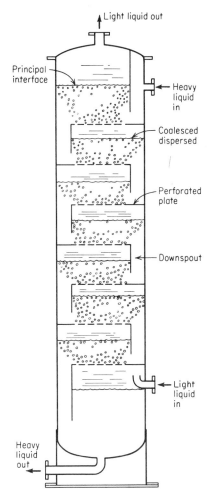

Fig. 10.14   *Perforated-plate extractor, arranged for light liquid dispersed.*

because (1) axial mixing of the continuous phase is confined to the region between trays and does not spread throughout the tower, and (2) the dispersed-phase droplets coalesce and are re-formed at each tray, destroying the tendency to establish concentration gradients within the drops which persist for the entire tower height.   A tower of simple design is shown in Fig. 10.14, where the general arrangement of plates and downspouts is much the same as for gas-liquid contact except that no weir is required. The figure shows the arrangement for light liquid dispersed.   Light liquid passes through the perforations, and the bubbles rise through the heavy continuous phase and coalesce into a layer, which accumulates beneath each plate.   The heavy liquid flows across each plate through the rising droplets and passes through the downspouts to the plate below.   By turning the tower as shown upside down, the downspouts become "upspouts" and carry the light liquid from plate to plate, while the heavy liquid flows through the perforations and is dispersed into drops.   As an alternative, the heavy liquid may be dispersed in one part of the tower and the light liquid in the other, while the principal interface is maintained in the central portion of the tower. Interface taps to remove scum accumulating at the interface may be included between each tray, or special bypasses may be arranged.[15]

Perforation diameters of $\frac{1}{8}$ to $\frac{1}{4}$ in., $\frac{1}{2}$ to $\frac{3}{4}$ in. apart, may be used, and these may either be drilled or better punched (Fig. 10.12) to eliminate wetting of the plate by the dispersed liquid which interferes with drop formation. The best velocity of liquid through the perforations ought to be established by pilot-plant tests, but in the absence of experimental information it is recommended that it be kept within the range 0.4 to 1.0 ft/sec. At lower velocities the diameter of the tower will be unnecessarily large, and all perforations may not operate, while at higher velocities the many fine droplets which form will be likely to be carried from tray to tray through the downspout by the continuous phase. At the recommended velocities the liquid flowing through the perforations will probably "stream," and droplets will not form at the perforations, but rather at the ends of jets which extend from the plate.

The tower will flood if excessive quantities of dispersed-phase droplets are carried through the downspout, entrained in the continuous phase. The velocity of the liquid in the downspouts, V_d, should therefore be lower than the settling velocity of all except the smallest droplets, those smaller than $\frac{1}{32}$ in. diameter, for example.[15] The settling velocity of the drops may be estimated through Fig. 10.11. The plate spacing should be sufficient so that (1) the "streamers" of dispersed liquid from the perforations break up into drops before coalescing into the layer of liquid on the next plate; (2) the linear velocity of the continuous liquid is not greater than that in the downspout, to avoid excessive entrainment; and (3) the tower may be entered through hand- or manholes in the sides for cleaning.

The tower will also flood if the dispersed liquid accumulates to a depth greater than the length of the downspout. The depth of dispersed liquid accumulating on each tray is determined by the pressure drop required for counterflow of the liquids,[5]

$$h = h_C + h_D \tag{10.6}$$

where h is the total thickness of the layer, while h_C and h_D are the contributions from the flow of each liquid. The head required for the dispersed phase h_D is that necessary to overcome interfacial tension effects at the perforations h_σ plus that necessary to cause flow through the orifices h_0,

$$h_D = h_\sigma + h_0 \tag{10.7}$$

The value of h_0 may be computed from the usual orifice equation with a coefficient of 0.67,

$$h_0 = \frac{(V_0^2 - V_n^2)\rho_D}{2g_C(0.67)^2 \Delta\rho} \tag{10.8}$$

where V_n is based on A_n, the net tower cross section, $A_t - A_d$. h_σ, which is important only when the dispersed phase flows slowly, may be computed from

$$h_\sigma = \frac{6\sigma}{d_{p,0.1} \Delta\rho} \tag{10.9}$$

where $d_{p,0.1}$ is the drop diameter produced at perforation velocities $V_0' = 0.1$ ft/sec. At perforation velocities where jets of dispersed liquid issue from the perforations, h_σ may be omitted, and $h_D = h_0$.

The head required for flow of the continuous phase h_C includes losses owing to (1) friction in the downspout, which is ordinarily negligible, (2) contraction and expansion upon entering and leaving the downspout, equal to 0.5 and 1.0 "velocity heads," respectively, and (3) the two abrupt changes in direction each equivalent to 1.47 velocity heads. The value of h_C is therefore substantially 4.5 velocity heads, or

$$h_C = \frac{4.5 V_d^2 \rho_C}{2 g_c \, \Delta \rho} \tag{10.10}$$

Illustration 10.2. Design a perforated tray tower for the extraction of illustration 10.1 with ether as the dispersed phase.

Solution. The perforations will be made $3/16$ in. diameter. $d_o = 3/16(12) = 0.01561$ ft, and the area of each perforation $= \pi(0.01561)^2/4 = 0.000191$ sq ft.   A perforation velocity $V_o' = 1.0$ ft/sec will be used, and $V_o = 3,600$ ft/hr.

For 180 cu ft ether/hr, $180/3,600(0.000191) = 262$ perforations per plate.   If placed on the corners of $3/4$-in. equilateral triangles, 0.89 sq ft of the tower cross section must be devoted to perforations.

The velocity of the aqueous phase in the downspout will be set at the settling velocity of ether droplets $1/32$ in. diameter, $d_p = 1/32(12) = 0.0026$ ft. $P^{0.15} = 11.03$, as in Illustration 10.1.   The ordinate of Fig. 10.11 becomes $4(17.4)(0.0026^2)(11.03)/3(8.90)(10^{-4}) = 1.95$, and the abscissa is therefore 0.8.   Therefore,

$$\frac{\text{Re}}{P^{0.15}} = \frac{0.0026 V_t (63.0)}{3.1(2.42)(11.03)} = 0.8$$

$$V_t = 405 \text{ ft/hr}$$

and V_d will be set at this value.

For 120 cu ft/hr of aqueous liquid, the downspout cross section is therefore $A_d = 120/405 = 0.296$ sq ft.   The tower cross section devoted to downspouts and perforations $= 2(0.296) + 0.89 = 1.482$ sq ft.   Keeping the perforations at least 1 in. from the walls of the tower to allow for a ring support for the plate, and 1 in. from the downspouts brings the total tower cross section to $A_t = 1.71$ sq ft, corresponding to a diameter 1.475 or 1.5 ft.   For a tower arranged as in Fig. 10.14, the segmental downspouts are formed of chords 15 in. long, set at 5 in. from the tower center.   The distance between trays will be set at 12 in., and the downspouts will extend 6 in. below each plate.

The net area $A_n = A_t - A_d = 1.5 - 0.296 = 1.204$ sq ft, and the dispersed-phase velocity based on this is $V_n = 180/1.204 = 149.5$ ft/hr.
Eq. (10.8):

$$h_o = \frac{[(3,600)^2 - (149.5)^2]45.6}{2(4.18)(10^8)(0.67)^2(17.4)} = 0.0905 \text{ ft}$$

At this perforation velocity, h_σ may be omitted, and $h_D = 0.0905$ ft.
Eq. (10.10):

$$h_C = \frac{4.5(405)^2(63.0)}{2(4.18)(10^8)(17.4)} = 0.00321 \text{ ft}$$

Eq. (10.6): $h = 0.00312 + 0.0905 = 0.0936$ ft

This corresponds to 1.12 in., and the tower will therefore not flood.

Agitated countercurrent extractors

The extraction towers previously described are very similar to towers used for gas-liquid contact, where density differences between liquid and gas are of the order of 50 lb/cu ft or more, available to provide the energy for adequate dispersion of one fluid in the other.   In liquid extraction, where density differences are likely to be one-tenth as large or less, good dispersion of systems with high interfacial tension is impossible in such towers, and mass-transfer rates are poor.   For such systems, dispersion is best brought about by mechanical agitation of the liquids, whereupon good mass-transfer rates are developed.   Some examples of such extractors follow.   Except for pulse columns, they are proprietary devices for which complete design procedures have not been made publicly available, and the manufacturers are best consulted. Some of their characteristics have been reviewed.[27]

The *Mixco Lightnin CMContactor (Oldshue-Rushton extractor)*[3,16] of Fig. 10.15 uses flat-blade turbine impellers to disperse and mix the liquids and depends upon the horizontal compartmenting plates to reduce vertical axial mixing.

The *Rotating-disk Contactor (RDC)*[20,26] (Fig. 10.16) is somewhat similar, except that the vertical baffles are omitted and the agitation is brought about by rotating flat disks, which usually turn at higher speeds than turbine-type impellers.

The *Scheibel-York* extractor[24] is shown only in a short section in Fig. 10.17.   The paddle-type impellers are surrounded by a shroud baffle.   For systems of low interfacial tension, the agitation sections may be alternated with sections filled with woven

Baffle

Light liquid ou.

Heavy liquid in

Perforated distributor

Impeller

Compartment baffle

Light liquid in

Heavy liquid out

Fig. 10.15   *Mixco Lightnin CMContactor (Mixing Equipment Co.).*

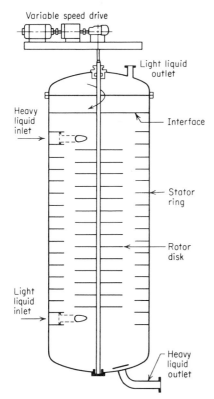

Variable speed drive

Light liquid
outlet

Heavy
liquid
inlet

Interface

Stator
ring

Rotor
disk

Light
liquid
inlet

Heavy
liquid
outlet

Fig. 10.16 *Rotating-disk Contactor (RDC) (General American Transportation Corp.).*

Rotating shaft

Turbine impeller

Horizontal
stationary
baffle

Wire mesh

Tie rod

Fig. 10.17 *Scheibel-York extractor (York Process Equipment Co.).*

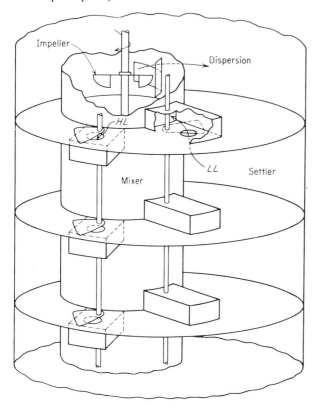

Fig. 10.18 *Treybal extractor (schematic). Recycle provisions not shown. LL = light liquid, HL = heavy liquid. (U.S. Stoneware, Inc.)*

wire mesh, as shown.   For systems of high interfacial tension the wire-mesh sections are omitted.

The *Treybal* extractor[29] (Fig. 10.18) is in reality a vertically arranged mixer-settler cascade, thus essentially eliminating axial mixing.   The mixing compartments, vertically in line, are surrounded by the settlers for each stage.   Baffles within the mixers assist the turbine impellers to pump the liquids, and provision is available for interface-level control and intrastage recycling of liquids between settler and mixer of the same stage (see page 412).

In *pulsed extractors*,[14,32] a rapid (30 to 250/min) reciprocating motion of short amplitude ($\frac{1}{4}$ to 1 in.) is hydraulically transmitted to the liquid contents.   Since no moving parts are present within the extractors, they have found particular use in handling radioactive solutions in atomic-energy work, where they can be put behind heavy radiation shields without the necessity for maintenance.   The most common arrangement is that of Fig. 10.19; the perforated plates, which have no downspouts, are drilled with very small holes so that ordinarily flow of liquid will not occur.   The pulsing superimposed upon the liquids alternately forces light and heavy liquids through the perforations.   Packed columns may also be pulsed,[7] as indeed may any type of extractor.   Although the mass-transfer rates are thereby improved, the flow capacities become lower.

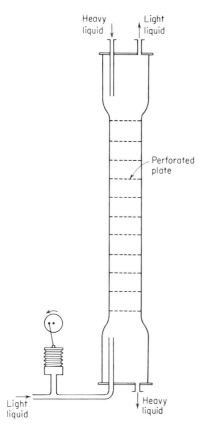

Heavy
liquid

Light
liquid

Perforated
plate

Light
liquid

Heavy
liquid

Fig. 10.19   *Pulse column.*

Centrifugal extractors

The most important of these is the Podbielniak extractor[2,10] (Fig. 10.20).   The cylindrical drum contains perforated, concentric shells, and is rapidly rotated on the horizontal shaft (2,000 to 5,000 rpm).   Liquids enter through the shaft: heavy liquid is led to the center of the drum, light liquid to the periphery.   The heavy liquid flows radially outward, displacing the light liquid inwardly, and both are led out through the shaft.   These extractors are especially useful for liquids of very small density difference and where very short residence times are essential, as in some pharmaceutical applications.

LIQUID EQUILIBRIA

Extraction involves the use of systems composed of at least three substances, and in most cases all three components appear in both insoluble phases.   The following notation scheme will be used to describe the concentrations and amounts of these ternary mixtures, for purposes of discussing both equilibria and material balances.

Fig. 10.20   *Podbielniak centrifugal extractor (schematic).*   (*Podbielniak, Inc.*)

Notation scheme

1. *A* and *B* are pure, substantially insoluble liquids, and *C* is the distributed solute.   Mixtures to be separated by extraction are composed of *A* and *C*, and *B* is the extracting solvent.

2. The same letter will be used to indicate the quantity of a solution or mixture and the location of the mixture on a phase diagram.   Quantities are measured in pounds for batch operations, lb/hr for continuous operation.   Thus,

E = lb/hr of solution E, an extract, shown on a phase diagram by point E
R = lb/hr of solution R, a raffinate, shown on a phase diagram by point R
B = lb/hr of solvent B

Solvent-free (*B*-free) quantities are indicated by primed letters.   Thus,

E' = lb *B*-free solution/hr, shown on a phase diagram by point E
$E = E'(1 + N_E)$

3. x = weight fraction C in the solvent-lean (*A*-rich), or raffinate, liquids
y = weight fraction C in the solvent-rich (*B*-rich), or extract, liquids
$x' = x/(1 - x)$ = lb C/lb non-*C* in the raffinate liquids
$y' = y/(1 - y)$ = lb C/lb non-*C* in the extract liquids
X = weight fraction C in the raffinate liquids on a *B*-free basis, lb C/(lb A + lb C)
Y = weight fraction C in the extract liquids on a *B*-free basis, lb C/(lb A + lb C)
N = weight fraction B on a *B*-free basis, lb B/(lb A + lb C)

Subscripts identify the solution or mixture to which the concentration terms refer. Stages are identified by number.   Thus, $x_3 =$ wt fraction C in the raffinate from stage 3, $Y_3 =$ wt fraction C (B-free basis) in the extract from stage 3, etc.   For other solutions identified by a letter on a phase diagram, the same letter is used as an identifying subscript.   Thus, $x_M =$ wt fraction C in the mixture M.

An asterisk specifically identifies equilibrium concentrations where the condition of equilibrium is emphasized.   Thus, $y_E^* =$ wt fraction C in the equilibrium solution E.

4. Throughout the discussion of equilibria, material balances, and stagewise calculations, mole fractions, mole ratios, and pound moles may be consistently substituted for weight fractions, weight ratios, and pounds, respectively.

Equilateral-triangular coordinates

These are used extensively in the chemical literature to describe graphically the concentrations in ternary systems.   It is the property of an equilateral triangle that the sum of the perpendicular distances from any point within the triangle to the three sides equals the altitude of the triangle.   We may therefore let the altitude represent 100 percent composition and the distances to the three sides the percents or fractions of the three components.   Refer to Fig. 10.21.   Each apex of the triangle represents one of the pure components, as marked.   The perpendicular distance from any point such as K to the base AB represents the percentage of C in the mixture at K, the distance to the base AC the percentage of B, and that to the base CB the percentage of A.   Thus $x_K = 0.4$.   Any point on a side of the triangle represents a binary mixture.   Point D, for example, is a binary containing 80% A, 20% B.   All points on the line DC represent mixtures containing the same ratio of A to B and may be considered as mixtures originally at D to which C has been added.   If R lb of a mixture at point R is added to E lb of a mixture at E, the new mixture is shown on the straight line RE at point M, such that

$$\frac{R}{E} = \frac{\text{line } ME}{\text{line } RM} = \frac{x_E - x_M}{x_M - x_R} \tag{10.11}$$

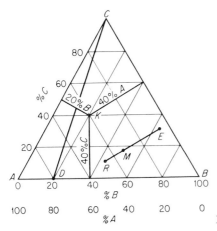

Fig. 10.21   *Equilateral-triangular coordinates.*

Alternatively the composition corresponding to point M can be computed by material balances, as will be shown later. Similarly, if a mixture at M has removed from it a mixture of composition E, the new mixture is on the straight line EM extended in the direction away from E, and located at R so that Eq. (10.11) applies.

Equation (10.11) is readily established. Refer to Fig. 10.22, which again shows R lb of mixture at R added to E lb of mixture at E. Let M represent the pounds of new mixture as well as the composition on the figure. Line $RL =$ wt fraction C in $R = x_R$, line $MO =$ wt fraction C in $M = x_M$, and line $ET =$ wt fraction C in $E = x_E$. A total material balance,

$$R + E = M$$

A balance for component C,

$$R(\text{line } RL) + E(\text{line } ET) = M(\text{line } MO)$$
$$Rx_R + Ex_E = Mx_M$$

Eliminating M,

$$\frac{R}{E} = \frac{\text{line } ET - \text{line } MO}{\text{line } MO - \text{line } RL} = \frac{x_E - x_M}{x_M - x_R}$$

But line $ET -$ line $MO =$ line EP, and line $MO -$ line $RL =$ line $MK =$ line PS. Therefore

$$\frac{R}{E} = \frac{\text{line } EP}{\text{line } PS} = \frac{\text{line } ME}{\text{line } RM}$$

The following discussion is limited to those types of systems which most frequently occur in liquid-extraction operations. For a complete consideration of the very many types of systems which may be encountered, the student is referred to one of the more comprehensive texts on the phase rule.[21]

Systems of three liquids—one pair partially soluble

This is the most commonly encountered type of system in extraction, and typical examples are water (A)–chloroform (B)–acetone (C), and benzene (A)–water (B)–acetic acid (C). The triangular coordinates are used as *isotherms*, or diagrams at constant temperature. Refer to Fig. 10.23a. Liquid C dissolves completely in A and B, but A and B dissolve only to a limited extent in each other to give rise to the saturated liquid solutions at L (A-rich) and at K (B-rich). The more insoluble the liquids A

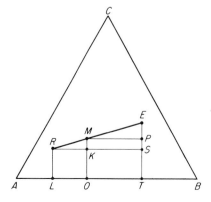

Fig. 10.22 *The mixture rule.*

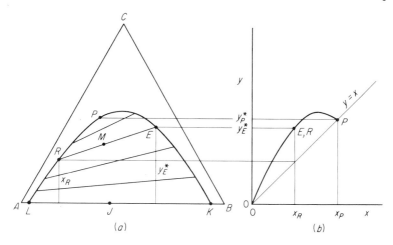

Fig. 10.23   *System of three liquids, A and B partially miscible.*

and B, the nearer the apexes of the triangle will points L and K be located.   A binary mixture J, anywhere between L and K, will separate into two insoluble liquid phases of compositions at L and K, the relative amounts of the phases depending upon the position of J, according to the principle of Eq. (10.11).

Curve $LRPEK$ is the binodal solubility curve, indicating the change in solubility of the A- and B-rich phases upon addition of C.   Any mixture outside this curve will be a homogeneous solution of one liquid phase.   Any ternary mixture underneath the curve, such as M, will form two insoluble, saturated liquid phases of equilibrium compositions indicated by R (A-rich) and E (B-rich).   The line RE joining these equilibrium compositions is a tie line, which must necessarily pass through point M representing the mixture as a whole.   There are an infinite number of tie lines in the two-phase region, and only a few are shown.   They are rarely parallel and usually change their slope slowly in one direction as shown.   In a relatively few systems the direction of the tie-line slope changes, and one tie line will be horizontal.   Such systems are said to be "solutropic."   Point P, the *plait point*, the last of the tie lines and the point where the A-rich and B-rich solubility curves merge, is ordinarily not at the maximum value of C on the solubility curve.

The percentage of C in solution E is clearly greater than that in R, and it is said that in this case the distribution of C favors the B-rich phase.   This is conveniently shown on the distribution diagram (Fig. 10.23b), where the point (E,R) lies above·the diagonal $y = x$.   The ratio y^*/x, the *distribution coefficient*, is in this case greater than unity.   The concentrations of C at the ends of the tie lines, when plotted against each other, give rise to the distribution curve shown.   Should the tie lines on Fig. 10.23a slope in the opposite direction, with C favoring A at equilibrium, the distribution curve will lie below the diagonal.   The distribution curve may be used for interpolating between tie lines when only a few have been experimentally determined.   Other methods of interpolation are also available.[27]

Effect of temperature. To show the effect of temperature in detail requires a three-dimensional figure, as in Fig. 10.24a. In this diagram, temperature is plotted vertically, and the isothermal triangles are seen to be sections through the prism. For most systems of this type, the mutual solubility of A and B increases with increasing temperature, and above some temperature t_4, the critical solution temperature, they dissolve completely. The increased solubility at higher temperatures influences the ternary equilibria considerably, and this is best shown by projection of the isotherms onto the base triangle as in Fig. 10.24b. Not only does the area of heterogeneity decrease at higher temperatures, but the slopes of the tie lines may also change. Liquid-extraction operations, which depend upon the formation of insoluble liquid phases, must be carried on at temperatures below t_4. Other temperature effects, which are less common, are also known.[21,27]

Effect of pressure. Except at very high pressures, the influence of pressure on the liquid equilibrium is so small that it may generally be ignored. All the diagrams shown are therefore to be considered as having been plotted at sufficiently high pressure to maintain a completely condensed system, i.e., above the vapor pressures of the solutions. However, should the pressure be sufficiently reduced so that it becomes less than the vapor pressure of the solutions, a vapor phase will appear, and the liquid equilibrium will be interrupted. Such an effect on a binary solubility curve of the type APB of Fig. 10.24a is shown in Fig. 9.8.

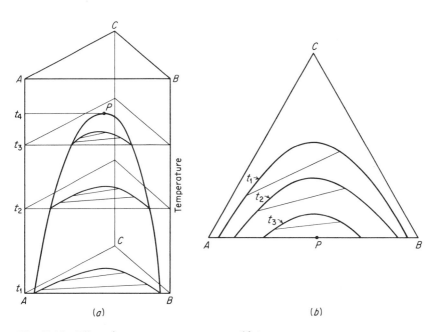

Fig. 10.24 *Effect of temperature on ternary equilibria.*

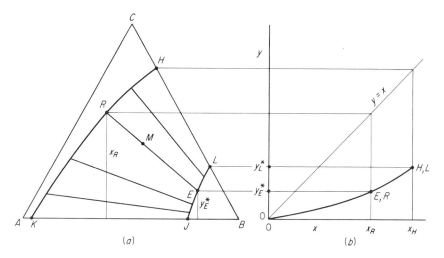

Fig. 10.25 *System of three liquids, A-B and B-C partially miscible.*

Systems of three liquids—two pairs partially soluble

This type is exemplified by the system chlorobenzene (A)–water (B)–methyl ethyl ketone (C), where A and C are completely soluble, while the pairs A-B and B-C show only limited solubility.   Refer to Fig. 10.25a, a typical isotherm.   At the prevailing temperature, points K and J represent the mutual solubilities of A and B and points H and L those of B and C.   Curves KRH (A-rich) and JEL (B-rich) are the ternary solubility curves, and mixtures outside the band between these curves form homogeneous single-phase liquid solutions.   Mixtures such as M, inside the heterogeneous area, form two liquid phases at equilibrium at E and R, joined on the diagram by a tie line.   The corresponding distribution curve is shown in Fig. 10.25b.

Effect of temperature. Increased temperature usually increases the mutual solubilities and at the same time influences the slope of the tie lines.   Figure 10.26 is typical of the effect that may be expected.   Above the critical solution temperature of the binary B-C at t_3, the system is similar to the first type discussed.   Other temperature effects are also possible.[21,27]

Systems of two partially soluble liquids and one solid

When the solid does not form compounds such as hydrates with the liquids, the system will frequently have the characteristics of the isotherm of Fig. 10.27, an example of which is the system naphthalene (C)–aniline (A)–isooctane (B).   Solid C dissolves in liquid A to form a saturated solution at K and in liquid B to give the saturated solution at L. A and B are soluble only to the extent shown at H and J.   Mixtures in the regions $AKDH$ and $BLGJ$ are homogeneous liquid solutions.   The curves KD and

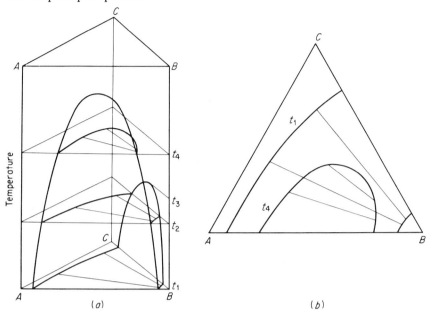

Fig. 10.26   *Effect of temperature on ternary liquid equilibria.*

GL show the effect of adding A and B upon the solubilities of the solid.   In the region $HDGJ$ two liquid phases form: if C is added to the insoluble liquids H and J to give a mixture M, the equilibrium liquid phases will be R and E, joined by a tie line.   All mixtures in the region CDG consist of three phases, solid C, and saturated liquid solutions at D and G.   Liquid-extraction operations are usually confined to the region of the two liquid phases, which is that corresponding to the distribution curve shown.

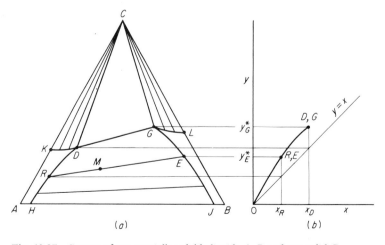

Fig. 10.27   *System of two partially soluble liquids A, B and one solid C.*

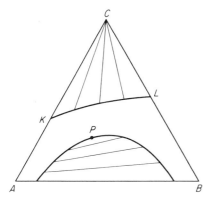

Fig. 10.28 *System of two partially soluble liquids A, B and one solid C.*

Increased temperature frequently changes these systems to the configuration shown in Fig. 10.28.

Other coordinates

Because the equilibrium relationship can rarely be expressed algebraically with any convenience, extraction computations must usually be made graphically on a phase diagram.   The coordinate scales of equilateral triangles are necessarily always the same, and in order to be able to expand one concentration scale relative to the other, rectangular coordinates may be used.   One of these is formed by plotting concentrations of B as abscissa against concentrations of C (x and y) as ordinate, as in Fig. 10.29a.   Unequal scales may be used in order to expand the plot as desired.   Equation (10.11) applies for mixtures on Fig. 10.29a, regardless of any inequality of the scales.

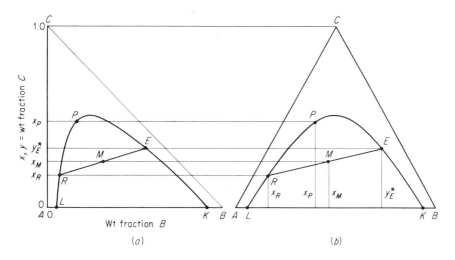

Fig. 10.29 *Rectangular coordinates.*

Another rectangular coordinate system involves plotting as abscissa the weight fraction C on a B-free basis, X and Y in the A- and B-rich phases, respectively, against N, the B-concentration on a B-free basis, as ordinate, as shown in the upper part of Fig. 10.30. This has been plotted for a system of two partly miscible pairs, such as that of Fig. 10.25.

The similarity of such diagrams to the enthalpy-concentration diagrams of Chap. 9 is clear. In extraction, the two phases are produced by addition of solvent, in distillation by addition of heat, and solvent becomes the analog of heat. This is emphasized by the ordinate of the upper part of Fig. 10.30. Tie lines such as QS can be projected to X, Y coordinates, as shown in the lower figure, to produce a solvent-free distribution graph similar to those of distillation. The mixture rule on these coordinates (see the upper part of Fig. 10.30) is

$$\frac{M'}{N'} = \frac{Y_N - Y_P}{Y_P - Y_M} = \frac{X_N - X_P}{X_P - X_M} = \frac{\text{line } NP}{\text{line } PM} \qquad (10.12)$$

where M' and N' are the B-free weights of these mixtures.

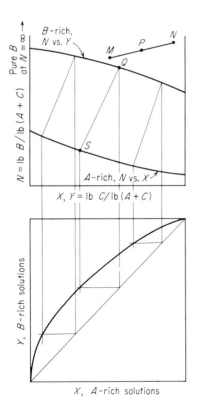

Fig. 10.30 *Rectangular coordinates, solvent-free basis, for a system of two partly miscible liquid pairs.*

Multicomponent systems

The simplest system of four components occurs when two solutes distribute between two solvents, e.g., the distribution of formic and acetic acids between the partly soluble solvents water and carbon tetrachloride.   Complete display of such equilibria requires a three-dimensional graph[27] which is difficult to work with, but frequently we can simplify this to the distribution (*xy*) curves, one for each solute, such as that for a single solute in Fig. 10.23*b*.   More than four components cannot be conveniently dealt with graphically.

Choice of solvent

There is usually a wide choice among liquids to be used as solvents for extraction operations.   It is unlikely that any particular liquid will exhibit all the properties considered desirable for extraction, and some compromise is usually necessary.   The following are the quantities to be given consideration in making a choice:

1. *Selectivity.*   The effectiveness of solvent *B* for separating a solution of *A* and *C* into its components is measured by comparing the ratio of *C* to *A* in the *B*-rich phase to that in the *A*-rich phase at equilibrium.   The ratio of the ratios, the separation factor, or selectivity, β, is analogous to the relative volatility of distillation.   If *E* and *R* are the equilibrium phases,

$$\beta = \frac{(\text{wt fraction } C \text{ in } E)/(\text{wt fraction } A \text{ in } E)}{(\text{wt fraction } C \text{ in } R)/(\text{wt fraction } A \text{ in } R)}$$

$$= \frac{y_E^*(\text{wt fraction } A \text{ in } R)}{x_R(\text{wt fraction } A \text{ in } E)} \tag{10.13}$$

For all useful extraction operations the selectivity must exceed unity, the more so the better.   If the selectivity is unity, no separation is possible.

Selectivity usually varies considerably with solute concentration, and in systems of the type shown in Fig. 10.23 it will be unity at the plait point.   In some systems it passes from large values through unity to fractional values, and these are analogous to azeotropic systems of distillation.

2. *Distribution coefficient.*   This is the ratio y^*/x at equilibrium.   While it is not necessary that the distribution coefficient be larger than 1, large values are very desirable since less solvent will then be required for the extraction.

3. *Insolubility of solvent.*   Refer to Fig. 10.31.   For both systems shown, only those *A-C* mixtures between *D* and *A* can be separated by use of the solvents *B* or *B'*, since mixtures richer in *C* will not form two liquid phases with the solvents.   Clearly the solvent in Fig. 10.31*a*, which is the more insoluble of the two, will be the more useful.   In systems of the type shown in Figs. 10.25*a* and 10.27*a*, if the solubility of *C* in *B* is small (point *L* near the *B* apex), the *capacity* of solvent *B* to extract *C* is small, and large amounts of solvent are then required.

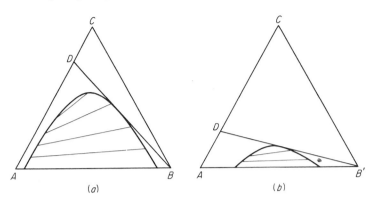

Fig. 10.31 *Influence of solvent solubility on extraction.*

4. *Recoverability.* It is always necessary to recover the solvent for reuse, and this must ordinarily be done by another of the mass-transfer operations, most frequently distillation. If distillation is to be used, the solvent should form no azeotrope with the extracted solute, and mixtures should show high relative volatility for low-cost recovery. That substance in the extract, either solvent or solute, which is present as the lesser quantity should be the more volatile in order to reduce heat costs. If the solvent must be volatilized, its latent heat of vaporization should be small.

5. *Density.* A difference in densities of the saturated liquid phases is necessary, both for stagewise and continuous-contact equipment operation. The larger this difference the better. In systems of the type shown in Fig. 10.23, the density difference for equilibrium phases will become less as C concentrations increase and will be zero at the plait point. It may reverse in sign before reaching the plait point, in which case continuous-contact equipment cannot be specified to operate at the concentrations at which the density difference passes through zero.

6. *Interfacial tension.* The larger the interfacial tension, the more readily will coalescence of emulsions occur, but the more difficult will the dispersion of one liquid in the other be. Coalescence is usually of greater importance, and interfacial tension should therefore be high. Interfacial tension between equilibrium phases in systems of the type shown in Fig. 10.23 falls to zero at the plait point.

7. *Chemical reactivity.* The solvent should be stable chemically and inert toward the other components of the system and toward the common materials of construction.

8. *Viscosity, vapor pressure, and freezing point.* These should be low for ease in handling and storage.

9. The solvent should be *nontoxic, nonflammable,* and of *low cost.*

STAGEWISE CONTACT

Extraction in equipment of the stage type may be carried on according to a variety of flow sheets, depending upon the nature of the system and the extent of separation desired.   In the discussion which follows it is to be understood that each stage is a *theoretical* or *ideal* stage, such that the effluent extract and raffinate solutions are in equilibrium with each other.   Each stage must include facilities for contacting the insoluble liquids and separating the product streams.   A combination of a mixer and a settler may therefore constitute a stage, and in multistage operation these may be arranged in cascades as desired.   In the case of countercurrent multistage operation, it is also possible to use towers of the multistage type, as described earlier.

Single-stage extraction

This may be a batch or a continuous operation.   Refer to Fig. 10.32.   The flow sheet shows the extraction stage.   Feed F lb (if batch) or F lb/hr (if continuous) contains substances A and C at x_F weight fraction C.   This is contacted with S_1 lb (or lb/hr) of a solvent, principally B, containing y_S weight fraction C, to give the equilibrium extract E_1 and raffinate R_1, each measured in pounds or pounds per hour.   Solvent recovery then involves separate removal of solvent B from each product·stream (not shown).

The operation may be followed in either of the phase diagrams as shown.   If the solvent is pure B ($y_S = 0$), it will be plotted at the B apex, but sometimes it has been recovered from a previous extraction and therefore contains a little A and C as well, as shown by the location of S.   Adding S to F produces in the extraction stage a mixture M_1 which, on settling, forms the equilibrium phases E_1 and R_1 joined by the tie

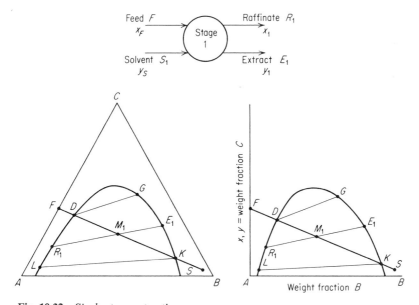

Fig. 10.32   *Single-stage extraction.*

line through M_1. A total material balance is

$$F + S_1 = M_1 = E_1 + R_1 \tag{10.14}$$

and point M_1 may be located on line FS by the mixture rule, Eq. (10.11), but it is usually more satisfactory to locate M_1 by computing its C concentration. Thus, a C balance provides

$$Fx_F + S_1 y_S = M_1 x_{M1} \tag{10.15}$$

from which x_{M1} may be computed. Alternatively, the amount of solvent to provide a given location for M_1 on the line FS may be computed:

$$\frac{S_1}{F} = \frac{x_F - x_{M1}}{x_{M1} - y_S} \tag{10.16}$$

The quantities of extract and raffinate may be computed by the mixture rule, Eq. (10.11), or by the material balance for C:

$$E_1 y_1 + R_1 x_1 = M_1 x_{M1} \tag{10.17}$$

$$E_1 = \frac{M_1(x_{M1} - x_1)}{y_1 - x_1} \tag{10.18}$$

and R_1 can be determined through Eq. (10.14).

Since two insoluble phases must form for an extraction operation, point M_1 must lie within the heterogeneous liquid area, as shown. The minimum amount of solvent is thus found by locating M_1 at D, which would then provide an infinitesimal amount of extract at G, and the maximum amount of solvent is found by locating M_1 at K, which provides an infinitesimal amount of raffinate at L. Point L represents also the raffinate with the lowest possible C concentration, and if a lower value were required, the recovered solvent S would have to have a lower C concentration.

Computations for systems of two insoluble liquid pairs, or with a distributed solute which is a solid, are made in exactly the same manner, and Eqs. (10.14) to (10.18) all apply.

All the computations may also be made on a solvent-free basis, as in the upper part of Fig. 10.33, if the nature of this diagram makes it convenient. If solvent S is pure B, its N value is infinite, and the line FS is then vertical. Products E_1 and R_1 lie on a tie line through M_1 representing the entire mixture in the extractor. Material balances for use with this diagram must be made on a B-free basis. Thus,

$$F' + S' = M_1' = E_1' + R_1' \tag{10.19}$$

where the primes indicate B-free weight (the feed is normally B-free, and $F = F'$). A balance for C is

$$F'X_F + S'Y_S = M_1' X_{M1} = E_1' Y_1 + R_1' X_1 \tag{10.20}$$

and for B,

$$F'N_F + S'N_S = M_1' N_{M1} = E_1' N_{E1} + R_1' N_{R1} \tag{10.21}$$

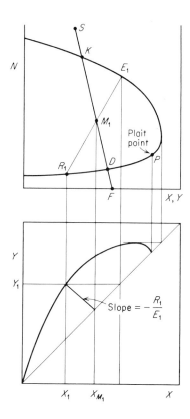

Fig. 10.33 *Single-stage extraction, solvent-free coordinates.*

(ordinarily, $N_F = 0$ since the feed contains no B). The coordinates of M'_1 may be computed, point M_1 located on line FS, the tie line located, and the B-free weights, E'_1 and R'_1, computed:

$$E'_1 = \frac{M'_1(X_{M1} - X_1)}{Y_1 - X_1} \tag{10.22}$$

and R'_1 is obtained through Eq. (10.19). The total weights of the saturated extract and raffinate are then

$$E_1 = E'_1(1 + N_{E1}) \qquad R_1 = R'_1(1 + N_{R1}) \tag{10.23}$$

If the solvent is pure B, whence $N_S = \infty$, these equations still apply, with the simplification that $S' = 0$, $Y_S = 0$, $S'N_S = B$, and $F' = M'_1$. Minimum and maximum amounts of solvent correspond to putting M_1 at D and K on the figure, as before.

Equations (10.19) and (10.20) lead to

$$\frac{R'_1}{E'_1} = \frac{Y_1 - X_{M1}}{X_{M1} - X_1} \tag{10.24}$$

When the equilibrium extract and raffinate are located on the lower diagram of Fig. 10.33, Eq. (10.24) is seen to be that of the operating line shown, of slope $-R'_1/E'_1$.

The single stage is seen to be analogous to the flash vaporization of distillation, with solvent replacing heat. If pure B is used as solvent, the operating line on the lower figure passes through the 45° line at X_F, which completes the analogy (see Fig. 9.14).

Multistage crosscurrent extraction

This is an extension of single-stage extraction, wherein the raffinate is successively contacted with fresh solvent, and may be done continuously or in batch. Refer to Fig. 10.34, which shows the flow sheet for a three-stage extraction. A single final raffinate results, and the extracts may be combined to provide the composited extract, as shown. As many stages may be used as desired.

Computations are shown on triangular and on solvent-free coordinates. All the material balances for a single stage of course now apply to the first stage. Subsequent stages are dealt with in the same manner, except of course that the "feed" to any stage is the raffinate from the preceding stage. Thus, for any stage n,

Total balance:
$$R_{n-1} + S_n = M_n = E_n + R_n \tag{10.25}$$

C balance:
$$R_{n-1}x_{n-1} + S_n y_S = M_n x_{Mn} = E_n y_n + R_n x_n \tag{10.26}$$

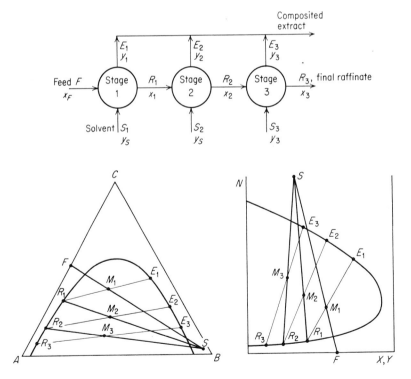

Fig. 10.34 *Crosscurrent extraction.*

For the solvent-free coordinates,

$A + C$ balance:
$$R'_{n-1} + S'_n = M'_n = E'_n + R'_n \tag{10.27}$$

C balance:
$$R'_{n-1}X_{n-1} + S'_nY_S = M'_nX_{Mn} = E'_nY_n + R'_nX_n \tag{10.28}$$

B balance:
$$R'_{n-1}N_{R,n-1} + S'_nN_S = M'_nN_{Mn} = E'_nN_{En} + R'_nN_{Rn} \tag{10.29}$$

from which the quantities can be calculated for either type of graph.

Unequal amounts of solvent may be used in the various stages, and even different temperatures, in which case each stage must be computed with the help of a phase diagram at the appropriate temperature. For a given final raffinate concentration, less total solvent will be used the greater the number of stages.

Illustration 10.3. One hundred pounds of a solution of acetic acid (C) and water (A) containing 30% acid is to be extracted three times with isopropyl ether (B) at 20°C, using 40 lb of solvent in each stage. Determine the quantities and compositions of the various streams. How much solvent would be required if the same final raffinate concentration were to be obtained with one stage?

Solution. The equilibrium data at 20°C are listed below [*Trans. AIChE*, **36**, 628 (1940), with permission]. The horizontal rows give the concentrations in equilibrium solutions. The system is of the type shown in Fig. 10.29, except that the tie lines slope downward toward the B apex. The rectangular coordinates of Fig. 10.29a will be used, but only for acid concentrations up to $x = 0.30$. These are plotted in Fig. 10.35.

	Water layer			Isopropyl ether layer	
Wt % acetic acid $100x$	Water	Isopropyl ether	Acetic acid $100y^*$	Water	Isopropyl ether
0.69	98.1	1.2	0.18	0.5	99.3
1.41	97.1	1.5	0.37	0.7	98.9
2.89	95.5	1.6	0.79	0.8	98.4
6.42	91.7	1.9	1.93	1.0	97.1
13.30	84.4	2.3	4.82	1.9	93.3
25.50	71.1	3.4	11.40	3.9	84.7
36.70	58.9	4.4	21.60	6.9	71.5
44.30	45.1	10.6	31.10	10.8	58.1
46.40	37.1	16.5	36.20	15.1	48.7

Stage 1. $F = 100$ lb, $x_F = 0.30$, $y_S = 0$, $S_1 = B_1 = 40$ lb.

Eq. (10.14):
$$M_1 = 100 + 40 = 140 \text{ lb}$$

Eq. (10.15):
$$100(0.30) + 40(0) = 140x_{M1} \qquad x_{M1} = 0.214$$

Point M_1 is located on line FB. With the help of a distribution curve, the tie line passing through M_1 is located as shown, and $x_1 = 0.258$, $y_1 = 0.117$ wt fraction acetic acid.

Eq. (10.18):
$$E_1 = \frac{140(0.214 - 0.258)}{0.117 - 0.258} = 43.6 \text{ lb}$$

Eq. (10.14):
$$R_1 = 140 - 43.6 = 96.4 \text{ lb}$$

Stage 2. $S_2 = B_2 = 40$ lb.

Eq. (10.25):
$$M_2 = R_1 + B_2 = 96.4 + 40 = 136.4 \text{ lb}$$

Eq. (10.26):
$$96.4(0.258) + 40(0) = 136.4x_{M2} \qquad x_{M2} = 0.1822$$

Point M_2 is located on line R_1B and the tie line R_2E_2 through M_2. $x_2 = 0.227$, $y_2 = 0.095$.   Eq. (10.18) becomes

$$E_2 = \frac{M_2(x_{M2} - x_2)}{y_2 - x_2} = \frac{136.4(0.1822 - 0.227)}{0.095 - 0.227} = 46.3 \text{ lb}$$

Eq. (10.25):
$$R_2 = M_2 - E_2 = 136.4 - 46.3 = 90.1 \text{ lb}$$

Stage 3. In a similar manner, $B_3 = 40$, $M_3 = 130.1$, $x_{M3} = 0.1572$, $x_3 = 0.20$, $y_3 = 0.078$, $E_3 = 45.7$, and $R_3 = 84.4$.   The acid content of the final raffinate is $0.20(84.4) = 16.88$ lb.
The composited extract is $E_1 + E_2 + E_3 = 43.6 + 46.3 + 45.7 = 135.6$ lb, and its acid content $= E_1y_1 + E_2y_2 + E_3y_3 = 13.12$ lb.
If an extraction to give the same final raffinate concentration, $x = 0.20$, were to be done in one stage, the point M would be at the intersection of tie line R_3E_3 and line BF of Fig. 10.35, or at $x_M = 0.12$.   The solvent required would then be, by Eq. (10.16), $S_1 = 100(0.30 - 0.12)/(0.12 - 0) = 150$ lb, instead of the total of 120 required in the three-stage extraction.

Insoluble liquids. When the extraction solvent and feed solution are insoluble and remain so at all concentrations of the distributed solute which are encountered in the operation, the computations may be simplified.   For this purpose, the equilibrium

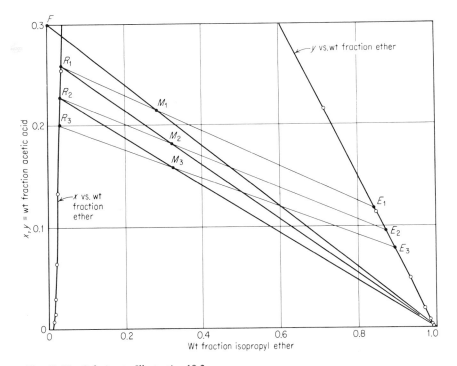

Fig. 10.35 *Solution to Illustration* 10.3.

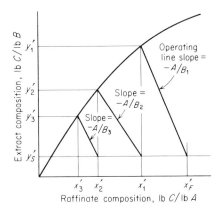

Extract composition, lb C/lb B

y_1'

y_2'

y_3'

y_S'

Operating
line slope =
$-A/B_1$

Slope =
$-A/B_2$

Slope =
$-A/B_3$

x_3' x_2' x_1' x_F'

Raffinate composition, lb C/lb A

Fig. 10.36 *Crosscurrent extraction with an insoluble solvent.*

concentrations are plotted as in Fig. 10.36, $x' = x/(1 - x)$ against $y' = y/(1 - y)$. Since the liquids A and B are insoluble, there are A lb of this substance in all raffinates. Similarly, the extract from each stage contains all the solvent B fed to that stage. A solute-C balance about any stage n is then

$$Ax_{n-1}' + B_n y_S' = B_n y_n' + Ax_n' \qquad (10.30)$$

$$-\frac{A}{B_n} = \frac{y_S' - y_n'}{x_{n-1}' - x_n'} \qquad (10.31)$$

This is the operating-line equation for stage n, of slope $-A/B_n$, passing through points (x_{n-1}', y_S') and (x_n', y_n'). The construction for a three-stage extraction is shown in Fig. 10.36, where for each stage a line is drawn of slope appropriate to that stage. Each operating line intersects the equilibrium curve at the raffinate and extract compositions. No raffinate of concentration smaller than that in equilibrium with the entering solvent is possible.

Solute concentrations for these cases are sometimes also conveniently expressed as mass/volume. Equations (10.30) and (10.31) then apply with x' and y' expressed as mass solute/volume, and A and B as volume/time (or volumes for batch operations).

Illustration 10.4. Nicotine (C) in a water (A) solution containing 1 % nicotine is to be extracted with kerosene (B) at 20°C. Water and kerosene are essentially insoluble. (*a*) Determine the percentage extraction of nicotine if 100 lb of feed solution is extracted once with 150-lb solvent. (*b*) Repeat for three ideal extractions using 50-lb solvent each.

Solution. Equilibrium data are provided by Claffey et al., *Ind. Eng. Chem.*, **42**, 166 (1950), and expressed as lb nicotine/lb liquid, they are as follows:

$x' = \dfrac{\text{lb nicotine}}{\text{lb water}}$	0	0.001011	0.00246	0.00502	0.00751	0.00998	0.0204
$y'* = \dfrac{\text{lb nicotine}}{\text{lb kerosene}}$	0	0.000807	0.001961	0.00456	0.00686	0.00913	0.01870

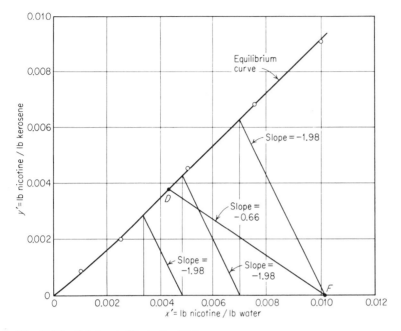

Fig. 10.37 *Solution to Illustration* 10.4.

a. $x_F = 0.01$ wt fraction nicotine, $x_F' = 0.01/(1 - 0.01) = 0.0101$ lb nicotine/lb water. $F = 100$ lb. $A = 100(1 - 0.01) = 99$ lb water. $A/B = {}^{99}\!/_{150} = 0.66$.

Refer to Fig. 10.37, which shows the equilibrium data and the point F representing the composition of the feed. From F, line FD is drawn of slope -0.66, intersecting the equilibrium curve at D, where $x_1' = 0.00425$ and $y_1' = 0.00380$ lb nicotine/lb liquid. The nicotine removed from the water is therefore $99(0.0101 - 0.00425) = 0.580$ lb, or 58% of that in the feed.

b. For each stage, $A/B = {}^{99}\!/_{50} = 1.98$. The construction is started at F, with operating lines of slope -1.98. The final raffinate composition is $x_3' = 0.0034$, and the nicotine extracted is $99(0.0101 - 0.0034) = 0.663$ lb, or 66.3% of that in the feed.

Continuous countercurrent multistage extraction

The flow sheet for this type of operation is shown in Fig. 10.38. Extract and raffinate streams flow from stage to stage in countercurrent and provide two final products, raffinate R_{N_p} and extract E_1. For a given degree of separation, this type of operation requires fewer stages for a given amount of solvent, or less solvent for a fixed number of stages, than the crosscurrent methods described above.

Fig. 10.38 *Countercurrent multistage extraction.*

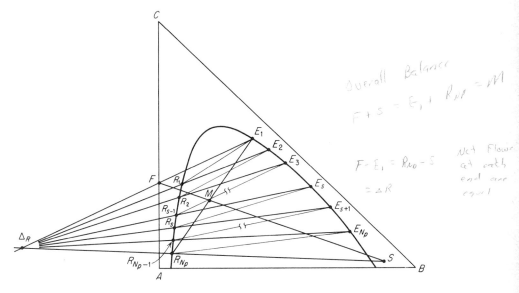

Handwritten annotations beside the figure:

Overall Balance

$F + S = E_1 + R_{Np} = M$

Net Flows
at each
end are
equal

$F - E_1 = R_{Np} - S$

$= \Delta R$

Fig. 10.39 *Countercurrent multistage extraction.*

The graphical treatment is developed in Fig. 10.39 on rectangular coordinates. Construction on the equilateral triangle is identical with this. A total material balance about the entire plant is

$$F + S = E_1 + R_1 = M \tag{10.32}$$

Point M may be located on line FS through a balance for substance C,

$$Fx_F + Sy_S = E_1y_1 + R_{Np}x_{Np} = Mx_M \tag{10.33}$$

$$x_M = \frac{Fx_F + Sy_S}{F + S} \tag{10.34}$$

Equation (10.32) indicates that M must lie on line $R_{Np}E_1$, as shown. Rearrangement of Eq. (10.32) provides

$$R_{Np} - S = F - E_1 = \Delta_R \tag{10.35}$$

where Δ_R, a difference point, is the net flow outward at the last stage N_p. According to Eq. (10.35), the extended lines E_1F and SR_{Np} must intersect at Δ_R, as shown in Fig. 10.39. This intersection may in some cases be located at the right of the triangle. A material balance for stages s through N_p is

$$R_{s-1} + S = R_{Np} + E_s \tag{10.36}$$

or

$$R_{Np} - S = R_{s-1} - E_s = \Delta_R \tag{10.37}$$

so that the difference in flow rates at a location between any two adjacent stages is constant, Δ_R. Line E_sR_{s-1} extended must therefore pass through Δ_R, as on the figure.

The graphical construction is then as follows. After location of points F, S, M, E_1, R_{Np}, and Δ_R, a tie line from E_1 provides R_1 since extract and raffinate from the first ideal stage are in equilibrium. A line from Δ_R through R_1 when extended provides E_2, a tie line from E_2 provides R_2, etc. The lowest possible value of x_{Np} is that given by the A-rich end of a tie line which, when extended, passes through S.

As the amount of solvent is increased, point M representing the overall plant balance moves toward S on Fig. 10.39 and point Δ_R moves farther to the left. At an amount of solvent such that lines E_1F and SR_{Np} are parallel, point Δ_R will be at an infinite distance. Greater amounts of solvent will cause these lines to intersect on the right-hand side of the diagram rather than as shown, with point Δ_R nearer B for increasing solvent quantities. The interpretation of the difference point is, however, still the same: a line from Δ_R intersects the two branches of the solubility curve at points representing extract and raffinate from adjacent stages.

If a line from point Δ_R should coincide with a tie line, an infinite number of stages will be required to reach this condition. The maximum amount of solvent for which this occurs corresponds to the minimum solvent/feed ratio which may be used for the specified products. The procedure for determining the minimum amount of solvent is indicated in Fig. 10.40. All tie lines below that marked JK are extended to line SR_{Np}, to give intersections with line SR_{Np} as shown. The intersection farthest from S (if on the left-hand side of the diagram) or nearest S (if on the right) represents the difference point for minimum solvent, as at point Δ_{Rm} (Fig. 10.40). The actual position of Δ_R must be farther from S (if on the left) or nearer to S (if on the right) for a finite number of stages. The larger the amount of solvent, the fewer the number of stages. Usually, but not in the instance shown, the tie lines which when extended pass through F, i.e., tie line JK, will locate Δ_{Rm} for minimum solvent.

When the number of stages is very large, the construction indicated in Fig. 10.41 may be more convenient. A few lines are drawn at random from point Δ_R to intersect the two branches of the solubility curve as shown, where the intersections do not now necessarily indicate streams between two actual adjacent stages. The C

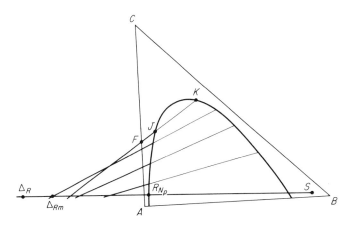

Fig. 10.40 *Minimum solvent for countercurrent extraction.*

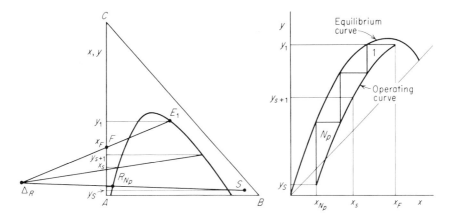

Fig. 10.41   *Transfer of coordinates to distribution diagram.*

concentrations x_s and y_{s+1} corresponding to these are plotted on x, y coordinates as shown to provide an operating curve. Tie-line data provide the equilibrium curve y^* vs. x, and the theoretical stages are stepped off in the manner used for gas absorption and distillation.

Figure 10.42 shows the construction for solvent-free coordinates. The B-free material balance for the entire plant is

$$F' + S' = E_1' + R_{Np}' = M' \tag{10.38}$$

where ordinarily $F = F'$ since the feed is usually B-free. M' is therefore on the line FS at X_M calculated by a C balance

$$F'X_F + S'Y_S = M'X_M \tag{10.39}$$

If pure B is used as solvent, $S' = 0$, $S'Y_S = 0$, $F' = M'$, $X_M = X_F$, and point M is vertically above F.

Line E_1R_{Np} must pass through M. Then

$$R_{Np}' - S' = F' - E_1' = \Delta_R' \tag{10.40}$$

The balance for stages s through N_p is

$$R_{Np}' - S' = R_{s-1}' - E_s' = \Delta_R' \tag{10.41}$$

where Δ_R' is the difference in solvent-free flow, out — in, at stage N_p, and the constant difference in solvent-free flows of the streams between any two adjacent stages. Line E_sR_{s-1} extended, where s is any stage, must therefore pass through Δ_R on the graph.

The graphical construction is then as follows. After locating points F, S, M, E_1, R_{Np}, and Δ_R, a tie line from E_1 provides R_1, line $\Delta_R R_1$ extended locates E_2, etc. If the solvent is pure B ($N_S = \infty$), line $R_{Np}\Delta_R$ is vertical.

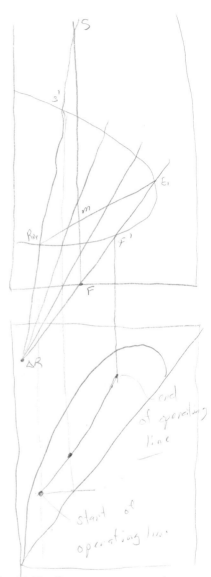

Fig. 10.42 *Countercurrent extraction solvent-free coordinates.*

A C balance, stages s through N_p, following Eq. (10.40) is

$$R'_{s-1}X_{s-1} - E'_s Y_s = \Delta'_R X_{\Delta R} \tag{10.42}$$

A B balance is

$$R'_{s-1}N_{R,s-1} - E'_s N_{Es} = \Delta'_R N_{\Delta R} \tag{10.43}$$

Elimination of Δ'_R between Eqs. (10.40) to (10.42) provides

$$\frac{R'_{s-1}}{E'_s} = \frac{Y_s - X_{\Delta R}}{X_{s-1} - X_{\Delta R}} = \frac{N_{Es} - N_{\Delta R}}{N_{R,n-1} - N_{\Delta R}} \tag{10.44}$$

Thus, the ratio of flows R'_{s-1}/E'_s may be obtained from the ratio of line lengths $E_s\Delta_R/R_{s-1}\Delta_R$ on the upper part of Fig. 10.42, or as the slope of the chord from (X_{s-1}, Y_s) to $X_{\Delta R}$ on the $45°$ diagonal of the lower diagram, as shown. The difference-point coordinates are

$$\Delta'_R \begin{cases} N_{\Delta R} = \dfrac{\text{difference in } B \text{ flow, out } - \text{ in, at stage } N_p}{\text{net flow out, } B\text{-free}} \\[2em] X_{\Delta R} = \dfrac{\text{difference in } C \text{ flow, out } - \text{ in, at stage } N_p}{\text{net flow out, } B\text{-free}} \end{cases}$$

and Δ'_R is analogous to the Δ_W of distillation (see Chap. 9).

As the solvent/feed ratio is increased, Δ_R on Fig. 10.42 moves lower, and the minimum solvent is determined by the lowest point of intersection of all extended tie lines with the line SR_{Np}. A practical Δ_R must be located below this, corresponding to larger amounts of solvent.

Solvent recovery by extraction. While most processes use distillation or evaporation to recover the solvent from the product solutions of liquid extraction, it is not uncommon to recover solvent by liquid extraction. A typical example is the recovery of penicillin from the acidified fermentation broth in which it occurs by extraction with amyl acetate as solvent, followed by stripping of the penicillin from the solvent by extracting it into an aqueous buffer solution. The amyl acetate is then returned to the first extraction. The calculations of such solvent-recovery operations are made in the same manner as those for the first extraction.

Illustration 10.5. Two thousand pounds per hour of an acetic acid (C)–water (A) solution, containing 30% acid, is to be countercurrently extracted with isopropyl ether (B) to reduce the acid concentration to 2% in the solvent-free raffinate product. (a) Determine the minimum amount of solvent which may be used. (b) Determine the number of theoretical stages if 5,000 lb/hr of solvent is used.

Solution. The equilibrium data of Illustration 10.3 are plotted on triangular coordinates in Fig. 10.43. The tie lines have been omitted for reasons of clarity.

a. $F = 2,000$ lb/hr; $x_F = 0.30$ wt fraction acetic acid, corresponding to point F on the figure. R'_{Np} is located on the AC base at 2% acid, and line BR'_{Np} intersects the water-rich solubility curve at R_{Np}, as shown. In this case the tie line J which when extended passes through F provides the conditions for minimum solvent, and this intersects line $R_{Np}B$ on the right of the figure nearer B than

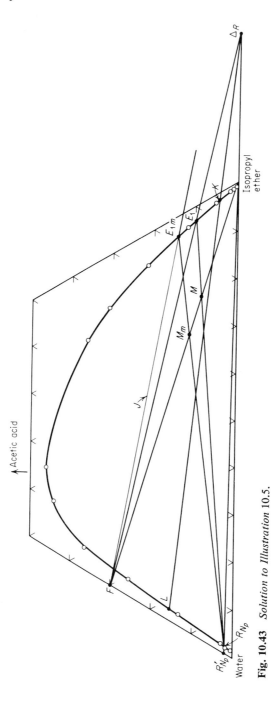

Fig. 10.43   *Solution to Illustration 10.5.*

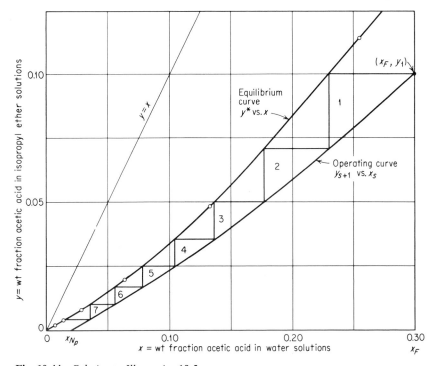

Fig. 10.44   *Solution to Illustration* 10.5.

any other lower tie line.   Tie line *J* provides the minimum E_1 as shown at $y_1 = 0.143$.   Line $E_{1m}R_{Np}$ intersects line *FB* at M_m, for which $x_M = 0.114$.

Eq. (10.34), with $y_s = 0$ and $S = B$:

$$B_m = \frac{Fx_F}{x_M} - F = \frac{2,000(0.30)}{0.114} - 2,000 = 3,260 \text{ lb/hr, min solvent rate}$$

b. For $B = 5,000$ lb solvent/hr [Eq. (10.34) with $y_s = 0$ and $S = B$],

$$x_M = \frac{Fx_F}{F + B} = \frac{2,000(0.30)}{2,000 + 5,000} = 0.0857$$

and point *M* is located as shown on line *FB*.   Line $R_{Np}M$ extended provides E_1 at $y_1 = 0.10$.   Line FE_1 is extended to intersect line $R_{Np}B$ at Δ_R.   Random lines such as *OKL* are drawn to provide y_{s+1} at *K* and x_s at *L*, as follows:

y_{s+1}	0	0.01	0.02	0.04	0.06	0.08	$0.10 = y_1$
x_s	0.02	0.055	0.090	0.150	0.205	0.250	$0.30 = x_F$

These are plotted on Fig. 10.44 as the operating curve, along with the tie-line data as the equilibrium curve.   There are required 7.6 theoretical stages.   The weight of extract may be obtained by an

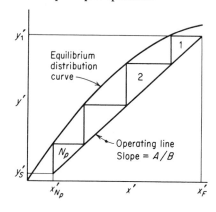

Fig. 10.45   *Countercurrent extraction, insoluble solvent.*

acid balance,

$$E_1 = \frac{M(x_M - x_{Np})}{y_1 - x_{Np}} = \frac{7,000(0.0857 - 0.02)}{0.10 - 0.02} = 5,750 \text{ lb/hr}$$

and

$$R_{Np} = M - E_1 = 7,000 - 5,750 = 1,250 \text{ lb/hr}$$

Insoluble liquids. When the liquids A and B are insoluble over the range of solute concentrations encountered, the stage computation is made more simply on x', y' coordinates. For this case, the solvent content of all extracts and the A content of all raffinates are constant. An overall plant balance for substance C is

$$By'_S + Ax'_F = Ax'_{Np} + By'_1 \tag{10.45}$$

or

$$\frac{A}{B} = \frac{y'_1 - y'_S}{x'_F - x'_{Np}} \tag{10.46}$$

which is the equation of a straight line, the operating line, of slope A/B, through points (y'_1, x'_F), (y'_S, x'_{Np}). For stages 1 through s, similarly,

$$\frac{A}{B} = \frac{y'_1 - y'_{s+1}}{x'_F - x'_s} \tag{10.47}$$

and Fig. 10.45 shows the construction for stages. x' and y' may also be expressed as mass/volume, with A and B as volume/time.

For the special case where the equilibrium curve is of constant slope $m' = y'^*/x'$, Eq. (5.50) applies,

$$\frac{x'_F - x'_{Np}}{x'_F - y'_S/m'} = \frac{(m'B/A)^{Np+1} - m'B/A}{(m'B/A)^{Np+1} - 1} \tag{10.48}$$

where $m'B/A$ is the extraction factor. This may be used in conjunction with Fig. 5.16, with $(x'_{Np} - y'_S/m')/(x'_F - y'_S/m')$ as ordinate and $m'B/A$ as parameter.

Illustration 10.6. One thousand pounds per hour of a nicotine (C)–water (A) solution containing 1% nicotine is to be countercurrently extracted with kerosene at 20°C to reduce the nicotine content to 0.1%. (*a*) Determine the minimum kerosene rate. (*b*) Determine the number of theoretical stages required if 1,150 lb of kerosene is used per hour.

Solution. The equilibrium data of Illustration 10.4 are plotted in Fig. 10.46.

a. $F = 1,000$ lb/hr, $x_F = 0.01$, $A = 1,000(1 - 0.01) = 990$ lb water/hr, $y_S = 0$.

$$x_F' = \frac{0.01}{1 - 0.01} = 0.0101 \text{ lb nicotine/lb water}$$

$$x_{Np} = 0.001 \qquad x_{Np}' = \frac{0.001}{1 - 0.001} = 0.001001 \text{ lb nicotine/lb water}$$

The operating line starts at point L ($y' = 0$, $x' = 0.001001$) and for infinite stages passes through K on the equilibrium curve at x_F'. $y_K' = 0.0093$. Therefore

$$A/B_m = (0.0093 - 0)/(0.0101 - 0.001001) = 1.021,$$

and $B_m = A/1.021 = 990/1.021 = 969$ lb kerosene/hr.

b. $B = 1,150$ lb/hr, $A/B = 990/1,150 = 0.860$.

Eq. (10.46):
$$\frac{y_1'}{x_F' - x_{Np}'} = \frac{y_1'}{0.0101 - 0.001001} = 0.860$$

$$y_1' = 0.00782 \text{ lb nicotine/lb kerosene}$$

The operating line is drawn through (y_1', x_F'), and 8.3 theoretical stages are determined graphically. Alternatively, at the dilute end of the system, $m' = dy'^*/dx' = 0.798$, and

$$m'B/A = 0.798(1,150)/990 = 0.928.$$

At the concentrated end, $m' = 0.953$, and $m'B/A = 0.953(1,150)/990 = 1.110$. The average is $[0.928(1.110)]^{0.5} = 1.01$. $x_{Np}'/x_F' = 0.001001/0.0101 = 0.099$, and Fig. 5.16 indicates 8.4 theoretical stages.

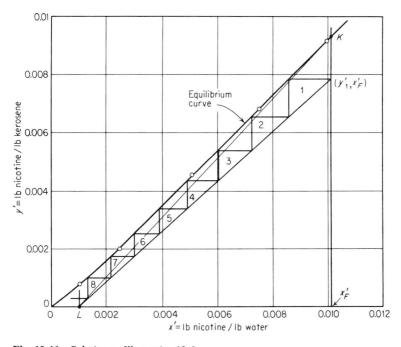

Fig. 10.46 *Solution to Illustration 10.6.*

Continuous countercurrent extraction with reflux

Whereas in ordinary countercurrent operation the richest possible extract product leaving the plant is at best only in equilibrium with the feed solution, the use of reflux at the extract end of the plant can provide a product even richer, as in the case of the rectifying section of a distillation column.   Reflux is not needed at the raffinate end of the cascade since, unlike the case of distillation, where heat must be carried in from the reboiler by a vapor reflux, in extraction the solvent (the analog of heat) may enter without need for a carrier stream.

An arrangement for this is shown in Fig. 10.47.   The feed to be separated into its components is introduced more or less centrally into the cascade, through which extract and raffinate liquids are passing countercurrently.   The concentration of solute C is increased in the extract-enriching section by countercurrent contact with a raffinate liquid rich in C.   This is provided by removing the solvent from extract E_1 to produce the solvent-free stream E', part of which is removed as extract product P'_E and part returned as reflux R_0.   The raffinate-stripping section of the cascade is the same as the countercurrent extractor of Fig. 10.38, and C is stripped from the raffinate by countercurrent contact with solvent.

Graphical determination of stages required for such operations is usually inconvenient to carry out on triangular coordinates[27] because of crowding, and only the use of N, X, Y coordinates will be described.   For the stages in the raffinate stripping section, Fig. 10.47, the developments for simple countercurrent extraction, Eqs. (10.41) to (10.44) apply, and this section of the plant needs no further consideration.

In the extract-enriching section, an $A + C$ balance about the solvent separator is

$$E'_1 = E' = P'_E + R'_0 \qquad (10.49)$$

Let Δ_E represent the net rate of flow outward from this section.   Then, for its $A + C$ content,

$$\Delta'_E = P'_E \qquad (10.50)$$

and for its C content,

$$X_{\Delta E} = X_{PE} \qquad (10.51)$$

while for its B content,

$$B_E = \Delta'_E N_{\Delta E} \qquad (10.52)$$

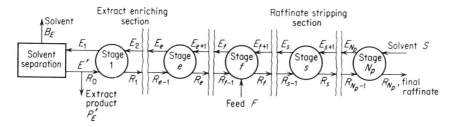

Fig. 10.47   *Countercurrent extraction with reflux.*

The point Δ_E is plotted on Fig. 10.48, which is drawn for a system of two partly miscible component pairs. For all stages through e, an $A + C$ balance is

$$E'_{e+1} = P'_E + R'_e = \Delta'_E + R'_e \qquad (10.53)$$

or

$$\Delta'_E = E'_{e+1} - R'_e \qquad (10.54)$$

A C balance,

$$\Delta'_E X_{\Delta E} = E'_{e+1} Y_{e+1} - R'_e X_{Re} \qquad (10.55)$$

and a B balance,

$$\Delta'_E N_{\Delta E} = E'_{e+1} N'_{E,e+1} - R'_e N_{Re} \qquad (10.56)$$

Since e is any stage in this section, lines radiating from point Δ_E cut the solubility curves of Fig. 10.48 at points representing extract and raffinate flowing between any two adjacent stages. Δ_E is therefore a difference point, constant for all stages in this section, whose coordinates mean

$$\Delta'_E \begin{cases} N_{\Delta E} = \dfrac{\text{difference in } B \text{ flow, out} - \text{in}}{\text{net flow out, } B\text{-free}} = \dfrac{B \text{ out}}{(A + C) \text{ out}} \\[3mm] X_{\Delta E} = \dfrac{\text{difference in } C \text{ flow, out} - \text{in}}{\text{net flow out, } B\text{-free}} = \dfrac{C \text{ out}}{(A + C) \text{ out}} \end{cases}$$

Alternating tie lines and lines from Δ_E then establish the stages, starting with stage 1 and continuing to the feed stage. Figure 10.48 also shows the raffinate-stripping stages as well, developed as before for countercurrent extraction.

Solving Eq. (10.53) with (10.55) and (10.56) produces the internal reflux ratio at any stage,

$$\frac{R'_e}{E'_{e+1}} = \frac{N_{\Delta E} - N_{E.e+1}}{N_{\Delta E} - N_{Re}} = \frac{X_{\Delta E} - Y_{e+1}}{X_{\Delta E} - X_{Re}} = \frac{\text{line } \Delta_E E_{e+1}}{\text{line } \Delta_E R_e} \qquad (10.57)$$

This may be computed from line lengths on the upper diagram of Fig. 10.48 or from the slope of a chord on the lower diagram, as shown. The external reflux ratio is

$$\frac{R'_0}{P'_E} = \frac{R_0}{P'_E} = \frac{N_{\Delta E} - N_{E1}}{N_{E1}} \qquad (10.58)$$

which may be used to locate Δ_E for any specified reflux ratio.

Material balances may also be made over the entire plant. For $A + C$,

$$F' + S' = P'_E + R'_{Np} \qquad (10.59)$$

Using Eqs. (10.40) and (10.50), this becomes

$$F' = \Delta'_R + \Delta'_E \qquad (10.60)$$

where normally $F = F'$. Point F must therefore lie on a line joining the two difference points, and the optimum location of the feed stage is represented by the tie line which

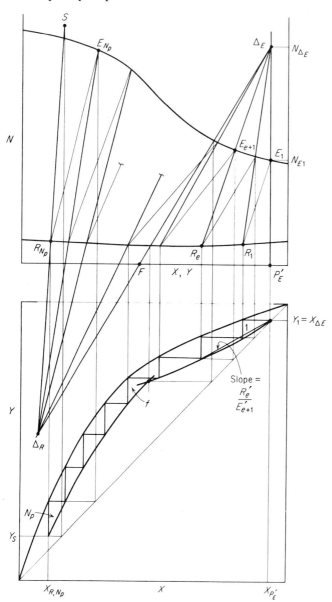

Fig. 10.48 *Countercurrent extraction with reflux.*

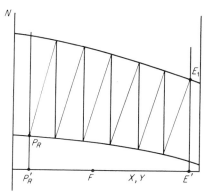

Fig. 10.49   *Total reflux.*

crosses line $\Delta_R F \Delta_E$, as shown.   The similarity of Fig. 10.48 to the enthalpy-concentration diagram of distillation is clear, and the two become completely analogous when solvent S is pure B.

The higher the location of Δ_E (and the lower Δ_R), the larger the reflux ratio and the smaller the number of stages.   When R_0/P'_E is infinite (infinite reflux ratio or total reflux), $N_{\Delta E} = \infty$, and the minimum number of stages results.   The capacity of the plant falls to zero, feed must be stopped, and solvent B_E is recirculated to become S. The configuration is shown in Fig. 10.49 on N, X, Y coordinates.   The corresponding XY diagram uses the $45°$ diagonal as operating lines for both sections of the cascade.

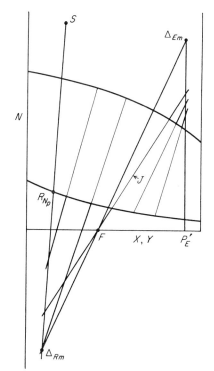

Fig. 10.50   *Determination of minimum reflux ratio.*

An infinity of stages is required if a line radiating from either Δ_E or Δ_R coincides with a tie line, and the greatest reflux ratio for which this occurs is the *minimum reflux ratio*. This may be determined as in Fig. 10.50. Tie lines to the left of J are extended to intersect line SR_{Np+1}, and those to the right of J are extended to line $P'_E E_1$. Points Δ_{Em} and Δ_{Rm} for the minimum reflux ratio are established by selecting the intersections farthest from $N = 0$, consistent with the requirement that Δ_R, Δ_E, and F must always lie on the same straight line. Frequently tie line J, which when extended passes through F, will establish the minimum reflux ratio, and always if the XY equilibrium distribution curve is everywhere concave downward.

Illustration 10.7. One thousand pounds per hour of a solution containing 50% ethylbenzene (A) and 50% styrene (C) is to be separated at 25°C into products containing 10% and 90% styrene, respectively, with diethylene glycol (B) as solvent. (*a*) Determine the minimum number of theoretical stages. (*b*) Determine the minimum extract reflux ratio. (*c*) Determine the number of theoretical stages and the important flow quantities at an extract reflux ratio of 1.5 times the minimum value.

Solution. Equilibrium data of Boobar et al., *Ind. Eng. Chem.*, **43**, 2922 (1951), have been converted to a solvent-free basis and are tabulated below.

Hydrocarbon-rich solutions		Solvent-rich solutions	
X, lb styrene / lb hydrocarbon	N, lb glycol / lb hydrocarbon	Y^*, lb styrene / lb hydrocarbon	N, lb glycol / lb hydrocarbon
0	0.00675	0	8.62
0.0870	0.00817	0.1429	7.71
0.1883	0.00938	0.273	6.81
0.288	0.01010	0.386	6.04
0.384	0.01101	0.480	5.44
0.458	0.01215	0.557	5.02
0.464	0.01215	0.565	4.95
0.561	0.01410	0.655	4.46
0.573	0.01405	0.674	4.37
0.781	0.01833	0.833	3.47
1.00	0.0256	1.00	2.69

These are plotted on the solvent-free coordinate system of Fig. 10.51. The tie lines corresponding to these points are not drawn in, for purposes of clarity. $F = 1,000$ lb/hr, $X_F = 0.5$ wt fraction styrene, $X_{P'E} = 0.9$, $X_{R,Np} = 0.1$, all on a solvent-free basis. Point E_1 is located as shown. $N_{E1} = 3.10$.

a. Minimum theoretical stages are determined by drawing a tie line from E_1, a vertical line from R_1, a tie line from E_2, etc., until the raffinate product is reached, as shown. The minimum number of stages, corresponding to the constructed tie lines, is 9.5.

b. The tie line which when extended passes through F provides the minimum reflux ratios, since it provides intersections Δ_{Em} and Δ_{Rm} farthest from the line $N = 0$. From the plot, $N_{\Delta Em} = 20.76$.

Eq. (10.58):
$$\left(\frac{R_0}{P'_E}\right)_m = \frac{20.76 - 3.1}{3.1} = 5.70 \text{ lb reflux/lb extract product}$$

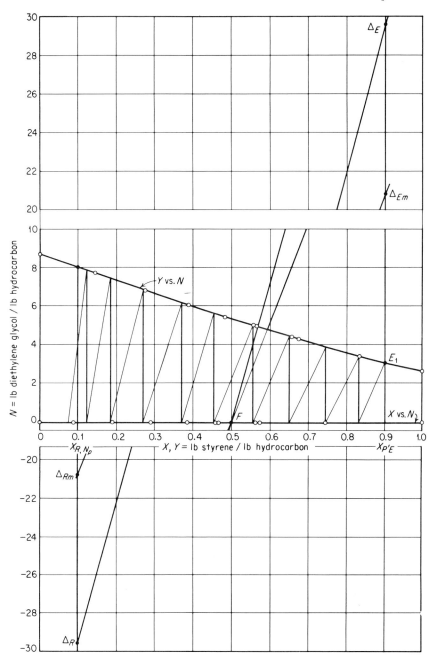

Fig. 10.51   *Solution to Illustration* 10.7.   *Minimum ideal stages at total reflux and location of difference points.*

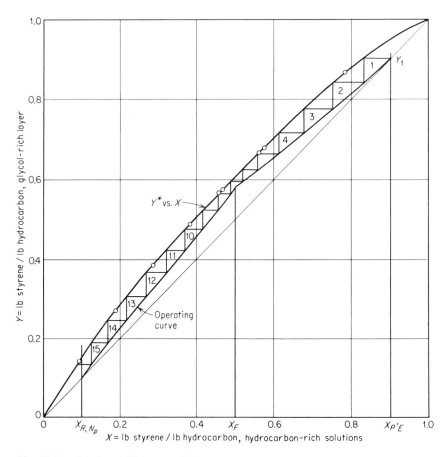

Fig. 10.52 *Solution to Illustration* 10.7.

c. For $R_0/P_E' = 1.5(5.70) = 8.55$ lb reflux/lb extract product [Eq. (10.58)],

$$8.55 = \frac{N_{\Delta E} - 3.1}{3.1}$$

and $N_{\Delta E} = 29.6$. Point Δ_E is plotted as shown. A straight line from Δ_E through F intersects line $X = 0.10$ at Δ_R. $N_{\Delta R} = -29.6$. Random lines are drawn from Δ_E for concentrations to the right of F, and from Δ_R for those to the left, and intersections of these with the solubility curves provide the coordinates of the operating curve (Fig. 10.52). The tie-line data plotted directly provide the equilibrium curve. The number of theoretical stages is seen to be 15.5, and the feed is to be introduced into the seventh from the extract-product end of the cascade.

From Fig. 10.51, $X_{R,Np} = 0.10$, $N_{R,Np} = 0.0082$. On the basis of 1 hr, an overall plant balance is

$$F = 1,000 = P_E' + R_{Np}'$$

A C balance,

$$FX_F = 500 = P_E'(0.9) + R_{Np}'(0.1)$$

Solving simultaneously, $P_E' = R_{N_p}' = 500$ lb/hr.

$$R_0 = R_0' = 8.55P_E' = 8.55(500) = 4,275 \text{ lb/hr}$$

Eq. (10.49): $$E_1' = R_0' + P_E' = 4,275 + 500 = 4,775 \text{ lb/hr}$$

$$B_E = E_1'N_{E1} = 4,775(3.10) = 14,800 \text{ lb/hr}$$

$$E_1 = B_E + E_1' = 14,800 + 4,775 = 19,575 \text{ lb/hr}$$

$$R_{N_p} = R_{N_p}'(1 + N_{R,N_p}) = 500(1.0082) = 504 \text{ lb/hr}$$

$$S = B_E + R_{N_p}'N_{R,N_p} = 14,800 + 500(0.0082) = 14,804 \text{ lb/hr}$$

Economic balances

Several types of economic balances may be made for the various flow sheets just described.   For example, the amount of solute extracted for a fixed solvent/feed ratio increases with increased number of stages, and therefore the value of the unextracted solute may be balanced against the cost of the extraction equipment required to recover it.   The amount of solvent per unit of feed, or reflux ratio in the case of the last flow sheet described, is also subject to economic balance.   For a fixed extent of extraction, the number of stages required decreases as solvent rate or reflux ratio increases.   Since the capacity of the equipment for handling the larger liquid flow must at the same time increase, the cost of equipment must then pass through a minimum.   The extract solutions become more dilute as solvent rate is increased, and consequently the cost of solvent removal increases.   The total cost, which is the sum of investment and operating costs, must pass through a minimum at the optimum solvent rate or reflux ratio.   In all such economic balances, the cost of solvent recovery will always be a major item and usually must include consideration of recovery from the saturated raffinate product as well as the extract.

Fractional extraction—separation of two solutes

If a solution contains two extractable solutes, both may be removed from the solution by countercurrent extraction with a suitable solvent, but it is impossible to produce any great degree of separation of the solutes by this method unless the ratio of their distribution coefficients is very large.

Separation to any extent may, however, be achieved, so long as their distribution coefficients are different, by the techniques of fractional extraction.   The simplest flow sheet for this is shown in Fig. 10.53.   Here solutes B and C, which constitute the

Fig. 10.53 *Fractional extraction.*

feed, are introduced into a countercurrent cascade where partly miscible solvents A and D flow countercurrently.   At the feed stage, both solutes distribute between the solvents, with solute B favoring solvent A, solute C favoring solvent D.   In the section to the left of the feed stage, solvent A preferentially extracts the B from D, and D leaves this section with a solute content rich in C.   In the section to the right of the feed stage, solvent D preferentially extracts the C from A, and A leaves with a solute content rich in B.

This operation will be considered only in its simplest form, where the solvents A and D are essentially immiscible and enter free of solutes and where solutes B and C distribute independently, i.e., the distribution of each is uninfluenced by the presence of the other. A and D will represent the weight rates of flow of these solvents, lb/hr, and concentrations will be expressed as

$$y' = \text{lb solute/lb } A \ (y'_B \text{ for solute } B,\ y'_C \text{ for solute } C)$$

$$x' = \text{lb solute/lb } D \ (x'_B \text{ for solute } B,\ x'_C \text{ for solute } C)$$

Consider the stages $1'$ through m'.   For *either* solute, a solute material balance is

$$Dx'_{m'+1} = Ay'_{m'} + Dx'_{1'} \tag{10.61}$$

or

$$\frac{D}{A} = \frac{y'_{m'} - 0}{x'_{m'+1} - x'_{1'}} \tag{10.62}$$

and we need only add the subscripts B or C to the concentrations to apply these to particular solutes.   Similarly, for stages 1 through m, for *either* solute, the balance is

$$Ay'_{m+1} = Dx'_m + Ay'_1 \tag{10.63}$$

$$\frac{D}{A} = \frac{y'_{m+1} - y'_1}{x'_m - 0} \tag{10.64}$$

Equations (10.62) and (10.64) represent the operating lines for each solute, one for each section of the cascade, of slope D/A.   Figure 10.54 shows the distribution diagrams

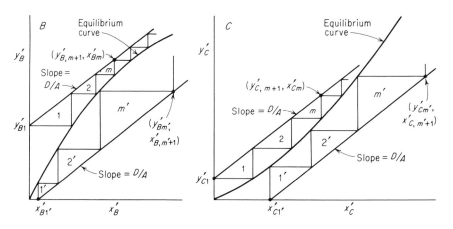

Fig. 10.54 *Fractional extraction, operating lines and stages.*

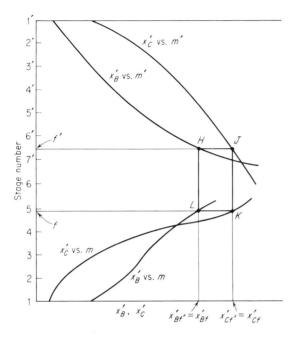

Fig. 10.55   *Feed-stage matching.*

for the solutes, each of which distrbiutes independently of the other.   The operating lines are also drawn on the figure, and the stages stepped off in the usual manner, beginning at stages 1 and 1'.

To determine the number of stages required in each section of the cascade, a match of concentrations and stage numbers at the point of feed introduction must be made.   At the feed stage (which is numbered f and f') for either solute f must be the same, f' must be the same, and the concentration must be the same when computed from each end of the cascade.   The match may be established by plotting the concentrations of both B and C in one of the solvents against stage number, as in Fig. 10.55.   The requirements listed above are then met where the rectangle $HJKL$ can be drawn in the manner shown.

It can be seen from Fig. 10.55 that the concentrations of both solutes is greatest at the feed stage, least at stages 1 and 1'.   Sufficient rates of solvent flow must be used to ensure that solute solubilities are not exceeded at the feed stage.   Changing the solvent ratio changes the total number of stages and the relative position of the feed stage, and there is always a solvent ratio for which the total number of stages is the least.

The number of stages may be reduced by use of solute reflux at either or both ends of the cascade.   Computation of this effect, treatment of cases where solute distributions are interdependent or solvent miscibility varies, and other special flow sheets are beyond the scope of this book, but these have been thoroughly worked out.[25,27]

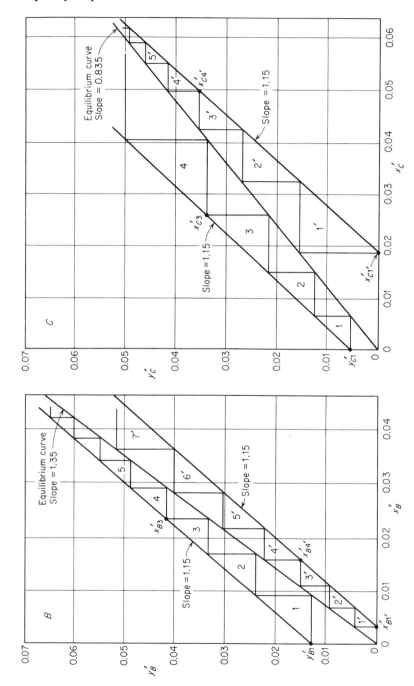

Fig. 10.56 *Solution to Illustration 10.8.*

Fig. 10.57 *Solution to Illustration 10.8, feed-stage matching.*

Illustration 10.8. A mixture containing 40% p-chloronitrobenzene (B) and 60% o-chloronitrobenzene (C) is to be separated at the rate of 100 lb/hr into products containing 80 and 15%, respectively, of the para isomer after removal of solvents. The insoluble solvents to be used are 2,400 lb/hr heptane (A) and 2,760 lb/hr aqueous methanol (D). The distribution coefficients are constant and independent, $y'_B{}^*/x'_B = 1.35$ and $y'_C{}^*/x'_C = 0.835$. Determine the number of ideal stages required and the position of the feed stage.

Solution. The para isomer (B) favors the heptane (A), and the ortho (C) favors the methanol (D). *Basis:* 1 hr. Feed = 100 lb = 40 lb B, 60 lb C. Let W = lb A-rich product, Z = lb D-rich product, after solvent removal. Then B and C balances are, respectively,

$$0.80W + 0.15Z = 40 \qquad 0.20W + 0.85Z = 60$$

from which $W = 38.5$ lb (30.8 lb B, 7.7 lb C), and $Z = 61.5$ lb (9.23 lb B, 52.27 lb C).

$$x'_{B1} = \frac{9.23}{2,760} = 0.00334 \qquad x'_{C1} = \frac{52.27}{2,760} = 0.01895$$

$$y'_{B1} = \frac{30.8}{2,400} = 0.01283 \qquad y'_{C1} = \frac{7.7}{2,400} = 0.00321$$

$D/A = 2,760/2,400 = 1.15$. The stages are constructed on Fig. 10.56, and the feed-stage match is shown on Fig. 10.57. From the latter, the feed stage is $f' = 6.6$ and $f = 4.6$. Therefore the total number of ideal stages is $6.6 + 4.6 - 1 = 10.2$ and the feed stage is the 4.6th from the solvent-D inlet.

Multicomponent systems

For most systems containing more than four components, the display of equilibrium data and the computation of stages is very difficult. Some of our most important separations involve hundreds of components whose identity is not even firmly established, as in the extraction of petroleum lubricating oils. In such cases, the stage requirements are best obtained in the laboratory, without detailed study of the equilibria. There are available small-scale mixer-settler extractors of stage efficiency essentially 100 percent, which may be used to study extraction processes,[27] but these must be run continuously to steady state. Countercurrent flow sheets, which are necessarily for continuous operation, can be simulated with small batches of feed and solvent in separatory funnels, however, and this is frequently most convenient and least costly.

Suppose, for example, it is desired to determine what products will be obtained from a five-stage countercurrent extraction of a complex feed flowing at F lb/hr with a solvent flowing at S lb/hr. Refer to Fig. 10.58. Here each circle represents a separatory funnel which, when adequately shaken and the liquids allowed to settle, will represent one ideal stage. Into funnel a are placed suitable amounts of feed and solvent in the ratio F/S, the mixture is shaken, settled, and the two phases separated. Extract layer E' is removed and raffinate R_a is contacted in funnel b with precisely the same amount of solvent S as used in funnel a. Raffinates and extracts, feeds and solvents, are moved and contacted in the manner indicated in the figure, care being taken each time to use precisely the same amount of feed and solvent at streams marked F and S as in funnel a.

Clearly extract E' and raffinate R' will not be the same as those produced by a continuous countercurrent extraction. Subsequent raffinates R'', R''', and extracts E'', E''', etc., will approach the desired result, however. One can follow the approach to steady state by observing any conveniently measured property of the raffinates and extracts (density, refractive index, etc.). The properties of R', R'', etc., will approach a constant value, as will those of E', E'', etc. If this has occurred by the time extract E_1 and raffinate R_5 in the upper part of Fig. 10.58 is reached, then funnels 1 through 5 represent in every detail the stages of the continuous cascade just below. Thus, for example, raffinate R_3 from funnel 3 will have all the properties and relative volume of raffinate R_3 of the continuous plant.

In a similar manner, flow sheets involving reflux and fractional extraction may also be studied.[1,27]

Stage efficiency

As in the case of gas-liquid contact, the performance of individual extraction stages can be described in terms of the approach to equilibrium actually realized by the effluent extract and raffinate streams. The Murphree stage efficiency may be expressed in terms of extract compositions as $\mathbf{E}_{ME}$ or in terms of raffinate compositions as $\mathbf{E}_{MR}$. Applying Eq. (5.39) to stage m of the countercurrent cascade of Fig. 10.59, for example,

$$\mathbf{E}_{ME} = \frac{y_m - y_{m+1}}{y_m^* - y_{m+1}} \qquad \mathbf{E}_{MR} = \frac{x_{m-1} - x_m}{x_{m-1} - x_m^*} \qquad (10.65)$$

where x_m and y_m represent the actual average effluent compositions and y_{m+1} and

Fig. 10.58 *Batch simulation of a countercurrent cascade.*

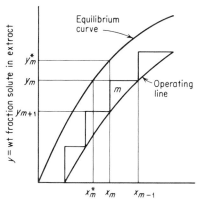

x = wt fraction solute in Raffinate

Fig. 10.59 *Murphree stage efficiency.*

x_{m-1} those of the streams entering the stage. Any other consistent set of concentration units may equally well be used. The overall stage efficiency E_O of a cascade is defined simply as the ratio of the number of ideal stages to the number of real stages required to bring about a given concentration change.

The available experimental data are so meager that few generalizations can be made. Pilot-plant experimentation for new designs is therefore essential.[30] Overall stage efficiencies for cascades of the mixer-settler type have been reported ranging from 0.75 to 1.0. On the other hand, individual Murphree stage efficiencies of 1.0 are easily obtained with agitated vessels, especially if they are baffled, even with systems of high interfacial tension for which dispersion is difficult. It seems quite probable, therefore, that overall efficiencies as low as the 0.75 occasionally reported for cascades may well be the result of incomplete settling of the liquids between stages.

The few data reported for perforated-tray towers have all been taken from small laboratory devices of only a few inches diameter, and the direct application of these data to the design of large-scale equipment is most risky. Overall efficiencies range from as low as 0.02 for systems of high interfacial tension which are difficultly dispersed to 1.0 for easily dispersed systems of low interfacial tension, with the bulk of the data falling in the range 0.25 to 0.50. There appears to be little effect of perforation size, up to 0.25 in., for any given system. Tray efficiencies increase with tray spacing, owing to the corresponding increased time of contact of the phases, but there is little improvement for spacing larger than 16 or 18 in. As will be shown later, it appears that the most rapid mass transfer occurs during the formation of droplets, owing probably to the continual formation of new interfacial surface, while that occurring during the passage of the drop through a layer of continuous liquid is slow owing to the relatively stagnant conditions inside the drop. For these reasons very large tray spacings offer no advantage.

Overall stage efficiencies for agitated equipment of the type shown in Figs. 10.15 to 10.17 and 10.19 depend to some extent on arbitrary definitions as to what constitutes real stages in these devices, and they are perhaps better treated as continuous-contact devices. The centrifugal extractor of Fig. 10.20 has been reported to offer the equivalent of 1 to 13 theoretical stages, depending upon the circumstances of operation.[2]

CONTINUOUS CONTACT

Countercurrent extraction as shown in Figs. 10.38, 10.47, and 10.53 may be carried out in any of the continuous-contact devices such as the spray, packed, and agitated towers previously described, as well as in the centrifugal-type extractors, although for the last, two extractors are needed for cases where feed is introduced into other than the ends of the cascade.

Consider the continuous-contact tower of Fig. 10.60, where extract and raffinate phases flow countercurrently. Although in the diagram the raffinate is shown flowing downward as if it were the more dense phase, it is to be understood that in some instances the solvent-rich, or extract, phase will be the heavier and will enter at the top. In either case, in what follows subscript 1 will always represent that end of the tower where the raffinate enters and extract leaves, while subscript 2 will indicate where

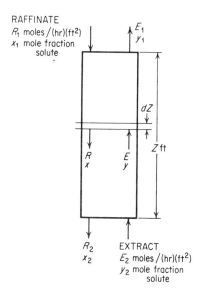

RAFFINATE
R_1 moles/(hr)(ft²)
x_1 mole fraction
solute

E_1
y_1

dZ

Z ft

R
x

E
y

R_2
x_2

EXTRACT
E_2 moles/(hr)(ft²)
y_2 mole fraction
solute

Fig. 10.60 *Continuous-contact tower.*

extract enters and raffinate leaves. We are presently unconcerned with the matter of which phase is dispersed and which is continuous. If the extractor is fed along the side, Fig. 10.60 and the relationships which follow apply separately to each section above and below the feed inlet.

Throughout this discussion, *unless otherwise specified*, x and y will refer to solute concentrations expressed as mole fractions in the raffinate and extract, respectively, and rates of flow of raffinate R and of extract E will be expressed as lb moles/(hr) (sq ft tower cross section). Except in special cases, the transfer of solute usually results in changes of mutual solubility of the contacted liquids, so that in general all components of the systems transfer from one phase to the other. The F-type mass-transfer coefficients are capable of handling this problem, but in reality our knowledge of mass-transfer rates in extractors is so poorly developed that we can ordinarily consider only the transfer of a single solute. This discussion is therefore limited to cases where the liquids are insoluble, only solute is transferred, and mutual solubility unchanged. In practice, however, the expressions developed are used for all cases.

It then follows that the equations derived for gas absorption apply. Thus, for the raffinate (which corresponds to the gas in gas absorption), we have the counterparts of Eqs. (8.21) to (8.25)

$$Z = \int_{x_2}^{x_1} \frac{R(1-x)_{iM}\,dx}{F_R a(1-x)(x-x_i)} = H_{tR}\int_{x_2}^{x_1} \frac{(1-x)_{iM}\,dx}{(1-x)(x-x_i)} = H_{tR}N_{tR} \quad (10.66)$$

$$H_{tR} = \frac{R}{F_R a} = \frac{R}{k_R a(1-x)_{iM}} \quad (10.67)$$

$$N_{tR} = \int_{x_2}^{x_1} \frac{(1-x)_{iM}\,dx}{(1-x)(x-x_i)} = \int_{x_2}^{x_1} \frac{dx}{x-x_i} + \frac{1}{2}\ln\frac{1-x_2}{1-x_1} \quad (10.68)$$

where x_i = interface concentration of solute

$\quad F_R, k_R$ = transfer coefficients for the raffinate phase

$\quad\quad H_{tR}$ = raffinate height of transfer unit

$\quad\quad N_{tR}$ = number of raffinate transfer units

$(1 - x)_{iM}$ = logarithmic mean of $1 - x$ and $1 - x_i$

The interface concentration corresponding to any bulk raffinate concentration x is found through Eq. (5.21) adapted to the present situation

$$\frac{1 - x_i}{1 - x} = \left(\frac{1 - y}{1 - y_i}\right)^{F_E/F_R} \tag{10.69}$$

This equation is plotted, for any value of (x,y) on the operating curve, to determine its intersection with the equilibrium curve at (x_i, y_i), just as for gas absorption.   As an approximation, a straight line of slope $-k_R/k_E$ is plotted from (x,y) on the operating line to obtain the intersection at (x_i, y_i).

Similarly, we have the corresponding expressions for the extract (corresponding to the liquid in gas absorption).

In reality, we know so little about the mass-transfer coefficients that the above expressions are of little use.   For practical reasons, even though not strictly applicable unless the equilibrium curve is of constant slope, it is usually necessary to deal with overall coefficients and transfer units.   These we may take from their gas-absorption counterparts:

$$Z = H_{tOR}N_{tOR} = H_{tOE}N_{tOE} \tag{10.70}$$

$$H_{tOR} = \frac{R}{F_{OR}a} = \frac{R}{K_R a(1 - x)_{*M}} \tag{10.71}$$

$$H_{tOE} = \frac{E}{F_{OE}a} = \frac{E}{K_E a(1 - y)_{*M}} \tag{10.72}$$

$$N_{tOR} = \int_{x_2}^{x_1} \frac{(1 - x)_{*M}\,dx}{(1 - x)(x - x^*)} = \int_{x_2}^{x_1} \frac{dx}{x - x^*} + \frac{1}{2}\ln\frac{1 - x_2}{1 - x_1} \tag{10.73}$$

$$N_{tOE} = \int_{y_2}^{y_1} \frac{(1 - y)_{*M}\,dy}{(1 - y)(y^* - y)} = \int_{y_2}^{y_1} \frac{dy}{y^* - y} + \frac{1}{2}\ln\frac{1 - y_1}{1 - y_2} \tag{10.74}$$

$$(1 - x)_{*M} = \frac{(1 - x^*) - (1 - x)}{\ln\left[(1 - x^*)/(1 - x)\right]} \tag{10.75}$$

$$(1 - y)_{*M} = \frac{(1 - y) - (1 - y^*)}{\ln\left[(1 - y)/(1 - y^*)\right]} \tag{10.76}$$

where x^* is the concentration in equilibrium with y, and y^* that in equilibrium with x.

Concentrations in Eqs. (10.70) to (10.76) are in mole fractions. *If x and y are expressed as weight fractions,* for convenience in use with the stage-calculation operating diagrams in terms of weight fractions,

$$N_{tOR} = \int_{x_2}^{x_1} \frac{dx}{x - x^*} + \frac{1}{2} \ln \frac{1 - x_2}{1 - x_1} + \frac{1}{2} \ln \frac{x_2(r - 1) + 1}{x_1(r - 1) + 1} \tag{10.77}$$

$$N_{tOE} = \int_{y_2}^{y_1} \frac{dy}{y^* - y} + \frac{1}{2} \ln \frac{1 - y_1}{1 - y_2} + \frac{1}{2} \ln \frac{y_1(r - 1) + 1}{y_2(r - 1) + 1} \tag{10.78}$$

where r is the ratio of molecular weights of nonsolute to solute. For weight-ratio concentrations,

$$N_{tOR} = \int_{x_2'}^{x_1'} \frac{dx'}{x' - x'^*} + \frac{1}{2} \ln \frac{1 + rx_2'}{1 + rx_1'} \tag{10.79}$$

$$N_{tOE} = \int_{y_2'}^{y_1'} \frac{dy'}{y'^* - y'} + \frac{1}{2} \ln \frac{1 + ry_1'}{1 + ry_2'} \tag{10.80}$$

Dilute solutions

For dilute solutions, only the integral terms of the above equations for N_{tOE} and N_{tOR} are important.   If in addition the equilibrium curve and operating line are straight over the concentration range encountered, it is readily shown in the manner of Chap. 8 that logarithmic averages of the terminal concentration differences are applicable

$$N_{tOR} = \frac{x_1 - x_2}{(x - x^*)_M} \qquad N_{tOE} = \frac{y_1 - y_2}{(y^* - y)_M} \tag{10.81}$$

The equivalent expressions in terms of mass-transfer coefficients are

$$R(x_1 - x_2) = E(y_1 - y_2) = K_R aZ(x - x^*)_M = K_E aZ(y - y^*)_M \tag{10.82}$$

If in addition the equivalent of Henry's law applies, so that the equilibrium-distribution curve is a straight line passing through the origin ($m = y^*/x = y/x^* = $ const), there is obtained, by a procedure exactly similar to that used previously in the case of gas absorption,

$$N_{tOR} = \frac{\ln \left[\frac{x_1 - y_2/m}{x_2 - y_2/m} \left(1 - \frac{R}{mE} \right) + \frac{R}{mE} \right]}{1 - R/mE} \tag{10.83}$$

Figure 8.20 represents a graphical solution, provided $(x_2 - y_2/m)/(x_1 - y_2/m)$ is considered the ordinate and mE/R the parameter.   Similarly for the extract-enriching section of a tower used with reflux, the same circumstances provide

$$N_{tOE} = \frac{\ln \left[\frac{y_2 - mx_1}{y_1 - mx_1} \left(1 - \frac{mE}{R} \right) + \frac{mE}{R} \right]}{1 - mE/R} \tag{10.84}$$

which is also solved graphically in Fig. 8.20 provided $(y_1 - mx_1)/(y_2 - mx_1)$ is the ordinate and R/mE the parameter.

For these dilute solutions, Eqs. (10.81), (10.83), and (10.84) may be used with concentrations in terms of weight fractions, in which case m must be defined in these terms as well while E and R are measured in lb/(hr)(sq ft). Weight ratios may also be used. Equations (10.81) and (10.82) are frequently used with concentrations expressed as c lb moles/cu ft, in which case the extract and raffinate flow rates are measured in terms of V cu ft/(hr)(sq ft) and the units of the appropriate mass-transfer coefficients are K_{LE} and K_{LR} lb moles/(hr)(sq ft)(Δc). The requirements of constant m (in whatever units it is measured) and straight line operating lines still of course apply.

Illustration 10.9. Determine the number of transfer units N_{tOR} for the extraction of Illustration 10.5, for the case where 5,000 lb/hr of solvent are used.

Solution. Define x and y in terms of weight fractions acetic acid. $x_1 = x_F = 0.30$; $y_2 = 0$; $x_2 = 0.02$; $y_1 = 0.10$. The operating diagram is already plotted in Fig. 10.43. From this plot, values of x and x^* are taken from the operating line and equilibrium curve at various values of y, as follows:

x	x^*	$\dfrac{1}{x - x^*}$
0.30	0.230	14.30
0.25	0.192	17.25
0.20	0.154	20.75
0.15	0.114	27.8
0.10	0.075	40.0
0.05	0.030	50.0
0.02	0	50.0

The area under a curve of x as abscissa against $1/(x - x^*)$ as ordinate (not shown) between $x = 0.30$ and $x = 0.02$ is determined to be 8.40. In these solutions, the mutual solubility of water and isopropyl ether is very small, so that r may be taken as $^{18}\!\!/_{60} = 0.30$. Eq. (10.77):

$$N_{tOR} = 8.40 + \frac{1}{2} \ln \frac{1 - 0.02}{1 - 0.30} + \frac{1}{2} \ln \frac{0.02(0.3 - 1) + 1}{0.30(0.3 - 1) + 1} = 8.46$$

The operating and equilibrium curves are nearly parallel in this case, so that N_{tOR} and N_p are nearly the same. The curvature of the lines makes the simplified methods for N_{tOR} inapplicable, however.

Illustration 10.10. Determine the number of transfer units N_{tOR} for the extraction of Illustration 10.6, when 1,150 lb/hr of kerosene are used.

Solution. Use weight-ratio concentrations, as in Illustration 10.6. $x_1' = x_F' = 0.0101$; $y_2' = 0$; $x_2' = 0.001001$; $y_1' = 0.0782$. The calculation may be done through Eq. (10.83) or the equivalent, Fig. 8.20.

$$\frac{x_2' - y_2'/m'}{x_1' - y_2'/m'} = \frac{0.001001}{0.0101} = 0.0909$$

The average $mE/R = m'B/A = 1.01$ (Illustration 10.6). From Fig. 8.20, $N_{tOR} = 8.8$.

Illustration 10.11. Leibson and Beckmann [*Chem. Eng. Progr.*, **49**, 405 (1953)] extracted diethylamine from water [20.4 cu ft/(hr) (sq ft)] with toluene [3.05 cu ft/(hr)(sq ft)] at 30.8°C, toluene dispersed, in a 6-in.-ID tower packed to a depth of 4 ft with ½-in. Raschig rings. The observed concentrations of diethylamine, in lb moles/cu ft, were water in $= 0.01574$, out $= 0.01450$; toluene in $= 0$, out 0.00860. At this temperature the distribution coefficient $=$ concn in water/concn in toluene $= 1.156$, and water and toluene are substantially insoluble at these diethylamine concentrations. (*a*) Determine the extraction characteristics of the packing for these conditions. (*b*) Compute the effluent concentrations if 8 ft of packing had been used.

Solution. a. The water solution is the raffinate and toluene the extract. Define $m'' = c_E^*/c_R = 1/1.156 = 0.865$.

$c_{E1} = 0.00860$, $c_{E2} = 0$, $c_{R1} = 0.01574$, $c_{R2} = 0.01450$ lb moles diethylamine/cu ft. Owing to the insolubility of the water and toluene, Eq. (10.82) may be written for this case as

$$V_E(c_{E1} - c_{E2}) = K_{LE}aZ(c_E^* - c_E)_M$$

where $V_E = 3.05$ cu ft extract/(hr)(sq ft), constant at these concentrations

$Z = 4$ ft

$c_{E1}^* = m''c_{R1} = 0.865(0.01574) = 0.01363$

$c_{E2}^* = m''c_{R2} = 0.865(0.01450) = 0.01254$

$$(c_E^* - c_E)_M = \frac{(c_{E2}^* - c_{E2}) - (c_{E1}^* - c_{E1})}{\ln\left[(c_{E2}^* - c_{E2})/(c_{E1}^* - c_{E1})\right]} = \frac{(0.01254 - 0) - (0.01363 - 0.00860)}{\ln\left[(0.01254 - 0)/(0.01363 - 0.00860)\right]}$$

$$= 0.00825 \text{ lb mole/cu ft.}$$

$$\therefore 3.05(0.00860 - 0) = K_{LE}a(4)(0.00825)$$

$$K_{LE}a = 0.795 \text{ lb mole/(hr)(cu ft)}(\Delta c_E)$$

Applying Eqs. (5.16) and (5.17) to this case, $K_{LR}a = m''K_{LE}a = 0.865(0.795) = 0.687$ lb mole/(hr)(cu ft)(Δc_R).

From Table 3.1, $K_Ea = cK_{LE}a$, where c is the molar density, lb moles/cu ft, of the extract phase. For these dilute solutions, the density (0.856 g/cu cm) and average molecular weight (92.1) of the extract are the same as those for pure toluene, so that $c = 0.856(62.3)/92.1 = 0.58$ lb mole/cu ft. Therefore $K_Ea = 0.58(0.795) = 0.461$ lb mole/(hr)(cu ft)(mole fraction).

$$E = V_Ec = 3.05(0.58) = 1.77 \text{ lb moles extract/(hr)(sq ft)}$$

$$H_{tOE} = \frac{E}{K_Ea} = \frac{1.77}{0.461} = 3.84 \text{ ft}$$

Alternatively,

$$H_{tOE} = \frac{V_E}{K_{LE}a} \qquad H_{tOR} = \frac{V_R}{K_{LR}a} = \frac{20.4}{0.687} = 29.7 \text{ ft}$$

b. For 8 ft of packing let c_{R2} be the exit concentration in the water and c_{E1} the exit concentration in the toluene. Equation (10.83) can be adapted to these units.

$$\frac{V_R}{m''V_E} = \frac{20.4}{0.865(3.05)} = 7.73$$

$$N_{tOR} = \frac{Z}{H_{tOR}} = \frac{8}{29.7} = 0.269 \qquad c_{R1} = 0.01574 \qquad c_{E2} = 0$$

$$\therefore 0.269 = \frac{\ln\left[(0.01574/c_{R2})(1 - 7.73) + 7.73\right]}{1 - 7.73}$$

$$c_{R2} = 0.01400 \text{ lb mole diethylamine/cu ft}$$

A material balance for diethylamine,

$$V_E(c_{E1} - c_{E2}) = V_R(c_{R1} - c_{R2})$$
$$3.05(c_{E1} - 0) = 20.4(0.01574 - 0.01400)$$
$$c_{E1} = 0.01163 \text{ lb mole/cu ft}$$

Performance of continuous-contact equipment

While over the past 30 years a considerable number of data has been accumulated, taken almost entirely from laboratory-size equipment of a few inches diameter, no satisfactory correlation of them has as yet been possible owing to the very large number of variables which influence extraction rates.   For the design of new extractors it is essential that pilot-plant experiments be performed under conditions as nearly like those expected in the large-scale equipment as possible.[30]   This discussion will therefore be limited to a brief consideration of the important variables, but no data for design will be presented.   Detailed study of many of the data is available elsewhere.[27]

The principal difficulty in obtaining an understanding of extractor performance lies with the very large number of variables which influence the performance.   The following at least have influence.

1.   The liquid system.
   a. Chemical identity and corresponding physical properties.   In this category may be included the presence or absence of surface-active agents, finely divided solids, and the like.
   b. Concentration of solute, since this influences physical properties.
   c. Direction of extraction, whether from aqueous to organic, from continuous to dispersed phase.
   d. Total flow rate of the liquids.
   e. Ratio of liquid flows.
   f. What liquid is dispersed.
2.   The equipment.
   a. Design, which includes not only the gross and obvious design such as whether the extractor is a packed- or sieve-tray tower, but also the details such as size and shape of packing and number of perforations in a plate.
   b. Nature and extent of mechanical agitation, whether rotary or pulsating, whether fast or slow.
   c. Materials of construction, which influence the relative wetting by the liquids.
   d. Height of the extractor and the end effects.
   e. Diameter of extractor and extent of axial mixing.

Except for possible interface effects due to surface-active substances, the overall resistance to mass transfer is made up of those residing in each of the fluids.   Thus Eqs. (5.16) and (5.17) provide the relation between mass-transfer coefficients, and in terms of heights of transfer units we have

$$H_{tOR} = H_{tR} + \frac{R}{mE} H_{tE} \tag{10.85}$$

$$H_{tOE} = H_{tE} + \frac{mE}{R} H_{tR} \tag{10.86}$$

It must be understood that in any equipment of this sort the dispersed phase may be either the extract or the raffinate and either the light or the heavy phase. The resistances to mass transfer in the contacted fluids are likely to depend strongly upon whether the phases in question are dispersed or continuous. It is best therefore to describe the equipment characteristics in terms of mass-transfer coefficients or heights of tranfer units written in terms of the continuous or dispersed phase, $K_C a$ and $K_D a$, or H_{tOC} and H_{tOD}, so that the resistance equations become

$$H_{tOD} = H_{tD} + \frac{L_D}{mL_C} H_{tC} \qquad (10.87)$$

$$H_{tOC} = H_{tC} + \frac{mL_C}{L_D} H_{tD} \qquad (10.88)$$

Some work has been done to establish the individual mass-transfer resistances by use of a technique similar to that found useful in humidification work. Thus, by allowing pure water and pure butanol in the absence of a third distributed substance to flow countercurrently through a tower and mutually to saturate each other, values of H_{tC} and H_{tD} can be obtained. A limited number of such studies with spray and packed towers has been made, but insufficient to permit regularization of the data.

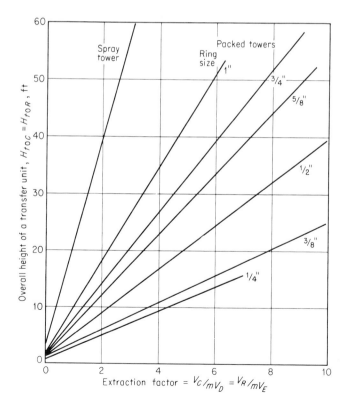

Fig. 10.61 *Extraction of diethylamine from water into toluene, toluene dispersed, in a 6-in.-diameter tower.* [*Data of Leibson and Beckmann: Chem. Eng. Progr.,* **49**, 405 (1953).]

In packed towers, H_{tD} for a given packing and system appears to be fairly constant, while H_{tC} varies with the ratio of liquid flow rates.   Despite this, Eq. (10.88) has frequently been successful in the empirical correlation of data for a given packing and system, as shown in Fig. 10.61.   Despite the linearity of the data, the slope and intercept of such lines should *not* be interpreted as H_{tD} and H_{tC}.[30]   The figure shows clearly the improved, i.e., lower, values of H_{tOC} for small packings as compared to large and the poor performance of a spray tower.   Economic considerations would generally put the extraction factor V_R/mV_E of the figure in the region of 1 or 2, so that for the smaller packings, values of H_{tOR} are not too unreasonably large.   Mechanically agitated extractors will show substantially lower values, however.

NOTATION FOR CHAPTER 10

a = interfacial surface, sq ft/cu ft active volume
a_p = surface of packing, sq ft/cu ft .
A = component A, lb liquid A/hr or lb (batch operations)
A_d = downspout cross section, sq ft
A_n = net tower cross section = $A_t - A_d$, sq ft
A_t = tower cross section, sq ft
B = component B, lb liquid B/hr or lb (batch operations)
c = concentration of solute, lb moles/cu ft solution
C = component C, lb substance C/hr or lb (batch operations)
C_D = drag coefficient = $4\Delta\rho\, d_p g/3\rho_C V_t^2$, dimensionless
d = differential operator
d_F = packing size, ft
d_{FC} = critical packing size, ft
d_o = nozzle or perforation diameter, ft
d_p = drop diameter, ft
D = component D, lb liquid D/hr
E = extract solution, lb/hr (staged extractors), lb (batch operations), lb moles/(hr)(sq ft) (continuous-contact extractors)
E' = solvent-free extract, lb/hr or lb (batch operation)
$\mathbf{E}_{ME}$ = Murphree extract-stage efficiency, fractional
$\mathbf{E}_{MR}$ = Murphee raffinate-stage efficiency, fractional
$\mathbf{E}_O$ = overall stage efficiency, fractional
F = feed or solution to be extracted, lb/hr or lb (batch operations)
    = mass-transfer coefficient, lb moles/(hr)(sq ft)
F' = feed, solvent-free basis, lb/hr or lb (batch operations)
g = acceleration due to gravity, ft/hr²
g_c = conversion factor, 4.17(10⁸)(lb mass)(ft)/(lb force)(hr²)
h = depth of dispersed liquid accumulating on a tray, ft
h_C = depth of dispersed liquid on a tray owing to flow of continuous liquid, ft
h_D = depth of dispersed liquid on a tray owing to flow of dispersed liquid, ft
h_o = head required to cause flow through an orifice, ft
h_σ = head required to overcome effect of interfacial tension, ft
H_t = height of a transfer unit, ft
k = mass-transfer coefficient, lb moles/(hr)(sq ft)(mole fraction)
K = overall mass-transfer coefficient, lb moles/(hr)(sq ft)(mole fraction)
K_L = overall mass-transfer coefficient, lb moles/(hr)(sq ft)(lb mole/cu ft)
ln = natural logarithm

L = superficial mass velocity, lb/(hr)(sq ft)
m = slope of the equilibrium-distribution curve = $dy*/dx = dy/dx*$, dimensionless
m' = slope of the equilibrium-distribution curve = $dy'*/dx' = dy'/dx'*$, dimensionless
M = mixture M, lb/hr or lb (batch operations)
M' = solvent-free mixture M, lb/hr or lb (batch operations)
N = solvent concentration, solvent-free basis, lb B/lb $(A + C)$
N_p = number of ideal stages, dimensionless
N_t = number of transfer units, dimensionless
P = dimensionless group defined by Eq. (10.5)
P'_E = solvent-free extract product, lb/hr
r = molecular weight nonsolute/molecular weight solute, dimensionless
R = raffinate solution, lb/hr (staged extractors), lb (batch operations), lb moles/(hr)(sq ft) (continuous-contact extractors)
R' = solvent-free raffinate, lb/hr or lb (batch operations)
Re = drop Reynolds number = $d_p V_t \rho_C/\mu_C$, dimensionless
s = a distance, Fig. 10.4 and Eq. (10.1), ft
  = stage s
S = solvent, lb/hr or lb (batch operations)
t = a distance, ft
T = tower diameter, ft
u = a distance, ft
V = superficial velocity based on tower cross section, ft/hr
V' = superficial velocity based on tower cross section, ft/sec
V_d = velocity through downspout, ft/hr
V_K = characteristic velocity, ft/hr
V_n = velocity based on A_n, ft/hr
V_O = velocity through orifice, ft/hr
V'_O = velocity through orifice, ft/sec
V_t = terminal settling velocity, ft/hr
We = drop Weber number = $d_p V_t^2 \rho_C/\sigma g_c$, dimensionless
x = concentration of C in A-rich (raffinate) phase, weight fraction (staged extractors), mole fraction (continuous-contact extractors)
x' = concentration of C in A-rich (raffinate) phase, lb C/lb non-C
  = concentration of solute in D-rich phase (fractional extraction), lb solute/lb nonsolute
X = concentration of C in A-rich (raffinate) phase, solvent-free basis, lb C/lb $(A + C)$
y = concentration of C in B-rich (extract) phase, weight fraction (staged extractors), mole fraction (continuous-contact extractors)
y' = concentration of C in B-rich (extract) phase, lb C/lb non-C
  = concentration of solute in A-rich phase (fractional extraction), lb solute/lb nonsolute
Y = concentration of C in B-rich (extract) phase, solvent-free basis, lb C/lb $(A + C)$
Z = active height, ft
β = selectivity, dimensionless
Δ = difference
Δ'_E = difference in flow rate, solvent-free basis, defined by Eq. (10.50)
Δ_R = difference in flow rate, defined by Eq. (10.35)
Δ'_R = difference in flow rate, solvent-free basis, defined by Eq. (10.41)
ϵ = volume void fraction in a packed bed, dimensionless
μ = viscosity, lb mass/(ft)(hr) = $2.42\mu'$
μ_W = viscosity of water, lb mass/(ft)(hr)
μ' = viscosity, centipoises
π = 3.1416
ρ = density, lb mass/cu ft
σ = interfacial tension, lb force/ft = $6.85(10^{-5})\sigma'$

$\sigma' =$ interfacial tension, dynes/cm
$\phi_D =$ volume fraction dispersed phase, dimensionless

Subscripts:

$C =$ continuous phase
$D =$ dispersed phase
$e =$ stage e
$E =$ extract
$f =$ flooding condition
$F =$ feed
$H =$ heavy, or more dense, phase
$i =$ interface
$L =$ light, or less dense, phase
$m =$ stage m; minimum (reflux ratio or solvent/feed ratio)
$M =$ mixture M; logarithmic mean
$N_p =$ last stage of a cascade
$O =$ orifice or nozzle
$ =$ overall (with $\mathbf{E}$, H_t, and N_t)
$R =$ raffinate
$s =$ stage s
$S =$ solvent
$1 =$ stage 1; that end of a continuous-contact tower where feed or raffinate enters
$2 =$ stage 2; that end of a continuous-contact tower where extract or solvent enters

Superscript:

$* =$ in equilibrium with bulk concentration of other phase

REFERENCES

1. Alders, L.: "Liquid-Liquid Extraction," 2d ed., Elsevier Publishing Company, Amsterdam, 1959.
2. Barson, N., and G. H. Beyer: *Chem. Eng. Progr.*, **49**, 243 (1953).
3. Bibaud, R. E., and R. E. Treybal: *AIChE J.*, **12**, 472 (1966).
4. Blanding, F. H., and J. C. Elgin: *Trans. AIChE*, **38**, 305 (1942).
5. Bussolari, R., S. Schiff, and R. E. Treybal: *Ind. Eng. Chem.*, **45**, 2413 (1953).
6. Crawford, J. W., and C. R. Wilke: *Chem. Eng. Progr.*, **47**, 423 (1951).
7. Feick, G., and H. M. Anderson: *Ind. Eng. Chem.*, **44**, 404 (1952).
8. Hayworth, C. B., and R. E. Treybal: *Ind. Eng. Chem.*, **42**, 1174 (1950).
9. Hu, S., and R. C. Kintner: *AIChE J.*, **1**, 42 (1955).
10. Jacobson, F. M., and G. H. Beyer: *AIChE J.*, **2**, 283 (1956).
11. Johnson, A. I., and L. Braida: *Can. J. Chem. Eng.*, **35**, 165 (1957).
12. Keith, F. W., and A. N. Hixson: *Ind. Eng. Chem.*, **47**, 258 (1955).
13. Laity, D. S., and R. E. Treybal: *AIChE J.*, **3**, 176 (1957).
14. Mar, B. W., and A. L. Babb: *Ind. Eng. Chem.*, **51**, 1011 (1959).
15. Mayfield, F. D., and W. L. Church: *Ind. Eng. Chem.*, **44**, 2253 (1952).
16. Oldshue, J. Y., and J. H. Rushton: *Chem. Eng. Progr.*, **48**, 297 (1952).
17. Overcashier, R., H. A. Kingsley, and R. B. Olney: *AIChE J.*, **2**, 529 (1956).
18. Pratt, H. R. C., and coworkers: *Trans. Inst. Chem. Engrs.* (*London*), **29**, 89, 110, 126 (1951); **31**, 57, 70, 78 (1953); **35**, 267 (1957).
19. Quinn, J. A., and D. B. Sigloh: *Can. J. Chem. Eng.*, **41**, 15 (1963).
20. Reman, G. H., and R. B. Olney: *Chem. Eng. Progr.*, **51**, 141 (1955).
21. Ricci, J. E.: "The Phase Rule and Heterogeneous Equilibrium," D. Van Nostrand Company, Inc., Princeton, N.J., 1951.

22. Rushton, J. H., E. W. Costich, and H. J. Everett: *Chem. Eng. Progr.*, **46**, 395, 467 (1950).
23. Sareen, S. S., P. M. Rose, R. C. Gudeson, and R. C. Kintner: *AIChE J.*, **12**, 1045 (1966).
24. Scheibel, E. G.: *AIChE J.*, **2**, 74 (1956).
25. Scheibel, E. G.: *Chem. Eng. Progr.*, **62**(9), 76 (1966).
26. Strand, C. P., R. B. Olney, and G. H. Ackerman: *AIChE J.*, **8**, 252 (1962).
27. Treybal, R. E.: "Liquid Extraction," 2d ed., McGraw-Hill Book Co., New York, 1963.
28. Treybal, R. E.: *Ind. Eng. Chem. Fundamentals*, **3**, 185 (1964).
29. Treybal, R. E.: *Chem. Eng. Progr.*, **60**(5), 77 (1964).
30. Treybal, R. E.: *Chem. Eng. Progr.*, **62**(9), 67 (1966).
31. Vermeulen, T., J. S. Moon, A. Hennico, and T. Miyauchi: *Chem. Eng. Progr.*, **62**(9), 95 (1966).
32. Woodfield, F. N., and G. Sege: *Chem. Eng. Progr. Symp. Ser.*, **50**(13), 14 (1954).

PROBLEMS

Problems 10.1 to 10.7 refer to the system water (A)–chlorobenzene (B)–pyridine (C) at 25°C. Equilibrium tie-line data, interpolated from those of Peake and Thompson, *Ind. Eng. Chem.*, **44**, 2439 (1952), are in weight percents.

Pyridine	Chlorobenzene	Water	Pyridine	Chlorobenzene	Water
0	99.95	0.05	0	0.08	99.92
11.05	88.28	0.67	5.02	0.16	94.82
18.95	79.90	1.15	11.05	0.24	88.71
24.10	74.28	1.62	18.90	0.38	80.72
28.60	69.15	2.25	25.50	0.58	73.92
31.55	65.58	2.87	36.10	1.85	62.05
35.05	61.00	3.95	44.95	4.18	50.87
40.60	53.00	6.40	53.20	8.90	37.90
49.0	37.8	13.2	49.0	37.8	13.2

10.1. Plot the equilibrium data on the following coordinate systems: (*a*) triangular; (*b*) x and y against weight fraction B; (*c*) x against y.

10.2. Compute the selectivity of chlorobenzene for pyridine at each tie line, and plot selectivity against concentration of pyridine in water.

10.3. It is desired to reduce the pyridine concentration of 2,000 lb of an aqueous solution from 50 to 2% in a single batch extraction with chlorobenzene. What amount of solvent is required? Solve on triangular coordinates.

10.4. A 2,000-lb batch of pyridine-water solution, 50% pyridine, is to be extracted with an equal weight of chlorobenzene. The raffinate from the first extraction is to be reextracted with a weight of solvent equal to the raffinate weight, and so on ($B_2 = R_1$, $B_3 = R_2$, etc.). How many theoretical stages and what total solvent will be required to reduce the concentration of pyridine to 2% in the final raffinate? Solve on triangular coordinates.

10.5. Two thousand pounds per hour of a 50% pyridine–50% water solution is to be continuously and countercurrently extracted with chlorobenzene to reduce the pyridine concentration to 2%. Using the coordinate systems plotted in (*b*) and (*c*) of Prob. 10.1:

a. Determine the minimum solvent rate required, lb/hr.

  b.   If 2,040 lb solvent/hr is used, what are the number of theoretical stages and the saturated weights of extract and raffinate?   **Ans.:** 3 ideal stages.

  c.   Determine the number of transfer units N_{tOR} for the extraction of (*b*).   **Ans.:** 4.89.

  10.6.   The properties of the solutions have not been completely studied, but from those of the pure constituents the following properties are estimated:

	Density, lb/cu ft	Viscosity, centipoises	Interfacial tension, dynes/cm
Feed	62.1	1.0	8
Extract	65	1.3	
Raffinate	62.2	0.89	35
Solvent	68.5	1.25	

  For the extraction of Prob. 10.5*b* and *c*, chlorobenzene as dispersed phase,

  a.   Recommend a diameter of a tower packed with 1-in. ceramic rings, operating with a dispersed-phase holdup of 10%.   What approach to flooding does this represent?   **Ans.:** 1 ft 9 in.

  b.   Design a perforated tray suitable for the lower part of a tower.   Use $\frac{3}{16}$-in.-diameter perforations and a perforation velocity of 0.5 ft/sec.   Estimate the depth of dispersed liquid accumulating on the tray.

  10.7.   Can the separation of Prob. 10.5 be made by distillation at atmospheric pressure?

  10.8.   Water-dioxane solutions form a minimum-boiling azeotrope at atmospheric pressure and cannot be separated by ordinary distillation methods.   Benzene forms no azeotrope with dioxane and may be used as an extraction solvent.   At 25°C, the equilibrium distribution of dioxane between water and benzene [*J. Am. Chem. Soc.*, **66**, 282 (1944)] is as follows:

Wt % dioxane in water	5.1	18.9	25.2
Wt % dioxane in benzene	5.2	22.5	32.0

  At these concentrations water and benzene are substantially insoluble.   One thousand pounds of a 25% dioxane–75% water solution is to be extracted with benzene to remove 95% of the dioxane. The benzene is dioxane-free.

  a.   Calculate the solvent requirement for a single batch operation.

  b.   If the extraction were done with equal amounts of solvent in five crosscurrent stages, how much solvent would be required?

  10.9.   One thousand pounds per hour of a 25% solution of dioxane in water is to be continuously extracted in countercurrent fashion with benzene to remove 95% of the dioxane.   Equilibrium data are given in Prob. 10.8.

  a.   What is the minimum solvent requirement, lb/hr?

  b.   If 900 lb/hr of solvent is used, how many theoretical stages are required?   **Ans.:** 6.1 ideal stages.

  c.   How many transfer units N_{tOR} correspond to the extraction of (*b*)?

  10.10.   An aqueous solution contains 25% acetone by weight together with a small amount of an undesired contaminant.   For the purpose of a later process, it is necessary to have the acetone dissolved in water without the impurity.   To accomplish this, the solution will be extracted countercurrently with trichloroethane, which extracts the acetone but not the impurity.   The extract will then be countercurrently extracted with pure water in a second extractor to give the desired product water solution, and the recovered solvent will be returned to the first extractor. It is required to obtain 98% of the acetone in the final product. Water and trichloroethane are insoluble over the acetone-concentration range involved, and the distribution coefficient (lb acetone/lb trichloroethane)/(lb acetone/lb water) = 1.65 = const.

a. What is the largest concentration of acetone possible in the recovered solvent?

b. How many stages would be required in each extractor to obtain the acetone in the final water solution at the same concentration as in the original solution?

c. If recovered solvent contains 0.005 lb acetone/lb trichloroethane, if 1 lb trichloroethane/lb water is used in the first extractor, and if the same number of stages is used in each extractor, what concentration of acetone in the final product will result?

10.11. Twenty-four cubic feet per hour of water, containing 0.02 lb mole diethylamine/cu ft, is to be extracted countercurrently with 27.7 cu ft toluene/hr at 30.8°C, in order to remove 90% of the diethylamine. Determine the required height and diameter of a tower packed with 1-in. unglazed porcelain rings, operated at 50% of the flooding velocity.

Equilibrium distribution data are given in Illustration 10.11 and values of H_{tOR} in Fig. 10.61. The densities and viscosities of the liquids may be taken as those of pure water and toluene, and the interfacial tension is estimated to be 30 dynes/cm.

Problems 10.12 to 10.14 refer to the system cottonseed oil (*A*)–liquid propane (*B*)–oleic acid (*C*) at 98.5°C, 625 psia. Smoothed equilibrium tie-line data of Hixson and Bockelmann, *Trans. AIChE,* **38,** 891 (1942), in weight percents, are as follows:

Cottonseed oil	Oleic acid	Propane	Cottonseed oil	Oleic acid	Propane
63.5	0	36.5	2.30	0	97.7
57.2	5.5	37.3	1.95	0.76	97.3
52.0	9.0	39.0	1.78	1.21	97.0
46.7	13.8	39.5	1.50	1.90	96.6
39.8	18.7	41.5	1.36	2.73	95.9
31.0	26.3	42.7	1.20	3.8	95.0
26.9	29.4	43.7	1.10	4.4	94.5
21.0	32.4	46.6	1.0	5.1	93.9
14.2	37.4	48.4	0.8	6.1	93.1
8.3	39.5	52.2	0.7	7.2	92.1
4.5	41.1	54.4	0.4	6.1	93.5
0.8	43.7	55.5	0.2	5.5	94.3

10.12. Plot the equilibrium data on the following coordinate systems: (*a*) *N* against *X* and *Y*; (*b*) *X* against *Y*.

10.13. One hundred pounds of a cottonseed oil–oleic acid solution containing 25% acid is to be extracted twice in crosscurrent fashion, each time with 1,000 lb of propane. Determine the compositions, percent by weight, and the weights of the mixed extracts and the final raffinate. Determine the compositions and weights of the solvent-free products. Make the computations on the coordinates plotted in Prob. 10.12*a*.

10.14. One thousand pounds per hour of a cottonseed oil–oleic acid solution containing 25% acid is to be continuously separated into products containing 2 and 90% acid (solvent-free compositions) by countercurrent extraction with propane.   Make the following computations on the coordinate systems of Prob. 10.12a and b:

   a.   What is the minimum number of theoretical stages required?   **Ans.:** 5.
   b.   What is the minimum external extract-reflux ratio required?   **Ans.:** 3.08.
   c.   For an external extract-reflux ratio of 4.5, determine the number of theoretical stages, the position of the feed stage, and the quantities, in lb/hr, of the following streams: E_1, B_E, E', R_0, R_{Np}, P'_E, and S.   **Ans.:** 10.5 ideal stages.
   d.   What do the equilibrium data indicate as to the maximum purity of oleic acid that could be obtained?

   Problems 10.15 and 10.16 refer to the system oxalic and succinic acids distributed between water and n-amyl alcohol.   The acids distribute practically independently of each other, and for present purposes they will be considered to do so.   Equilibrium concentrations, expressed as g acid/liter, are:

Either acid in water	0	20	40	60
Oxalic in alcohol	0	6.0	13.0	21.5
Succinic in alcohol	0	12.0	23.5	35.0

The water and amyl alcohol are essentially immiscible.   In the calculations, express acid concentrations as g/liter and solvent rates as liters/time.

   10.15.   A water solution containing 50 g each of oxalic and succinic acids per liter of water is to be extracted countercurrently with n-amyl alcohol (free of acid) to recover 95% of the oxalic acid.
   a.   Compute the minimum solvent required, liters alcohol/liter water.
   b.   If an alcohol/water ratio of 3.8 liters/liter is used, compute the number of ideal stages required and the solvent-free analysis of the extract product.   **Ans.:** 9 ideal stages.

   10.16.   A mixture of succinic (B) and oxalic (C) acids containing 50% of each is to be separated into products each 90% pure on a solvent-free basis, using n-amyl alcohol (A) and water (D) by a fractional extraction.
   a.   Calculate the number of ideal stages and the location of the feed stage if 9 liters of alcohol and 4 liters of water are used per 100 g of acid feed.   **Ans.:** 12.75 stages.
   b.   Investigate the effect of solvent ratio on the number of stages, keeping the total liquid flow constant.   What is the least number of stages required and the corresponding solvent ratio?

PART FOUR
SOLID-FLUID
OPERATIONS

The mass-transfer operations in this category to be considered in detail are adsorption, drying, and leaching. Others which are less frequently used are included in Part 5. Adsorption involves contact of solids with either liquids or gases, with mass transfer in the direction fluid to solid. Drying involves gas-solid, and leaching liquid-solid, contact, with mass transfer in each case in the direction solid to fluid. In many but not all applications, the last two may be considered as special cases of desorption, the reverse of adsorption. Adsorption is thus more general, in principle at least, and is considered first.

Theoretically, at least, the same apparatus and equipment useful for gas-solid or liquid-solid contact in adsorption should also be useful in the corresponding operations of drying and leaching. In practice, however, we find special types of apparatus in all three categories. This is probably the result of many years of development of the practical applications of these operations without the realization that basically they are very similar. For example, we find considerable inventive genius applied to the development of equipment for the continuous gas-solid operations of adsorption, but little application of the results to the problem of drying. Many clever devices have been developed for continuous leaching of solids with liquids, but there is little application of these to the practical problems of adsorption from liquids. Ideal devices have not yet been invented. But we may reasonably expect a reduction in the number of equipment types and greater interapplication among the three operations as the many problems of solids handling are eventually solved.

In developing the quantitative treatment of these operations, particularly the diverse applications of adsorption, considerable simplification results if advantage is taken of the resemblances to the gas and liquid operations previously considered.   This introduces many problems of mathematical notation, however, and the student is advised to pay more than ordinary attention to the tables of notation at the end of each chapter.   Complete consistency with the notation of the previous chapters seemed impossible to realize.

CHAPTER ELEVEN
ADSORPTION AND
ION EXCHANGE

The adsorption operations exploit the ability of certain solids preferentially to concentrate specific substances from solution onto their surfaces. In this manner, the components of either gaseous or liquid solutions may be separated from each other. A few examples will indicate the general nature of the separations possible and at the same time demonstrate the great variety of practical applications. In the field of gaseous separations, adsorption is used to dehumidify air and other gases, to remove objectionable odors and impurities from industrial gases such as carbon dioxide, to recover valuable solvent vapors from dilute mixtures with air and other gases, and to fractionate mixtures of hydrocarbon gases containing such substances as methane, ethylene, ethane, propylene, and propane. Typical liquid separations include the removal of moisture dissolved in gasoline, decolorization of petroleum products and aqueous sugar solutions, removal of objectionable taste and odor from water, and the fractionation of mixtures of aromatic and paraffinic hydrocarbons.

These operations are all similar in that the mixture to be separated is brought into contact with another insoluble phase, the adsorbent solid, and the unequal distribution of the original constituents between the adsorbed phase on the solid surface and the bulk of the fluid then permits a separation to be made. All the techniques previously found valuable in the contact of insoluble fluids are useful in adsorption. Thus we have batchwise single-stage and continuous multistage separations and separations analogous to countercurrent absorption and stripping in the field of gas-liquid contact and to rectification and extraction with the use of reflux. In addition, the rigidity and immobility of a bed of solid adsorbent particles makes possible useful application of semicontinuous methods which are not at all practicable when two fluids are contacted.

Another solid-liquid operation of great importance is ion exchange, the reversible exchange of ions between certain solids and an electrolyte solution, which permits the separation and fractionation of electrolytic solutes. It is, of course, chemical in nature but involves not only the interaction of the ions with the solid but also diffusion of ions within the solid phase. Although the phenomenon may be more complex than adsorption, the general techniques and the results obtained are very similar. The special features of ion exchange are considered separately at the end of this chapter.

Types of adsorption

We must distinguish at the start between two types of adsorption phenomena, physical and chemical.

Physical adsorption, or "van der Waals" adsorption, a readily reversible phenomenon, is the result of intermolecular forces of attraction between molecules of the solid and the substance adsorbed. When, for example, the intermolecular attractive forces between a solid and a gas are greater than those existing between molecules of the gas itself, the gas will condense upon the surface of the solid even though its pressure may be lower than the vapor pressure corresponding to the prevailing temperature. Such a condensation will be accompanied by an evolution of heat, in amount usually somewhat larger than the latent heat of vaporization and of the order of the heat of sublimation of the gas. The adsorbed substance does not penetrate within the crystal lattice of the solid and does not dissolve in it but remains entirely upon the surface. If, however, the solid is highly porous, containing many fine capillaries, the adsorbed substance will penetrate these interstices if it wets the solid. The equilibrium vapor pressure of a concave liquid surface of very small radius of curvature is lower than that of a large flat surface, and the extent of adsorption is correspondingly increased. In any case, at equilibrium the partial pressure of the adsorbed substance equals that of the contacting gas phase, and by lowering the pressure of the gas phase or by raising the temperature the adsorbed gas is readily removed or desorbed in unchanged form. Industrial adsorption operations of the type we shall consider depend upon this reversibility for recovery of the adsorbent for reuse, for recovery of the adsorbed substance, or for the fractionation of mixtures. Reversible adsorption is not confined to gases but is observed in the case of liquids as well.

Chemisorption, or activated adsorption, is the result of chemical interaction between the solid and the adsorbed substance. The strength of the chemical bond may vary considerably, and identifiable chemical compounds in the usual sense may not actually form, but the adhesive force is generally much greater than that found in physical adsorption.   The heat liberated during chemisorption is usually large, of the order of the heat of chemical reaction.   The process is frequently irreversible, and on desorption the original substance will often be found to have undergone a chemical change.   The same substance which, under conditions of low temperature, will undergo substantially only physical adsorption upon a solid will sometimes exhibit chemisorption at higher temperatures, and both phenomena may occur at the same time. Chemisorption is of particular importance in catalysis but will not be considered here.

Nature of adsorbents

Adsorbent solids are usually used in granular form, varying in size from roughly $\frac{1}{2}$ in. in diameter to as small as 50 μ.   The solids must possess certain engineering properties depending upon the application to which they are put   If they are used in a fixed bed through which a liquid or gas is to flow, for example, they must not offer too great a pressure drop for flow nor must they easily be carried away by the flowing stream.   They must have adequate strength and hardness so as not to be reduced in size during handling or crushed in supporting their own weight in beds of the required thickness.   If they are to be transported frequently in and out of bins, they should be free-flowing.   These are properties which are readily recognized.

The adsorptive ability of solids is quite another matter.   Adsorption is a very general phenomenon, and even common solids will adsorb gases and vapors at least to a certain extent.   For example, every student of analytical chemistry has observed with annoyance the increase in weight of a dried porcelain crucible on a humid day during an analytical weighing, owing to the adsorption of moisture from the air upon the crucible surface.   But only certain solids exhibit sufficient specificity and adsorptive capacity to make them useful as industrial adsorbents.   Since solids are frequently very specific in their ability to adsorb certain substances in large amounts, the chemical nature of the solid evidently has much to do with its adsorption characteristics.   But mere chemical identity is insufficient to characterize its usefulness.   In liquid extraction, all samples of pure butyl acetate will extract acetic acid from a water solution with identical ability.   The same is not true for the adsorption characteristics of silica gel with respect to water vapor, for example.   Much depends on its method of manufacture and on its prior history of adsorption and desorption.

Large surface per unit weight seems essential to all useful adsorbents.   Particularly in the case of gas adsorption, the significant surface is not the gross surface of the granular particles which are ordinarily used but rather the very much larger surface of the internal pores of the particles.   The pores are usually very small, sometimes of the order of a few molecular diameters in width, but their large number provides an enormous surface for adsorption.   It is estimated, for example, that a typical gasmask charcoal has an effective surface of 1,000,000 sq m/kg.[33]   There are many other properties evidently of great importance which are not at all understood, and we must depend largely on empirical observation for recognition of adsorptive ability.   The following is a list of the principal adsorbents in general use.   For a complete description the student is referred to a more extensive treatment of the subject.[21,33]

1. *Fuller's earths.* These are natural clays, the American varieties coming largely from Florida and Georgia. They are chiefly magnesium aluminum silicates in the form of the minerals attapulgite and montmorillonite. The clay is heated and dried, during which operation it develops a porous structure, ground, and screened. Commercially available sizes range from coarse granules to fine powders. The clays are particularly useful in decolorizing, neutralizing, and drying such petroleum products as lubricating oils, transformer oils, kerosenes, and gasolines, as well as vegetable and animal oils. By washing and burning the adsorbed organic matter accumulating upon the clay during use, the adsorbent may be reused many times.

2. *Activated clays.* These are bentonite or other clays which show essentially no adsorptive ability unless activated by treatment with sulfuric or hydrochloric acid. Following such treatment, the clay is washed, dried, and ground to a fine powder. It is particularly useful for decolorizing petroleum products and is ordinarily discarded after a single application.

3. *Bauxite.* This is a certain form of naturally occurring hydrated alumina which must be activated by heating to temperatures varying from 450 to 1500°F in order to develop its adsorptive ability. It is used for decolorizing petroleum products and for drying of gases and may be reactivated by heating.

4. *Alumina.* This is a hard, hydrated aluminum oxide which is activated by heating to drive off the moisture. The porous product is available as granules or powders, and it is used chiefly as a desiccant for gases and liquids. It may be reactivated for reuse.

5. *Bone char.* This is obtained by the destructive distillation of crushed, dried bones at temperatures in the range 1100 to 1600°F. It is used chiefly in the refining of sugar and may be reused after washing and burning.

6. *Decolorizing carbons.* These are variously made by (*a*) mixing vegetable matter with inorganic substances such as calcium chloride, carbonizing, and leaching away the inorganic matter, (*b*) mixing organic matter such as sawdust, etc., with porous substances such as pumice stone, followed by heating and carbonizing to deposit the carbonaceous matter throughout the porous particles, and (*c*) carbonizing wood, sawdust, and the like, followed by activation with hot air or steam. They are used for a great variety of purposes, including the decolorizing of solutions of sugar, industrial chemicals, drugs, and dry-cleaning liquids, water purification, and refining of vegetable and animal oils.·

7. *Gas-adsorbent carbon.* This is made by carbonization of coconut shells, fruit pits, coal, and wood. It must be activated, essentially a partial oxidation process, by treatment with hot air or steam. It is available in granular or pelleted form and is used for recovery of solvent vapors from gas mixtures, in gas masks, and for the fractionation of hydrocarbon gases. It is revivified for reuse by evaporation of the adsorbed gas.

8. *Silica gel.* This is a hard, granular, very porous product made from the gel precipitated by acid treatment of sodium silicate solution. Its moisture content prior to use varies from roughly 4 to 7 percent, and it is used principally for dehydration of air and other gases, in gas masks, and for fractionation of hydrocarbons. It is revivified for reuse by evaporation of the adsorbed matter.

9. *Molecular sieves.* These are porous, synthetic zeolite crystals, metal aluminosilicates. The "cages" of the crystal cells can entrap adsorbed matter, and the diameter of the passageways, controlled by the crystal composition, regulates the size of the molecules which may enter or be excluded. The sieves can thus separate according to molecular size, but they also separate by adsorption according to molecular polarity and degree of unsaturation. They are used for dehydration of gases and liquids, separation of gas and liquid hydrocarbon mixtures, and in a great variety of processes. They are regenerated by heating or elution.

ADSORPTION EQUILIBRIA

The great bulk of the experimental data pertaining to adsorption represents equilibrium measurements. Many of them were gathered in an attempt to provide corroboration for one or another of the many theories which have been advanced in an

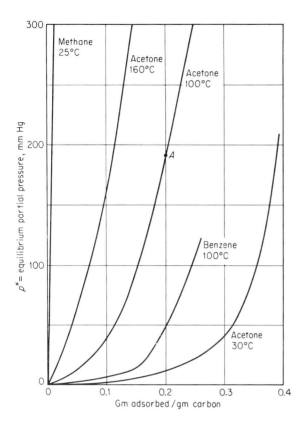

Fig. 11.1 *Equilibrium adsorption on an activated carbon.*

attempt to explain the adsorption phenomena. No one theory has yet been devised which satisfactorily explains even a majority of the observations, and this discussion is therefore limited simply to a description of the more commonly observed adsorption characteristics. The theories are reviewed elsewhere.[5,6,43]

SINGLE GASES AND VAPORS

In many respects the equilibrium adsorption characteristics of a gas or vapor upon a solid resemble the equilibrium solubility of a gas in a liquid. Figure 11.1 shows several equilibrium adsorption isotherms for a particular activated carbon as adsorbent, where the concentration of adsorbed gas (the adsorbate) on the solid is plotted against the equilibrium partial pressure $p*$ of the vapor or gas at constant temperature. Curves of this sort are analogous to those of Fig. 8.1. At 100°C, for example, pure acetone vapor at a pressure of 190 mm Hg is in equilibrium with an adsorbate concentration of 0.2 g adsorbed acetone/g carbon, point A. Increasing the pressure of the acetone will cause more to be adsorbed, as the rising curve indicates, and decreasing the pressure of the system at A will cause acetone to be desorbed from the carbon.

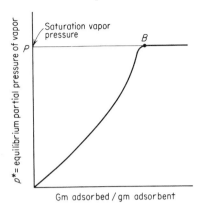

Fig. 11.2 *Typical complete-adsorption isotherm.*

While not determined experimentally in this case, it is known that the 100°C isotherm for acetone will continue to rise only to a pressure of 2,790 mm Hg, the saturation vapor pressure of acetone at this temperature. At higher pressures, no acetone can exist in the vapor state at this temperature but instead will condense entirely to a liquid. It will thus be possible to obtain indefinitely large concentrations of the substance on the solid at pressures higher than the vapor pressure, as at point *B* (Fig. 11.2). However, concentrations in excess of that corresponding to point *B* indicate liquefaction, but not necessarily adsorption of the vapor. Gases above their critical temperature, of course, do not show this characteristic.

Different gases and vapors are adsorbed to different extents under comparable conditions. Thus benzene (Fig. 11.1) is more readily adsorbed than acetone at the same temperature and gives a higher adsorbate concentration for a given equilibrium pressure. As a general rule, vapors and gases are more readily adsorbed the higher their molecular weight and the lower their critical temperature, although chemical differences such as the extent of unsaturation in the molecule also influence the extent of adsorption. The so-called permanent gases are usually adsorbed only to a relatively small extent, as the methane isotherm of Fig. 11.1 indicates.

Adsorption isotherms are not always concave to the pressure axis. The shapes shown in Fig. 11.3 have all been observed for various systems. Here the ordinate is plotted as equilibrium partial pressure p^* divided by the saturation vapor pressure P of the adsorbed substance (actually, the relative saturation) in order to place all the curves on a comparable basis.

It will be recalled that a change of liquid solvent alters profoundly the equilibrium solubility of a gas except in the case of ideal liquid solutions. In a similar fashion the equilibrium curves for acetone, benzene, and methane on silica gel as adsorbent would be entirely different from those of Fig. 11.1. Indeed, differences in the origin and method of preparation of an adsorbent will result in significant differences in the equilibrium adsorption as well. For this reason, many of the data gathered years ago are no longer of practical value, since methods of preparing adsorbents, and consequently the corresponding adsorbent capacities, have improved greatly over the

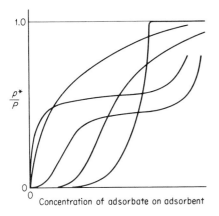

Concentration of adsorbate on adsorbent   **Fig. 11.3**   *Types of adsorption isotherms for vapors.*

years.   Repeated adsorption and desorption will also frequently alter the characteristics of a particular adsorbent, owing perhaps to progressive changes in the pore
structure within the solid.

Adsorption hysteresis

The curves of Fig. 11.1 are true equilibrium curves and therefore represent completely
reversible phenomena.   The conditions corresponding to point A on the figure, for
example, can be obtained either by adsorption onto fresh carbon or by desorption of a
sample with an initially higher adsorbate concentration.   Occasionally, however,
different equilibria result, at least over a part of an isotherm, depending upon whether
the vapor is adsorbed or desorbed, and this gives rise to the hysteresis phenomenon
indicated in Fig. 11.4.   This may be the result of the shape of the openings to the
capillaries and pores of the solid or of complex phenomena of wetting of the solid by
the adsorbate.   In any case, when hysteresis is observed, the desorption equilibrium
pressure is always lower than that obtained by adsorption.

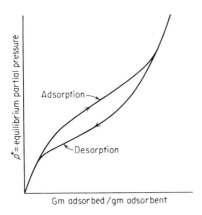

Gm adsorbed /gm adsorbent   **Fig. 11.4**   *Adsorption isotherms showing hysteresis.*

Effect of temperature

Since adsorption is an exothermic process, the concentration of adsorbed gas decreases with increased temperature at a given equilibrium pressure, as the several acetone isotherms of Fig. 11.1 indicate.

The reference-substance method of plotting, described in Chap. 8 for gas-liquid solubilities, is conveniently applicable also to adsorption data.[36] As reference substance it is best to use the pure substance being adsorbed, unless the temperatures are above the critical temperature. Figure 11.5, for example, was prepared for the adsorption of acetone vapor on activated carbon with acetone as reference substance. The abscissa of the logarithmic coordinates was marked with the vapor pressure of pure acetone, and the corresponding saturation temperatures were also marked. The equilibrium partial pressure of adsorbate was plotted on the ordinate. Points of equal temperature for the vapor pressure of pure acetone and the partial pressure of adsorbate were then plotted. Thus, point A of Fig. 11.1 ($p^* = 190$ mm Hg, 100°C) was plotted on Fig. 11.5 at A, where $P = 2{,}790$ mm Hg, the vapor pressure of acetone at 100°C. Points of constant adsorbate concentration (isosteres) form straight lines with few exceptions, and thus only two points are required to establish each.

Figure 11.6 shows all the same data plotted in such a manner as to reduce all the measurements to a single curve, thereby permitting considerable extension of meager

Fig. 11.5 *Reference-substance plot of equilibrium adsorption of acetone on an activated carbon.* [*Data of Josefewitz and Othmer: Ind. Eng. Chem.*, **40**, 739 (1948).]

Fig. 11.6 *Adsorption of acetone on an activated carbon, 30 to 200°C.*

data.   The free energy of compression of 1 mole of a gas from the equilibrium adsorption pressure p^* to the vapor pressure P, the "adsorption potential," is $RT \ln (P/p^*)$. In the case of single substances, when this quantity is plotted against adsorbate concentration, a single curve results for all temperatures, at least over a moderate temperature range.[14]   The ordinate of Fig. 11.6 is proportional to this quantity.   More complex methods of expressing the adsorbate concentration may be used to provide improved and extended correlations of the data.

Heat of adsorption

The *differential heat of adsorption* $(-\bar{H})$ is defined as the heat liberated at constant temperature when unit quantity of vapor is adsorbed upon a large quantity of solid already containing adsorbate.   Such a large quantity of solid is used that the adsorbate concentration is unchanged.   The *integral heat of adsorption* at any concentration X

of adsorbate upon the solid is defined as the enthalpy of the adsorbate-adsorbent combination minus the sum of the enthalpies of unit weight of pure solid adsorbent and sufficient pure adsorbed substance (before adsorption) to provide the required concentration X, all at the same temperature. These are both functions of temperature and adsorbate concentration for any system.

Othmer and Sawyer[36] have shown that plots of the type shown in Fig. 11.5 are useful in estimating the heat of adsorption, which may be calculated in a manner similar to that for the latent heat of vaporization of a pure liquid (see Chap. 7). Thus, the slope of an isostere of Fig. 11.5 is

$$\frac{d \ln p^*}{d \ln P} = \frac{(-\bar{H})M}{\lambda_r M_r} \tag{11.1}$$

where $\bar{H}$, Btu/lb of vapor adsorbed, is referred to the pure vapor and λ_r is the latent heat of vaporization of the reference substance at the same temperature, Btu/lb. M and M_r are the molecular weights of the vapor and reference substance, respectively. If $\bar{H}$ is computed at constant temperature for each isostere, then the integral heat of adsorption at this temperature may be computed from the relation

$$\Delta H'_A = \int_0^X \bar{H} \, dX \tag{11.2}$$

$\Delta H'_A$, Btu/lb of adsorbate-free solid, is referred to the pure vapor, and X is the adsorbate concentration, lb adsorbate/lb solid. The integral may be evaluated graphically by determining the area under a curve of $\bar{H}$ against X. The integral heat of adsorption referred to solid and the adsorbed substance in the liquid state is $\Delta H_A = \Delta H'_A + \lambda X$, Btu/lb solid. The quantities $\bar{H}$, ΔH_A, and $\Delta H'_A$ are negative quantities if heat is evolved during adsorption.

Illustration 11.1. Estimate the integral heat of adsorption of acetone upon activated carbon at 30°C as a function of adsorbate concentration.

Solution. Refer to Fig. 11.5. The isosteres for various concentrations are straight on this diagram, and their slopes are measured with the help of a millimeter rule. In the accompanying table, column 1 lists the adsorbate concentrate of each isostere and column 2 the corresponding slope.

X, $\dfrac{\text{lb acetone}}{\text{lb carbon}}$	Slope of isostere	Differential heat of adsorption, $\bar{H}$, Btu/lb acetone	Integral heat of adsorption, Btu/lb carbon	
			$\Delta H'_A$, referred to acetone vapor	ΔH_A, referred to acetone liquid
(1)	(2)	(3)	(4)	(5)
0.05	1.170	−275	−12.8	−0.9
0.10	1.245	−295	−27.1	−3.4
0.15	1.300	−308	−42.1	−6.5
0.20	1.310	−310	−57.6	−10.2
0.25	1.340	−318	−73.3	−14.0
0.30	1.327	−314	−89.1	−18.0

Since in this case the adsorbate and reference substance are the same, $M = M_r$ and consequently $\bar{H} = -\lambda_r$ (slope of isostere). At 30°C, $\lambda_r = \lambda$, the latent heat of vaporization of acetone $= 237$ Btu/lb. Column 3 of the table lists values of $\bar{H}$ calculated in this manner.

Column 3 was plotted as ordinate against column 1 as abscissa (not shown). The area under the curve between $X = 0$ and any value of X is listed in column 4 as the corresponding integral heat of adsorption, referred to acetone vapor. Thus the area under the curve between $X = 0$ and $X = 0.20 = -57.6$. If 0.20 lb acetone vapor at 30°C is adsorbed on 1 lb fresh carbon at 30°C and the product brought to 30°C, 57.6 Btu will be evolved.

Column 5, the integral heat of adsorption referred to liquid acetone, is computed from the relation $\Delta H_A = \Delta H_A' + \lambda X$. Thus, at $X = 0.20$, $\Delta H_A = -57.6 + 237(0.20) = -10.2$ Btu/lb carbon.

VAPOR AND GAS MIXTURES

It is necessary to distinguish between mixtures depending upon whether one or several of the components are adsorbed.

One component adsorbed

In the case of many mixtures, particularly vapor-gas mixtures, only one component is appreciably adsorbed. This would be the circumstance for a mixture of acetone vapor and methane in contact with activated carbon (Fig. 11.1), for example. In such instances, the adsorption of the vapor will be substantially unaffected by the presence of the poorly adsorbed gas, and the adsorption isotherm for the pure vapor will be applicable provided the equilibrium pressure is taken as the *partial* pressure of the vapor in the vapor-gas mixture. The isotherms for acetone (Fig. 11.1) thus apply for mixtures of acetone with any poorly adsorbed gas such as nitrogen, hydrogen, and the like. This is similar to the corresponding case of gas-liquid solubility.

Binary gas or vapor mixtures, both components appreciably adsorbed

When both components of a binary gas or vapor mixture are separately adsorbed to roughly the same extent, the amount of either one adsorbed from the mixture will be affected by the presence of the other. Since such systems are composed of three components when the adsorbent is included, the equilibrium data are conveniently shown in the manner used for ternary liquid equilibria in Chap. 10. For this purpose it is convenient to consider the solid adsorbent as being analogous to liquid solvent in extraction operations. However, adsorption is greatly influenced by both temperature and pressure, unlike liquid solubility, which is scarcely affected by pressure under ordinary circumstances. Equilibrium diagrams are consequently best plotted at constant temperature and constant total pressure, and they are therefore simultaneously *isotherms* and *isobars*.

A typical system is shown in Fig. 11.7 on triangular and rectangular coordinates. The properties of these coordinate systems and the relations between them were considered in detail in Chap. 10. Even though mole fraction is generally a more convenient concentration unit in dealing with gases, the figure is plotted in terms of weight-fraction compositions since the molecular weight of the adsorbent is uncertain.†

---

† Alternatively, some arbitrary molecular weight could be assigned to the adsorbent.

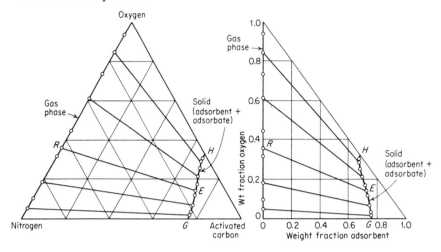

Fig. 11.7 *System oxygen–nitrogen–activated carbon,* $-150°C$, *1 atm, concentrations expressed as weight fractions.* [*Data of Maslan, Altman, and Aberth: J. Phys. Chem.,* **57**, 106 (1953).]

Since the adsorbent is not volatile and does not appear in the gas phase, the equilibrium gas compositions fall upon one axis of either graph, as shown.   Points G and H represent the adsorbate concentration for the individual pure gases and the curve GEH that of gas mixtures.   Tie. lines such as line RE join equilibrium compositions of the gas and adsorbate.   The fact that the tie lines do not, when extended, pass through the adsorbent apex indicates that under the prevailing conditions the adsorbent can be used to separate the binary gas mixture into its components.   The separation factor, or *relative adsorptivity,* similar to relative volatility in distillation or selectivity in liquid extraction, is obtained by dividing the equilibrium ratio of gas compositions in the adsorbate (as at point E) by the ratio in the gas (as at R).   The relative adsorptivity must be larger than unity if the adsorbent is to be useful for separating the components of the gas mixture.   In the system of Fig. 11.7 the more strongly adsorbed of the two pure gases (oxygen) is also selectively adsorbed from any mixture. This appears to be true for most mixtures, although an inversion of the relative adsorptivity in some systems (analogous to azeotropism in distillation) is certainly a possibility.

    Especially when the extent of adsorption is small, it will be more convenient to express compositions on an adsorbent-free basis and to plot them in the manner of Fig. 11.8.   Such diagrams are also analogous to those used in liquid extraction (Fig. 10.30, for example), where adsorbent solid and extraction solvent play an analogous role, and to the enthalpy-concentration diagrams of distillation, where heat is analogous to adsorbent.   The adsorption characteristics of the binary gas mixture acetylene-ethylene on silica gel for one temperature and pressure are shown in Fig. 11.8a.   In the upper portion of this figure, the gas phase appears entirely along the abscissa of the plot owing to the absence of adsorbent in the gas.   The adsorbent-free equilibrium compositions corresponding to the tie lines may be plotted in the lower half of the diagram, as at point (R,E), to produce a figure analogous to the xy diagram of distillation.   Silica gel selectively adsorbs acetylene from these gas mixtures.

The powerful influence of the adsorbent on the equilibrium is demonstrated with the same gas mixture by Fig. 11.8b, where activated carbon is the adsorbent.   Not only is the extent of adsorption greater than for silica gel so that the curve GH is lower than the corresponding curve for silica gel, but in addition the relative adsorptivity is reversed: ethylene is selectively adsorbed on activated carbon.   In both cases, however, that gas which is separately more strongly adsorbed on each adsorbent is selectively adsorbed from mixtures.   If a condition corresponding to azeotropism should arise, the curve of the lower half of these figures would cross the 45° diagonal line.   In cases such as Fig. 11.8b, it will generally be preferable to plot compositions

Fig. 11.8   *Adsorption of acetylene-ethylene on (a) silica gel and (b) activated carbon, at 25°C, 1 atm.   [Data of Lewis et al.: J. Am. Chem. Soc.,* **72,** *1157 (1950).]*

in terms of the more strongly adsorbed gas (ethylene), to keep the appearance of the diagram similar to those used previously in liquid extraction.

Effect of change of pressure or temperature

The available data are meager, and generalizations are very difficult to make. Lowering the pressure will of course reduce the amount of adsorbate upon the adsorbent, as shown in the upper half of Fig. 11.9. In those cases investigated over

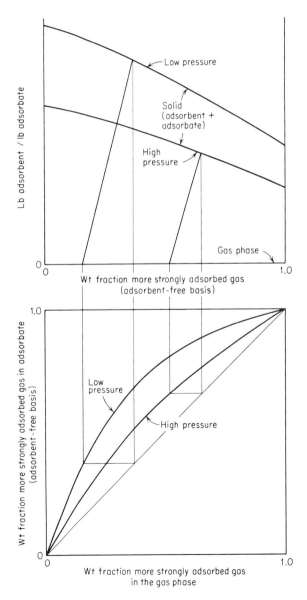

Fig. 11.9 *Effect of pressure on adsorption isotherms for binary gas mixtures.*

any appreciable pressure range[12,30] the relative adsorptivity of paraffin hydrocarbons on carbon decreased at increased pressure, as shown in the lower part of this figure, just as it does in the case of distillation. Owing to the increased tendency toward liquid condensation in the absorbent capillaries at higher pressures, the equilibrium may simply be shifting toward the ordinary vapor-liquid equilibrium with increased pressure, and in each of the investigated cases this corresponded to lower separation factor. Increasing the temperature at constant pressure will decrease the amount adsorbed from a mixture and will influence the relative adsorptivity as well, but in a manner for which no generalizations can now be made. A beginning has been made on the estimation of the adsorption of mixed vapors whose liquid solutions are not ideal.[20]

LIQUIDS

When an adsorbent solid is immersed in a pure liquid, the evolution of heat, known as the heat of wetting, is evidence that adsorption of the liquid does occur. But immersion does not provide an effective method of measuring the extent of adsorption. No appreciable volume change of the liquid which might be used as a measure of adsorption is ordinarily observed, while withdrawal of the solid and weighing it will not distinguish between the adsorbed liquid and that which is mechanically occluded. This problem does not exist in the case of adsorption of gases, where the change in weight of the solid owing to adsorption is readily measured.

Adsorption of solute from dilute solution

When an adsorbent is mixed with a binary solution, adsorption of both solute and solvent occurs. Since the total adsorption cannot be measured, the relative or apparent adsorption of solute is determined instead. The customary procedure is to treat a known volume of solution with a known weight of adsorbent, V cu ft solution/lb adsorbent. As a result of preferential adsorption of solute, the solute concentration of the liquid is observed to fall from the initial value c_0 to the final equilibrium value c^* lb solute/cu ft liquid. The apparent adsorption of solute, neglecting any volume change in the solution, is then $V(c_0 - c^*)$ lb solute adsorbed/lb adsorbent. This is satisfactory for dilute solutions when the fraction of the original solvent which may be adsorbed is small.

Correction is sometimes made for the volume of the solute apparently adsorbed. Thus, the initial solvent content of this solution is $V(1 - c_0/\rho)$, and on the assumption that no solvent is adsorbed, the volume of residual solution is $V(1 - c_0/\rho)/(1 - c^*/\rho)$. The apparent solute adsorption is then the difference between initial and final solute content of the liquid, $Vc_0 - [V(1 - c_0/\rho)/(1 - c^*/\rho)]c^*$ or $V(c_0 - c^*)/(1 - c^*/\rho)$. This, of course, still neglects solvent adsorption.

The apparent adsorption of a given solute depends upon the concentration of solute, the temperature, the solvent, and the type of adsorbent. Typical isotherms are shown in Fig. 11.10. Isotherms of all the indicated forms have been observed, for example, when a given solute is adsorbed on the same adsorbent, but from different

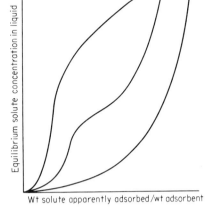

Fig. 11.10 *Typical adsorption isotherms for dilute solutions.*

solvents. The extent of adsorption of a given solute practically always decreases at increased temperature and usually is greater the smaller the solubility in the solvent. It is usually reversible, so that the same isotherm results whether solute is desorbed or adsorbed.

The Freundlich equation

Over a small concentration range, and particularly for dilute solutions, the adsorption isotherms may frequently be described by an empirical expression usually attributed to Freundlich,

$$c^* = k[V(c_0 - c^*)]^n \tag{11.3}$$

where $V(c_0 - c^*)$ is the apparent adsorption per unit weight of adsorbent and k and n are constants. Other concentration units are frequently used also, and while these

Fig. 11.11 *Adsorption from a dilute solution.* [*Data of Bartell, et al.: J. Phys. Chem.,* **33**, 676 (1929); *J. Phys. Colloid. Chem.,* **55**, 1456 (1951).*]

Fig. 11.12   *Decolorization of cylinder oil with clay.*
[*Data of Rogers, et al.: Ind. Eng. Chem.,* **18**, 164 (1926).]

will result in different values of k, for the dilute solutions for which the equation is applicable the value of n will be unaffected.   The form of the equation indicates that plotting the equilibrium solute concentration as ordinate against adsorbate content of the solid as abscissa on logarithmic coordinates will provide a straight line of slope n and intercept k.   Several typical isotherms are plotted in this manner in Fig. 11.11. The effect of the nature of the solvent on adsorption of benzoic acid on silica gel is shown by curves a and b, which follow Eq. (11.3) excellently over the concentration range shown.   The adsorption is less strong from benzene solutions, which is to be expected in view of the higher solubility of the acid in this solvent.   Curve c of this figure shows the deviation from linearity to be expected over large concentration ranges, although Eq. (11.3) is applicable for the lower concentration ranges.   Failure of the data to follow the equation at high solute concentrations may be the result of appreciable adsorption of the solvent which is not taken into account or simply general inapplicability of the expression.

The Freundlich equation is also frequently useful in cases where the actual identity of the solute is not known, as in the adsorption of colored substances from such materials as sugar solutions and mineral or vegetable oils.   In such cases, the concentration of solute may be measured by means of a colorimeter or spectrophotometer and expressed in terms of arbitrary units of color intensity, provided that the color scale used varies linearly with the concentration of the responsible solute. Figure 11.12 illustrates the application of this method of plotting the adsorption of colored substances from a petroleum fraction on two adsorbent clays.   Here the color concentrations of the solutions are measured on an arbitrary scale, and the concentration of adsorbate on the clay determined by measuring the change in color expressed in these terms when 100 g of oil is treated with various amounts of clay.

Adsorption from concentrated solutions

When the apparent adsorption of solute is determined over the entire range of concentrations from pure solvent to pure solute, curves such as those of Fig. 11.13 will result. Curves of the shape marked *a* occur when at all concentrations the solute is adsorbed more strongly relative to the solvent. At increasing solute concentrations, the extent of solute adsorption may actually continue to increase; yet the curve showing apparent solute adsorption necessarily returns to point *E*, since in a liquid consisting of pure solute alone there will be no concentration change on addition of adsorbent. In cases where both solvent and solute are adsorbed to nearly the same extent, the S-shaped curves of type *b* are produced. In the range of concentrations from *C* to *D*, solute is more strongly adsorbed than solvent. At point *D*, both are equally well adsorbed, and the apparent adsorption falls to zero. In the range of concentrations from *D* to *E*, solvent is more strongly adsorbed. Consequently, on addition of adsorbent to such solutions, the solute concentration of the liquid increases, and the quantity $V(c_0 - c^*)$ indicates an apparent *negative* solute adsorption.

The true adsorption of the substances may be estimated from apparent adsorption data if some mechanism for the process, such as the applicability of the Freundlich isotherm, separately for each component, is assumed.[3] In this manner, curves such as those of Fig. 11.14 can be computed from the S-shaped apparent adsorption data (note that such data characteristically show a situation analogous to azeotropism in distillation, with relative adsorptivity equal to unity at some liquid concentration). It has been shown, however, that such isotherms are not always applicable, and another approach is to determine the adsorption of a liquid solution by measuring that of the vapor in equilibrium with the liquid.[26,32]

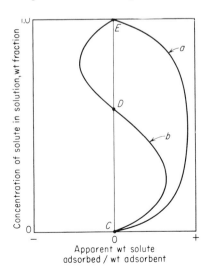

Concentration of solute in solution, wt fraction

Apparent wt solute
adsorbed / wt adsorbent

Fig. 11.13   *Apparent adsorption of solute from solutions.*

Fig. 11.14 *Calculated adsorption of benzene and ethanol by activated carbon (Bartell and Sloan.[3])*

ADSORPTION OPERATIONS

Adsorption is unique in the very diverse nature of its applications. For example, it is applied to such a wide variety of processes as recovery of vapors from dilute mixture with gases, solute recovery and removal of contaminants from solution, and the fractionation of gas and liquid mixtures. The techniques used include both stagewise and continuous-contacting methods, and these are applied to batch, continuous, and semicontinuous operations. Within each of these categories it is possible to recognize operations which are exactly analogous to those already discussed in previous chapters of this book. Thus, when only one component of a fluid mixture (either a gas or a liquid) is strongly adsorbed, the separation of the mixture is analogous for purposes of calculation to gas absorption, where the added insoluble phase is adsorbent in the present case and liquid solvent in the case of absorption. When both components of the fluid (either gas or liquid) are adsorbed strongly, the separation requires a fractionation procedure. The operation is then conveniently considered as being analogous to liquid extraction, where the added insoluble adsorbent corresponds to the use of solvent in extraction. By this means many simplifications in the treatment become possible.

I. STAGEWISE OPERATION

Liquid solutions, where the solute to be removed is adsorbed relatively strongly compared with the remainder of the solution, are treated in batch, semicontinuous, or continuous operations in a manner analogous to the mixer-settler operations of liquid extraction (*contact filtration*). Continuous countercurrent cascades may be simulated or actually realized by use of such techniques as fluidized beds.

Gases are treated for solute removal or for fractionation, usually with fluidized-bed techniques.

Contact filtration of liquids

Typical process applications include:

1. The collection of valuable solutes from dilute solutions, as, for example, the adsorption onto carbon of iodine from brines, after liberation of the element from its salts by oxidation; and the collection of insulin from dilute solutions.

2. The removal of undesirable contaminants from a solution.

Owing to the extremely favorable equilibrium distribution of solute toward the adsorbent which is frequently possible, adsorption becomes a powerful tool for the latter purpose, and most industrial applications of stagewise techniques fall into this category. Adsorption of colored substances from aqueous sugar solutions onto carbon, in order to provide a pure product and to assist the crystallization, is a typical example. Similarly, carbon is sometimes used to adsorb odorous substances from potable water, and grease is adsorbed from dry-cleaning liquids. The colors of petroleum and vegetable oils are lightened by treatment with clay.

Equipment and methods. As pointed out in Chap. 1, each stage requires the intimate contact of two insoluble phases for a time sufficient for a reasonable approach to equilibrium, followed by physical separation of the phases. The equipment used in applying these principles to adsorption is varied, depending upon the process application. That shown in Fig. 11.15 is very typical of many installations operated in a batchwise fashion. The liquid to be processed and the adsorbent are intimately mixed in the treating tank at the desired temperature for the required period of time,

Fig. 11.15 *Contact filtration. Schematic arrangement, for single-stage batch treatment of liquids.*

following which the thin slurry is filtered to separate the solid adsorbent and accompanying adsorbate from the liquid. The equipment is readily adaptable to multistage operation by providing additional tanks and filters as necessary. If the operation is to be made continuous, which is sometimes done in the decolorizing of petroleum lubricating oils, for example, centrifuges or a continuous rotary filter may be substituted for the filter press, or the solid may be allowed to settle out by virtue of its higher density when the mixture is passed through a large tank.

The type of adsorbent used depends upon the solution to be treated. Aqueous solutions are frequently treated with activated carbon especially prepared for the purpose at hand, whereas organic liquids such as oils are usually treated with inorganic adsorbents such as clays. Occasionally mixed adsorbents are used. High selectivity for the solute to be removed is desirable in order to reduce the amount of solid to be added. In any case, the adsorbent is applied in the form of a very finely ground powder, usually at least fine enough to pass entirely through a 200-mesh screen, and frequently very much finer.

The time required for the adsorbent and liquid to come to substantial equilibrium depends principally upon the concentration and particle size of the solid, the viscosity of the liquid, and the intensity of agitation. Agitation should be vigorous in order to ensure rapid contact of the adsorbent particles with all the liquid, and the latter will be the more rapid the larger the solid concentration. The flow regime should be turbulent so that adsorbent particles move relative to the bulk of the liquid, and this is promoted by the presence of baffles in the tank. Rotational motion accompanied by swirl and vortexing merely carries the particles along with the liquid and does not decrease the required time. Moreover, the air introduced by the vortex frequently has a deleterious effect on the solution owing to the oxidation of sensitive organic substances. The residual concentration of unadsorbed solute still remaining in solution usually varies with time in the manner indicated in Fig. 11.16, falling rapidly at first and approaching the equilibrium value asymptotically. A practical time for agitation is chosen as at point A, where the additional adsorption to be obtained by further contact is insignificant, and this may be of the order of 10 to 30 min. Agitation should be continued during filtration in order to avoid segregation of the fine and coarser particles of the adsorbent.

The highest convenient temperature should be used during the mixing, since the resulting decreased liquid viscosity increases both the rate of diffusion of solute and the ease with which the adsorbent particles may move through the liquid. Usually the equilibrium adsorption is decreased to a small extent at higher temperatures, but this is more than compensated for by the increased rate of approach to equilibrium. Operations are sometimes conducted at the boiling point of the liquid if this temperature will cause no injury to the substances involved. In the clay treatment of petroleum-lubricant fractions the adsorbent-oil mixture may be pumped through a tubular furnace to be heated to as much as 250 to 300°F, and for very heavy oils even to 600 to 700°F. If the adsorbed substance is volatile, however, the equilibrium extent of adsorption will be much more strongly affected by temperature and such material is best handled at ordinary temperatures.

Owing to the large quantity of solution usually treated relative to the amount of adsorption occurring, the temperature rise resulting from release of the heat of adsorption may usually be ignored.

The method of dealing with the spent adsorbent depends upon the particular system under consideration. The filter cake is usually washed to displace the solution held within the pores of the cake, but relatively little adsorbate will be removed in this manner. If the adsorbate is the desired product, it may be desorbed by contact of the solid with a solvent other than that which comprises the original solution, one in which the adsorbate is more soluble. This may be done by washing the cake in the filter or by dispersing the solid into a quantity of the solvent. If the adsorbate is volatile, it may be desorbed by reduction of the partial pressure of the adsorbate over the solid by passage of steam or warm air through the solid. In the case of activated

Fig. 11.16   *Approach to equilibrium, batch adsorption.*

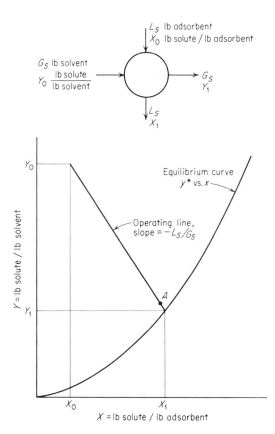

Fig. 11.17 *Single-stage adsorption.*

carbon adsorbents, care must be taken to avoid too high temperatures in using air for this purpose, in order to avoid combustion of the carbon. In the case of most decolorizing operations, the adsorbate is of no value and is difficultly desorbed. The adsorbent may then be revivified by burning off the adsorbate, followed by reactivation. Usually only a limited number of such revivifications is possible before the adsorbent ability is severely reduced, whereupon the solid is discarded.

Single-stage operation. The schematic flow sheet for this type of operation, when done in either batch or continuous fashion, is shown in the upper part of Fig. 11.17. Here the circle represents all the equipment and procedures constituting one stage. The operation is essentially analogous to a single-stage gas absorption, where the solution to be treated corresponds to a "gas" and the solid adsorbent to a "liquid." Since the amount of adsorbent used is ordinarily very small with respect to the amount of solution treated, and since the solute to be removed is adsorbed much more strongly than the other constituents present, the adsorption of the latter may be ignored. Furthermore the adsorbent is insoluble in the solution. Adopting a notation scheme similar to that used for gas absorption, the solution to be treated contains G_S lb unadsorbed substance or solvent, and the adsorbable solute concentration is reduced from Y_0 to Y_1 lb solute/lb solvent. The adsorbent is added to the extent of L_S lb adsorbate-free solid, and the solute adsorbate content increases from X_0 to X_1 lb solute/lb adsorbent. If fresh adsorbent is used, $X_0 = 0$, and in cases of continuous operation G_S and L_S are measured in terms of lb/hr.†

Equating the solute removed from the liquid to that picked up by the solid,

$$G_S(Y_0 - Y_1) = L_S(X_1 - X_0) \tag{11.4}$$

On X, Y coordinates this represents a straight operating line, through points of coordinates (X_0, Y_0) and (X_1, Y_1) of slope $-L_S/G_S$. If the stage is a theoretical or ideal stage, the effluent streams are in equilibrium, so that the point (X_1, Y_1) lies on the equilibrium adsorption isotherm. This is shown on the lower portion of Fig. 11.17. The equilibrium curve should be that obtaining at the final temperature of the operation. If insufficient time of contact is allowed, so that equilibrium is not reached, the final liquid and solid concentrations will correspond to some point such as A (Fig. 11.17), but ordinarily equilibrium is approached very closely.

The use of Eq. (11.4) assumes that the amount of liquid mechanically retained with the solid (but not adsorbed) after filtration or settling is negligible. This is quite satisfactory for most adsorption, since the quantity of solid employed is ordinarily very small with respect to that of the liquid treated. If the operation under consideration is *desorption*, and if again the quantity of liquid retained mechanically by the solid is negligible, Eq. (11.4) applies, but the operating line lies below the equilibrium curve on Fig. 11.17. In this case, however, it is much more likely that the quantity of liquid retained mechanically with the solid will be an appreciable portion of the total liquid used, and the methods of calculation described in Chap. 13 for leaching should be used.

Application of the Freundlich equation. The Freundlich equation can frequently be applied to adsorption of this type, particularly since small adsorbable solute concentrations are usually involved. This may be written in the following form for the concentration units used here,

$$Y^* = mX^n \tag{11.5}$$

and, at the final equilibrium conditions,

$$X_1 = \left(\frac{Y_1}{m}\right)^{1/n} \tag{11.6}$$

Since the adsorbent used ordinarily contains no initial adsorbate and $X_0 = 0$, substitution in Eq. (11.4) yields

$$\frac{L_S}{G_S} = \frac{Y_0 - Y_1}{(Y_1/m)^{1/n}} \tag{11.7}$$

† For the dilute solutions ordinarily used other consistent units may be applied to these terms. Thus, Y may be expressed as lb solute/lb solution (or lb solute/cu ft solution) and G_s as lb (or cu ft, respectively) of solution. When the adsorbed solute is colored matter whose concentration is measured in arbitrary units, the latter may be considered as Y units of color/lb or cu ft solution and the adsorbate concentration on the solid X as units of color/lb adsorbent.

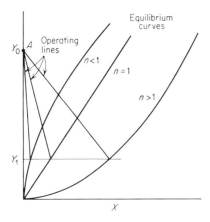

Fig. 11.18   *Single-stage adsorption, Freundlich equilibrium curves.*

This permits analytical calculation of the adsorbent/solution ratio for a given change in solution concentration, Y_0 to Y_1.

Refer to Fig. 11.18, where three typical Freundlich isotherms are shown. The isotherm is straight for $n = 1$, concave upward for $n > 1$, and concave downward for $n < 1$. If in each case the solution concentration is to be reduced from Y_0 to Y_1, the three operating lines radiating from point A apply. The slope of the operating line is in each case directly proportional to the adsorbent/solution ratio. It is generally stated[18] that values of n in the range 2 to 10 represent good, 1 to 2 moderately difficult, and less than 1 poor adsorption characteristics. In the case of the last, impractically large adsorbent dosages may be required for appreciable fractional removal of solute.

Multistage crosscurrent operation. The removal of a given amount of solute may be accomplished with greater economy of adsorbent if the solution is treated with separate small batches of adsorbent rather than in a single batch, with filtration between each stage. This method of operation is sometimes called "split-feed" treatment, and it is usually done in batch fashion, although continuous operation is also possible. Economy is particularly important when activated carbon, a fairly expensive adsorbent, is used. The savings are greater the larger the number of batches used but result at the expense of greater filtration and other handling costs. It is therefore rarely economical to use more than two stages. In rare instances, the adsorption may be irreversible, so that separate adsorbent dosages may be applied without intermediate filtration at considerable savings in operating costs.[17] This is by far the exception rather than the rule, and when applied to ordinary reversible adsorption, it will provide the same end result as if all the adsorbent had been used in a single stage.

A schematic flow sheet and operating diagram for a typical operation of two ideal stages are shown in Fig. 11.19. The same quantity of solution is treated in each stage by amounts of adsorbent L_{S1} and L_{S2} lb in the two stages, respectively, to reduce the solute concentration of the solution from Y_0 to Y_2. The material balances

are, for stage 1,

$$G_S(Y_0 - Y_1) = L_{S1}(X_1 - X_0) \tag{11.8}$$

and for stage 2,

$$G_S(Y_1 - Y_2) = L_{S2}(X_2 - X_0) \tag{11.9}$$

These provide the operating lines shown on the figure, each of a slope appropriate to the adsorbent quantity used in the corresponding stage. The extension to large numbers of stages is obvious. If the amounts of adsorbent used in each stage are equal, the operating lines on the diagram will be parallel. The least total amount of adsorbent will require unequal dosages in each stage except for the case where the equilibrium isotherm is linear, and in the general case this can be established only by a trial-and-error computation.

Application of the Freundlich equation. When the Freundlich expression [Eq. (11.5)] describes the adsorption isotherm satisfactorily and fresh adsorbent is used in each stage ($X_0 = 0$), the least total amount of adsorbent for a two-stage system can

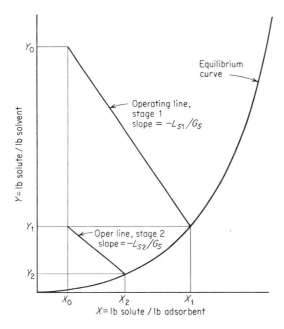

Fig. 11.19   *Two-stage crosscurrent adsorption.*

Fig. 11.20 *Solution to Eq.* (11.13). *Minimum total adsorbent, two-stage crosscurrent operation.*

be computed directly.[17,42] Thus, for stage 1,

$$\frac{L_{S1}}{G_S} = \frac{Y_0 - Y_1}{(Y_1/m)^{1/n}} \tag{11.10}$$

and, for stage 2,

$$\frac{L_{S2}}{G_S} = \frac{Y_1 - Y_2}{(Y_2/m)^{1/n}} \tag{11.11}$$

The total amount of adsorbent used is

$$\frac{L_{S1} + L_{S2}}{G_S} = m^{1/n} \left(\frac{Y_0 - Y_1}{Y_1^{1/n}} + \frac{Y_1 - Y_2}{Y_2^{1/n}} \right) \tag{11.12}$$

For minimum total adsorbent, $d[(L_1 + L_2)/G_S]/dY_1$ is set equal to zero, and since for a given case m, n, Y_0, and Y_2 are constants, this reduces to

$$\left(\frac{Y_1}{Y_2} \right)^{1/n} - \frac{1}{n} \frac{Y_0}{Y_1} = 1 - \frac{1}{n} \tag{11.13}$$

Equation (11.13) may be solved for the intermediate concentration Y_1, and the adsorbed quantities calculated by Eqs. (11.10) and (11.11). Figure 11.20 permits solutions of Eq. (11.13) without trial and error.

Multistage countercurrent operation. Even greater economy of adsorbent can be obtained by countercurrent operation. When batch methods of treating are used, this can only be simulated, for which the general scheme of batch simulation of countercurrent operations shown in Fig. 10.58 for liquid extraction is actually followed. The flow sheet of Fig. 11.21 then becomes the ultimate, steady-state result reached only after a number of cycles. However, truly continuous operation has also been used, as in the simultaneous dissolution of gold and silver from finely ground ore by cyanide solution and adsorption of the dissolved metal upon granular activated carbon in a three-stage operation. Coarse screens between agitated vessels separate the large carbon particles from the pulped ore–liquid mixture.[8]

A solute balance about the N_p stages is

$$G_S(Y_0 - Y_{Np}) = L_S(X_1 - X_{Np+1}) \tag{11.14}$$

which provides the operating line on the figure, through the coordinates of the terminal conditions (X_{Np+1}, Y_{Np}) and (X_1, Y_0) and of slope L_S/G_S. The number of theoretical stages required is found by drawing the usual staircase construction between equilibrium curve and operating line in the manner shown. Alternatively

Fig. 11.21   *Countercurrent multistage adsorption.*

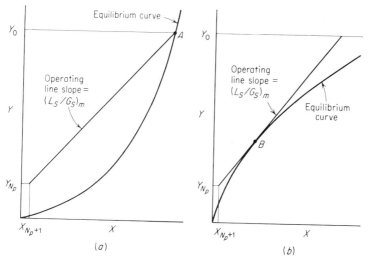

Fig. 11.22 *Operating lines and minimum adsorbent/solvent ratio for infinite stages.*

the adsorbent/solution ratio for a predetermined number of stages may be found by trial-and-error location of the operating line. If the operation is a *desorption* (corresponding to stripping in gas-liquid contact), the operating line falls below the equilibrium curve.

The minimum adsorbent/solvent ratio will be the largest which results in an infinite number of stages for the desired change of concentration. This corresponds to the operating line of largest slope which touches the equilibrium curve within the specified range of concentrations. For cases where the equilibrium isotherm is straight or concave upward, as in Fig. 11.22a, this will cause a *pinch* at the concentrated end of the cascade, as at point *A*. If the isotherm is concave downward (Fig. 11.22b), the pinch may occur at a point of tangency, as at point *B*, if Y_0 is sufficiently large. The situations are entirely analogous to those found in gas absorption (Fig. 8.7).

As the number of stages in a cascade is increased, the amount of adsorbent required at first decreases rapidly but approaches the minimum value only asymptotically. In practice, where intermediate filtration of solid from the liquid must be made between stages, it is rarely economical to use more than two stages in a countercurrent cascade.

In small-scale processing, there may be appreciable variation in the amounts of solution to be treated from one batch to the next. Furthermore, long periods of time may pass between batches, so that partially spent adsorbent must be stored between stages. Activated carbon particularly may deteriorate during storage through oxidation, polymerization of the adsorbate, or other chemical change, and in such cases the crosscurrent flow sheet may be more practical.

Application of the Freundlich equation. Trial-and-error calculation for the adsorbent/solvent ratio may be eliminated if the equilibrium curve may be conveniently described algebraically. If the equilibrium curve is linear, the Kremser equations (5.50) to (5.53) and Fig. 5.16 apply. More frequently the Freundlich expression (11.5) is useful, and fresh adsorbent ($X_{Np+1} = 0$) is used in the last stage.[37] For a typical two-stage cascade (Fig. 11.23) a solute material balance for the entire plant is

$$L_S(X_1 - 0) = G_S(Y_0 - Y_2) \tag{11.15}$$

Applying Eq. (11.5) to the effluents from the first ideal stage,

$$X_1 = \left(\frac{Y_1}{m}\right)^{1/n} \tag{11.16}$$

and combining these,

$$\frac{L_S}{G_S} = \frac{Y_0 - Y_2}{(Y_1/m)^{1/n}} \tag{11.17}$$

The operating line for the second ideal stage is shown on the figure and is given by

$$G_S(Y_1 - Y_2) = L_S X_2 = L_S\left(\frac{Y_2}{m}\right)^{1/n} \tag{11.18}$$

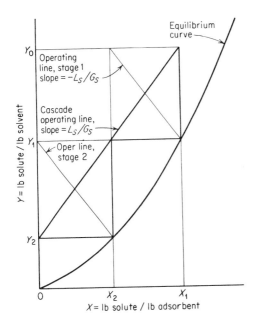

Fig. 11.23   *Two-stage countercurrent adsorption.*

$\dfrac{Y_2}{Y_0}$ = fraction unadsorbed, two stages

Fig. 11.24 *Solution to Eq. (11.19). Two-stage countercurrent adsorption.*

Eliminating L_S/G_S between Eqs. (11.17) and (11.18), there results

$$\frac{Y_0}{Y_2} - 1 = \left(\frac{Y_1}{Y_2}\right)^{1/n} \left(\frac{Y_1}{Y_2} - 1\right) \tag{11.19}$$

Equation (11.19) may be solved for the intermediate concentration Y_1 for specified terminal concentrations Y_0 and Y_2, and L_S/G_S is then given by Eq. (11.17). Figure 11.24 will assist in the solution of Eq. (11.19). The savings in adsorbent by countercurrent operation over single stage are greater, the greater the value of n.

Illustration 11.2. An aqueous solution containing a valuable solute is colored by small amounts of an impurity. Prior to crystallization, the impurity is to be removed by adsorption on a decolorizing carbon which adsorbs only insignificant amounts of the principal solute. A series of laboratory tests was made by stirring various amounts of the adsorbent into batches of the original solution until equilibrium was established, yielding the following data at constant temperature:

Lb carbon/lb soln	0	0.001	0.004	0.008	0.02	0.04
Equilibrium color	9.6	8.6	6.3	4.3	1.7	0.7

The color intensity was measured on an arbitrary scale, proportional to the concentration of the colored substance.   It is desired to reduce the color to 10% of its original value, 9.6.   Determine the quantity of fresh carbon required per 1,000 lb of solution (*a*) for a single-stage operation, (*b*) for a two-stage crosscurrent process using the minimum total amount of carbon, and (*c*) for a two-stage countercurrent operation.

Solution.   The experimental data must first be converted to a suitable form for plotting the equilibrium isotherm.   For this purpose, define Y as units of color per pound of solution and X as units of color adsorbed per pound of carbon.   The solutions may be considered as dilute in color, so that operating lines will be straight on X, Y coordinates expressed in this manner.   The calculations are made in the manner indicated below.

Lb carbon / Lb soln	Y^* = equilibrium color, units/lb soln	X = adsorbate concn, units/lb carbon
0	9.6	
0.001	8.6	$(9.6 - 8.6)/0.001 = 1{,}000$
0.004	6.3	$(9.6 - 6.3)/0.004 = 825$
0.008	4.3	663
0.02	1.7	395
0.04	0.7	223

The equilibrium data, when plotted on logarithmic coordinates, provide a straight line, so that the Freundlich equation applies (see Fig. 11.25).   The slope of the line is $1.66 = n$, and, at $X = 663$, $Y^* = 4.3$.   Therefore [Eq. (11.5)]

$$m = \frac{4.3}{663^{1.66}} = 8.91(10^{-5})$$

The Freundlich equation is therefore

$$Y^* = 8.91(10^{-5})X^{1.66}$$

The equilibrium data may also be plotted on arithmetic coordinates (Fig. 11.26).

Fig. 11.25   *Equilibrium data, Illustration* 11.2.

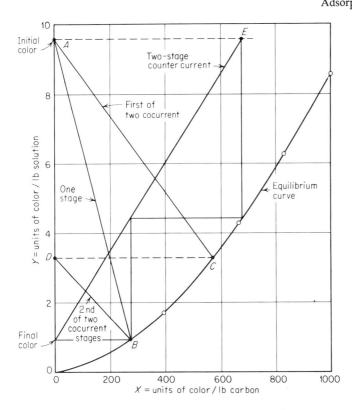

Fig. 11.26 *Solution to Illustration 11.2.*

a. Single-stage operation. $Y_0 = 9.6$ units of color/lb soln,

$$Y_1 = 0.10(9.6) = 0.96 \text{ unit/lb soln}$$

Let $G_s = 1,000$ lb soln. Since fresh carbon is to be used, $X_0 = 0$. On Fig. 11.26, point A representing the initial solution and fresh adsorbent is located, and point B is located on the equilibrium curve at the color concentration of the final solution. At B, $X_1 = 260$. Therefore [Eq. (11.4)]

$$\frac{L_s}{G_s} = \frac{Y_0 - Y_1}{X_1 - X_0} = \frac{9.6 - 0.96}{270 - 0} = 0.032 \text{ lb carbon/lb soln}$$

and $$L_s = 0.032(1,000) = 32.0 \text{ lb carbon/1,000 lb soln}$$

Alternatively, since the Freundlich equation applies, use Eq. (11.7)

$$\frac{L_s}{G_s} = \frac{Y_0 - Y_1}{(Y_1/m)^{1/n}} = \frac{9.6 - 0.96}{[0.96/8.91(10^{-5})]^{1/1.66}} = 0.032 \text{ lb carbon/lb soln}$$

$$L_s = 0.032(1,000) = 32.0 \text{ lb carbon/1,000 lb soln}$$

b. Two-stage crosscurrent operation. The minimum total amount of carbon may be found on Fig. 11.26 by a trial-and-error procedure. Thus, point C on the equilibrium curve is assumed, the operating lines AC and DB drawn, and the values of L_{s1} and L_{s2} computed by Eqs. (11.8) and (11.9). The position of point C is changed until the sum of L_{s1} and L_{s2} is a minimum. The position of C in Fig. 11.26 is the final value, and its coordinates are $(X_1 = 565, Y_1 = 3.30)$. $X_2 = 270$ (at B).

Eq. (11.8):
$$L_{S1} = \frac{G(Y_0 - Y_1)}{X_1 - X_0} = \frac{1,000(9.6 - 3.30)}{565 - 0} = 11.14 \text{ lb}$$

Eq. (11.9)
$$L_{S2} = \frac{G(Y_1 - Y_2)}{X_2 - X_0} = \frac{1,000(3.30 - 0.96)}{270 - 0} = 8.67 \text{ lb}$$

$$L_{S1} + L_{S2} = 11.14 + 8.67 = 19.81 \text{ lb carbon}/1,000 \text{ lb soln}$$

Alternatively, since the Freundlich equation applies, use Fig. 11.20: $Y_2/Y_0 = 0.96/9.6 = 0.10$, $n = 1.66$. From the figure, $Y_1/Y_0 = 0.344$. $Y_1 = 0.344(9.6) = 3.30$.

Eq. (11.10):
$$\frac{L_{S1}}{G_S} = \frac{Y_0 - Y_1}{(Y_1/m)^{1/n}} = \frac{9.6 - 3.30}{[3.30/8.91(10^{-5})]^{1/1.66}}$$

$$= 0.01114 \text{ lb carbon/lb soln into 1st stage}$$

Eq. (11.11):
$$\frac{L_{S2}}{G_S} = \frac{Y_1 - Y_2}{(Y_2/m)^{1/n}} = \frac{3.30 - 0.96}{[0.96/8.91(10^{-5})]^{1/1.66}}$$

$$= 0.00867 \text{ lb carbon/lb soln into 2d stage}$$

Total carbon required $= (0.01114 + 0.00867)1,000 = 19.81 \text{ lb}/1,000 \text{ lb soln}$

c. Two-stage countercurrent operation. $Y_0 = 9.6$, $Y_2 = 0.96$, $X_{Np+1} = 0$. The operating line is located by trial on Fig. 11.26 until two stages may be drawn between operating line and equilibrium curve, as shown. From the figure at E, $X_1 = 675$.

Eq. (11.14):
$$L_S = \frac{G_S(Y_0 - Y_2)}{X_1 - X_{Np+1}} = \frac{1,000(9.6 - 0.96)}{675 - 0}$$

$$= 12.80 \text{ lb carbon}/1,000 \text{ lb soln}$$

Alternatively, $Y_2/Y_0 = 0.96/9.6 = 0.10$; $n = 1.66$. From Fig. 11.24, $Y_2/Y_1 = 0.217$, and $Y_1 = Y_2/0.217 = 0.96/0.217 = 4.42$.

Eq. (11.17):
$$\frac{L_S}{G_S} = \frac{Y_0 - Y_2}{(Y_1/m)^{1/n}} = \frac{9.6 - 0.96}{[4.42/8.91(10^{-5})]^{1/1.66}}$$

$$= 0.01280 \text{ lb carbon/lb soln}$$

and
$$L = 0.01280(1,000) = 12.80 \text{ lb carbon}/1,000 \text{ lb soln}$$

Stage efficiency

The resistance to the attainment of equilibrium during batch operation will be the sum of at least the following resistances: (1) The resistance to mass transfer of the solute through the liquid surrounding each adsorbent particle. This may be minimized by maintaining a high degree of turbulence through intensive agitation. (2) The resistance to diffusion of the solute through the liquid in the pores of the solid, from the outside of the particles to the inner surface where adsorption will occur. The liquid in the pores will be stagnant, uninfluenced by the turbulence in the liquid surrounding the particles, and the solute transfer is by a process of molecular diffusion. The path of the diffusion is relatively long and tortuous, and the rate may be described by an effective diffusivity or a pore-shape factor, characteristic of such "structure-sensitive" diffusion (see Chap. 4). (3) The resistance to adsorption itself. This will exist if there is any finite time for the solute molecules to be adsorbed once they have arrived at the point on the surface where they are finally held. For example, it is conceivable that some orientation of the solute molecules with respect to the surface might be required before actual adsorption would occur. For a given system and type of adsorbent, neither the second nor third of these would be under the control of the operator of the process.

The fairly complex mathematical analysis of these resistances in the unsteady state characteristic of a batch operation has been summarized.[22,41] The internal diffusional resistance of the common adsorbents, i.e., other than certain ion-exchange resins, has not been established. It is known that ordinarily, under high agitation intensities, the mass-transfer resistance of the fluid surrounding the solid particles is negligible and the particle mass-transfer resistance controls.

Under industrial conditions it is usually possible to reach substantial equilibrium between adsorbent and solution within a reasonable time, and stage efficiencies are therefore essentially unity. For the present at least it will be best to establish the necessary time of contact for this experimentally, using actual samples of the adsorbent and solution to be treated, at the same adsorbent/solution ratio as it is planned to use ultimately. The tests could be made on a small scale provided that for both small-scale test and large-scale operation the intensity of agitation is sufficient substantially to eliminate the resistance of the liquid film surrounding the adsorbent particles. Otherwise large-scale tests would be required.

Fluidized and teeter beds

These have been used to a limited extent for recovery of vapors from vapor-gas mixtures,[2,10] for desorption (see drying, Chap. 12), for fractionation of light hydrocarbon vapors with carbon,[11] and a few others. In the case of liquid treating, there have been applications of ion exchange. Applications will unquestionably increase in number.

Consider a bed of granular solids up through which a gas flows, the gas being fairly uniformly distributed over the bottom cross section of the bed. At low gas rates, the gas suffers a pressure drop which may be estimated by Eq. (6.36). As the gas velocity is increased, the pressure drop eventually equals the sum of the weight of the solids per unit area of bed and the friction of the solids at the container walls. If the solids are free flowing, an increment in the gas velocity causes the bed to expand, and the gas pressure drop will equal the weight/area of the bed. Further increase in gas velocity causes further enlargement of the bed, and voidage increases sufficiently for the solid particles to move about locally. This is the condition of a "quiescent fluidized bed." Still further increase in gas velocity further expands the bed, the solid particles move about freely (indeed they are thoroughly circulated throughout the bed), and well-defined bubbles of gas may form and rise through the bed. The bed appears much like a boiling liquid, a distinct interface between the top of the solids and the escaping gas remains evident, and the gas pressure drop is not much different from that of the quiescent fluidized state. This is the condition used for adsorption. Further increase in gas velocity continues to expand the bed, and eventually the solids are carried away with the gas.

Squires[39] has distinguished between *fluidized* beds and *teeter* beds. Fluidized beds are produced by fine powders, usually smaller than 20 mesh and ranging down to 325 mesh, and will retain a great range of particle sizes within the bed, with little particle attrition. They usually operate with superficial gas velocities of the order of 2 ft/sec or less, which may be 10 times that for minimum fluidization. Teeter beds are produced with coarser particles, up to 10 mesh commonly. Gas velocities of from 5 to 10 ft/sec may be used, which may only be twice that for minimum fluidization. There is little gas bubbling, and the size range of particles retained is relatively small. In general, better fluid-solids contacting is obtained in teeter beds, and most adsorption applications are in this category. Solids may also be fluidized by liquids, and these will be ordinarily in the teeter-bed category.

Since the first introduction of these techniques for fluid-solid contact in 1948, with the principal application in the catalysis of gaseous chemical reactions, a very large technology for their design has developed. This is still not in a condition which permits summary for design purposes in the space available here, however, and the works of Leva[31] and Zenz[44,45] should be consulted for such details. The discussion here is limited to the computation of stage requirements and does not include the mechanical design.

Adsorption of a vapor from a gas. Figure 11.27 shows an arrangement typical of that required for adsorption of a vapor from a nonadsorbed gas, in this case drying of air with silica gel.[10] In the upper part of the tower, the gel is contacted countercurrently with the air to be dried on perforated trays in relatively shallow beds, the gel moving from tray to tray through downspouts. In the lower part of the tower, the gel is regenerated by similar contact with hot gas, which desorbs and carries off the moisture. The dried gel is then recirculated by air lift to the top of the tower. In cases where the adsorbed vapor is to be recovered, regeneration might include steam stripping of a carbon adsorbent with distillation or decantation of the condensed water–organic vapor mixture, followed by air drying of the adsorbent before reuse, and obvious changes in the flow sheet would be necessary.

If adsorption is isothermal, the calculations for ideal stages can be made in the same manner as for contact filtration of liquids [Fig. 11.21, Eq. (11.14)], and the same is true for desorption-regeneration. Ordinarily, however, the adsorber will operate adiabatically, and there may be a considerable rise in temperature owing to adsorption (or fall, in the case of desorption). Since the equilibrium then changes with stage number, the calculations are then done stage by stage, much in the manner of gas absorption. The same procedure will apply to any type of stage device and is not limited to fluidized beds. Thus, for the first n stages of the flow sheet of Fig. 11.21, a balance for adsorbable vapor is

$$G_S(Y_0 - Y_n) = L_S(X_1 - X_{n+1}) \tag{11.20}$$

and an enthalpy balance for adiabatic operation is

$$G_S(H_{G0} - H_{Gn}) = L_S(H_{L1} - H_{L,n+1}) \tag{11.21}$$

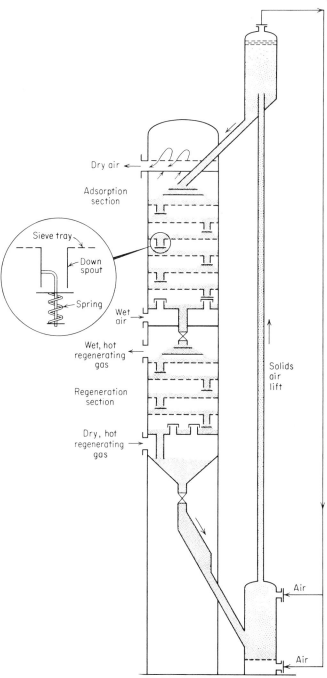

Fig. 11.27 *Fluidized bed, multistage countercurrent adsorber with regeneration. (After Ermenc.[10])*

where H_G = enthalpy of vapor-gas mixture, Btu/lb gas
$\quad\quad H_L$ = enthalpy of solid plus adsorbate, Btu/lb adsorbent.
If enthalpies are referred to solid adsorbent, nonadsorbed gas (component C), and the adsorbate (component A) as a liquid, all at a base temperature t_o, then

$$H_G = C_C(t_G - t_o) + Y[C_A(t_G - t_o) + \lambda_{Ao}] \tag{11.22}$$

where C_C = gas heat capacity, Btu/(lb)(°F)
$\quad\quad C_A$ = vapor heat capacity, Btu/(lb)(°F)
$\quad\quad \lambda_{Ao}$ = latent heat of vaporization of A at t_o, Btu/lb

$$H_L = C_B(t_L - t_o) + XC_{AL}(t_L - t_o) + \Delta H_A \tag{11.23}$$

where C_B = heat capacity of adsorbent (component B), Btu/(lb)(°F)
$\quad\quad C_{AL}$ = heat capacity of liquid A, Btu/(lb)(°F)
$\quad\quad \Delta H_A$ = integral heat of adsorption at X and t_o, Btu/lb adsorbent.
Gas and solid leaving an ideal stage are in thermal and concentration equilibrium. Some trial and error is required in the use of these equations with the equilibrium data, of a nature depending on the problem, as shown in Illustration 11.3.

Illustration 11.3. A mixture of nitrogen and acetone vapor, 5 mole % acetone, 1 atm, 30°C (86°F), is to be countercurrently contacted with gas-adsorbent carbon in a fluidized-bed tray tower to reduce the acetone content to 0.01 mole %. Revivified carbon will enter at 40°C (104°F), at the rate 1.5 lb carbon/lb nitrogen, acetone-free initially. Adsorption will be adiabatic, and pressure drop will be ignored. Compute the number of ideal stages required.

Solution. A base temperature t_o = 86°F will be used. Heat capacities are C_A (acetone vapor) = 0.35, C_{AL} (acetone liquid) = 0.54, C_B (carbon) = 0.20, and C_C (nitrogen) = 0.26, all as Btu/(lb)(°F). λ_{Ao} = 237 Btu/lb. The adsorption equilibria of Fig. 11.5 and heats of adsorption of Illustration 11.1 will be used.

Basis: G_S = 1 lb nitrogen, L_S = 1.5 lb carbon. Mol wt acetone = 58.1, of nitrogen = 28.

$$Y_0 = \frac{0.05}{0.95}\left(\frac{58.1}{28}\right) = 0.1093 \text{ lb acetone/lb N}_2$$

$$Y_{Np} = \frac{0.0001}{0.9999}\left(\frac{58.1}{28}\right) = 0.000208 \text{ lb acetone/lb N}_2$$

$$X_{Np+1} = 0 \text{ lb acetone/lb carbon}$$

For the entire adsorber, Eq. (11.20) with $n = N_p$:

$$1(0.1093 - 0.000208) = 1.5(X_1 - 0)$$

$$X_1 = 0.0727 \text{ lb acetone/lb carbon}$$

From the data of Illustration 11.1, ΔH_A = −1.8 Btu/lb carbon. Eq. (11.22) for the entering gas ($t_G = t_o$ = 86°F): H_{G0} = 0.1093(237) = 25.9 Btu/lb N$_2$. Eq. (11.23) for the entering carbon ($t_{L,Np+1}$ = 104°F): $H_{L,Np+1}$ = 0.20(104 − 86) = 3.6 Btu/lb carbon.

Stage calculations will be made from the bottom upward. To begin, the temperature of the effluent solid is required. This will be obtained by an enthalpy balance about the entire adsorber but requires first an estimate of the effluent-gas temperature. After several trials, assume $t_{G,Np}$ = 127°F (to be checked later).

Eq. (11.22): $H_{G,N_p} = 0.26(127 - 86) + 0.000208[0.35(127 - 86) + 237]$

$= 10.75$ Btu/lb N_2

Eq. (11.21) with $n = N_p$: $1(25.9 - 10.75) = 1.5(H_{L1} - 3.6)$

$H_{L1} = 14.20$ Btu/lb carbon

Eq. (11.23) for the solid effluent:

$H_{L1} = 14.20 = 0.20(t_{L1} - 86) + 0.0727(0.54)(t_{L1} - 86) - 1.8$

$t_{L1} = 153°F$

The gas leaving stage 1 is in equilibrium with solid at $X_1 = 0.0727$, $t_{L1} = 153°F$.   From Fig. 11.5 (extrapolation and interpolation will be required, for which a cross plot, $\log p^*$ vs. $\log X$, is useful), the equilibrium partial pressure of acetone $= 8.0$ mm Hg.

$$Y_1 = \frac{8.0}{760 - 8} \frac{58.1}{28} = 0.0221 \text{ lb acetone/lb } N_2$$

Eq. (11.22): $H_{G1} = 0.26(153 - 86) + 0.0221[0.35(153 - 86) + 237]$

$= 23.15$ Btu/lb N_2

Eq. (11.20) with $n = 1$: $1(0.1093 - 0.0221) = 1.5(0.0727 - X_2)$

$X_2 = 0.0147$ lb acetone/lb carbon

From Illustration 11.1, $\Delta H_A = -0.12$ Btu/lb carbon.

Eq. (11.21) with $n = 1$: $1(25.9 - 23.15) = 1.5(14.20 - H_{L2})$

$H_{L2} = 12.37$ Btu/lb carbon

Eq. (11.23): $12.37 = 0.20(t_{L2} - 86) + 0.0147(0.54)(t_{L2} - 86) - 0.12$

$t_{L2} = 146°F$

At $X_2 = 0.0147$, $t_2 = 146°F$, the equilibrium partial pressure of acetone $= 0.6$ mm Hg.

$$Y_2 = \frac{0.6}{760 - 0.6} \frac{58.1}{28} = 0.00164 \text{ lb acetone/lb } N_2$$

In similar fashion, $H_{G2} = 16.02$, $X_3 = 0.001$, $H_{L3} = 7.60$, $t_{L3} = 124°F = t_{G3}$, $Y_3 = 0.000021$, all in the same units as before.

The gas leaving tray 3 is at 124°F (acceptable check with assumed 127°F) and an unnecessarily low acetone concentration.   About 2.5 ideal trays are required, and an exact integral number can be obtained with some slight change in the carbon/nitrogen ratio.

There are limited data on mass- and heat-transfer coefficients for fluidized beds[44,45] with which to estimate tray efficiencies after gas velocities and bed depths have been established.

Fractionation of a vapor mixture. For the separation of a vapor mixture consisting of, for example, two adsorbable components for which the adsorbent exhibits a relative adsorptivity, calculations are made in the manner for moving beds to locate operating lines and equilibrium curves [Eqs. (11.31) to (11.43) and Fig. 11.35].

Ideal stages may then be determined by the usual step construction on the lower part of such a figure.

II. CONTINUOUS CONTACT

In these operations the fluid and adsorbent are in contact throughout the entire apparatus, without periodic separation of the phases. The operation may be carried out in strictly continuous, steady-state fashion, characterized by movement of the solid as well as the fluid. Alternatively, owing to the rigidity of the solid adsorbent particles, it is also possible to operate advantageously in semicontinuous fashion, characterized by a moving fluid but stationary solid. This results in unsteady-state conditions, where compositions in the system change with time.

STEADY-STATE–MOVING-BED ADSORBERS

Steady-state conditions require continuous movement of both fluid and adsorbent through the equipment at constant rate, with no change in composition at any point in the system with passage of time. If parallel flow of solid and fluid is used, the net result is at best a condition of equilibrium between the effluent streams, or the equivalent of one theoretical stage. It is the purpose of these applications to develop separations equivalent to many stages, however, and hence only countercurrent operations need be considered. There are applications in treating gases and liquids, for purposes of collecting solute and fractionation, through ordinary adsorption and ion exchange.

Equipment

It is only in relatively recent years that satisfactory large-scale devices for the continuous contacting of a granular solid and a fluid have been developed. These have had to overcome the difficulties of obtaining uniform flow of solid particles and fluid without "channeling" or local irregularities, as well as those of introducing and removing the solid continuously into the vessel to be used.

One such device, developed specifically for fractionation of light hydrocarbon gases with a dense, very hard, active coconut-shell or fruit-pit carbon, is the *Hypersorber*[4,25] (Fig. 11.28), which contains exceptionally interesting devices for the solids-gas-handling problems. Feed gas is introduced more or less centrally. In the "adsorption" section, the more readily adsorbed components are adsorbed upon the descending solid, and the top product consists of poorly adsorbed components. Solid passing to the "rectifying" section below the feed point contains all the constituents of the feed, and in this section a rising stream of gas displaces the more volatile constituents, which pass upward. The adsorbate on the solid leaving this section is then rich in the readily adsorbed constituents. This constitutes the fractionation. In the stripping section, the adsorbate is removed by heating and steaming the solid, part of the desorbed gas is removed as product, and part is returned to the rectifying section as reflux. The solid is recycled to the top by a gas lift.

Figure 11.29 shows the device used for disengaging a product gas stream: the

Fig. 11.28 *Hypersorber for continuous, counter-current fractionation of a gas into two products. (Union Oil Co. of California.)*

gas collects under the tray and is removed from several points in the tower periphery, while the short pipes carry adsorbent downward through the tray and whatever gas is desired to the upper section.   The same device is used for introducing the feed. Figure 11.30 is a schematic representation of the adsorbent flow-controlling device at the bottom of the Hypersorber.   The solid must pass through two sets of down-comers, the upper set fixed and the lower set kept in constant reciprocating motion.

Fig. 11.29 *Device for disengaging solid and gas for Hypersorber.*[4] *(With permission of the American Institute of Chemical Engineers.)*

Fig. 11.30 *Adsorbent flow-control device for Hypersorber.*[25] *(With permission of the American Institute of Chemical Engineers.)*

The adsorbent enters the lower set only when they are in juxtaposition with the upper.   The reciprocating motion then carries the entrapped solid to openings in the lower plate, through which it is discharged.   This device successfully produces a rodlike flow of the compacted solids in the tower.

In the case of liquid treating, far less elaborate devices have been used.   Solids may be introduced to the top of the tower by a screw feeder or simply from a bin by gravity flow.   Withdrawal of solids at the bottom may be accomplished by several types of devices, e.g., a revolving compartmented valve similar to revolving doors for buildings; it is not generally possible to remove solids entirely free of liquid.[40]

The Higgins contactor,[16,23] developed initially for ion exchange but useful for solids-liquid contacting generally, is unique in the intermittent nature of its operation. Figure 11.31 shows it schematically as arranged for simple solute collection.   In Fig. 11.31a, the temporarily stationary upper bed of solids is contacted with liquid flowing downward, so that fluidization does not occur.   In the lower bed, the solid is regenerated by an eluting liquid.   After several minutes, the liquid flow is stopped, valves are turned as shown in Fig. 11.31b, and the liquid-filled piston pump is moved as shown for a period of several seconds, whereupon solid is moved hydraulically in clockwise fashion.   At Fig. 11.31c, with the valves readjusted to their original

Fig. 11.31 *Higgins contactor, schematic (solids shown shaded).*

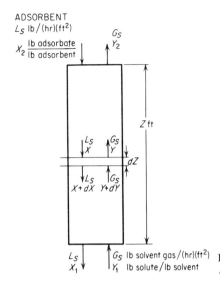

ADSORBENT
L_S lb/(hr)(ft²)

$X_2 \dfrac{\text{lb adsorbate}}{\text{lb adsorbent}}$

G_S
Y_2

Z ft

L_S G_S
X Y

dZ

L_S G_S
$X+dX$ $Y+dY$

L_S G_S lb solvent gas/(hr)(ft²)
X_1 Y_1 lb solute/lb solvent

Fig. 11.32   *Continuous countercurrent adsorption of one component.*

position, movement of solid is completed, and liquid flows are started to complete the cycle.   Operation, although intermittent and cyclic, is nearly the same as for truly continuous countercurrent operation.   Other schemes, for fractionation, for example, are readily arranged.

One component adsorbed

For purposes of computation, the operations are best considered as analogous to gas absorption, with a solid adsorbent replacing the liquid solvent.   Refer to Fig. 11.32. The notation used resembles that for gas absorption for a binary gas mixture: G_S and L_S are the superficial mass velocities of solute-free fluid and adsorbate-free solid, respectively, and solute concentrations are expressed as lb solute/lb solute-free substance.   A solute balance about the entire tower is

$$G_S(Y_1 - Y_2) = L_S(X_1 - X_2) \tag{11.24}$$

and about the upper part

$$G_S(Y - Y_2) = L_S(X - X_2) \tag{11.25}$$

These establish the operating line on X, Y coordinates, a straight line of slope L_S/G_S joining the terminal conditions (X_1, Y_1) and (X_2, Y_2) (Fig. 11.33).   The solute concentrations X and Y at any level in the tower fall upon this line.   An equilibrium-distribution curve appropriate to the system and to the prevailing temperature and pressure may also be plotted on the figure as shown.   This will fall below the operating line for adsorption and above for desorption.   In the same fashion as for absorbers, the minimum solid/fluid ratio is given by the operating line of maximum slope which anywhere touches the equilibrium curve.

The simplifying assumption found useful in gas absorption, that the temperature of the fluid remains substantially constant in adiabatic operations, will be satisfactory only in the case of solute collection from dilute liquid solutions and is unsatisfactory for estimating temperatures in the case of gases. Calculation of the temperature effect when heats of adsorption are large is very complex.[1,38] The present discussion is limited to isothermal operation.

The resistance to mass transfer of solute from the fluid to the adsorbed state on the solid will include that residing in the gas surrounding the solid particles, that corresponding to the diffusion of solute through the gas within the pores of the solid, and possibly an additional resistance at the time of adsorption. During physical adsorption, the last of these will probably be negligible. If the remaining resistances may be characterized by an overall gas mass-transfer coefficient based on a_p, the outside surface of the solid particles, $K_Y a_p$, then the rate of solute transfer over the differential height of adsorber dZ (Fig. 11.32) may be written in the usual manner as

$$L_S \, dX = G_S \, dY = K_Y a_p (Y - Y^*) \, dZ \qquad (11.26)$$

where Y^* is the equilibrium composition in the gas corresponding to the adsorbate composition X. The driving force $Y - Y^*$ is then represented by the vertical distance between operating line and equilibrium curve (Fig. 11.33). Rearranging Eq. (11.26) and integrating define the number of transfer units N_{tOG},

$$N_{tOG} = \int_{Y_2}^{Y_1} \frac{dY}{Y - Y^*} = \frac{K_Y a_p \, dZ}{G_S} = \frac{Z}{H_{tOG}} \qquad (11.27)$$

where

$$H_{tOG} = \frac{G_S}{K_Y a_p} \qquad (11.28)$$

The integral of Eq. (11.27) is ordinarily evaluated graphically and the active height Z determined through knowledge of the height of a transfer unit H_{tOG}, characteristic of the system.

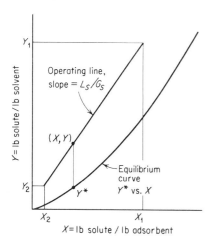

Fig. **11.33** *Continuous countercurrent adsorption of one component.*

The use of an overall coefficient or overall height of a transfer unit implies that the resistance to mass transfer within the pores of the solid particles may be characterized[9] by an individual mass-transfer coefficient $k_S a_p$ or height of a transfer unit H_{tS}, thus,

$$\frac{G_S}{K_Y a_p} = \frac{G_S}{k_Y a_p} + \frac{m G_S}{L_S} \frac{L_S}{k_S a_p} \tag{11.29}$$

or

$$H_{tOG} = H_{tG} + \frac{m G_S}{L_S} H_{tS} \tag{11.30}$$

where $m = dY^*/dX$, the slope of the equilibrium curve.

The resistance within the fluid surrounding the particles H_{tG}, or the corresponding coefficient $k_Y a_p$, may be estimated for moving beds through the correlations available for fixed beds (Table 3.3). Owing to the rigidity of each solid particle and the unsteady-state diffusional conditions existing within each particle as it travels through the adsorber, the use of a mass-transfer coefficient k_S, with an implied linear concentration-difference driving force, is not strictly correct, and Eqs. (11.27) to (11.30) are sound only when the mass-transfer resistance of the fluid surrounding the particles is of controlling size. Ordinarily, however, the diffusional resistance within the particles is of major importance, and for these conditions, which space does not permit consideration of here, the work of Vermeulen[22,41] should be consulted.

Illustration 11.4. Eagleton and Bliss[9] have measured the individual resistances to mass transfer residing in the fluid and within the solid during adsorption of water vapor from air by silica gel, using a fixed-bed semicontinuous method of operation. For low moisture contents of the air, they found that

$$k_Y a_p = 188 G'^{0.55} \text{ lb H}_2\text{O}/(\text{hr})(\text{cu ft})(\Delta Y)$$

and

$$k_S a_p = 217 \text{ lb H}_2\text{O}/(\text{hr})(\text{cu ft})(\Delta X)$$

where G' is the mass velocity of the gas, lb/(hr)(sq ft). Their silica gel had an apparent bed density of 41.9 lb/cu ft, an average particle size of 0.068-in. diameter, and the external surface of the particles was 10.58 sq ft/lb.

It is desired to estimate the height of a continuous countercurrent isothermal adsorber for the drying of air at 80°F, atmospheric pressure, from an initial humidity of 0.005 to a final humidity of 0.0001 lb water/lb dry air. The entering gel will be dry. (*Note:* So-called "dry" silica gel must contain a minimum of about 5% water if it is to retain its adsorptive capacity. Moisture measurements as ordinarily reported do not include this.) A gel rate of 500 lb/(hr)(sq ft) and an air rate of 1,000 lb dry air/(hr)(sq ft) will be used. For the moisture concentrations to be encountered here, the equilibrium adsorption isotherm at 80°F, 1 atm (see Illustration 11.7), may be taken as substantially straight and described by the expression $Y^* = 0.0185X$.

Solution. $Y_1 = 0.005$, $Y_2 = 0.0001$ lb H$_2$O/lb dry air. $L_S = 500$ lb/(hr)(sq ft), $G_S = 1,000$ lb/(hr)(sq ft), $X_2 = 0$ lb H$_2$O/lb dry gel.

Eq. (11.24):

$$X_1 = \frac{G_S(Y_1 - Y_2)}{L_S} + X_2 = \frac{1,000(0.005 - 0.0001)}{500}$$

$$= 0.0098 \text{ lb H}_2\text{O/lb dry gel}$$

$$Y_2^* = \text{humidity of air in equilibrium with entering gel} = 0$$

$$Y_1^* = 0.0185 X_1 = 0.0185(0.0098) = 0.0001815 \text{ lb H}_2\text{O/lb dry gel}$$

Since operating line and equilibrium curve will both be straight on X, Y coordinates, the average driving force is the logarithmic average [Eqs. (8.44) to (8.45)].

$$Y_1 - Y_1^* = 0.005 - 0.0001815 = 0.00482$$

$$Y_2 - Y_2^* = 0.0001 - 0 = 0.0001$$

$$\text{Av } \Delta Y = \frac{0.00482 - 0.0001}{\ln (0.00482/0.0001)} = 0.001217$$

$$N_{tOG} = \frac{Y_1 - Y_2}{\Delta Y} = \frac{0.005 - 0.0001}{0.001217} = 4.03$$

If the fixed-bed data are to be used for estimating mass-transfer coefficients for a moving bed of solids, the relative mass velocity of air and solid is appropriate. The linear rate of flow of the solid downward is $500/41.9 = 11.95$ ft/hr, where 41.9 is the apparent density. The density of this substantially dry air at 80°F, 1 atm, is 0.0737 lb/cu ft, and its superficial linear velocity upward is $1,000/0.0737 = 13,590$ ft/hr. The relative linear velocity of air and solid is $13,590 + 11.95 = 13,602$ ft/hr, and the relative mass velocity of the air is $13,602(0.0737) = 1,004$ lb/(hr)(sq ft) $= G'$.

$$H_{tG} = \frac{G_S}{k_Y a_p} = \frac{G_S}{188 G'^{0.55}} = \frac{1,000}{188(1,004)^{0.55}} = 0.118 \text{ ft}$$

$$H_{tS} = \frac{L_S}{k_S a_p} = \frac{500}{217} = 2.30 \text{ ft}$$

$$\frac{mG_S}{L_S} = \frac{0.0185(1,000)}{500} = 0.037$$

Eq. (11.30):
$$H_{tOG} = 0.118 + 0.037(2.30) = 0.203 \text{ ft}$$
$$Z = N_{tOG} H_{tOG} = 4.03(0.203) = 0.83 \text{ ft} \quad \textbf{Ans.}$$

Note: The gas-phase mass-transfer coefficient in this case is smaller than that given by item 5, Table 3.3, perhaps because of the very small diameter (0.63 in.) of the bed in which it was measured.

Two components adsorbed; fractionation

When several components of a gas mixture are appreciably adsorbed, fractionation is required for their separation, and a device such as the Hypersorber may be used. This discussion is confined to binary gas mixtures.

For purposes of computation, it is easiest to recall the similarity between the adsorption operation and continuous countercurrent extraction with reflux. Solid adsorbent as the added insoluble phase is analogous to extraction solvent, the adsorbate is analogous to the solvent-free extract, and the fluid stream is similar to the raffinate. Computations may then be made using the methods and equations of Chap. 10 [Eqs. (10.41) to (10.44) and (10.49) to (10.60) with Fig. 10.48]. Some simplification is possible, however, owing to the complete insolubility of adsorbent in the mixture to be separated.

Refer to Fig. 11.34, a schematic representation of the adsorber. Feed enters at the rate of F lb/(hr)(sq ft), containing components A and C. The adsorbate-free adsorbent enters the top of the tower at the rate of B lb/(hr)(sq ft) and flows countercurrent to the gas entering at the bottom at the rate of R_1 lb/(hr)(sq ft). Compositions in the gas stream are expressed as x weight fraction C, the more strongly adsorbed

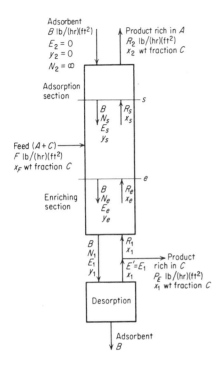

Feed $(A + C)$ →
F lb/(hr)(ft²)
x_F wt fraction C

Fig. 11.34 *Continuous fractionation.*

substance. E represents the weight of adsorbent-free adsorbate $A + C$ upon the solid, lb/(hr)(sq ft), and N the ratio, lb adsorbent/lb adsorbate. At any point in the adsorber, $B \doteq NE$. The adsorbate composition is expressed as y weight fraction component C, on an adsorbent-free basis. Solid leaves the adsorber at the bottom, is stripped of its adsorbate in the desorption section, and the desorbed fluid is split into two streams, the reflux R_1 and the C-rich product P_E. At the top the fluid leaving is the A-rich product, R_2 lb/(hr)(sq ft). The arrangement is very similar to that shown in Fig. 10.47. Calculations are made on a phase diagram of the type shown in the upper part of Fig. 11.8a, with N plotted as ordinate, x and y as abscissa.

Let Δ_E represent the net adsorbent-free flow downward and out of the adsorber. Then $\Delta_E = P_E$, and the coordinates of point Δ_E on the phase diagram are $(N_{\Delta E} = B/P_E, y_{\Delta E} = x_1)$. At the bottom of the adsorber, $B = N_1 E_1$ and

$$E_1 = E' = P_E + R_1 = \Delta_E + R_1 \tag{11.31}$$

An A-C balance below section e of the enriching section is

$$E_e = P_E + R_e = \Delta_E + R_e \tag{11.32}$$

and, for substance C,

$$E_e y_e = P_E x_1 + R_e x_e = \Delta_E x_1 + R_e x_e \tag{11.33}$$

while for adsorbent it becomes

$$N_e E_e = N_{\Delta E}\, \Delta_E = B \tag{11.34}$$

Δ_E therefore represents the difference $E_e - R_e$ for any level in the enriching section. Equations (11.32) and (11.34) provide a measure of the internal reflux ratio,

$$\frac{R_e}{E_e} = \frac{N_{\Delta E} - N_e}{N_{\Delta E}} = 1 - \frac{N_e}{N_{\Delta E}} \tag{11.35}$$

and at the bottom of the tower the external reflux ratio is

$$\frac{R_1}{P_E} = \frac{R_1}{E_1 - R_1} = \frac{N_{\Delta E} - N_1}{N_1} = \frac{N_{\Delta E}}{N_1} - 1 \tag{11.36}$$

At the top of the adsorber let Δ_R represent the difference between flows of adsorbate and unadsorbed gas, and since $E_2 = 0$, $\Delta_R = -R_2$. The coordinates of Δ_R on the phase diagram are then ($N_{\Delta R} = -B/R_2$, $x_{\Delta R} = x_2$). Material balances above section s are then, for A and C,

$$R_s = E_s + R_2 = E_s - \Delta_R \tag{11.37}$$

for C,

$$R_s x_s = E_s y_s + R_2 x_2 = E_s y_s - \Delta_R x_2 \tag{11.38}$$

and for adsorbent,

$$B = N_s E_s = \Delta_R N_{\Delta R} \tag{11.39}$$

Equations (11.37) and (11.39) provide the internal reflux ratio,

$$\frac{R_s}{E_s} = \frac{N_s - N_{\Delta R}}{-N_{\Delta R}} = 1 - \frac{N_s}{N_{\Delta R}} \tag{11.40}$$

Overall balances about the entire plant are

$$F = R_2 + P_E \tag{11.41}$$

$$F x_F = R_2 x_2 + P_E x_1 \tag{11.42}$$

The definitions of Δ_R and Δ_E, together with Eq. (11.42), provide

$$\Delta_R + F = \Delta_E \tag{11.43}$$

The graphical interpretation of these relations on the phase diagram is the same as that for the corresponding situations in extraction and is shown in detail in Illustration 11.5 below.

If a stage-type device (fluidized beds, for example) is used, the number of ideal stages is readily obtained by the usual step construction on the lower part of a diagram such as Fig. 11.35. For continuous contact,

$$N_{tOG} = \frac{Z}{H_{tOG}} = \int_{p_2}^{p_1} \frac{dp}{p - p^*} = \int_{x_2}^{x_1} \frac{dx}{x - x^*} - \ln \frac{1 + (r - 1)x_1}{1 + (r - 1)x_2} \tag{11.44}$$

where $r = M_A/M_C$ and

$$H_{tOG} = \frac{G}{K_G a_p P_t} \tag{11.45}$$

This may be applied separately to the enriching and adsorption sections. It assumes equimolar counterdiffusion of A and C, which is not strictly the case, but refinement at this time is unwarranted in view of the sparsity of the data.[24] It is also subject to the same limitations considered on page 536.

Illustration 11.5. Determine the number of transfer units and adsorbent circulation rate required to separate a gas containing 60% ethylene C_2H_4 and 40% propane C_3H_8 by volume into products containing 5 and 95% C_2H_4 by volume, isothermally at 25°C and 2.25 atm, using activated carbon as the adsorbent and a reflux ratio of twice the minimum. (*Note:* Hypersorbers customarily operate at reflux ratios closer to the minimum in order to reduce the adsorbent circulation rate. The present value is used in order to make the graphical solution clear.)

Solution. Equilibrium data for this mixture at 25°C and 2.25 atm have been estimated from the data of Lewis et al., *Ind. Eng. Chem.*, **42**, 1319, 1326 (1950), and are plotted in Fig. 11.35. C_3H_8 is the more strongly adsorbed component, and compositions in the gas and adsorbate are expressed as weight fraction C_3H_8. Tie lines have been omitted in the upper part of the plot, and the equilibrium compositions are shown instead in the lower part.

Molecular weights are 28.0 for C_2H_4 and 44.1 for C_3H_8. The feed-gas composition is then $x_F = 0.4(44.1)/[0.4(44.1) + 0.6(28.0)] = 0.512$ wt fraction C_3H_8. Similarly $x_1 = 0.967$, and $x_2 = 0.0763$ wt fraction C_3H_8.

Basis: 100 lb feed gas.

Eqs. (11.41) and (11.42):
$$100 = R_2 + P_E$$
$$100(0.512) = R_2(0.0763) + P_E(0.967)$$

Solving simultaneously, $R_2 = 51.1$ lb, $P_E = 48.9$ lb.

Point F at x_F and point E_1 at x_1 are located on the diagram as shown. From the diagram, N_1 (at point E_1) = 4.57 lb carbon/lb adsorbate. The minimum reflux ratio is found as it is for extraction. In this case, the tie line through point F locates Δ_{Em}, and $\Delta_{Em} = 5.80$.

$$\left(\frac{R_1}{P_E}\right)_m = \frac{5.80}{4.57} - 1 = 0.269 \text{ lb reflux gas/lb product}$$

$$(R_1)_m = 0.269 P_E = 0.269(48.9) = 13.15 \text{ lb}$$

$$(E_1)_m = (R_1)_m + P_E = 13.15 + 48.9 = 62.1 \text{ lb}$$

$$B_m = N_1(E_1)_m = 4.57(62.1) = 284 \text{ lb carbon/100 lb feed}$$

At twice the minimum reflux ratio, $R_1/P_E = 2(0.269) = 0.538$.

Eq. (11.36):
$$0.538 = \frac{N_{\Delta E}}{4.57} - 1$$

$$N_{\Delta E} = 7.03 \text{ lb carbon/lb adsorbate}$$

and point Δ_E is located on the diagram.

$$R_1 = 0.538 P_E = 0.538(48.9) = 26.3 \text{ lb}$$

$$E_1 = R_1 + P_E = 26.3 + 48.9 = 75.2 \text{ lb}$$

$$B = N_1 E_1 = 4.57(75.2) = 344 \text{ lb carbon/100 lb feed}$$

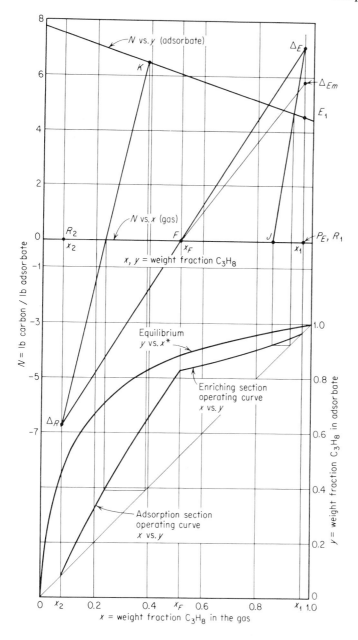

Fig. 11.35 *So ution to Illustration* 11.5.

Point Δ_R may be located by extending line $\Delta_E F$ to intersect the line $x = x_2$. Alternatively, $N_{\Delta_R} = -B/R_2 = -344/51.1 = -6.74$ lb carbon/lb adsorbate. Random lines such as line $\Delta_R K$ are drawn from Δ_R, and the intersections with the equilibrium curves are projected downward in the manner shown to provide the adsorption-section operating curve. Similarly random lines such as line $\Delta_E J$ are drawn from Δ_E, and intersections projected downward to provide the enriching-section operating curve. The horizontal distance between operating and equilibrium curves on the lower diagram is the driving force $x - x^*$ of Eq. (11.44).   The following were determined from the diagram:

x	x^*	$\dfrac{1}{x - x^*}$
$x_1 = 0.967$	0.825	7.05
0.90	0.710	5.26
0.80	0.60	5.00
0.70	0.50	5.00
0.60	0.43	5.89
$x_F = 0.512$	0.39	8.20
0.40	0.193	4.83
0.30	0.090	4.76
0.20	0.041	6.29
$x_2 = 0.0763$	0.003	13.65

The third column was plotted as ordinate against the first as abscissa, the area under the curve between x_1 and x_F was 2.65, and that between x_F and x_2 was 2.67.   Further, $r = 28.0/44.1 = 0.635$. Applying Eq. (11.44) to the enriching section,

$$N_{tOG} = 2.65 - \ln \frac{1 + (0.635 - 1)0.967}{1 + (0.635 - 1)0.512} = 2.52$$

and to the adsorption section,

$$N_{tOG} = 2.67 - \ln \frac{1 + (0.635 - 1)0.512}{1 + (0.635 - 1)0.0763} = 2.53$$

The total $N_{tOG} = 2.52 + 2.53 = 5.1$.

UNSTEADY STATE—FIXED-BED ADSORBERS

Owing to the inconvenience and relatively high cost of continuously transporting solid particles as required in steady-state operations, it is frequently found more economical to pass the fluid mixture to be treated through a stationary bed of adsorbent.   As increasing amounts of fluid are passed through such a bed, the solid adsorbs increasing amounts of solute, and an unsteady state prevails.   This technique is very widely used and finds application in such diverse fields as the recovery of valuable solvent vapors from gases, purifying air as with gas masks, dehydration of gases and liquids, decolorizing mineral and vegetable oils, the concentration of valuable solutes from liquid solutions, and many others.

The adsorption wave

Consider the case of a binary solution, either gas or liquid, containing a strongly adsorbed solute at concentration c_0.   The fluid is to be passed continuously down through a relatively deep bed of adsorbent initially free of adsorbate.   The uppermost layer of solid, in contact with the strong solution entering, at first adsorbs solute rapidly and effectively, and what little solute is left in the solution is substantially all

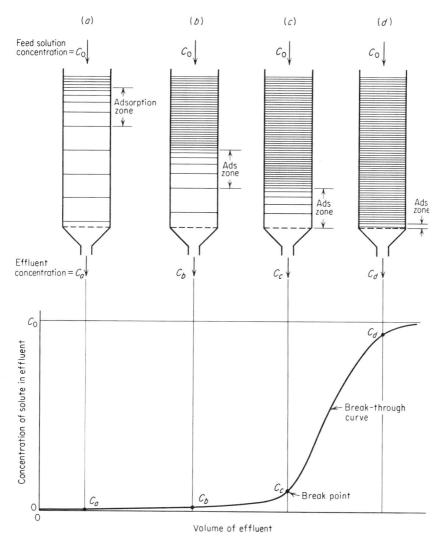

Fig. 11.36   *The adsorption wave.*

removed by the layers of solid in the lower part of the bed.   The effluent from the bottom of the bed is practically solute-free as at c_a in the lower part of Fig. 11.36. The distribution of adsorbate in the solid bed is indicated in the sketch in the upper part of this figure at a, where the relative density of the horizontal lines in the bed is meant to indicate the relative concentration of adsorbate.   The uppermost layer of the bed is practically saturated, and the bulk of the adsorption takes place over a relatively narrow adsorption zone in which the concentration changes rapidly, as shown.   As solution continues to flow, the adsorption zone moves downward as a wave, at a rate ordinarily very much more slowly than the linear velocity of the fluid through the bed. At a later time, as at b in the figure, roughly half of the bed is saturated with solute, but the effluent concentration c_b is still substantially zero. At c in the figure the lower portion of the adsorption zone has just reached the bottom of the bed, and the concentration of solute in the effluent has suddenly risen to an appreciable value c_c for the first time. The system is said to have reached the "break-point." The solute concentration in the effluent now rises rapidly as the adsorption zone passes through the bottom of the bed and at d has substantially reached the initial value c_0. The portion of the effluent concentration curve between positions c and d is termed the "breakthrough" curve. If solution continues to flow, little additional adsorption takes place since the bed is for all practical purposes entirely in equilibrium with the feed solution.

If a vapor is being adsorbed adiabatically from a gas mixture in this manner, the evolution of the heat of adsorption causes a temperature wave to flow through the adsorbent bed in a manner somewhat similar to the adsorption wave,[29] and the rise in temperature of the bed at the fluid outlet may sometimes be used as a rough indication of the breakpoint. In the case of adsorption from liquids the temperature rise is usually relatively small.

The shape and time of appearance of the breakthrough curve influence greatly the method of operating a fixed-bed adsorber. The curves generally have an S shape, but they may be steep or relatively flat and in some cases considerably distorted. If the adsorption process were infinitely rapid, the breakthrough curve would be a straight vertical line in the lower part of Fig. 11.36. The actual rate and mechanism of the adsorption process, the nature of the adsorption equilibrium, the fluid velocity, the concentration of solute in the feed, and the length of the adsorber bed·particularly if the solute concentration in the feed is high, all contribute to the shape of the curve produced for any system. The breakpoint is very sharply defined in some cases and in others poorly defined. Generally the breakpoint time decreases with decreased bed height, increased particle size of adsorbent, increased rate of flow of fluid through the bed, and increased initial solute content of the feed. There is a critical minimum bed height below which the solute concentration in the effluent will rise rapidly from the first appearance of effluent. In planning new processes it is best to determine the breakpoint and breakthrough curve for a particular system experimentally under conditions resembling as much as possible those to be encountered in the process.

Adsorption of vapors

One of the most important applications of fixed-bed adsorbers is in the recovery of valuable solvent vapors. Solids saturated with solvents such as alcohol, acetone, carbon disulfide, benzene, and others may be dried by evaporation of the solvent into an air stream, and the solvent vapor may be recovered by passing the resulting vapor-gas mixture through a bed of activated carbon. The very favorable adsorption equilibrium provided by a good grade of carbon for vapors of this sort permits substantially complete vapor recovery, 99 to 99.8 percent, from gas mixtures containing

Fig. 11.37   *Adsorber for solvent vapors, schematic.* [*Logan, U.S. Patent* 2,180,712 (1939).]

as little as 0.5 to 0.05 percent of the vapor by volume.[7] Air-vapor mixtures of concentration well below the explosive limits may thus be handled. In most such adsorption plants it is necessary to operate with a small drop in pressure through the bed of adsorbent in order to keep power costs low. Therefore granular rather than powdered adsorbents are used, and bed depths are relatively shallow (12 to 36 in.) and large in cross section. The superficial gas velocity may be in the range 0.8 to 1.8 ft/sec. A typical arrangement of the adsorption vessel is shown in Fig. 11.37.

In a typical operation the air-vapor mixture, if necessary cooled to 90 to 100°F and filtered free of dust particles which might clog the pores of the adsorbent, is admitted to the adsorbent bed. If the breakthrough curve is steep, the effluent air, substantially free of vapor, may be discharged to the atmosphere until the breakpoint is reached, whereupon the influent stream must be diverted to a second adsorber, while the first is regenerated. On the other hand, if the breakthrough curve is flat so that at the breakpoint a substantial portion of the adsorbent remains unsaturated with adsorbate, the gas may be permitted to flow through a second adsorber in series with the first until the carbon in the first is substantially all saturated. The influent mixture is then passed through the second and a third adsorber in series, while the first is regenerated. Such operation is relatively unusual, however, except for liquids.[13]

After gas flow has been diverted from an adsorber, the carbon is usually desorbed by admission of low-pressure steam. This lowers the partial pressure of the vapor in contact with the solid and provides by condensation the necessary heat of desorption. The steam-vapor effluent from the carbon is condensed and the condensed solvent recovered by decantation from the water if it is water-insoluble or by rectification if an aqueous solution results. When desorption is complete, the carbon is saturated with adsorbed water. This moisture is readily displaced by many vapors and evaporated into the air when the air-vapor mixture is readmitted to the carbon, and indeed much of the heat evolved during adsorption of the vapor may be used in desorbing the water, thus maintaining moderate bed temperatures. If the moisture interferes with vapor adsorption, the bed may first be dried by admitting heated air and then cooled by unheated air, prior to reuse for vapor recovery. Figure 11.38 shows a typical

Fig. 11.38 *Solvent-recovery adsorption plant.* [*After Benson and Courouleau, Chem. Eng. Progr.,* **44,** *466 (1948), with permission.*]

plant layout arranged for this method of operation. Mantell[33] provides many other operating details.

Moist gases may be dried of their water content by passing them through beds of activated silica gel, alumina, bauxite, or molecular sieves. Especially if the gases are under appreciable pressures, moderately deep beds are used since the pressure drop will still be only a small fraction of the total pressure. Towers containing the adsorbent may be as much as 30 ft tall or more, but in such instances the solid is best supported on trays at intervals of 4 or 5 ft in order to minimize the compression of the bed resulting from pressure drop. After the bed has reached the maximum practical moisture content, the adsorbent may be regenerated, either by application of heat by steam coils embedded in the adsorbent or by admitting heated air or gas. Liquids such as gasoline, kerosene, and transformer oil may also be dehydrated by passage through beds of activated alumina. High-temperature (450°F) steam followed by application of vacuum provided by a steam-jet ejector may be used for regenerating the adsorbent.

Illustration 11.6. A solvent-recovery plant is to recover 800 lb/hr of ethyl acetate vapor from a mixture with air at a concentration of 1.8 lb vapor/1,000 cu ft air at 90°F, 1 atm pressure. The adsorbent will be activated carbon, 6 to 8 mesh (av particle diam 0.0091 ft, apparent density of individual particles 45 lb/cu ft, and apparent density of the packed bed 30 lb/cu ft). The carbon is capable of adsorbing 0.45 lb vapor/lb carbon up to the breakpoint. The adsorption cycle will be set at 3 hr to allow sufficient time for regeneration. Determine the amount of carbon required, choose suitable dimensions for the carbon beds, and estimate the pressure drop.

Solution. In 3 hr the vapor to be adsorbed is 3(800) = 2,400 lb. The carbon required per bed = 2,400(1/0.45) = 5,330 lb. Two beds will be necessary, one adsorbing while the other is being regenerated. Total carbon required is 2(5,330) = 10,660 lb.

The volume of each bed will be 5,330/30 = 178 cu ft. If the bed depth is 1.5 ft, the cross section is 178/1.5 = 119 sq ft, say 7 by 17 ft, and it may be installed horizontally in a suitable vessel such as that shown in Fig. 11.37.

The pressure drop may be estimated by Eq. (6.36). At 90°F, 1 atm, the viscosity of air = 0.018 centipoise, or 0.018(2.42) = 0.0436 lb/(ft)(hr), and the density is $(^{29}/_{359})(^{492}/_{550}) = 0.0723$ lb/cu ft. One cubic foot of the bed, weighing 30 lb, contains $^{30}/_{45} = 0.667$ cu ft of solid particles. The fractional void content of the bed (space between particles, but not including pore volume) is $1 - 0.667 = 0.333 = \epsilon$.

The volumetric rate of air flow = 800(1,000)/1.8 = 445,000 cu ft/hr, and the superficial mass velocity = 445,000(0.0723)/119 = 270 lb/(hr)(sq ft) (linear velocity = 1.04 ft/sec). The particle Reynolds number = $\mathrm{Re} = d_p G/\mu = 0.0091(270)/0.0436 = 56.3$.

Eq. (6.36) (Chap. 6 notation):

$$\frac{\Delta P}{Z} \frac{g'_c \epsilon^3 d_p \rho_G}{(1 - \epsilon) G'^2} = \frac{150(1 - \epsilon)}{\mathrm{Re}} + 1.75$$

$$\frac{\Delta P(4.17)(10^8)(0.333)^3(0.0091)(0.0723)}{1.5(1 - 0.333)(270)^2} = \frac{150(1 - 0.333)}{56.3} + 1.75$$

$$\Delta P = 25.5 \text{ lb/sq ft, or } 25.5 \frac{12}{62.4} = 4.9 \text{ in. water}$$

Adsorption of liquids; percolation

The dehydration of liquids by stationary beds of adsorbent has already been mentioned. In addition, the colors of petroleum products, such as lubricating oils and transformer oils, and of vegetable oils are commonly reduced by percolation through beds of decolorizing clays; sugar solutions are deashed and decolorized by percolation through bone char; and many other liquid-treating operations use these semibatch methods.

In such service, the bed of adsorbent is commonly called a "filter." It may be installed in a vertical cylindrical vessel fitted with a dished or conical bottom, of diameter ranging up to as much as 15 ft and height up to 30 ft. In the case of decolorizing clays, the beds may contain as much as 50 tons of adsorbent. The granular adsorbent is supported on a screen or blanket, in turn supported by a perforated plate.

The liquid flow is ordinarily downward, either under the force of gravity alone or under pressure from above. At the start of the operation, the adsorbent bed is frequently allowed to "soak" for a time in the first portions of the feed liquid, in order to displace air from the adsorbent particles before the percolation is begun. In decolorizing operations, the concentration of impurity in the initial effluent liquid is usually much smaller than the specifications of the product require, and the breakthrough curve is frequently rather flat. Consequently it is common practice to allow the effluent liquid to accumulate in a receiving tank below the filter and to blend or composite it until the blended liquid reaches the largest acceptable concentration of impurity. In this way, the largest possible adsorbate concentration may be accumulated upon the solid.

When the solid requires revivification, the flow of liquid is stopped and the liquid in the filter drained. The solid may then be washed in place with an appropriate solvent, e.g., water in the case of sugar-refining filters, naphtha in the case of petroleum products. If necessary the solvent is then removed by admission of steam, following which the solid may be dumped from the filter and reactivated by burning or other suitable procedure, depending upon the nature of the adsorbent.

Elution

Desorption of the adsorbed solute by a solvent is called *elution*. The desorption solvent is the *elutant*, the effluent stream containing the desorbed solute and eluting solvent is the *eluate*. The *elution curve* is a plot of the solute concentration in the eluate against quantity of eluate, as in Fig. 11.39. The initial rise in solute concentration of the eluate, OA in the figure, is found when the void spaces between the adsorbent particles are initially filled with fluid remaining from the adsorption. In the case of liquids, if the bed is drained prior to elution, the elution curve starts at A. If elution is stopped after eluate corresponding to C has been withdrawn, the area under the curve $OABC$ represents the quantity of solute desorbed. For a successful process, this must equal the solute adsorbed during an adsorption cycle, else solute will build up in the bed from one cycle to the next.

Chromatography

Imagine a solution containing two solutes, A and B, which are differently adsorbed at equilibrium, A more strongly. A small quantity of this solution, insufficient to

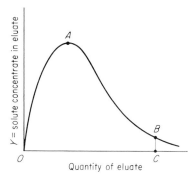

Fig. 11.39 *Elution of a fixed bed.*

saturate all but a small quantity of the adsorbent, is passed through an adsorbent bed, whereupon both solutes are retained in the upper portion of the bed to give rise to adsorbate concentrations as indicated in Fig. 11.40*a*. A suitable elutant is now passed through the bed, whereupon solute *B* is more readily desorbed than *A*. At *b*, *c*, and *d* in the figure, the solutes are seen both to be desorbed, only to be readsorbed and redesorbed at lower positions in the bed, but the wave of *B* concentration moves more rapidly downward than that of *A*.† At *e*, solute *B* has been washed out of the

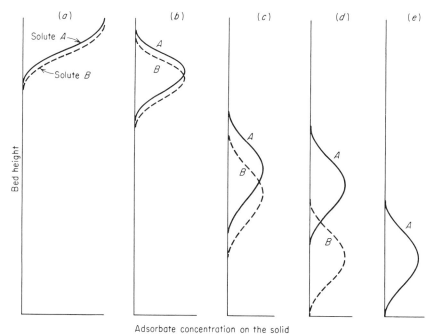

Fig. 11.40 *Chromatographic separation of two solutes.*

† The adsorption bands in some cases have different colors, depending upon the chemical nature of the solutes, and from this arose the terms *chromatographic adsorption* and *chromatography*.

solid, leaving essentially all the A behind.   The curves of Fig. 11.40 are idealized, since in reality their shape may change as the concentration waves pass down the column.   If the adsorption (or desorption) zone heights are short relative to the height of the bed, and if the selectivity of the adsorbent is sufficiently great, essentially complete separation of the solutes is possible.   This technique is the basis of very powerful methods of analysis of mixtures, both gas and liquid, and variants are used for industrial purposes.   *Partition chromatography* accomplishes a similar result, using a liquid contained in the pores of a solid as an immobilized solvent for solute separation, rather than adsorption itself.

Rate of adsorption in fixed beds

The design of a fixed-bed adsorber, and the prediction of the length of the adsorption cycle between revivifications, requires knowledge of the percentage approach to saturation at the breakpoint, as shown in Illustration 11.6.   This in turn requires the designer to predict the time of the breakpoint and the shape of the breakthrough curve.   The unsteady-state circumstances of fixed-bed adsorption and the many factors which influence the adsorption make such computations for the general case very difficult.[22,41]   The following simplified treatment due to Michaels[34] is readily used but is limited to isothermal adsorption from dilute feed mixtures and to cases where the equilibrium adsorption isotherm is concave to the solution-concentration axis, where the adsorption zone is constant in height as it travels through the adsorption column, and where the height of the adsorbent bed is large relative to the height of the adsorption zone.   Many industrial applications fall within these restrictions.   The development here is in terms of adsorption from a gas, but it is equally applicable to treatment of liquids.   Nonisothermal cases have also been treated.[29]

Consider the idealized breakthrough curve of Fig. 11.41.   This results from the flow of a solvent gas through an adsorbent bed at the rate of G_S lb/(hr)(sq ft), entering with an initial solute concentration Y_0 lb solute/lb solvent gas.   The total solute-free effluent after any time is w lb/sq ft of bed cross section.   The breakthrough curve is steep, and the solute concentration in the effluent rises rapidly from essentially zero to that in the incoming gas.   Some low value Y_B is arbitrarily chosen as the breakpoint concentration, and the adsorbent is considered as essentially exhausted when the effluent concentration has risen to some arbitrarily chosen value Y_E, close to Y_0.   We are concerned principally with the quantity of effluent w_B at the breakpoint and the shape of the curve between w_B and w_E.   The total effluent accumulated during the appearance of the breakthrough curve is $w_a = w_E - w_B$.   The adsorption zone, of constant height Z_a ft, is that part of the bed in which the concentration change from Y_B to Y_E is occurring at any time.

Let θ_a be the time required for the adsorption zone to move its own height down the column, after the zone has been established.   Then

$$\theta_a = \frac{w_a}{G_S} \tag{11.46}$$

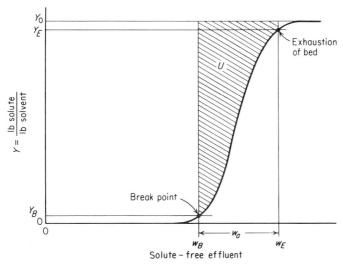

Fig. 11.41   *Idealized breakthrough curve.*

Let θ_E be the time required for the adsorption zone to establish itself and move out of the bed.   Then

$$\theta_E = \frac{W_E}{G_S} \qquad (11.47)$$

If the height of the adsorbent bed is Z ft, and if θ_F is the time required for the formation of the adsorption zone,

$$Z_a = Z\frac{\theta_a}{\theta_E - \theta_F} \qquad (11.48)$$

The quantity of solute removed from the gas in the adsorption zone from the breakpoint to exhaustion is U lb solute/sq ft of bed cross section.   This is given by the shaded area of Fig. 11.41, which is

$$U = \int_{w_B}^{w_E} (Y_0 - Y)\, dw \qquad (11.49)$$

If, however, all the adsorbent in the zone were saturated with solute, it would contain $Y_0 w_a$ lb solute/sq ft.   Consequently at the breakpoint, when the zone is still within the column, the fractional ability of the adsorbent in the zone still to adsorb solute is

$$f = \frac{U}{Y_0 w_a} = \frac{\displaystyle\int_{w_B}^{w_E} (Y_0 - Y)\, dw}{Y_0 w_a} \qquad (11.50)$$

If $f = 0$, so that the adsorbent in the zone is essentially saturated, the time of formation of the zone at the top of the bed θ_F should be substantially the same as the time required for the zone to travel a distance equal to its own height, θ_a. On the other hand, if $f = 1.0$, so that the solid in the zone contains essentially no adsorbate, the zone-formation time should be very short, essentially zero. These limiting conditions, at least, are described by

$$\theta_F = (1 - f)\theta_a \tag{11.51}$$

Equations (11.48) and (11.51) provide

$$Z_a = Z\frac{\theta_a}{\theta_E - (1 - f)\theta_a} = Z\frac{w_a}{w_E - (1 - f)w_a} \tag{11.52}$$

The adsorption column, Z ft tall and of unit cross-sectional area, contains $Z\rho_S$ lb adsorbent, where ρ_S is the apparent packed density of the solid in the bed. If this were all in equilibrium with the entering gas and therefore completely saturated at an adsorbate concentration X_T lb adsorbate/lb solid, the adsorbate weight would be $Z\rho_S X_T$ lb. At the breakpoint, the adsorption zone of height Z_a ft is still in the column at the bottom, but the rest of the column, $Z - Z_a$ ft, is substantially saturated. At the breakpoint, therefore, the adsorbed solute is $(Z - Z_a)\rho_S X_T + Z_a\rho_S(1 - f)X_T$ lb. The fractional approach to saturation of the column at the breakpoint is therefore[15]

$$\text{Degree of saturation} = \frac{(Z - Z_a)\rho_S X_T + Z_a\rho_S(1 - f)X_T}{Z\rho_S X_T} = \frac{Z - fZ_a}{Z} \tag{11.53}$$

In the fixed bed of adsorbent, the adsorption zone in reality moves downward through the solid, as we have seen. Imagine instead, however, that the solid moves upward through the column countercurrent to the fluid at sufficient velocity so that the adsorption zone remains stationary within the column, as in Fig. 11.42a. Here the solid leaving at the top of the column is shown in equilibrium with the entering gas, and all solute is shown as having been removed from the effluent gas. This would, of course, require an infinitely tall column, but our concern will be primarily with the concentrations at the levels corresponding to the extremities of the adsorption zone. The operating line over the entire tower is

$$G_S(Y_0 - 0) = L_S(X_T - 0) \tag{11.54}$$

or

$$\frac{L_S}{G_S} = \frac{Y_0}{X_T} \tag{11.55}$$

Since the operating line passes through the origin of Fig. 11.42b, at any level in the column the concentration of solute in the gas Y and of adsorbate upon the solid X are then related by

$$G_S Y = L_S X \tag{11.56}$$

Over the differential height dZ, the ratio of adsorption is

$$G_S \, dY = K_Y a_p (Y - Y^*) \, dZ \tag{11.57}$$

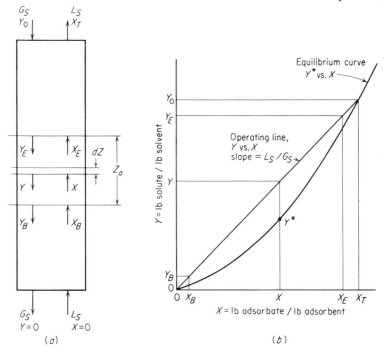

Fig. 11.42   *The adsorption zone.*

For the adsorption zone, therefore,

$$N_{tOG} = \int_{Y_B}^{Y_E} \frac{dY}{Y - Y^*} = \frac{Z_a}{H_{tOG}} = \frac{Z_a}{G_S/K_Y a_p} \tag{11.58}$$

where N_{tOG} is the overall number of gas transfer units in the adsorption zone.   For any value of Z less than Z_a, assuming H_{tOG} remains constant with changing concentrations,

$$\frac{Z \text{ at } Y}{Z_a} = \frac{w - w_B}{w_a} = \frac{\displaystyle\int_{Y_B}^{Y} \frac{dY}{Y - Y^*}}{\displaystyle\int_{Y_B}^{Y_E} \frac{dY}{Y - Y^*}} \tag{11.59}$$

Equation (11.59) should permit plotting the breakthrough curve by graphical evaluation of the integrals.

In addition to the restrictions outlined at the beginning, the success of this analysis largely hinges upon the constancy of $K_Y a_p$ or H_{tOG} for the concentrations within the adsorption zone.   This will, of course, depend upon the relative constancy of the resistances to mass transfer in the fluid and within the pores of the solid. Illustration 11.7 demonstrates the method of using the equations in a typical case.

Illustration 11.7. Air at 80°F, 1 atm, with a humidity of 0.00267 lb water/lb dry air is to be dehumidified by passage through a fixed bed of the silica gel used in Illustration 11.4. The depth of the adsorbent bed is to be 2 ft. The air will be passed through the bed at a superficial mass velocity of 95.5 lb/(hr)(sq ft), and the adsorption will be assumed to be isothermal. The breakpoint will be considered as that time when the effluent air has a humidity of 0.0001 lb water/lb dry air, and the bed will be considered exhausted when the effluent humidity is 0.0024 lb water/lb dry air. Mass-transfer coefficients are given in Illustration 11.4 for this gel. Estimate the time required to reach the breakpoint.

Solution. The equilibrium data are plotted in Fig. 11.43. The gel is initially "dry," and the effluent air initially of so low a humidity as to be substantially dry, so that the operating line passes through the origin of the figure. The operating line is then drawn to intersect the equilibrium curve at $Y_0 = 0.00267$ lb water/lb dry air. $Y_B = 0.0001$, $Y_E = 0.0024$ lb water/lb dry air.

In the accompanying table, column 1 lists values of Y on the operating line between Y_B and Y_E and column 2 the corresponding values of Y^* taken from the equilibrium curve at the same value of X. From these the data of column 3 were computed. A curve (not shown) of column 1 as abscissa, column 3 as ordinate was prepared and integrated graphically between each value of Y in the table and Y_B, to give in column 4 the numbers of transfer units corresponding to each value of Y (thus, for example, the area under the curve from $Y = 0.0012$ to $Y = 0.0001$ equals 4.438). The total number of transfer units corresponding to the adsorption zone is $N_{tOG} = 9.304$, in accordance with Eq. (11.58).

Y, lb H$_2$O lb dry air (1)	Y^*, lb H$_2$O lb dry air (2)	$\dfrac{1}{Y - Y^*}$ (3)	$\displaystyle\int_{Y_B}^{Y} \dfrac{dY}{Y - Y^*}$ (4)	$\dfrac{w - w_B}{w_a}$ (5)	$\dfrac{Y}{Y_0}$ (6)
$Y_B = 0.0001$	0.00003	14,300	0	0	0.0374
0.0002	0.00007	7,700	1.100	0.1183	0.0749
0.0004	0.00016	4,160	2.219	0.2365	0.1498
0.0006	0.00027	3,030	2.930	0.314	0.225
0.0008	0.00041	2,560	3.487	0.375	0.300
0.0010	0.00057	2,325	3.976	0.427	0.374
0.0012	0.000765	2,300	4.438	0.477	0.450
0.0014	0.000995	2,470	4.915	0.529	0.525
0.0016	0.00123	2,700	5.432	0.584	0.599
0.0018	0.00148	3,130	6.015	0.646	0.674
0.0020	0.00175	4,000	6.728	0.723	0.750
0.0022	0.00203	5,880	7.716	0.830	0.825
$Y_E = 0.0024$	0.00230	10,000	9.304	1.000	0.899

By dividing each entry in column 4 by 9.304, the values in column 5 were determined in accordance with Eq. (11.59). Column 6 was obtained by dividing each entry in column 1 by $Y_0 = 0.00267$, and column 6 plotted against column 5 provides a dimensionless form of the breakthrough curve between w_B and w_E (Fig. 11.44). Equation (11.53) may be written as

$$f = \frac{\displaystyle\int_{w_B}^{w_E} (Y_0 - Y)\,dw}{Y_0 w_a} = \int_0^{1.0} \left(1 - \frac{Y}{Y_0}\right) d\frac{w - w_B}{w_a}$$

from which it is seen that f equals the entire area above the curve of Fig. 11.44 up to $Y/Y_0 = 1.0$. By graphical integration, $f = 0.530$.

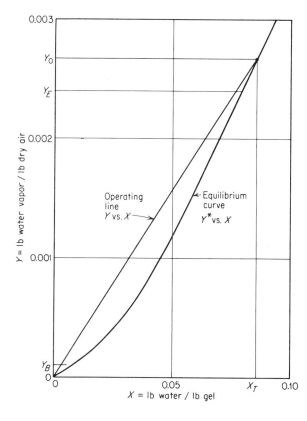

Fig. 11.43 *Solution to Illustration 11.7.*

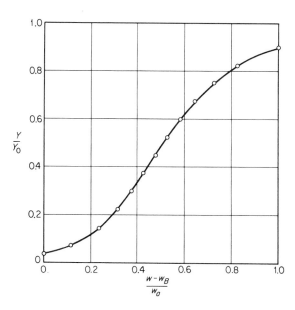

Fig. 11.44 *Calculated breakthrough curve for Illustration 11.7.*

The mass-transfer rates are given in equation form in Illustration 11.4.   For a mass velocity of air equal to 95.5 lb/(hr)(sq ft), $k_Y a_p = 188(95.5)^{0.55} = 2{,}310$ lb H_2O/(hr)(cu ft)(ΔY), and $k_S a_p = 217$ lb H_2O/(hr)(cu ft)(ΔX).

From Fig. 11.43, $X_T = 0.0858$ lb water/lb gel.

Eq. (11.55):
$$L_S = \frac{Y_0 G_S}{X_T} = \frac{0.00267(95.5)}{0.0858} = 2.97$$

The average slope of the equilibrium curve is $\Delta Y/\Delta X = 0.0185$, whence $mG_S/L_S = 0.0185(95.5)/2.97 = 0.595$.   Equations (11.29) and (11.30):

$$H_{tG} = \frac{G_S}{k_Y a_p} = \frac{95.5}{2{,}310} = 0.0413 \text{ ft} \qquad H_{tS} = \frac{L_S}{k_S a_p} = \frac{2.97}{217} = 0.0137 \text{ ft}$$

$$H_{tOG} = H_{tG} + \frac{mG_S}{L_S} H_{tS} = 0.0413 + 0.595(0.0137) = 0.0495 \text{ ft}$$

Eq. (11.58):
$$Z_a = N_{tOG} H_{tOG} = 9.304(0.0495) = 0.460 \text{ ft}$$

The height of the bed $= Z = 2$ ft.   Therefore [Eq. (11.53)]:

$$\text{Degree of bed saturation at breakpoint} = \frac{2 - 0.53(0.460)}{2} = 0.878 \text{ or } 87.8\%$$

The bed contains 2 cu ft gel/sq ft of cross section, and since the bed density is 41.9 lb/cu ft (Illustration 11.4), the weight of the gel $= 2(41.9) = 83.8$ lb/sq ft.   At 87.8% of equilibrium with the incoming air, the gel contains $83.8(0.878)(0.0858) = 6.30$ lb water/sq ft cross section.   The air introduces $95.5(0.00267) = 0.255$ lb water/(hr)(sq ft), and hence the breakpoint occurs at $6.30/0.255 = 24.7$ hr after air is admitted initially, and $w_B = 24.7(95.5) = 2{,}360$ lb air/sq ft cross section.   If the entire bed were in equilibrium with the entering gas, the adsorbed water would be $83.8(0.0858) = 7.18$ lb/sq ft, and hence $U = 7.18 - 6.30 = 0.88$ lb/sq ft $=$ ability of the bed still to adsorb.   Therefore $w_A = U/fY_0 = 0.88/0.53(0.00267) = 620$ lb air/sq ft.

The circumstances of this calculation correspond to run $S2$ of Eagleton and Bliss,[9] whose observed breakthrough curve (their fig. 5) agrees excellently with Fig. 11.44.   However, they observed that 180 lb air/sq ft flowed through while the effluent humidity rose from $Y/Y_0 = 0.1$ to 0.8, whereas the curve of Fig. 11.44 predicts this amount to be $(0.79 - 0.17)620 = 384$ lb/sq ft.   It is noteworthy that better agreement is obtained if the correlation of Table 3.3 is used for the gas-phase mass-transfer coefficient in the above calculations.

ION EXCHANGE

Ion-exchange operations are essentially metathetical chemical reactions between an electrolyte in solution and an insoluble electrolyte with which the solution is contacted. The mechanisms of these reactions and the techniques used to bring them about resemble those of adsorption so closely that for most engineering purposes ion exchange may be simply considered as a special case of adsorption.

Principles of ion exchange[19,27,28,35]

The ion-exchange solids first used were porous, natural or synthetic minerals containing silica, the zeolites, such as the mineral $Na_2O \cdot Al_2O_3 \cdot 4SiO_2 \cdot 2H_2O$, for example. Positively charged ions (cations) of a solution which are capable of diffusing through the pores will exchange with the Na^+ ions of such a mineral, and the latter is therefore called a cation exchanger. For example,

$$Ca^{++} + Na_2R \rightarrow CaR + 2Na^+$$

where R represents the residual material of the zeolite. In this manner "hard" water containing Ca^{++} may be softened by contact with the zeolite, the less objectionable Na^+ replacing the Ca^{++} in solution and the latter becoming immobilized in the solid. The reaction is reversible, and after saturation with Ca^{++} the zeolite may be regenerated by contact with a solution of salt,

$$CaR + 2NaCl \rightarrow Na_2R + CaCl_2$$

Later certain carbonaceous cation exchangers were manufactured by treating substances such as coal with reagents such as fuming sulfuric acid, and the like. The resulting exchangers can be regenerated to a hydrogen form, HR, by treatment with acid rather than salt. Thus, hard water containing $Ca(HCO_3)_2$ would contain H_2CO_3 after removal of the Ca^{++} by exchange, and since the carbonic acid is readily removed by degasification procedures, the total solids content of the water may be reduced in this manner. Early applications of ion exchangers using these principles were largely limited to water-softening problems.

In 1935, synthetic resinous ion exchangers were introduced. For example, certain synthetic, insoluble polymeric resins containing sulfonic, carboxylic, or phenolic groups can be considered as consisting of an exceedingly large anion and a replaceable or exchangeable cation. These make exchanges of the following type possible,

$$Na^+ + HR \rightleftharpoons NaR + H^+$$

and different cations will exchange with the resin with different relative ease. The Na^+ immobilized in the resin may be exchanged with other cations or with H^+, for example, much as one solute may replace another adsorbed upon a conventional adsorbent. Similarly synthetic, insoluble polymeric resins containing amine groups and anions may be used to exchange anions in solution. The mechanism of this action is evidently not so simple as in the case of the cation exchangers, but for present purposes it may be considered simply as an ion exchange. For example,

$$R\overset{}{N}H_3OH + Cl^- \rightleftharpoons RNH_3Cl + OH^-$$

$$H^+ + OH^- \rightarrow H_2O$$

where RNH_3 represents the immobile cationic portion of the resin. Such resins may be regenerated by contact with solutions of sodium carbonate or hydroxide. The synthetic ion-exchange resins are available in a variety of formulations of different exchange abilities, usually in the form of fine, granular solids or beads, 16 to 325 mesh. The individual beads are frequently nearly perfect spheres.

Techniques and applications

All the operational techniques ordinarily used for adsorption are used also for ion exchange. Thus we have batch or stagewise treatment of solutions, fluidized- and

fixed-bed operations, and continuous countercurrent operations. Fixed-bed per-
colations are most common. Chromatographic methods have been used for
fractionation of multicomponent ionic mixtures. Applications have been made in
the treatment of ore slurries ("resin-in-pulp") for collection of metal values.

In addition to the water-softening applications mentioned above, the complete
deionization of water may be accomplished by percolation first through a cation
exchanger and then through an anion exchanger. By using a bed formed of an
intimate mixture of equivalent amounts of a strong cationic and a strong anionic
exchange resin, simultaneous removal of all ions at neutrality is possible. For
purposes of regeneration, such mixed-bed resins are separated by hydraulic classification through particle size and density differences for the two resin types, and these
are regenerated separately. The ion exchangers have also been used for treatment
and concentration of dilute waste solutions. Perhaps the most remarkable application of exchange resins has been to the separation of the rare-earth metals, using
chromatographic techniques.

In *ion exclusion*, a resin is presaturated with the same ions as in a solution. It
can then reject ions in such a solution but at the same time absorb nonionic organic
substances such as glycerin, and the like, which may also be in the solution. The
organic matter may then later be washed from the resin in an ion-free state.

Equilibria

The equilibrium distribution of an ion between an exchange solid and a solution can
be described graphically by plotting isotherms in much the same manner used for
ordinary adsorption. Various empirical equations for these isotherms, such as the
Freundlich equation (11.3), have sometimes been applied to them. It is also possible
to apply equations of the mass-action type to the exchange reaction. For example,
for the cationic exchange

$$Na^+ + R^-H^+ \rightleftharpoons R^-Na^+ + H^+$$
$$\text{(soln)} \quad \text{(solid)} \quad \text{(solid)} \quad \text{(soln)}$$

the mass-action-law constant is

$$\alpha = \frac{[R^-Na^+]_{\text{solid}}[H^+]_{\text{soln}}}{[R^-H^+]_{\text{solid}}[Na^+]_{\text{soln}}} = \left[\frac{Na^+}{H^+}\right]_{\text{solid}}\left[\frac{H^+}{Na^+}\right]_{\text{soln}} \tag{11.60}$$

where the square brackets [ ] indicate the use of some suitable equilibrium-
concentration unit. The quantity α is thus seen to be an expression of relative
adsorptivity, in this case of relative adsorptivity of Na^+ to H^+. Since the solution
and the solid remain electrically neutral during the exchange process, we can write

$$\alpha = \frac{X}{X_0 - X}\frac{c_0 - c^*}{c^*} = \frac{X/X_0}{1 - X/X_0}\frac{1 - c^*/c_0}{c^*/c_0} \tag{11.61}$$

where c_0 is in this case the initial concentration of $Na^+ + H^+$ in the solution and
consequently the total of these at any time, c^* the equilibrium Na^+ concentration
after exchange, X the equilibrium concentration of Na^+ in the solid, and X_0 the

concentration if all H^+ were replaced by Na^+, all expressed as equivalents per unit volume or mass. In the general case for any system, the relative adsorptivity α at a given temperature varies with total cationic concentration c_0 in the solution and also with c. In some cases, α has been found to be essentially constant with varying c at fixed c_0.

Rate of ion exchange

The rate of ion exchange depends, like ordinary adsorption, upon rates of the following individual processes: (1) diffusion of ions from the bulk of the liquid to the external surface of an exchanger particle; (2) inward diffusion of ions through the solid to the site of exchange; (3) exchange of the ions; (4) outward diffusion of the released ions to the surface of the solid; (5) diffusion of the released ions from the surface of the solid to the bulk of the liquid. In some instances, the kinetics of the exchange reaction (3) may be controlling, but in others the rate of reaction is apparently very rapid in comparison with the rate of diffusion. The diffusion rates can be described by appropriate mass-transfer coefficients for equi-equivalent counterdiffusion through the solid and through the liquid, and in some instances at least it appears that the resistance to diffusion in the liquid phase may be controlling.

For cases where the exchange reactions are rapid in comparison with the rates of mass transfer, the methods of design developed for conventional adsorbers may be applied to ion-exchange operations directly. Some modification of the units of the terms in the various equations may be desirable, owing to the customary use of concentrations expressed as equivalents per unit volume in the cgs system. The following example illustrates this:

Illustration 11.8. A synthetic ion-exchange resin in bead form is to be used for collecting and concentrating the copper in a dilute waste solution. The feed contains $CuSO_4$ at a concentration of 20 milligram equivalents (meq) Cu^{++}/liter and is to be treated at the rate of 10,000 gal/hr. A continuous system is planned: the solution to be treated and regenerated resin will flow countercurrently through a vertical tower, where 99% of the Cu^{++} of the feed will be exchanged; the resin will be regenerated in a second tower by countercurrent contact with 2 N sulfuric acid. The necessary data are provided by Selke and Bliss, *Chem. Eng. Progr.*, **47**, 529 (1951).

For collection of Cu^{++}. A superficial liquid velocity of 2.2 liters/(hr)(sq cm) will be used for which the mass-transfer rate is 2.0 meq Cu^{++}/(hr)(g resin)(meq Cu^{++}/liter). The regenerated resin will contain 0.30 meq Cu^{++}/g, and 1.2 times the minimum resin/solution ratio will be used.

For regeneration of the resin. The superficial liquid velocity will be 0.17 liter/(hr)(sq cm), for which the mass-transfer rate is 0.018 meq Cu^{++}/(hr)(g resin)(meq Cu^{++}/liter). The acid will be utilized to the extent of 70%.

Compute the necessary rates of flow of resin and the amount of resin holdup in each tower.

Solution. Equilibria for the Cu^{++}–H^+ exchange are provided by Selke and Bliss at two concentration levels, 20 and 2,000 meq cation/liter. These are shown in Fig. 11.45a and b, respectively.

Collection of Cu^{++}. Feed soln = 10,000(3.785) = 37,850 liters/hr. $c_1 = 20$ meq Cu^{++}/liter, $c_2 = 0.01(20) = 0.20$ meq Cu^{++}/liter. Cu^{++} exchanged = 37,850(20 − 0.20) = 750,000 meq/hr.

$X_2 = 0.30$ meq Cu^{++}/g. The point (c_2, X_2) is plotted on Fig. 11.45a. For the minimum resin/solution ratio and an infinitely tall tower, the operating line passes also through point P at $X = 4.9$ on this figure, corresponding to equilibrium with c_1. The minimum resin rate is then 750,000/(4.9 − 0.30) = 163,000 g/hr. For 1.2 times the minimum, the resin rate is 1.2(163,000) = 196,000

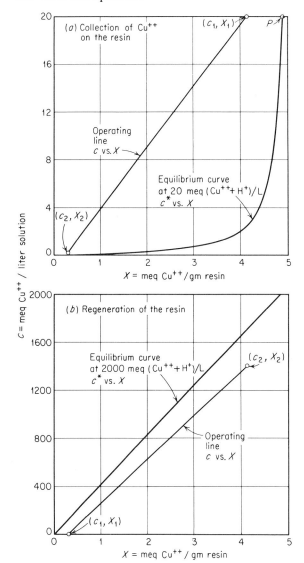

Fig. 11.45   *Solution to Illustration 11.8.*

g/hr, or 430 lb/hr.   A copper balance,

$$750,000 = 196,000(X_1 - 0.30)$$

$$X_1 = 4.12 \text{ meq Cu}^{++}/\text{g resin}$$

The point (c_1, X_1) is plotted on Fig. 11.45a, and the operating line may be drawn as a straight line at these low concentrations.

The quantity of resin in the tower may be obtained by application of the rate equation written in a form appropriate to the units of the quantities involved.   Adapting Eq. (11.26) to this case, we have

$$V \, dc = \frac{K'_L a_p}{\rho_s} (c - c^*) \, d(SZ\rho_s)$$

where V = liters liquid/hr
$\quad c$ = concn Cu^{++}, meq/liter, in the soln
$\quad c*$ = concn Cu^{++} in the soln at equilibrium with the resin
$K'_L a_p / \rho_S$ = overall liquid mass-transfer coefficient, meq/(hr)(g resin)(meq/liter)
$\quad K'_L$ = overall liquid mass-transfer coefficient, meq/(hr)(sq cm)(meq/liter)
$\quad a_p$ = surface of resin particles, sq cm/cu cm
$\quad \rho_S$ = packed density of resin, g/cu cm
$SZ\rho_S$ = resin in tower, g
$\quad S$ = cross section of tower, sq cm
$\quad Z$ = height of tower, cm

Rearranging this equation and integrating,

$$ SZ\rho_S = \frac{V}{K'_L a_p / \rho_S} \int_{c_2}^{c_1} \frac{dc}{c - c*} $$

For values of c on the operating line between c_1 and c_2, the corresponding values of $c*$ from the equilibrium curve at the same value of X are obtained as follows:

c	20	16	12	8	4	2	1	0.2
$c*$	2.4	1.9	0.5	0.25	0.10	0.05	0.02	0
$\dfrac{1}{c - c*}$	0.0568	0.0710	0.0870	0.129	0.256	0.513	1.02	5.0

A curve (not shown) of $1/(c - c*)$ as ordinate, c as abscissa, is plotted and integrated graphically between the limits c_1 and c_2. The area under the curve is 5.72. (*Note:* This is the number of transfer units N_{tOL}.) Substituting in the integrated equation,

$$ \text{Resin holdup} = SZ\rho_S = \frac{37,850(5.72)}{2.0} = 108,300 \text{ g, or 239 lb} $$

Regeneration of resin. Cu^{++} to be exchanged = 750,000 meq/hr, requiring as many meq H$^+$/hr. For a 70% utilization of acid, the acid feed must contain $750,000/0.70 = 1,071,000$ meq H$^+$/hr, or $1,071,000/2,000 = 536$ liters/hr of 2 N acid.
$c_1 = 0$, $c_2 = 750,000/536 = 1,400$ meq Cu^{++}/liter. $X_1 = 0.30$, $X_2 = 4.12$ meq Cu^{++}/g resin. The points (c_1, X_1) and (c_2, X_2) are plotted on Fig. 11.45b and the operating line drawn. Integration of the rate equation for this case, where both operating and equilibrium lines are straight, provides

$$ V(c_2 - c_1) = \frac{K'_L a_p}{\rho_S} (SZ\rho_S)(c* - c)_m $$

where $(c* - c)_m$ is the logarithmic average of the driving forces at the extremities of the tower and the other symbols have the same meaning as before.

$$ c_1^* - c_1 = 120 - 0 = 120 \qquad c_2^* - c_2 = 1,700 - 1,400 = 300 \text{ meq Cu}^{++}/\text{liter} $$

$$ (c* - c)_m = \frac{300 - 120}{\ln (300/120)} = 196.5 \text{ meq Cu}^{++}/\text{liter} $$

Substituting in the rate equation,

$$ 750,000 = 0.018(SZ\rho_S)(196.5) $$

$$ SZ\rho_S = 212,000 \text{ g, or 476 lb, resin holdup in regeneration tower} $$

The resin should be water-rinsed before reintroducing it into the adsorption tower.   The Cu^{++} in the effluent solution has been concentrated $1,400/20 = 70$ times, equivalent to the evaporation of 9,857 gal of water/hr from the original solution.

NOTATION FOR CHAPTER 11

a_p = external surface of solid particles, sq ft/cu ft of packed volume
B = rate of adsorbent flow in continuous fractionators, lb adsorbate-free solid/(hr)(sq ft)
c = solute concentration in solution, lb/cu ft or, in the case of ion exchange, equivalents/unit volume
C_A = heat capacity of a vapor, Btu/(lb)(°F)
C_{AL} = heat capacity of a liquid, Btu/(lb)(°F)
C_B = heat capacity of adsorbent, Btu/(lb)(°F)
C_G = heat capacity of unadsorbed gas, Btu/(lb)(°F)
d = differential operator
E = rate of flow of adsorbate, lb/(hr)(sq ft)
f = fractional ability of adsorbent zone to adsorb solute, dimensionless
F = feed rate, lb/(hr)(sq ft)
G = total rate of flow of gas, lb moles/(hr)(sq ft)
G' = total rate of flow of gas, lb/(hr)(sq ft)
G_s = solvent in solution, or unadsorbed gas, lb in a batch process or lb/(hr)(sq ft) in a continuous process
$\bar{H}$ = differential heat of adsorption, Btu/lb adsorbate
H_G = enthalpy of gas, Btu/lb solute-free gas
H_L = enthalpy of solid and adsorbed solute, Btu/lb adsorbate-free solid
H_{tG} = height of gas transfer unit, ft
H_{tOG} = overall height of gas transfer unit, ft
H_{tS} = height of solid transfer unit, ft
ΔH_A = integral heat of adsorption, Btu/lb adsorbent, referred to liquid adsorbate
$\Delta H_A'$ = integral heat of adsorption, Btu/lb adsorbent, referred to vapor adsorbate
k = constant
k_Y = gas mass-transfer coefficient, lb/(hr)(sq ft)(lb solute/lb solvent gas)
K_G = overall gas mass-transfer coefficient, lb moles/(hr)(sq ft)(atm)
K_Y = overall gas mass-transfer coefficient, lb/(hr)(sq ft)(lb solute/lb solvent gas)
ln = natural logarithm
log = common logarithm
L_s = adsorbate-free adsorbent, lb in a batch process or lb/(hr)(sq ft) in a continuous process
m = constant
   = in Eqs. (11.29) and (11.30), slope of the equilibrium adsorption isotherm = dY^*/dX, dimensionless
M = molecular weight, lb/lb mole
n = constant
N = adsorbent concentration, lb adsorbate-free adsorbent/lb adsorbate
N_p = number of theoretical stages in a cascade, dimensionless
N_{tOG} = overall number of gas transfer units, dimensionless
p = partial pressure, atm, unless otherwise indicated
P = vapor pressure, atm, unless otherwise indicated
P_E = product rich in the more strongly adsorbed substance, lb/(hr)(sq ft)
P_t = total pressure, atm
r = molecular weight poorly adsorbed gas/molecular weight strongly adsorbed gas, dimensionless
R = rate of flow of gas in a continuous fractionator, lb/(hr)(sq ft)
   = gas constant, (cu ft)(atm)/(lb mole)(°R)
   = nonexchanged portion of an ion exchanger

t_G = gas temperature, °F

t_L = adsorbent temperature, °F

t_o = base temperature for enthalpy computation, °F

T = absolute temperature, °R (°K on Fig. 11.6)

U = solute adsorbed in the adsorption zone, fixed-bed adsorbers, lb/(hr) (sq ft)

V = quantity of solution, cu ft solution/lb adsorbent

w = in a semibatch process, quantity of effluent from fixed-bed adsorber, lb solute-free effluent/ sq ft

$w_a = w_E - w_B$

w_B = quantity of effluent from fixed-bed adsorber at the breakpoint, lb solute-free effluent/ sq ft

w_E = quantity of effluent from fixed-bed adsorber at bed exhaustion, lb solute-free effluent/ sq ft

x = concentration of more strongly adsorbed substance in the fluid, weight fraction

X = adsorbate concentration, lb solute adsorbed/lb adsorbent, or, for ion exchange, equivalents/ unit mass or volume

X_T = adsorbate concentration of a fixed-bed adsorber, when in equilibrium with entering fluid, lb solute/lb adsorbent

y = composition of adsorbate, weight fraction more strongly adsorbed substance, adsorbent-free basis

Y = concentration of solute in fluid, lb solute/lb solvent

Y_B = concentration of solute in effluent from fixed-bed adsorber at the breakpoint, lb solute/lb ˙ solvent

Y_E = concentration of solute in effluent from fixed-bed adsorber at bed exhaustion, lb solute/lb solvent

Z = active height of adsorber, ft

Z_a = height of adsorption zone in fixed-bed adsorber, ft

α = mass-action-law constant or relative adsorptivity, dimensionless

Δ = difference

θ = time, hr

θ_a = time required for adsorption zone to move a distance Z_a through the fixed bed, hr

θ_E = time required to reach bed exhaustion, hr

θ_F = time of formation of adsorption zone, hr

λ = latent heat of vaporization, Btu/lb

ρ = fluid density, lb/cu ft

ρ_S = apparent packed density of an adsorbent bed, lb solid/cu ft packed space

Subscripts:

e = within the enriching section of a continuous fractionator

F = pertaining to the feed

m = minimum

n = stage n

o = at a base temperature t_o

r = reference subsance

0 = initial

1 = stage 1; bottom of a continuous-contact adsorber

2 = stage 2; top of a continuous-contact adsorber

Superscript

$*$ = equilibrium

REFERENCES

1. Amundsen, N. R.: *Ind. Eng. Chem.*, **48,** 26 (1956).
2. Anon.: *Chem. Eng.*, **70,** Apr. 15, 92 (1963).
3. Bartell, F. E., and C. K. Sloan: *J. Am. Chem. Soc.*, **51,** 1643 (1929).
4. Berg, C.: *Trans. AIChE.*, **42,** 665 (1946); *Chem. Eng. Progr.*, **47,** 585 (1951).
5. Boer, J. H. de: "The Dynamical Character of Adsorption," Oxford Press, Oxford, 1953.
6. Brunauer, S.: "Adsorption of Gases and Vapors," Princeton University Press, Princeton, N.J., 1943.
7. Courouleau, P. H., and R. E. Benson: *Chem. Eng.*, **55**(3), 112 (1948).
8. Denver Equipment Company: *Deco Trefoil*, Jan.–Feb., 1966, p. 26.
9. Eagleton, L. C., and H. Bliss: *Chem. Eng. Progr.*, **49,** 543 (1953).
10. Ermenc, E. D.: *Chem. Eng.*, **68,** May 27, 87 (1961).
11. Etherington, L. D., R. J. Fritz, E. W. Nicholson, and H. W. Scheeline: *Chem. Eng. Progr.*, **52,** 274 (1956).
12. Etherington, L. D., R. E. D. Haney, W. A. Herbst, and H. W. Scheeline: *AIChE J.*, **2,** 65 (1956).
13. Fornwalt, H. J., and R. A. Hutchins: *Chem. Eng.*, **73,** Apr. 11, 179; May 9, 155 (1966).
14. Goldman, F., and M. Polanyi: *Z. Physik. Chem.*, **132,** 321 (1928).
15. Halle, E. von: personal communication, 1964.
16. Hancher, C. W., and S. H. Jury: *Chem. Eng. Progr. Symp. Ser.*, **55**(24), 87 (1959).
17. Helby, W. A., in J. Alexander (ed.), "Colloid Chemistry," vol. VI, p. 814, Reinhold Publishing Corporation, New York, 1946.
18. Helby, W. A.: *Chem. Eng.*, **59**(10), 153 (1952).
19. Helfferich, F.: "Ion Exchange," McGraw-Hill Book Company, New York, 1962.
20. Henson, T. L., and R. L. Kabel: *AIChE J.*, **12,** 606 (1966).
21. Hersh, C. K.: "Molecular Sieves," Reinhold Publishing Corporation, New York, 1961.
22. Hiester, N. K., T. Vermeulen, and G. Klein: sec. 16 in "The Chemical Engineers' Handbook," 4th ed., McGraw-Hill Book Company, New York, 1963.
23. Higgins, I. R., and J. T. Roberts: *Chem. Eng. Progr. Symp. Ser.*, **50**(14), 87 (1954).
24. Kapfer, W. H., M. Malow, J. Happel, and C. J. Marsel: *AIChE J.*, **2,** 456 (1956).
25. Kehde, H., R. G. Fairfield, J. C. Frank, and L. W. Zahnstecker: *Chem. Eng. Progr.*, **44,** 575 (1948).
26. Kipling, J. J., and D. A. Tester: *J. Chem. Soc.*, **1952,** 4123.
27. Kunin, R.: "Elements of Ion Exchange," Reinhold Publishing Corporation, New York, 1960.
28. Kunin, R.: "Ion Exchange Resins," John Wiley & Sons, Inc., New York, 1958.
29. Leavitt, F. W.: *Chem. Eng. Progr.*, **58**(8), 54 (1962).
30. Lewis, W. K., E. R. Gilliland, B. Chertow, and W. P. Cadogen: *Ind. Eng. Chem.*, **42,** 1319, 1326 (1950).
31. Leva, M.: "Fluidization," McGraw-Hill Book Company, New York, 1959.
32. Lloyd, C. L., and B. L. Harris: *J. Phys. Chem.*, **58,** 899 (1954).
33. Mantell, C. L.: "Adsorption," 2d ed., McGraw-Hill Book Company, New York, 1951.
34. Michaels, A. S.: *Ind. Eng. Chem.*, **44,** 1922 (1952).
35. Nachod, F. C., and J. Schubert: "Ion Exchange Technology," Academic Press Inc., New York, 1956.
36. Othmer, D. F., and F. G. Sawyer: *Ind. Eng. Chem.*, **35,** 1269 (1943).
37. Sanders, M. T.: *Ind. Eng. Chem.*, **20,** 791 (1928).
38. Siegmund, C. W., W. D. Munro, and N. R. Amundsen: *Ind. Eng. Chem.*, **48,** 43 (1956).
39. Squires, A. M.: *Chem. Eng. Progr.*, **58**(4), 66 (1962).
40. Swinton, E. A., D. E. Weiss et al.: *Australian J. Appl. Sci.*, **4,** 316, 510, 519, 530, 543 (1953).
41. Vermeulen, T., in T. B. Drew and J. W. Hoopes (eds.), "Advances in Chemical Engineering," vol. II, p. 147, Academic Press Inc., New York, 1958.

42. Walker, W. H., W. K. Lewis, W. H. McAdams, and E. R. Gilliland: "Principles of Chemical Engineering," 3d ed., p. 511, McGraw-Hill Book Company, New York, 1937.

43. Young, D. M., and A. D. Croswell: "Physical Adsorption of Gases," Butterworth & Co. (Publishers), Ltd., London, 1962.

44. Zenz, F. A.: in A. Acrivos (ed.), "Modern Chemical Engineering," vol. 1, p. 269, Reinhold Publishing Corporation, New York, 1963.

45. Zenz, F. A., and D. F. Othmer: "Fluidization and Fluid-particle Systems," Reinhold Publishing Corporation, New York, 1960.

PROBLEMS

11.1 The equilibrium adsorption of acetone vapor on an activated carbon at 30°C is given by the following data:

G adsorbed/carbon	0	0.1	0.2	0.3	0.35
Partial pressure acetone, mm Hg	0	2	12	42	92

The vapor pressure of acetone at 30°C is 283 mm Hg.

A liter flask contains air and acetone vapor at 1 atm and 30°C, with a relative saturation of the vapor of 35%. Two grams of fresh activated carbon is introduced into the flask, and the flask is sealed. Compute the final vapor concentration at 30°C and the final pressure. Neglect the adsorption of air.

11.2. A solution of washed, raw cane sugar, 48% sucrose by weight, is colored by the presence of small quantities of impurities. It is to be decolorized at 80°C by treatment with an adsorptive carbon in a contact filtration plant. The data for an equilibrium adsorption isotherm were obtained by adding various amounts of the carbon to separate batches of the original solution and observing the equilibrium color reached in each case. The data, with the quantity of carbon expressed on the basis of the sugar content of the solution, are as follows:

Lb carbon/lb dry sugar	0	0.005	0.01	0.015	0.02	0.03
% of color removed	0	47	70	83	90	95

The original solution has a color concentration of 20, measured on an arbitrary scale, and it is desired to reduce the color to 2.5% of its original value.

a. Convert the equilibrium data to $Y^* = $ color units/lb sugar, $X = $ color units/lb carbon. Do they follow the Freundlich equation? If so, what are the equation constants?

b. Calculate the necessary dosage of fresh carbon, per 1,000 lb of solution, for a single-stage process. **Ans.:** 20.4 lb.

c. Calculate the necessary carbon dosages per 1,000 lb of solution for a two-stage crosscurrent treatment, using the minimum total amount of fresh carbon. **Ans.:** 10.54 lb.

d. Calculate the necessary carbon dosage per 1,000 lb of solution for a two-stage counter-current treatment. **Ans.:** 6.24 lb.

11.3. The sugar refinery of Prob. 11.2 must treat also a raw cane sugar solution, 48 wt % sucrose, of original color 50, based on the same color scale used in Prob. 11.2. The color scale is such that colors are additive, i.e., equal weights of solution of color 20 and color 50 will give a solution of color $(20 + 50)/2 = 35$. The same adsorption isotherm describes the color removal of the darker solution as that of Prob. 11.2. Equal quantities of the dark solution and that of Prob. 11.2 must both be decolorized to a color 0.5.

  a. In a single-stage process, will it be more economical of carbon first to blend the original solutions and to treat the blend, or to treat each separately to color 0.5 and to blend the finished products?

  b. Repeat for a two-stage crosscurrent treatment, fresh carbon in each stage, arranged for the minimum carbon in each case.

  c. Repeat for a countercurrent two-stage treatment.

  d. The following treating scheme was suggested: The light-colored solution is to be treated in a two-stage countercurrent plant to the final desired color. The spent carbon from this operation is to be used to treat an equal weight of the dark solution, and the carbon is then revivified. The residual dark solution is then finished to the desired final color with the necessary amount of fresh carbon. Sketch a flow sheet and an operating diagram (freehand) for the entire process. Determine whether there is any saving of carbon over that for the arrangement of part (*c*).

  e. Determine whether the scheme of Fig. 11.46 offers any economies of carbon.

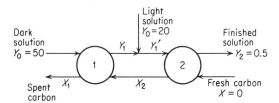

Fig. 11.46 *Flow sheet for Prob. 11.3e.*

11.4. Prove that for crosscurrent two-stage treatment of liquid solutions by contact filtration, when the adsorption isotherm is linear, the least total adsorbent results if the amounts used in each stage are equal.

11.5. For adsorption from dilute liquid solutions in stagewise countercurrent operations, where the Freundlich equation describes the adsorption equilibrium, derive analytical expressions in terms of n, m, Y_0, and Y_{Np} for the minimum adsorbent/solvent ratio when fresh adsorbent is used. Cover both cases of Fig. 11.22.

11.6. Nitrogen dioxide, NO_2, produced by a thermal process for fixation of nitrogen is to be removed from a dilute mixture with air by adsorption on silica gel in a continuous countercurrent adsorber. The gas entering the adsorber at the rate of 1,000 lb/hr contains 1.5% NO_2 by volume, and 90% of the NO_2 is to be removed. Operation is to be isothermal at 25°C, 1 atm. The entering gel will be free of NO_2. The equilibrium adsorption isotherm at this temperature is given by the following data [Foster and Daniels, *Ind. Eng. Chem.*, **43**, 986 (1951)]:

Partial pressure NO_2, mm Hg	0	2	4	6	8	10	12
G NO_2/100 g gel	0	0.4	0.9	1.65	2.60	3.65	4.85

  a. Calculate the minimum weight of gel required per hour.

  b. For twice the minimum gel rate, calculate the number of transfer units required.

  c. A superficial air rate of 300 lb/(hr)(sq ft) is to be used. Assume that the characteristics of the gel are the same as those described in Illustration 11.4. Modify the gas mass-transfer coefficient of Illustration 11.4 so that it will apply to the transfer of NO_2 rather than water. Modify the solid-phase mass-transfer coefficient to apply for NO_2 on the assumption that the transfer in the pores of the solid is by molecular diffusion through the gas filling the pores. The diffusivity of NO_2 in air is estimated to be 0.136 sq cm/sec at 25°C, 1 atm.

Estimate the value of H_{tOG}, and calculate the corresponding height of the adsorber. **Ans.:** 9.5 ft.

11.7. Lewis et al., *J. Am. Chem. Soc.*, **72**, 1157 (1950), report the following for the simultaneous adsorption of acetylene and ethylene from mixtures of the two on silica gel at 1 atm, 25°C (reprinted with permission of the American Chemical Society):

Mole fraction ethylene in adsorbate	Mole fraction ethylene in gas, at equilibrium	Mg moles mixture adsorbed/g adsorbent
0.0686	0.2422	1.622
0.292	0.562	1.397
0.458	0.714	1.298
0.592	0.814	1.193
0.630	0.838	1.170
0.864	0.932	1.078

A gas containing equimolar amounts of acetylene and ethylene is to be fractionated in a continuous countercurrent adsorber, to yield products containing 98 and 2% acetylene by volume. Assume the temperature to remain constant at 25°C and the pressure to be 1 atm. Calculate the number of transfer units and the gel circulation rate per 1,000 cu ft feed gas, using 1.2 times the minimum gel circulation rate. **Ans.:** $N_{tOG} = 15.3$.

11.8. The sulfur content of an oil is to be reduced by percolation through a bed of adsorbent clay. Laboratory tests with the clay and oil in a representative percolation filter show the following instantaneous sulfur contents of the effluent oil as a function of the total oil passing through the filter [adapted from Kaufman, *Chem. Met. Eng.*, **30**, 153 (1924)]:

Bbl oil/ton clay	0	10	20	50	100	200	300	400
% sulfur	0.011	0.020	0.041	0.067	0.0935	0.118	0.126	0.129

Assume that the specific gravity of the oil is unchanged during the percolation. The untreated oil has a sulfur content of 0.134%, and a product containing 0.090% sulfur is desired.

a. If the effluent from the filter is composited, what yield of satisfactory product may be obtained per ton of clay? **Ans.:** 240 bbl.

b. If the effluent from the filter is continually and immediately withdrawn and blended with just sufficient untreated oil to give the desired sulfur content in the blend, what quantity of product may be obtained per ton of clay? **Ans.:** 159.4 bbl.

11.9. A laboratory fixed-bed adsorption column filled with a synthetic sulfonic acid cation-exchange resin in the acid form is to be used to remove Na^+ ions from an aqueous solution of sodium chloride. The bed depth is 33.5 cm, and the solution to be percolated through the bed contains 0.120 meq Na^+/cu cm. At saturation, the resin contains 2.02 meq Na^+/cu cm resin. The solution will be passed through the bed at a superficial linear velocity of 0.31 cm/sec. For this resin, Michaels[34] reports that the overall liquid mass-transfer rate $K'_L a_p = 0.86 v_L^{0.5}$ where v_L is the superficial liquid velocity, cm/sec, and $K'_L a_p$ is expressed as meq Na^+/(sec)(cu cm)(meq/cu cm). The relative adsorptivity of Na^+ with respect to H^+ for this resin is $\alpha = 1.20$, and this is constant for the prevailing concentration level.   Define the breakpoint concentration as 5% of the initial solution concentration, and assume that practical bed exhaustion occurs when the effluent concentration is 95% of the initial.   Estimate the volume of effluent at the breakpoint, per unit bed cross section.   **Ans.:** 427 cu cm/sq cm.

Note: For these circumstances, Michaels[34] observed that the adsorption-zone height was 23.8 cm, that the breakpoint occurred after 382 ± 10 cu cm effluent/sq cm bed cross section was collected and that the holdup of liquid in the bed was 14.5 ± 2.5 cu cm solution/sq cm bed cross section. Compare the calculated results with these.

CHAPTER TWELVE
DRYING

The term *drying* refers generally to the removal of moisture from a substance. It is so loosely and inconsistently applied that some restriction in its meaning is necessary in the treatment to be given the subject here. For example, a wet solid such as wood, cloth, or paper may be dried by evaporation of the moisture either into a gas stream or without the benefit of the gas to carry away the vapor, but the mechanical removal of such moisture by expression or centrifuging is not ordinarily considered drying. A solution may be "dried" by spraying it in fine droplets into a hot, dry gas, which results in evaporation of the liquid, but evaporation of the solution by boiling in the absence of a gas to carry away the moisture is not ordinarily considered a drying operation. A liquid such as benzene may be "dried" of any small water content by an operation which is really distillation, but the removal of a small amount of acetone by the same process would not usually be called drying. Gases and liquids containing small amounts of water may be dried by adsorption operations, as discussed in Chap. 11. This discussion will be largely limited to the removal of moisture from solids and liquids by evaporation into a gas stream. In practice, the moisture is so frequently water and the gas so frequently air that this combination will provide the basis for most of the discussion. It is important to emphasize, however, that the equipment, techniques, and relationships are equally applicable to other systems as well.

EQUILIBRIUM

The moisture contained in a wet solid or liquid solution exerts a vapor pressure to an extent depending upon the nature of the moisture, the nature of the solid, and the temperature. If then a wet solid is exposed to a continual supply of fresh gas containing a fixed partial pressure of the vapor p, the solid will either lose moisture by evaporation or gain moisture from the gas until the vapor pressure of the moisture of the solid equals p. The solid and the gas are then in equilibrium, and the moisture content of the solid is termed its equilibrium-moisture content at the prevailing conditions.

Insoluble solids

A few typical equilibrium-moisture relationships are shown in Fig. 12.1, where the moisture in each case is water. Here the equilibrium partial pressure p of the water vapor in the gas stream has been divided by the vapor pressure of pure water P to give the relative saturation or relative humidity (see Chap. 7) of the gas, since the curves are then applicable over a modest range of temperatures instead of being useful for one temperature only. Consider the curve for wood. If the wood contained initially a very high moisture content, say 0.35 lb water/lb dry solid, and were exposed to a continual supply of air of 0.6 relative humidity, the wood would lose moisture by evaporation until its equilibrium concentration corresponding to point A on the curve were eventually reached. Further exposure to this air, for even indefinitely long periods, would not bring about additional loss of moisture from the solid.

Fig. 12.1 *Equilibrium water content of some common solids at about 25°C. (From "International Critical Tables," vol. 2, pp. 322–325, with permission.)*

The moisture content could, however, be reduced further by exposure of the solid to air of lower relative humidity, but to remove all the moisture would require exposure to perfectly dry air, corresponding to the origin of the curve. The moisture contained in the wood up to a concentration corresponding to point *B* in the figure, which exerts a vapor pressure less than that of pure water, may be moisture contained inside the cell walls of the plant structure, moisture in loose chemical combination with the cellulosic material, moisture present as a liquid solution of soluble portions of the solid and as a solid solution, moisture held in small capillaries and crevasses throughout the solid or otherwise adsorbed upon the surface. Such moisture is called *bound water*. If exposed to saturated air, the wood may have any moisture content greater than 0.3 lb/lb dry solid (point *B*), and moisture in excess of that at *B*, *unbound water*, exerts the vapor pressure of pure water at the prevailing temperature.

The equilibrium moisture for a given species of solid may depend upon the particle size or specific surface, if the moisture is largely physically adsorbed. Different solids have different equilibrium-moisture curves, as shown in the figure. Generally, inorganic solids which are insoluble in the liquid and which show no special adsorptive properties, such as the zinc oxide in the figure, show relatively low equilibrium-moisture contents, while spongy, cellular materials, especially those of vegetable origin such as the tobacco in the figure, generally show large equilibrium moisture contents. The equilibrium partial pressure for a solid is independent of the nature of the dry gas provided the latter is inert to the solid and is the same in the absence of noncondensable gas also. The same solids, if wet with liquids other than water, will show different equilibrium curves. The effect of large changes in temperature may frequently be shown in the form of a reference-substance plot as in Fig. 11.5.[46] It is seen that the equilibrium moisture is similar in many respects to the adsorption equilibria discussed in Chap. 11.

Hysteresis

Many solids exhibit different equilibrium-moisture characteristics depending upon whether the equilibrium is reached by condensation (adsorption) or evaporation (desorption) of the moisture. A typical example is shown in Fig. 12.2, and this curve somewhat resembles that of Fig. 11.4. In drying operations, it is the desorption equilibrium which is of particular interest, and this will always show the larger of the two equilibrium-moisture contents for a given partial pressure of vapor. The moisture picked up by a dry solid when exposed to moist air, i.e., the adsorption equilibrium, is sometimes called *regain*, and knowledge of this has practical value in the consideration of drying operations. For example, in the case of Fig. 12.2, it will be of little use to dry the solid to a water content below that corresponding to point *A* if it is expected to expose the dried material to air of 0.6 relative humidity later. If it is important that the solid be kept at a lower moisture content, it would have to be packaged or stored immediately out of contact with the air in a moisture-impervious container.

Fig. **12.2** *Equilibrium water content of a sulfite pulp, showing hysteresis.* [*Seborg, Ind. Eng. Chem.* **29**, 160 (1937).]

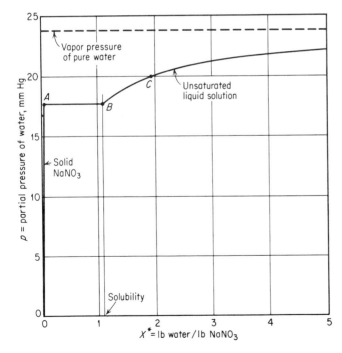

Fig. **12.3** *Equilibrium moisture content of sodium nitrate at 25°C.*

Soluble solids

Solids which are soluble in the liquid in question ordinarily show insignificant equilibrium-moisture contents when exposed to gases whose partial pressure of vapor is less than that of the saturated solution of the solid.   Refer to Fig. 12.3, where the characteristics of sodium nitrate–water are shown.   A saturated solution of sodium nitrate in water at 25°C exerts a partial pressure of water (*B*) equal to 17.7 mm Hg, and more dilute solutions exert higher partial pressures, as shown by curve *BC*. When exposed to air containing a partial pressure of water less than 17.7 mm Hg, a solution will evaporate, and the residual solid will retain only a negligible amount of adsorbed moisture as shown by the curve from the origin to point *A* and will appear dry. If the solid is exposed to air containing a higher water-vapor content, say 20 mm Hg, moisture will be adsorbed to such an extent that the solid will completely dissolve, or *deliquesce*, to produce the corresponding solution at *C*.   Solids of very low solubility, when exposed to ordinary atmospheric air, will not deliquesce since the equilibrium partial pressure of their saturated solutions is greater than that ordinarily found in the air.

Hydrated crystals may show more complicated relationships, such as those of Fig. 12.4 for the system copper sulfate–water at 25°C.   Three hydrates are formed in this system, as the figure indicates.   The anhydrous salt shows a negligible equilibrium-moisture content, which would in any case consist merely of adsorbed water upon the surface of the crystals.   If exposed to air containing a partial pressure of water less than 7.8 and more than 5.6 mm Hg, the salt will take on sufficient water to form the trihydrate, and the crystals will have negligible adsorbed water other than the water

Fig. 12.4 *Equilibrium moisture of copper sulfate at 25°C (not to scale).*

of crystallization.   The conditions will correspond to a point such as point A on the figure.   If the moisture content of the air is then reduced to slightly less than 5.6 mm Hg, the trihydrate will lose moisture (*effloresce*) to form the monohydrate, while at 5.6 mm Hg any proportion of mono- and trihydrate may coexist.   Similarly, if the moisture content of the air is increased to slightly more than 7.8 mm Hg, additional moisture will be adsorbed until the pentahydrate is formed.   If the moisture content of the air exceeds 23.1 mm Hg, the salt will deliquesce.

Definitions

For convenient reference, certain terms used to describe the moisture content of substances are summarized below.

Moisture content, wet basis.   The moisture content of a solid or solution is usually described in terms of weight percent moisture, and unless otherwise qualified this is ordinarily understood to be expressed on the wet basis, i.e., as (lb moisture/lb wet solid)100 = [lb moisture/(lb dry solid + lb moisture)]100 = $100X/(1 + X)$.

Moisture content, dry basis.   This is expressed as lb moisture/lb dry solid = X. Percentage moisture, dry basis = $100X$.

Equilibrium moisture X^*.   This is the moisture content of a substance when at equilibrium with a given partial pressure of the vapor.

Bound moisture.   This refers to the moisture contained by a substance which exerts an equilibrium vapor pressure less than that of the pure liquid at the same temperature.

Unbound moisture.   This refers to the moisture contained by a substance which exerts an equilibrium vapor pressure equal to that of the pure liquid at the same temperature.

Free moisture.   Free moisture is that moisture contained by a substance in excess of the equilibrium moisture: $X - X^*$.   Only free moisture can be evaporated,

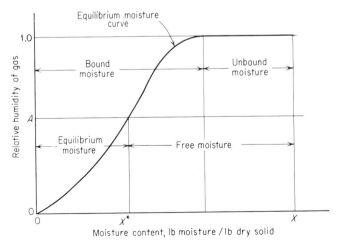

Fig. 12.5   *Types of moisture.*

and the free moisture content of a solid depends upon the vapor concentration in the gas.

These relations are shown graphically in Fig. 12.5 for a solid of moisture content X exposed to a gas of relative humidity A.

Illustration 12.1. A wet solid is to be dried from 80 to 5% moisture, wet basis. Compute the moisture to be evaporated, per 1,000 lb of dried product.
    Solution

$$\text{Initial moisture content} = \frac{0.80}{1 - 0.80} = 4.00 \text{ lb water/lb dry solid}$$

$$\text{Final moisture content} = \frac{0.05}{1 - 0.05} = 0.0527 \text{ lb water/lb dry solid}$$

$$\text{Lb dry solid in product} = 1,000(0.95) = 950 \text{ lb}$$
$$\text{Moisture to be evapd} = 950(4 - 0.0527) = 3,750 \text{ lb}$$

DRYING OPERATIONS

Drying operations may be broadly classified according to whether they are batch or continuous. These terms are applied specifically from the point of view of the substance being dried. Thus the operation termed *batch drying* is usually in fact a semibatch process wherein a quantity of the substance to be dried is exposed to a continually flowing stream of air into which the moisture evaporates. In continuous operations, the substance to be dried as well as the gas passes continually through the equipment. No typically stagewise methods are ordinarily used, and all operations involve continuous contact of the gas and the drying substance.

The equipment used for drying may be classified according to any of the following categories:

1. *Method of operation, i.e., batch or continuous.* Batch, or semibatch, equipment is operated intermittently or cyclically under unsteady-state conditions: the drier is charged with the substance, which remains in the equipment until dry, whereupon the drier is emptied and recharged with a fresh batch. Continuous driers are usually operated in steady-state fashion.

2. *Method of supplying the heat necessary for evaporation of the moisture.* In *direct* driers, the heat is supplied entirely by direct contact of the substance with the hot gas into which evaporation takes place. In *indirect* driers, the heat is supplied quite independently of the gas used to carry away the vaporized moisture. For example, heat may be supplied by conduction through a metal wall in contact with the substance, or less frequently by exposure of the substance to infrared radiation or by dielectric heating. In the case of the last, the heat is generated inside the solid by a high-frequency electric field.

3. *Nature of the substance to be dried.* The substance may be a rigid solid such as wood or fiberboard, a flexible material such as cloth or paper, a granular solid such as a mass of crystals, a thick paste or a thin slurry, or a solution.   If it is a solid, it may be fragile or sturdy.   The physical form of the substance and the diverse methods of handling necessary have perhaps the greatest influence on the type of drier used.

I. BATCH DRYING

Drying in batches is a relatively expensive operation and is consequently limited to small-scale operations, to pilot-plant and development work, and to drying valuable materials whose total cost will be little influenced by added expense in the drying operation.

Direct driers

The construction of such driers depends greatly upon the nature of the substance being dried.   *Tray driers*, also called cabinet, compartment, or shelf driers, are used for drying solids which must be supported on trays.   This may include pasty materials such as wet filter cakes from filter presses, lumpy solids which must be spread upon trays, and similar materials.   A typical device, shown schematically in Fig. 12.6, consists of a cabinet containing removable trays on which the solid to be dried is spread.   After loading, the cabinet is closed, and steam-heated air is blown across and between the trays to evaporate the moisture (cross-circulation drying).   Inert gas, even superheated steam,[6,16] rather than air may be used if the liquid to be evaporated is combustible.   When the solid has reached the desired degree of dryness, the cabinet is opened and the trays replaced with a new batch.   Figure 12.7 shows a simple modification, a *truck drier*, where the trays are racked upon trucks

Fig. 12.6   *Typical tray drier.*   (*Proctor and Schwartz, Inc.*)

Fig. 12.7   *Two-truck drier.*   (*Proctor and Schwartz, Inc.*)

which may be rolled into and out of the cabinet.   Since the trucks may be loaded
and unloaded outside the drier, considerable time may be saved between drying
cycles.   Other obvious modifications of the design are also used, depending upon
the nature of the drying substance.   Thus, skeins of fibers such as rayon may be
hung from poles, and wood or boardlike materials may be stacked in piles, the layers
separated from each other by spacer blocks.

In the case of granular materials, the solid may be arranged in thin beds supported
on screens so that air or other gas may be passed through the beds.   This results in
very much more rapid drying.   A typical device for this purpose, a batch *through-
circulation drier*, is shown schematically in Fig. 12.8.   Crystalline solids and materials
which are naturally granular such as silica gel may be dried in this manner directly.
In the case of others, some sort of preliminary treatment to put them into satisfactory
form, *preforming*, is necessary.   Pastes, for example, those resulting from precipitation of pigments or other solids, may be preformed by (1) extrusion into short,
spaghettilike rods, (2) granulation, i.e., forcing them through screens, or (3) by
briquetting.[21]

One of the most important difficulties in the use of driers of the type described
is the nonuniformity of moisture content found in the finished product taken from
various parts of the drier.   This is largely the result of inadequate and nonuniform
air movement inside the drier.   It is important to eliminate stagnant air pockets and
to maintain reasonably uniform air humidity and temperature throughout the drier.
In order to do this, large volumes of air must be blown over the trays, if possible at

Fig. 12.8 *Through-circulation drier.* *(Proctor and Schwartz, Inc.)*

velocities ranging up to 10 or 20 ft/sec if the solid will not blow from the trays at these air rates. This may be accomplished by blowing large quantities of heated fresh air only once through the drier, but the loss of heat in the discharged air will then usually be prohibitive in cost. Instead, it is the practice to admit only relatively small quantities of fresh air and to recirculate the bulk of it, sometimes as much as 80 to 95 percent.[44] This may be done inside the drier, as shown, for example, in Fig. 12.6, with dampers in the inlet and outlet pipes to regulate the extent of recirculation. The louvers at each tray level may then be adjusted so as to ensure as nearly uniform air velocity over each tray as possible. Alternatively, the heaters and fans may be installed outside the drier, with ductwork and dampers to permit more careful control of the relative amounts of fresh and recirculated air admitted to the drier itself. It is important also that the trays in such driers be filled level to the brim but not overloaded, so that uniform free space for air movement is available between trays.

The recirculation of large quantities of air necessarily raises the humidity of the air in the drier considerably above that of the fresh air. Low percentage humidity and consequently reasonably rapid drying rates are then obtained by using as high a temperature as practicable. The drier must then be thoroughly insulated, not only to conserve heat but also to maintain the inside walls at temperatures above the dew point of the air to prevent condensation of moisture upon the walls. Specially conditioned, low-humidity air is not used except where low-temperature drying is necessary to avoid damage to the product.

Illustration 12.2. The drier of Fig. 12.6 contains trays arranged in a tier of 10, each on racks 4 in. apart, each tray 1.5 in. deep. Each tray is 3 ft wide, and there are 150 sq ft of drying surface. It is desired that the air entering the trays (position 1 on the figure) have a dry-bulb temperature of 200°F and humidity 0.05 lb water/lb dry air. Atmospheric air enters at 80°F, humidity 0.01. The air velocity over the trays at the entrance to the trays is to be 10 ft/sec. At a time when the solid being dried is losing water at a constant rate of 60 lb evaporated/hr, determine the percentage recirculation of air and the conditions of the air in the various parts of the drier.

Solution. At position 1, $Y_1 = 0.05$ lb water/lb dry air, $t_{G1} = 200°F$, and the humid volume (Table 7.1) is $[0.0252 + 0.0405(0.05)](200 + 460) = 17.97$ cu ft/lb dry air.

$$\text{Free area for flow between trays} = \frac{3(4 - 1.5)(11)}{12} = 6.87 \text{ sq ft}$$

$$\text{Rate of air flow to trays} = 10(60)(6.87) = 4,120 \text{ cu ft/min, or } 4,120/17.97$$

$$= 230 \text{ lb dry air/min (at position 1)}$$

The rate of evaporation is $^{60}/_{60} = 1.0$ lb water/min, and the humidity at 2 (Fig. 12.6) is therefore $(0.05 + 1)/230 = 0.0544$ lb water/lb dry air. Assuming adiabatic drying, the temperature at 2 may be found on the adiabatic-saturation line (Fig. 7.5), drawn through the conditions at 1, and at $Y_2 = 0.0544$, $t_{G2} = 184°F$.

The condition of the air at 4, and the discharged air, must be the same as at 1. An overall water balance about the drier therefore is

$$G(0.05 - 0.01) = 1.0 \text{ lb water evapd/min}$$

$$G = 25 \text{ lb dry air/min enter and leave}$$

The quantity of air at 3 and 4 (Fig. 12.6) is therefore $230 + 25 = 255$ lb dry air/min, and at position 4 the humid volume must be 17.97 cu ft/lb dry air. The volumetric rate through the fan is therefore $255(17.97) = 4,600$ cu ft/min. The percentage of air recycled is $^{230}/_{255}(100) = 90.1\%$.

The enthalpy of the air at 2 (and at 1) is 99.5 Btu/lb dry air (Fig. 7.5, saturated enthalpy at the adiabatic-saturation temperature, 116°F), and that of the fresh air is 22.4 Btu/lb dry air. Assuming complete mixing, the enthalpy of the air at 3 is, by an enthalpy balance, $[99.5(230) + 22.4(25)]/255 = 92.0$ Btu/lb dry air. Since its humidity is 0.05, its dry bulb temperature (Fig. 7.5) is 173.5°F. The heater must apply $255(99.5 - 92.0) = 1910$ Btu/min, neglecting heat losses.

The dew-point temperature of the air (Fig. 7.5) at 1, 3, and 4 is 104.5°F, and at 2 it is 107°F. The drier should be sufficiently well insulated so that the inside surface will not fall to a temperature of 107°F.

The general humidity level in the drier may be altered during the drying cycle. This may be especially important in the case of certain solids which warp, shrink, develop surface cracks, or "case-harden" when dried too rapidly. A cake of soap of high moisture content, for example, if exposed to very dry, hot air, will lose moisture by evaporation from the surface so fast that water will not move rapidly enough from the center of the cake to the surface to keep pace with the evaporation. The surface then becomes hard and impervious to moisture (case-hardened), and drying stops even though the average water content of the cake is still very high. In the case of other solids, such as wood, for example, shrinkage at the surface may cause cracks or warping. Such substances should be dried slowly at first with air of high humidity, and drier air may be used only after the bulk of the water has been removed.

Driers of the type described are relatively cheap to build and have low maintenance costs. They are, however, expensive to operate owing to low heat economy and high labor costs. Each time the drier is opened for unloading and loading, the temperature of the interior falls and all the metal parts of the drier must be heated again to the operating temperature when operation is resumed. Steam consumption for heating the air will generally not be less than 2.5 lb steam/lb water evaporated and may be as high as 10, especially for cases where the moisture content of the product is reduced to very low levels.[17] The labor requirement for loading, unloading, and supervision of the drying cycle is high.

Indirect driers

Vacuum shelf driers are tray driers whose cabinets, made of cast-iron or steel plates, are fitted with tightly closing doors so that they may be operated at subatmospheric pressure. No air is blown or recirculated through such driers. The trays containing the solid to be dried rest upon hollow shelves through which warm water or steam is passed to provide the necessary heat for vaporization of moisture. The heat is conducted to the solid through the metal of the shelves and trays. After loading and sealing, the air in the drier is evacuated by a mechanical vacuum pump or steam jet ejector, and distillation of the moisture proceeds. The vapors usually pass to a condenser, where they are liquefied and collected, and only noncondensable gas is removed by the pump. *Agitated pan driers,*[43] which may be used to dry pastes or slurries in small batches, are shallow, circular pans, 3 to 6 ft in diameter and 1 to 2 ft deep, with flat bottoms and vertical sides. The pans are jacketed for admission of steam or hot water for heating. The paste, or slurry, in the pan is stirred and scraped by a set of rotating plows, in order to expose new material to the heated surface. Moisture is evaporated into the atmosphere in the case of atmosphere pan driers, or the pan may be covered and operated under vacuum. *Vacuum rotary driers* are steam-jacketed cylindrical shells, arranged horizontally, in which a slurry, or paste, may be dried in vacuum. The slurry is stirred by a set of rotating agitator blades attached to a central horizontal shaft which passes through the ends of the cylindrical shell. Vaporized moisture passes through an opening in the top to a condenser, and noncondensable gas is removed by a vacuum pump. The dried solid is discharged through a door in the bottom of the drier.

Driers of this category are expensive to build and to operate. Consequently they are used only for valuable materials which must be dried at low temperatures or in the absence of air to prevent damage, such as certain pharmaceutical products, or where the moisture to be removed is an expensive or poisonous organic solvent which must be recovered more or less completely.

Freeze drying. Substances which may not be heated even to moderate temperatures, such as foodstuffs and certain pharmaceuticals, may be dried by this method.[18] The substance to be dried is customarily frozen by exposure to very cold air and placed in a vacuum chamber, where the moisture sublimes and is pumped off by steam-jet ejectors or mechanical vacuum pumps. An alternative method of freezing is by flash vaporization of part of the moisture under vacuum, although foodstuffs which are not rigid in the unfrozen state may be damaged by this procedure. Some foods, beef for example, evidently contain capillary channels, and the water vapor diffuses from the receding ice surface through these channels as drying proceeds.[13] In other cases diffusion through cell walls must occur. In any event, one of the major problems is to supply the heat necessary for sublimation: as the plane of sublimation recedes, heat must be driven through larger thicknesses of dried matter of poor thermal conductivity, requiring increasing temperature differences which may damage the product. Radiant heat is used, and dielectric heat is a possibility although an expensive one. Still an additional method, useful for granular products, is through-circulation drying with air instead of pumping off the water by vacuum pump.

The rate of batch drying

In order to set up drying schedules and to determine the size of equipment, it is necessary to know the time which will be required to dry a substance from one moisture content to another under specified conditions. We shall also wish to estimate the influence that different drying conditions will have upon the time for drying. Our knowledge of the mechanism of drying is so incomplete that it is necessary with few exceptions to rely upon at least some experimental measurements for these purposes. Measurements of the rate of batch drying are relatively simple to make and provide much information not only for batch but also for continuous operation.

Drying tests. The rate of drying may be determined for a sample of a substance by suspending it in a cabinet or duct, in a stream of air, from a balance. The weight of the drying sample may then be measured as a function of time. Certain precautions must be observed if the data are to be of maximum utility. The sample should not be too small. Further, the following conditions should resemble as closely as possible those expected to prevail in contemplated large-scale operation: (1) The sample should be similarly supported in a tray or frame. (2) It should have the same ratio of drying to nondrying surface. (3) It should be subjected to similar conditions of radiant-heat transfer. (4) The air should have the same temperature, humidity, and velocity (both speed and direction with respect to the sample). If possible, several tests should be made on samples of different thicknesses. The dry weight of the sample should also be obtained.

The exposure of the sample to air of constant temperature, humidity, and velocity constitutes drying under *constant drying conditions*.

Rate-of-drying curve. From the data obtained during such a test, a curve of moisture content as a function of time (Fig. 12.9) may be plotted. This will be useful directly in determining the time required for drying larger batches under the same drying conditions. Much information can be obtained if the data are converted to rates of drying, expressed as N lb moisture evaporated/(hr)(sq ft), and plotted against moisture content, as in Fig. 12.10. This may be done by measuring the slopes of tangents drawn to the curve of Fig. 12.9 or by determining from the curve small changes in moisture content ΔX for corresponding small changes in time $\Delta \theta$ and calculating the rate as $N = -L_S \Delta X / A \Delta \theta$. Here L_S is the weight of dry solid, and A is the wet surface over which the gas blows and through which evaporation takes place in the case of cross-air circulation drying. In the case of through-circulation drying, A is the cross section of the bed measured at right angles to the direction of gas flow.

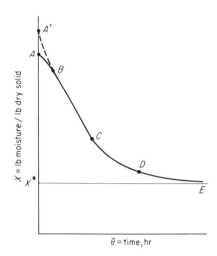

Fig. 12.9 *Batch drying, constant drying conditions.*

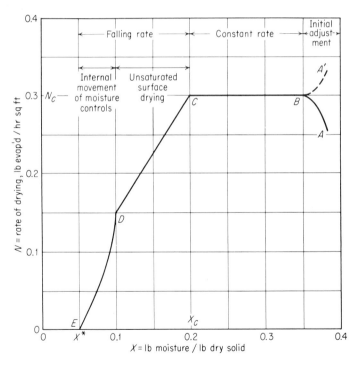

Fig. 12.10 *Typical rate-of-drying curve, constant drying conditions.*

The rate-of-drying curve is sometimes plotted with the ordinate expressed as lb moisture evaporated/(hr)(lb dry solid), which in the present notation is $-dX/d\theta$.

There are usually two major parts to the rate curve of Fig. 12.10, a period of constant rate and one of falling rate, as marked on the figure. While different solids and different conditions of drying will frequently give rise to curves of very different shape in the falling-rate period, the curve shown occurs frequently. Some of the differences which may arise will be considered later, but for the present let us briefly review the reasons generally advanced for the various parts of the curve shown.[12,26,39,41]

If a solid is initially very wet, the surface will be covered with a thin film of liquid, which we shall assume is entirely unbound moisture. When it is exposed to relatively dry air, evaporation will take place from the surface. The rate at which moisture evaporates can be described in terms of a gas mass-transfer coefficient k_Y and the difference in humidity of the gas at the liquid surface Y_s and in the main stream Y. Thus, for cross-circulation drying

$$N_c = k_Y(Y_s - Y) \tag{12.1}$$

The coefficient k_Y may be expected to remain constant as long as the speed and direction of gas flow past the surface do not change. The humidity Y_s is the saturated humidity at the liquid-surface temperature t_s and will therefore depend upon this temperature. Since evaporation of moisture absorbs latent heat, the liquid surface will come to, and remain at, an equilibrium temperature such that the rate of heat flow from the surroundings to the surface exactly equals the rate of heat absorption. Y_s therefore remains constant. Since in addition Y remains unchanged under constant drying conditions, the rate of evaporation must remain constant at the value N_c, as shown on Figs. 12.9 and 12.10 between points B and C. In the beginning, the solid and the liquid surface are usually colder than the ultimate surface temperature t_s, and the evaporation rate will increase while the surface temperature rises to its ultimate value during the period AB on these curves. Alternatively the equilibrium temperature t_s may be lower than the initial value, which will give rise to a curve $A'B$ while the initial adjustment occurs. The initial period is usually so short that it is ordinarily ignored in subsequent analysis of the drying times.

When the average moisture content of the solid has reached a value X_c, the *critical moisture content* (Fig. 12.10), the surface film of moisture has been so reduced by evaporation that further drying causes dry spots to appear upon the surface, and these occupy increasingly larger proportions of the exposed surface as drying proceeds. Since, however, the rate N is computed by means of the constant gross surface A, the value of N must fall even though the rate per unit of wet surface remains constant. This gives rise to the first part of the falling-rate period, the period of *unsaturated surface drying*, from points C to D (Figs. 12.9 and 12.10). Ultimately the original surface film of liquid will have entirely evaporated at an average moisture content for the solid corresponding to point D. This part of the curve may be missing entirely, or it may constitute the whole of the falling-rate period. In the case of some textiles, other explanations for the linear falling-rate period have been necessary.[30]

On further drying, the rate at which moisture may move through the solid, as a result of concentration gradients existing between the deeper parts and the surface, is the controlling step. As the moisture concentration generally is lowered by the drying, the rate of internal movement of moisture decreases. In some cases, evaporation may take place beneath the surface of the solid in a plane or zone which retreats deeper into the solid as drying proceeds. In any event, the rate of drying falls even more rapidly than before, as from D to E (Fig. 12.10). At point E, the moisture content of the solid has fallen to the equilibrium value X^* for the prevailing air humidity, and drying stops.

Time of drying. If it is desired to determine the time of drying a solid under the same conditions for which a drying curve such as Fig. 12.9 has been completely determined, one need merely read the difference in the times corresponding to the initial and final moisture contents from the curve.

Within limits, it is sometimes possible to estimate the appearance of a rate-of-drying curve such as Fig. 12.10 for conditions different from those used in the experiments. In order to determine the time for drying for such a curve, we may proceed as follows: The rate of drying is, by definition,

$$N = \frac{-L_s \, dX}{A \, d\theta} \tag{12.2}$$

Rearranging and integrating over the time interval while the moisture content changes from its initial value X_1 to its final value X_2,

$$\theta = \int_0^\theta d\theta = \frac{L_S}{A} \int_{X_2}^{X_1} \frac{dX}{N} \tag{12.3}$$

1. *The constant-rate period.* If the drying takes place entirely within the constant-rate period so that X_1 and $X_2 > X_c$ and $N = N_c$, Eq. (12.3) becomes

$$\theta = \frac{L_S(X_1 - X_2)}{A N_c} \tag{12.4}$$

2. *The falling-rate period.* If X_1 and X_2 are both less than X_c, so that drying occurs under conditions of changing N, we may proceed as follows:

a. General case. For any shape of falling-rate curve whatsoever, Eq. (12.3) may be integrated graphically by determining the area under a curve of $1/N$ as ordinate, X as abscissa, the data for which may be obtained from the rate-of-drying curve.

b. Special case. N is linear in X, as in the region BC of Fig. 12.10. In this case,

$$N = mX + b \tag{12.5}$$

where m is the slope of the linear portion of the curve and b is a constant. Substitution in Eq. (12.3) provides

$$\theta = \frac{L_S}{A} \int_{X_2}^{X_1} \frac{dX}{mX + b} = \frac{L_S}{mA} \ln \frac{mX_1 + b}{mX_2 + b} \tag{12.6}$$

But since $N_1 = mX_1 + b$, $N_2 = mX_2 + b$, and $m = (N_1 - N_2)/(X_1 - X_2)$, Eq. (12.6) becomes

$$\theta = \frac{L_S(X_1 - X_2)}{A(N_1 - N_2)} \ln \frac{N_1}{N_2} = \frac{L_S(X_1 - X_2)}{AN_m} \qquad (12.7)$$

where N_m is the logarithmic average of the rate N_1, at moisture content X_1, and N_2 at X_2.

Frequently the entire falling-rate curve may be taken as a straight line between points C and E (Fig. 12.10). It is often assumed to be so for lack of more detailed data. In this case

$$N = m(X - X^*) = \frac{N_c(X - X^*)}{X_c - X^*} \qquad (12.8)$$

and Eq. (12.7) becomes

$$\theta = \frac{L_S(X_c - X^*)}{N_c A} \ln \frac{X_1 - X^*}{X_2 - X^*} \qquad (12.9)$$

In any particular drying problem, either or both constant- and falling-rate periods may be involved, depending upon the relative values of X_1, X_2, and X_c. The appropriate equations and limits must then be chosen.

Illustration 12.3. A batch of the solid for which Fig. 12.10 is the drying curve is to be dried from 25 to 6% moisture under conditions identical to those for which the figure applies. The initial weight of the wet solid is 350 lb, and the drying surface is 1 sq ft/8 lb dry weight. Determine the time for drying.

Solution. The total weight of the batch is unimportant. $L_S/A = 8$. At 25% moisture, $X_1 = 0.25/(1 - 0.25) = 0.333$ lb moisture/lb dry solid. At 6% moisture, $X_2 = 0.06/(1 - 0.06) = 0.064$ lb moisture/lb dry solid. Inspection of Fig. 12.10 shows that both constant- and falling-rate periods are involved. The limits of moisture content in the equations for the different periods will be chosen accordingly.

Constant-rate period. From $X_1 = 0.333$ to $X_c = 0.200$. $N_c = 0.30$.

Eq. (12.4):
$$\theta = \frac{L_S(X_1 - X_c)}{AN_c} = \frac{8(0.333 - 0.200)}{1(0.30)} = 3.54 \text{ hr}$$

Falling-rate period. From $X_c = 0.200$ to $X_2 = 0.064$. Use Eq. (12.3). The following table is prepared from the data of Fig. 12.10:

X	N	$\dfrac{1}{N}$
0.20	0.300	3.33
0.18	0.266	3.76
0.16	0.239	4.18
0.14	0.208	4.80
0.12	0.180	5.55
0.10	0.150	6.67
0.09	0.097	10.3
0.08	0.070	14.3
0.07	0.043	23.3
0.064	0.025	40.0

A curve, not shown, is prepared of $1/N$ as ordinate, X as abscissa, and the area under the curve between $X = 0.20$ and $X = 0.064$ is 1.06.

Eq. (12.3): $\theta = \frac{8}{1}(1.06) = 8.48$ hr

The total drying time is therefore $3.54 + 8.48 = 12.02$ hr

Alternatively, since the drying curve is straight from $X = 0.20$ to $X = 0.10$, Eq. (12.7) may be used in this range of moisture contents,

$$\theta = \frac{L_S(X_c - X_D)}{A(N_c - N_D)} \ln \frac{N_c}{N_D} = \frac{8(0.20 - 0.10)}{1(0.30 - 0.15)} \ln \frac{0.30}{0.15} = 3.70 \text{ hr}$$

Graphical integration in the range $X = 0.1$ to $X = 0.064$ provides, through Eq. (12.3), an additional 4.79 hr, so that the total falling-rate time is $3.70 + 4.79 = 8.49$ hr.

As an approximation, the falling-rate period may be represented by a straight line from C to E (Fig. 12.10). The corresponding falling-rate time is, by Eq. (12.9),

$$\theta = \frac{L_S(X_c - X^*)}{N_c A} \ln \frac{X_c - X^*}{X_2 - X^*} = \frac{8(0.20 - 0.05)}{0.3(1)} \ln \frac{0.20 - 0.05}{0.064 - 0.05} = 9.5 \text{ hr}$$

The mechanisms of batch drying

We now consider the various portions of the rate-of-drying curve in more detail. Our present knowledge permits us to describe the drying process in the constant-rate period reasonably well, but our understanding of the falling-rate periods is very limited.

Cross-circulation drying

The constant-rate period. In this period, where surface evaporation of unbound moisture occurs, it has been shown that the rate of drying is established by a balance of the heat requirements for evaporation and the rate at which heat reaches the surface. Consider the section of a material drying in a stream of gas as shown in Fig. 12.11. The solid of thickness z_S ft is placed on a tray of thickness z_M ft. The whole is immersed in a stream of drying gas at temperature $t_G°$F and humidity Y lb moisture/lb dry gas, flowing at a mass velocity G lb/(hr)(sq ft). The evaporation

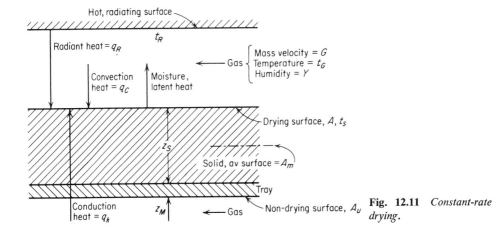

Fig. 12.11   Constant-rate drying.

of moisture takes place from the upper surface, A sq ft, which is at a temperature $t_s°$F. The drying surface receives heat from several sources: (1) q_c by convection from the gas stream; (2) q_k by conduction through the solid; (3) q_R by direct radiation from a hot surface at temperature $t_R°$F, as shown, all expressed as Btu/(hr)(sq ft). In accordance with the mechanism discussed earlier, the heat arriving at the surface by these methods is removed by the evaporating moisture, so that the surface temperature remains constant at t_s. The entire mechanism resembles the wet-bulb-thermometer process, complicated by the additional source of heat.

The rate of evaporation and the surface temperature may then be obtained by a heat balance.[38] If q represents the total heat arriving at the surface, then

$$q = q_c + q_R + q_k \tag{12.10}$$

Neglecting the heat required to superheat the evaporated moisture to the gas temperature and considering only the latent heat of vaporization λ_s, then the rate of evaporation N_c and the rate of heat flow are related,

$$N_c \lambda_s = q \tag{12.11}$$

The heat received at the surface by convection is controlled by the appropriate convection heat-transfer coefficient h_c,

$$q_c = h_c(t_G - t_s) \tag{12.12}$$

The heat received by radiation may be estimated by the usual means[23] and can also be expressed as a heat-transfer coefficient h_R,

$$q_R = \varepsilon(1,730)(10^{-12})(T_R^4 - T_s^4) = h_R(t_R - t_s) \tag{12.13}$$

$$h_R = \frac{\varepsilon(1,730)(10^{-12})(T_R^4 - T_s^4)}{t_R - t_s} \tag{12.14}$$

where ε is the emissivity of the drying surface and T_R and T_s are the absolute temperatures of the radiating and drying surfaces, in degrees Rankine. The heat received by convection and conduction through the solid may be computed by the usual methods for heat transfer through a series of resistances,

$$q_k = U_k(t_G - t_s) \tag{12.15}$$

$$U_k = \frac{1}{(1/h_c)(A/A_u) + (z_M/k_M)(A/A_u) + (z_S/k_S)(A/A_m)} \tag{12.16}$$

where h_c, the convection coefficient for the tray, may ordinarily be taken as the same as that for the drying surface, k_M and k_S are the thermal conductivities of the tray material and the drying solid, and A_u and A_m the nondrying surface and the average area of the drying solid, respectively. A thermal resistance at the junction of the drying solid and the tray material, and an effect of radiation to the tray, may be added to the terms of Eq. (12.16), if desired.

Combining Eqs. (12.1) and (12.10) to (12.15) permits calculation of the rate of drying,

$$N_c = \frac{q}{\lambda_s} = \frac{(h_c + U_k)(t_G - t_s) + h_R(t_R - t_s)}{\lambda_s} = k_Y(Y_s - Y) \qquad (12.17)$$

The surface temperature must be known in order to use the relationship. This may be obtained by consideration of the left-hand portions of Eq. (12.17), which may be rearranged to read

$$\frac{(Y_s - Y)\lambda_s}{h_c/k_Y} = \left(1 + \frac{U_k}{h_c}\right)(t_G - t_s) + \frac{h_R}{h_c}(t_R - t_s) \qquad (12.18)$$

The ratio h_c/k_Y applicable to flow of gases past wet-bulb thermometers [Eqs. (7.27) and (7.28)] may be used for present purposes, and for the system air-water vapor this ratio was shown to be substantially the same as the humid heat of the gas C_s. Since Y_s is the saturated humidity of the gas stream corresponding to t_s when unbound moisture is being evaporated, both these quantities may be found by solving Eq. (12.18) simultaneously with the saturated-humidity curve on a psychrometric chart.

If conduction through the solid and radiation effects is absent, Eq. (12.18) reduces to that for the wet-bulb thermometer [Eq. (7.26)] and the surface temperature is the wet-bulb temperature of the gas. The drying surfaces will also be at the wet-bulb temperature if the solid is dried from all surfaces in the absence of radiation. When pans or trays of drying material are placed one above another, as in Figs. 12.6 and 12.7, most of the solid will receive radiation only from the bottom of the pan immediately above it, and unless gas temperatures are very high, this is not likely to be very important. It is essential therefore not to overemphasize the heat received by radiation in conducting drying tests on single pairs of trays.

For flow of gas parallel to a smooth surface, it should be possible to determine both h_c and k_Y from item 3, Table 3.3. For high Reynolds numbers, in the range usually employed,

$$i_H = \frac{h_c}{C_p G} Pr^{\frac{2}{3}} = j_D = \frac{k_Y}{G_S} Sc^{\frac{2}{3}} = 0.036 \, Re_x^{-0.2} \qquad (12.19)$$

where Re_x is a length Reynolds number xG/μ, x being the length of the drying surface in the direction of gas flow. If the gas is air and the length of the surface is 1 ft, this provides $h_c = 0.0058G^{0.8}$, whereas in a detailed study of drying of sand in trays,[38] h_c was found to be $0.0128G^{0.8}$. Such discrepancies have been assigned to a number of causes: different "calming" lengths ahead of the drying surface,[31] the shape of the leading edge of the drying surface, and the fact that a Reynolds number based on equivalent duct diameter rather than length of surface may be more appropriate.[6] In the absence of more specific data, the following are recommended:

Air flow parallel to surface, $G = 500$ to $6,000$ lb/(hr)(sq ft)(2 to 25 ft/sec)

$$h_c = 0.01G^{0.8} \qquad (12.20)$$

Air flow perpendicular to surface,[28] $G = 800$ *to* $4,000$ $lb/(hr)(sq\ ft)(3$ *to* $15\ ft/sec)$

$$h_c = 0.37G^{0.37} \tag{12.21}$$

The relationships developed in Eqs. (12.17) to (12.21) permit direct estimates of the rate of drying during the constant-rate period, but they should not be considered as complete substitutes for experimental measurements. Perhaps their greatest value is in conjunction with limited experimental data in order to predict the effect of changing the drying conditions.

Effect of Gas Velocity. If radiation and conduction through the solid are negligible, N_c is proportional to $G^{0.8}$ for parallel flow of gas and to $G^{0.37}$ for perpendicular flow. If radiation and conduction are present, the effect of gas rate will be less important.

Effect of Gas Temperature. Increased air temperature increases the quantity $t_G - t_s$ and hence increases N_c. In the absence of radiation effects, and neglecting the variation of λ over moderate temperature ranges, N_c is directly proportional to $t_G - t_s$.

Effect of Gas Humidity. N_c varies directly as $Y_s - Y$, and consequently increasing the humidity lowers the rate of drying. Usually, changes in Y and t_G involve simultaneous changes in t_s and Y_s, and the effects are best estimated by direct application of Eq. (12.17).

Effect of Thickness of Drying Solid. If heat conduction through the solid occurs, Eqs. (12.15) and (12.16) indicate lowered values of N_c with increased solid thickness. However, conduction of heat through edge surfaces of pans and trays may be an important source of heat which can result in increased rate of drying if the edge surface is large. If nondrying surfaces are heat-insulated, or if drying occurs from all surfaces of the solid, N_c is independent of thickness. The *time* for drying between fixed moisture contents within the constant-rate period will then be directly proportional to thickness.

Illustration 12.4. An insoluble crystalline solid wet with water is placed in a 2- by 2-ft rectangular pan, 1 in. deep, made of $\frac{1}{32}$-in.-thick galvanized iron. The pan is placed in an air stream at 150°F, humidity 0.01 lb water/lb dry air, flowing parallel to the upper and lower surfaces at a velocity of 10 ft/sec. The surface of the solid is in direct sight of steam-heated pipes whose surface temperature is 250°F.

a. Make an estimate of the rate of drying at constant rate.

b. Reestimate the rate if the pan were thoroughly heat-insulated and if there were no radiation from the steam pipes.

Solution. a. $Y = 0.01$ lb water/lb dry air, $t_G = 150$°F. The humid volume of the air (Table 7.1) is $[0.0252 + 0.0405(0.01)](150 + 460) = 15.6$ cu ft/lb dry air.

$$\rho_G = \text{density of gas} = \frac{1.01}{15.6} = 0.0647\ \text{lb/cu ft}$$

$$G = 10(3,600)(0.0647) = 2,430\ \text{lb/(hr)(sq ft)}$$

Eq. (12.20):
$$h_c = 0.01(2430)^{0.8} = 5.10\ \text{Btu/(hr)(sq ft)(°F)}$$

Take the emissivity of the solid as $\varepsilon = 0.94$. $t_R = 250°F$, $T_R = 250 + 460 = 710°R$. Tentatively estimate t_s as $100°F$, and $T_s = 100 + 460 = 560°R$.

Eq. (12.14): $$h_R = \frac{0.94(1,730)(10^{-12})(710^4 - 560^4)}{250 - 100} = 1.70 \text{ Btu/(hr)(sq ft)(°F)}$$

Take $A_m = A = 2(2) = 4$ sq ft. The area of the sides of the pan $= 4(2)(\frac{1}{12}) = 0.667$ sq ft, and $A_u = 2(2) + 0.667 = 4.67$ sq ft for bottom and sides (this method of including the heat transfer through the sides is an oversimplification, but adequate for present purposes). Thermal conductivities are $k_M = 26$ for the metal of the pan, and $k_S = 2$ for the wet solid[38] (this value must be carefully chosen: it may bear no simple relation to the conductivities of either the dry solid or the moisture). $z_S = \frac{1}{12} = 0.0833$ ft, $z_M = 1/32(12) = 0.0026$ ft.

Eq. (12.16):
$$\frac{1}{U_k} = \frac{1}{5.10}\frac{1}{4.67} + \frac{0.0026}{26}\frac{4}{4.67} + \frac{0.0833}{2}\frac{4}{4}$$
$$U_k = 4.76 \text{ Btu/(hr)(sq ft)(°F)}$$

The humid heat of the air (Table 7.1) is $C_S = 0.24 + 0.45(0.01) = 0.245$, and λ_s at the estimated $100°F$ is $1,037$ Btu/lb.

Eq. (12.18):
$$\frac{(Y_s - 0.01)1,037}{0.245} = \left(1 + \frac{4.76}{5.10}\right)(150 - t_s) + \frac{1.70}{5.10}(250 - t_s)$$

This reduces to $Y_s = 0.0991 - 0.000541t_s$, which must be solved simultaneously with the saturated-humidity curve of the psychrometric chart for air–water vapor. This is most conveniently done graphically, as in Fig. 12.12, by plotting the equation on the pertinent portion of the psychrometric chart (Fig. 7.5). The line marked a on Fig. 12.12 is the above expression, and it intersects the saturated-humidity curve at $Y_s = 0.0445$, $t_s = 101°F$, the surface temperature, which is sufficiently close to the $100°F$ estimated previously to make recalculation unnecessary. At $101°F$, $\lambda_s = 1,036$ Btu/lb.

Eq. (12.17):
$$N_c = \frac{(5.10 + 4.76)(150 - 101) + 1.70(250 - 101)}{1,036}$$
$$= 0.712 \text{ lb water evapd/(hr)(sq ft)}$$

and the evaporation rate is $0.712(4) = 2.848$ lb water/hr.

b. Where no radiation or conduction of heat through the solid occurs, the drying surface assumes the wet-bulb temperature of the air. For the system air–water at this humidity, the adiabatic-saturation lines of the psychrometric chart serve as wet-bulb lines, and on Fig. 12.12 line b is the

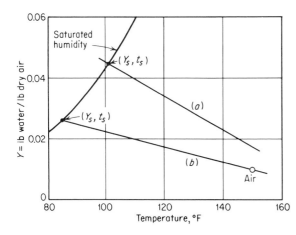

Fig. 12.12 Solution to Illustration 12.4.

adiabatic-saturation line through the point representing the air ($t_G = 150°F$, $Y = 0.01$). The line intersects the saturated-humidity curve at the wet-bulb conditions, $t_s = 84.5°F$, $Y_s = 0.026$. At this temperature, $\lambda_s = 1,045$ Btu/lb.

Eq. (12.17): $$N_c = \frac{h_c(t_G - t_s)}{\lambda_s} = \frac{5.10(150 - 84.5)}{1,045} = 0.320 \text{ lb/(hr)(sq ft)}$$

and the evaporation rate is $0.320(4) = 1.280$ lb water/hr.

When the air suffers a considerable change in temperature and humidity in its passage over the solid, as, for example, is indicated in Illustration 12.2, the rate of drying at the leading and trailing edge of the solid will differ and this accounts in part for the nonuniform drying frequently obtained in tray driers. This may be counteracted in part by periodic reversal of the air flow.

Movement of moisture within the solid. When surface evaporation occurs, there must be a movement of moisture from the depths of the solid to the surface. The nature of the movement influences the drying during the falling-rate periods. In order to appreciate the diverse nature of the falling-rate portions of the drying curve which have been observed, let us review very briefly some of the theories advanced to explain moisture movement and the relation of these to the falling-rate curves.

1. *Liquid diffusion.* Diffusion of liquid moisture may result because of concentration gradients between the depths of the solid, where the concentration is high, and the surface, where it is low. These gradients are set up during drying from the surface. This method of moisture transport is probably limited to cases where single-phase solid solutions are formed with the moisture, as in the case of soap, glue, gelatin, and the like; and to certain cases where bound moisture is being dried, as in the drying of the last portions of water from clays, flour, textiles, paper, and wood.[14] The general mechanism of this process is described in Chap. 4. It has been found that the moisture diffusivity usually decreases rapidly with decreased moisture content, so that diffusivities calculated in the manner of Illustration 4.5 are average values over the range of concentrations considered.

During the constant-rate period of drying such solids, the surface-moisture concentration is reduced, but the concentration in the depths of the solid remains high. The resulting high diffusivities permit movement of the moisture to the surface as fast as it can be evaporated, and the rate remains constant. When dry spots appear owing to the projection of portions of the solid into the gas film, a period of unsaturated surface evaporation results. The surface eventually dries to the equilibrium moisture content for the prevailing gas. Further drying occurs at rates which are entirely controlled by the diffusion rates within the solid, since these are slow at low moisture contents. If the initial constant-rate drying is very rapid, the period of unsaturated surface evaporation may not appear, and the diffusion-controlled falling-rate period begins immediately after the constant-rate period is completed,[40] as in Fig. 12.13.

X = lb moisture / lb dry solid   **Fig. 12.13** *Diffusion-controlled falling rate.*[40]

For many cases of drying where the diffusion mechanism has satisfactorily explained the rate of drying as a function of average moisture content, the distribution of moisture within the solid at the various stages of drying has not conformed to this mechanism.[14,29] The superficial applicability of the diffusion mechanism is then apparently accidental.

2. *Capillary movement.*[7,14,29,32,45] Unbound moisture in granular and porous solids such as clays, sand, paint pigments, and the like, moves through the capillaries and interstices of the solids by a mechanism involving surface tension, in the manner that oil moves through a lamp wick. The capillaries extend from small reservoirs of moisture in the solid to the drying surface. As drying proceeds, at first moisture moves by capillarity to the surface sufficiently rapidly to maintain a uniformly wetted surface and the rate of drying is constant. The water is replaced by air entering the solid through relatively few openings and cracks. The surface moisture is eventually drawn to spaces between the granules of the surface, the wetted area at the surface decreases, and the unsaturated-surface drying period follows. The subsurface reservoirs eventually dry up, the liquid surface recedes into the capillaries, evaporation occurs below the surface in a zone or plane which gradually recedes deeper into the solid, and a second falling-rate period results. During this period, diffusion of vapor within the solid will occur from the place of vaporization to the surface.

In the case of certain pastes dried in pans, the adhesion of the wet cake to the bottom of the pan may not permit ventilation of the subsurface passageways by gas. This may give rise to curves of the sort shown in Fig. 12.14. In this case, the usual constant-rate period prevailed during *a*. When the surface moisture was first depleted, liquid could not be brought to the surface by the tension in the capillaries since no air could enter to replace the liquid, the surface of moisture receded into the capillaries, and the rate fell during *b*. The solid eventually crumpled, admitting air to replace the liquid, whereupon capillary action brought this to the surface and the rate rose again, as at *c*.

3. *Vapor diffusion.*[32] Especially if heat is supplied to one surface of a solid while drying proceeds from another, the moisture may evaporate beneath the surface and diffuse outward as a vapor. Moisture particles in granular solids, which have been

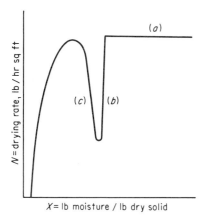

Fig. 12.14 *Effect of adhesion of a drying paste to the pan.*
[*After R. C. Ernst, et al.: Ind. Eng. Chem. 30, 1119 (1938).*]

isolated from the main portion of the moisture flowing through capillaries, may also be evaporated below the surface.

4. *Pressure.* Owing to shrinkage of the outside layers of a solid on drying, moisture may be squeezed to the surface.

Usually we can only speculate as to which of the mechanisms is appropriate to a particular solid and must rely on more or less empirical treatment of the experimental rates of drying.

Unsaturated-surface drying. During such a period the rate of drying N will usually vary linearly with moisture content X. Since the mechanism of evaporation during this period is the same as that in the constant-rate period, the effects of such variables as temperature, humidity, and velocity of the gas and thickness of the solid are the same as for constant-rate drying.

In some cases this period may constitute the whole of the falling-rate drying, giving rise to a curve of the type shown in Fig. 12.15. Equations (12.8) and (12.9)

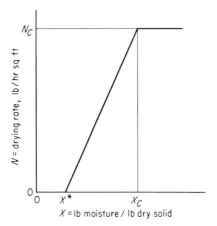

Fig. **12.15** *Linear falling rate.*

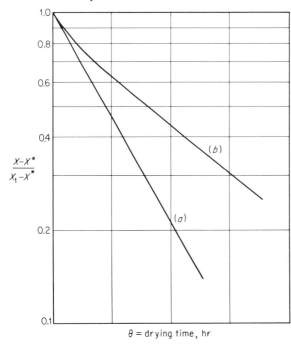

$\theta = $ drying time, hr

Fig. 12.16 *Empirical treatment of falling-rate data. (a) N varies linearly with X; (b) diffusion-controlled falling rate.*

then apply. Combining Eqs. (12.2), (12.8), and (12.17),

$$-\frac{dX}{d\theta} = \frac{k_Y A(X - X^*)(Y_s - Y)}{L_S(X_c - X^*)} \tag{12.22}$$

Noting that $L_S = z_S A \rho_S$, and letting $k_Y = f(G)$, then

$$-\frac{dX}{d\theta} = \frac{f(G)(X - X^*)(Y_s - Y)}{z_S \rho_S (X_c - X^*)} = \frac{\alpha f(G)(X - X^*)(Y_s - Y)}{z_S} \tag{12.23}$$

where $\alpha = $ const. This expression is sometimes used as an empirical description of the rates of drying for such cases. Alternatively, defining the time θ as that when the moisture content is X, Eq. (12.9) is readily transformed into

$$\ln \frac{X - X^*}{X_1 - X^*} = \frac{-N_c \theta}{\rho_S z_S (X_c - X^*)} \tag{12.24}$$

which suggests that falling-rate data of this nature will plot as a straight line, line a, on the semilogarithmic coordinates of Fig. 12.16. If drying tests are made under the same conditions for samples of different thickness, and so that heat is applied to the solid only through the drying surface, the slopes of such lines on this chart should be proportional to $-1/z_S$. The drying time between fixed moisture contents is then directly proportional to the solid thickness.

Internal-diffusion controlling. If a period of drying is developed where internal diffusion of moisture controls the rate, it can be expected that variables which influence the gas coefficients of heat or mass transfer will not influence the rate of drying. The drying rates should be independent of gas velocity, and humidity will be of importance only insofar as it controls the equilibrium-moisture concentration. When a semilogarithmic plot (Fig. 12.16) is prepared from drying data of this type, the curve b which results resembles those of Fig. 4.2. For a slab, the curves should be substantially straight at values of the ordinate below 0.6, with slopes proportional to $-1/z_S^2$. The drying time between fixed moisture contents should be proportional to the square of the thickness. Discrepancies may result because the initial moisture distribution is not uniform throughout the solid if a drying period precedes that for which diffusion controls, and because the diffusivity varies with moisture content.

Attempts have been made to describe rates of drying in the falling-rate period by means of overall coefficients of heat and mass transfer,[26] but these have not been too successful owing to the change in the individual resistances to transfer in the solid during the course of the drying.

Critical moisture content. The available data indicate that the average critical moisture content for a given type of solid depends upon the surface-moisture concentration. If drying during the constant-rate period is very rapid, and if the solid is thick, then steep concentration gradients are developed within the solid, and the falling rate begins at high average moisture contents. Generally, the critical moisture content will increase with increased drying rate and thickness of solid. It must usually be measured experimentally.

Through-circulation drying

When a gas passes through a bed of wet, granular solids, both a constant-rate and a falling-rate period of drying may result and the rate-of-drying curves may appear very much like that shown in Fig. 12.10.[21] Consider the case where the bed of solids has an appreciable thickness with respect to the size of the particles, as in Fig. 12.17.[2] The

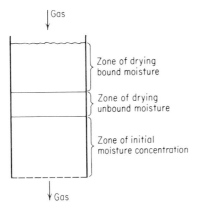

Fig. **12.17** *Through-circulation drying of thick beds of solids.*

evaporation of unbound moisture into the gas occurs in a relatively narrow zone which moves slowly through the bed, and unless the bed is internally heated, the gas leaving this zone is for all practical purposes saturated at the adiabatic-saturation temperature of the entering gas.   This is also the surface temperature of the wet particles.   The rate of drying is constant as long as the zone is entirely within the bed. When the zone first reaches the end of the bed, the rate of drying begins to fall because the gas no longer leaves in a saturated condition.   In other words, a *desorption* wave passes through the bed and the situation is much like that described for elution in fixed beds (Chap. 11).   However, the point of view of interest is the moisture content of the solid rather than the concentration changes occurring in the exit gas.   In the case of shallow beds composed of large particles, the gas leaves the bed unsaturated from the beginning,[21] but as long as each particle surface remains fully wet, there will still be a constant-rate period.   The falling rate then begins when the surface moisture is depleted.

The rate of drying of unbound moisture.[2] Consider a bed of uniform cross section as in Fig. 12.17, fed with a gas of humidity Y_1 at the rate of G_S lb dry gas/(hr)(sq ft bed cross section).   The maximum rate of drying N_{max} will occur if the gas leaving the bed is saturated at the adiabatic-saturation temperature, with humidity Y_{as},

$$N_{max} = G_S(Y_{as} - Y_1) \tag{12.25}$$

where N is expressed as lb moisture evaporated/(hr)(sq ft bed cross section).   In general, the gas will leave the bed at humidity Y_2, and the instantaneous rate of drying is

$$N = G_S(Y_2 - Y_1) \tag{12.26}$$

For a differential section of the bed where the gas undergoes a change in humidity dY and leaves at a humidity Y, the rate of drying is

$$dN = G_S \, dY = k_Y \, dS(Y_{as} - Y) \tag{12.27}$$

where S is the interfacial surface per square foot of bed cross section.   Letting a represent the interfacial surface per unit volume of bed whose thickness is z_S,

$$dS = a \, dz_S \tag{12.28}$$

and Eq. (12.27) becomes

$$\int_{Y_1}^{Y_2} \frac{dY}{Y_{as} - Y} = \int_0^{z_S} \frac{k_Y a \, dz_S}{G_S} \tag{12.29}$$

$$\ln \frac{Y_{as} - Y_1}{Y_{as} - Y_2} = N_{tG} = \frac{k_Y a z_S}{G_S} \tag{12.30}$$

where N_{tG} is the number of gas transfer units in the bed.   This equation is the same as Eq. (7.60), developed for a somewhat similar situation.   The mean driving force for evaporation is then the logarithmic mean of $Y_{as} - Y_1$ and $Y_{as} - Y_2$, in accordance with Eq. (7.61). Combining Eqs. (12.25), (12.26), and (12.30),

$$\frac{N}{N_{\max}} = \frac{Y_2 - Y_1}{Y_{as} - Y_1} = 1 - \frac{Y_{as} - Y_2}{Y_{as} - Y_1} = 1 - e^{-N_{tG}} = 1 - e^{-k_Y a z_S / G_S} \quad (12.31)$$

Equation (12.31) provides the rate of drying N if values of $k_Y a$ or N_{tG} can be determined. These have been established for certain special cases as follows:

  1. *Particles small* (10 *to* 200 *mesh, or* 0.08 *to* 0.0029 *in. diameter*) *with respect to bed depth* (*greater than* 0.45 *in.*); *drying of unbound water from the surface of nonporous particles.*[2] For this case,† the constant rate is given by $N_{\max}$ [Eq. (12.25)]. Equation (12.31) may be used for both constant and falling rates, since at high moisture contents the exponential term becomes negligible. The interfacial surface a varies with moisture content, and it is most convenient to express N_{tG} empirically as

$$N_{tG} = \frac{1.14}{d_p^{0.35}} \left(\frac{d_p G}{\mu} \right)^{0.215} (X \rho_S z_S)^{0.64} \quad (12.32)$$

where d_p is the particle diameter, feet, and ρ_S the apparent density of the bed, lb dry solid/cu ft. Through-drying of such beds in the ordinary equipment may involve a pressure drop for gas flow which is too high for practical purposes, especially if the particles are very small. Drying of such beds is done on continuous rotary filters (crystal-filter driers), however.

  2. *Particles large* (⅛ *to* ¾ *in. diameter*) *in shallow beds* (0.4 *to* 2.5 *in. thick*); *drying of unbound moisture from porous or nonporous particles.* During the constant-rate period the gas leaves the bed unsaturated, and the constant rate of drying is given by Eq. (12.31). For this purpose, k_Y is given by

$$k_Y = j_D G_S / Sc^{2/3} \quad (12.33)$$

and j_D in turn by item 5, Table 3.3. The interfacial surface may be taken as the surface of the particles. For air drying of water from solids, $Sc = 0.6$. Additional experimental data on a large number of preformed materials are also available.[21] During the falling-rate period, internal resistance to moisture movement may be important, and no general treatment is available. In many cases[21] it is found that semilogarithmic plots of the form of Fig. 12.16 are useful. If the line on this plot is straight, Eqs. (12.8) and (12.9) are applicable.

Drying of bound moisture. Presumably some adaptation of the methods used for adsorption in fixed beds (Chap. 11) could be made to describe this. No experimental confirmation is available, however.

---

  † In beds of finely packed solids containing a large percentage of liquid, the liquid is largely forced from between the solid particles by a mechanical process when gas is forced through the bed. See particularly Brownell and Katz, *Chem. Eng. Progr.*, **43**, 537, 601, 703 (1947). Only the last traces of moisture are removed by the drying process considered here.

Illustration 12.5. A cake of a crystalline precipitate is to be dried by drawing air through the cake. The particles of the cake are nonporous, of average diameter 0.008 in., and since they are insoluble in water have negligible equilibrium-moisture content.   The cake is 0.7 in. thick, and the apparent density is 85 lb dry solid/cu ft.   It is to be dried from 2.5 to 0.1% moisture.   The air will enter the cake at the rate of 175 lb dry air/(hr)(sq ft bed cross section), at a dry-bulb temperature of 90°F and 50% humidity.   Determine the time for drying.

Solution. $X_1 = 0.025/(1 - 0.025) = 0.0256$ lb water/lb dry solid; $X_2 = 0.001/(1 - 0.001) = 0.001001$ lb water/lb dry solid.   From Fig. 7.5, $Y_1 = 0.0158$ lb water/lb dry air; $t_{as} = 75°F$ (the adiabatic-saturation temperature) and $Y_{as} = 0.0190$ lb water/lb dry air. $G_S = 175$ lb dry air/(hr)(sq ft).

$$\text{Approx av } G = 175 + \frac{175(0.0158 + 0.0190)}{2} = 178 \text{ lb/(hr)(sq ft)}$$

Eq. (12.26): $N_{max} = 175(0.0190 - 0.0158) = 0.56$ lb evapd/(hr)(sq ft)

$$z_S = \frac{0.7}{12} = 0.0583 \text{ ft} \qquad d_p = \frac{0.008}{12} = 0.000665 \text{ ft} \qquad \rho_S = 85 \text{ lb dry solid/cu ft}$$

Viscosity of air at $(75 + 90)/2 = 82.5°F$ is 0.018 centipoise, and $\mu = 0.018(2.42) = 0.0286$ lb/ft hr.

$$\frac{d_p G}{\mu} = \frac{0.000665(178)}{0.0286} = 4.14$$

Eq. (12.32): $$N_{tG} = \frac{1.14(4.14)^{0.215}[X(85)(0.0583)]^{0.64}}{0.000665^{0.35}} = 59.1X^{0.64}$$

Eq. (12.31): $$N = 0.56(1 - e^{-59.1X^{0.64}})$$

The following table gives values of the rate N, lb evaporated/(hr)(sq ft), for various values of X, lb water/lb dry solid, in accordance with this expression.

X	0.0256	0.02	0.015	0.010	0.008	0.006	0.004	0.002	0.001
N	0.558	0.557	0.550	0.535	0.525	0.500	0.460	0.375	0.279

These provide the rate-of-drying curve of Fig. 12.18.   The time of drying is determined by finding the area under a curve of $1/N$ plotted against X, in accordance with Eq. (12.3).   The area

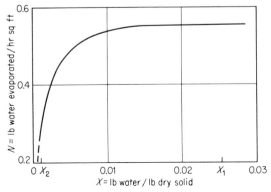

Fig. 12.18 *Solution to Illustration 12.5.*

under this curve (not shown) is 0.0473.   Since $L_S/A = \rho_S z_S = 85(0.0583) = 4.95$ lb dry solid/sq ft, the time for drying is, by Eq. (12.3),

$$\theta = 4.95(0.0473) = 0.234 \text{ hr, or 14 min}$$

Illustration 12.6. Wet, porous catalyst pellets in the form of small cylinders, 0.53 in. in diameter and 0.506 in. in height, are to be dried of their water content in a through-circulation drier.   The pellets are to be arranged in beds 2 in. deep on screens and are to be dried by air flowing at the rate of 800 lb dry air/(hr)(sq ft bed cross section), entering at 180°F dry-bulb temperature, humidity 0.01 lb water/lb dry air.   The apparent density of the bed is 37.9 lb dry solid/cu ft and the particle surface 86 sq ft/cu ft of bed.   Estimate the rate of drying, and the humidity and temperature of the air leaving the bed, during the constant-rate period.

Solution. $Y_1 = 0.01$ lb water/lb dry air, and, from Fig. 7.5, $Y_{as} = 0.031$ lb water/lb dry air at the corresponding adiabatic-saturation temperature (90°F). $G_S = 800$ lb dry air/(hr)(sq ft), and the approximate average $G = 800(1.016) = 815$ lb/(hr)(sq ft).   The approximate average air viscosity is 0.019 centipoise, or $\mu = 0.019(2.42) = 0.046$ lb/(ft)(hr).

The surface of each particle $= [\pi(0.53)^2(2)/4 + \pi(0.53)(0.506)]/144 = 0.0089$ sq ft.   The diameter of a sphere of equal area $= d_p = \sqrt{0.0089/\pi} = 0.0533$ ft. $a = 86$ sq ft/cu ft. $z_S = \frac{2}{12} = 0.1667$ ft.

The Reynolds number for the particles (Re" of item 5, Table 3.3) $= d_p G/\mu = 0.0533(815)/0.041 = 945$. $\epsilon = $ fraction voids (see Table 3.3) $= 1 - d_p a/6 = 1 - 0.0533(86)/6 = 0.237$.   Hence $j_D = 2.06/\epsilon(\text{Re}")^{0.575} = 0.169$.   Sc for air–water vapor $= 0.6$.

Eq. (12.33): $k_Y = 0.169(800)/(0.6)^{2/3} = 190.5$ lb water/(hr)(sq ft)(ΔY)

$$N_{tG} = \frac{k_Y a z_S}{G_S} = \frac{190.5(86)(0.1667)}{800} = 3.41$$

Eq. (12.25): $N_{max} = G_S(Y_{as} - Y_1) = 800(0.031 - 0.01) = 16.8$ lb/(hr)(sq ft)

Eq. (12.31): $\dfrac{N}{16.8} = \dfrac{Y_2 - 0.01}{0.031 - 0.01} = 1 - e^{-3.41}$

Therefore $N = 16.2$ lb water evapd/(hr)(sq ft) in the constant rate period, and $Y_2 = 0.0303$ lb water/lb dry air for the exit air.   The corresponding exit air temperature, from the adiabatic-saturation curve of Fig. 7.5 for the initial air, is 92.5°F.

Since

$$\frac{L_S}{A} = L_S z_S = 37.9(0.1667) = 6.31 \text{ lb dry solid/sq ft}$$

then Eq. (12.2):

$$\frac{-dX}{d\theta} = \frac{NA}{L_S} = \frac{16.2}{6.31} = 2.57 \text{ lb water/(hr)(lb dry solid) during constant rate}$$

These must be considered as estimates only, subject to check by drying-rate tests.

II. CONTINUOUS DRYING

Continuous drying offers the advantages that usually the equipment necessary is small relative to the quantity of product, the operation is readily integrated with continuous chemical manufacture without intermediate storage, the product has a more uniform moisture content, and the cost of drying per unit of product is relatively small.   As in the case of batch drying, the nature of the equipment used is greatly dependent upon the type of material to be dried. Either direct or indirect heating, and sometimes both, may be used.

In many of the direct driers to be described, the solid is moved through a drier while in contact with a moving gas stream. The gas and solid may flow in parallel or in countercurrent, or the gas may flow across the path of the solid. If heat is neither supplied within the drier nor lost to the surroundings, operation is adiabatic and the gas will lose sensible heat and cool down as the evaporated moisture absorbs latent heat of vaporization. By supplying heat within the drier, the gas may be maintained at constant temperature.

In *countercurrent* adiabatic operation, the hottest gas is in contact with the driest solid, and the discharged solid is therefore heated to a temperature which may approach that of the entering gas. This provides the most rapid drying, since especially in the case of bound moisture the last traces are the most difficult to remove, and this is done more rapidly at high temperatures. On the other hand, the dry solid may be damaged by being heated to high temperatures in this manner. In addition, the hot discharged solid will carry away considerable sensible heat, thus lowering the thermal efficiency of the drying operation.

In *parallel* adiabatic operation, the wet solid is contacted with the hottest gas. As long as unbound surface moisture is present, the solid will be heated only to the wet-bulb temperature of the gas, and for this reason even heat-sensitive solids may frequently be dried by fairly hot gas in parallel flow. For example, a typical flue gas resulting from combustion of a fuel, which may have a humidity of 0.03 lb water vapor/lb dry gas at 800°F, has a wet-bulb temperature of only about 150°F. In any event, the wet-bulb temperature can never exceed the boiling point of the liquid at the prevailing pressure. At the outlet of the drier, the gas will have been considerably cooled, and no damage will result to the dry solid. Parallel flow also permits greater control of the moisture content of the discharged solid, in cases where the solid must not be completely dried, through control of the quantity of gas passing through the drier and consequently its exit temperature and humidity.

Tunnel driers

These direct driers are essentially adaptations of the truck drier to continuous operation. They consist of relatively long tunnels through which trucks, loaded with trays filled with the drying solid, are moved in contact with a current of gas to evaporate the moisture. The trucks may be pulled continuously through the drier by a moving chain, to which they are attached. In a simpler arrangement, the loaded trucks are introduced periodically at one end of the drier, each displacing a truck at the other end. The time of residence in the drier must be sufficiently great to reduce the moisture content of the solid to the desired value. For relatively low-temperature operation the gas is usually steam-heated air, while for higher temperatures and especially for products which need not be kept scrupulously clean, flue gas from the combustion of a fuel may be used. Parallel or countercurrent flow of gas and solid may be used, or in some cases fans placed along the sides of the tunnel blow the gas through the trucks in crossflow. Operation may be essentially adiabatic, or the gas may be heated

Fig. 12.19 *Turbo-type drier. (Wyssmont Co., Inc.)*

by steam coils along its path through the drier, and operation may then be substantially at constant temperature. Part of the gas may be recycled, much as in the case of batch driers, for heat economy. Truck-type tunnel driers may be used for any material which may be dried on trays: crystals, filter cakes, pastes, pottery, and the like.

There are many modifications of the tunnel drier which are essentially the same in principle but different in detailed design owing to the nature of the material being dried. For example, skeins of wet yarn may be suspended from poles or racks which move through the tunnel drier. Hides may be stretched on frames which hang from conveyor chains passing through the drier. Material in continuous sheets, such as cloth, may move through the drier under tension, as in a continuous belt over a series of rollers, or may be hung in festoons from moving racks if it is to be dried in the absence of tension.

Turbo-type driers

Solids which ordinarily may be dried on trays, such as powdery and granular materials, heavy sludges and pastes, beads and crystalline solids, may be continuously dried in a turbo-type drier, a form of direct drier. The simplest of these is shown in Fig. 12.19. The drier is fitted with a series of annular trays arranged in a vertical stack. These rotate slowly (from a fraction to 1 rpm) about a vertical shaft. Each tray is provided with a slot cut into the tray, as well as a leveling rake for spreading the solid. Solid fed in at the top is spread upon the top tray to a uniform thickness, and as the tray revolves, the solid is pushed through the slot by a separate wiper rake, to fall upon the tray beneath. In this way, with overturning and respreading on each tray, the solid progresses to the discharge chute at the bottom of the drier. The drying gas flows upward through the drier, is circulated over the trays by slowly revolving turbine fans, and is reheated by internal heating pipes as shown.   The rate of drying will be faster than that experienced in a tray-equipped tunnel drier, owing to the frequent reloading of the solid on each tray.   Alternative arrangements are possible: external heating of the gas, recirculation of the gas, and arrangements for recovery of evaporated solvents may be provided.   In some installations the solid is carried upon a moving, endless conveyor, which is wound about the vertical axis of the drier in a close-pitched, screw-type spiral.   These driers are regularly built in sizes ranging from 6 to 20 ft in diameter and 6 to 25 ft high.   A few installations as tall as 60 ft have been made.

Through-circulation driers

Granular solids may be arranged in thin beds for through circulation of the gas, and, if necessary, pastes and filter cakes may be preformed into granules, pellets, or noodles as described in the case of batch driers.   In the continuous through-circulation drier of Fig. 12.20,[15] the solid is spread to a depth of 1.5 to 2 in. upon a moving endless conveyor which passes through the drier.   The conveyor is made of perforated plates or woven wire screens in hinged sections in order to avoid failure from repeated flexing of the screen.   Fans blow the heated air through the solid, usually upward through the wet solid, and downward after initial drying has occurred.   In this way, a more uniform moisture concentration throughout the bed is attained.   Much of the gas is usually recycled, and a portion is discarded continuously at each fan position in the drier.   For materials which permit the flow of gas through the bed in the manner shown, drying is much more rapid than for tray-type tunnel driers.

Fig. 12.20   *Continuous through-circulation (single-conveyor) drier with roller extruder.* (*Proctor and Schwartz, Inc.*)

Fig. 12.21 *Ruggles-Coles XW hot-air drier, manufactured by Hardinge Co., Inc.*

Rotary driers

This is a most important group of driers, suitable for handling free-flowing granular materials which may be tumbled about without concern over breakage. Figure 12.21 shows one form of such a drier, a direct countercurrent hot-air drier. The solid to be dried is continuously introduced into one end of a rotating cylinder, as shown, while heated air flows into the other. The cylinder is installed at a small angle to the horizontal, and the solid consequently moves slowly through the device. Inside the drier, lifting flights extending from the cylinder wall for the full length of the drier lift the solid and shower it down in a moving curtain through the air, thus exposing it thoroughly to the drying action of the gas. This lifting action also assists in the forward motion of the solid. At the feed end of the drier, a few short spiral flights assist in imparting the initial forward motion to the solid before the principal flights are reached. The solid must clearly be one which is neither sticky nor gummy, which might stick to the sides of the drier or tend to "ball" up. In such cases, recycling of a portion of the dried product may nevertheless permit use of a rotary drier.

The drier may be fed with hot flue gas rather than air, and if the gas leaves the drier at a sufficiently high temperature, discharging it through a stack may provide adequate natural draft to provide sufficient gas for drying. Ordinarily, however, an exhaust fan is used to pull the gas through the drier, since this provides more complete control of the gas flow. A dust collector, of the cyclone, filter, or washing type, may be interposed between the fan and the gas exit. A blower may also be provided at the gas entrance, thus maintaining a pressure close to atmospheric in the drier; this prevents leakage of cool air in at the end housings of the drier, and if the pressure is well balanced, outward leakage will also be minimized.

Rotary driers are made for a variety of operations. The following classification includes the major types.

1. *Direct heat, countercurrent flow.* For materials which may be heated to high temperatures, such as minerals, sand, limestone, clays, etc., hot flue gas may be used as the drying gas. For substances which should not be heated excessively, such as certain crystalline chemical products like ammonium sulfate and cane sugar, heated air may be used. The general arrangement is that shown in Fig. 12.21, and if flue gas is used, the heating coils are replaced by a furnace burning gas, oil, or coal.

2. *Direct heat, parallel flow.* Solids which may be dried with flue gas without

(a) Indirect rotary dryer

(b) Indirect, steam-tube rotary dryer

(c) Indirect-direct rotary dryer

Fig. 12.22 *Some rotary driers (schematic).*

fear of contamination but which must not be heated to high temperatures for fear of damage, such as gypsum, iron pyrites, and organic material such as peat and alfalfa, should be dried in a parallel-flow drier. The general construction is much like that of Fig. 12.21, except that the gas and solid both enter at the same end of the drier.

3. *Indirect heat, countercurrent flow.* For solids such as white pigments, and the like, which may be heated to high temperatures but which must remain out of contact with flue gas, the indirect drier indicated schematically in Fig. 12.22a may be used. As an alternative construction, the drier may be enclosed in a brick structure and completely surrounded by the hot flue gases. The air flow in such a drier may be kept to a minimum since the heat is supplied by conduction through the shell or central tube, and finely pulverized solids which dust severely may then be handled. For solids which must not be heated to high temperatures and for which indirect heat is desirable such as cattle feed, brewers' grains, feathers, and the like, the steam-tube drier, shown in Fig. 12.22b, may be used. This drier may or may not have lifting flights and may be built with one, two, or more concentric rows of steam-heated tubes. The tubes revolve with the drier, necessitating a special rotary joint where the steam is introduced and the condensate removed. This type of drier is frequently used when recovery of the evaporated liquid is necessary.

4. *Direct-indirect.* These driers, more economical to operate than the direct driers, may be used for solids which may be dried at high temperatures by flue gas, especially when fuel costs are high and when large percentages of moisture must be removed from the solid. A typical schematic arrangement is shown in Fig. 12.22c. In such a drier, the hot gas may enter the center tube at 1200 to 1800°F, cool to 400 to 900°F in its first passage through the drier, and on returning through the annular drying space cool further to 140 to 170°F at discharge. Lignite, coal, and coke may be dried in the inert atmosphere of such a drier at relatively high temperatures without danger of burning or dust explosion.

All these driers are available from various manufacturers in standard sizes, ranging from approximately 3 ft in diameter by 12 ft long to 10 ft in diameter by 100 ft long.

Holdup in rotary driers

The average time of passage, or retention time, of the solid in a drier must equal the required drying time if the solid is to emerge at the desired moisture content. It must be recognized of course that the retention time of individual particles may differ appreciably from the average,[27,37] and this can lead to nonuniformity of product quality. Several agencies bring about the movement of the solid particles through a rotary drier. Flight action is the lifting and dropping of particles by the flights on the drier shell: in the absence of air flow, each time the solid is lifted and dropped, it advances a distance equal to the product of the length of the drop and the slope of the drier. Kiln action is the forward rolling of the particles on top of each other in the bottom of the drier, as in a kiln without flights. The particles also bounce in a forward direction after being dropped from the flight. In addition, the forward motion of the solid is hindered by a counterflowing gas or assisted by parallel flow.

The holdup ϕ_D of solid is defined as the fraction of the drier volume occupied by the solid at any instant, and the average time of retention θ may be computed by dividing the holdup by the volumetric feed rate,

$$\theta = \frac{\phi_D Z \pi d^2/4}{(L_s/\rho_s)(\pi d^2/4)} = \frac{Z\phi_D \rho_s}{L_s} \tag{12.34}$$

where L_s/ρ_s = volumetric feed rate, cu ft/(hr)(sq ft drier cross section)

L_s = rate of flow of dry solids, lb/(hr)(sq ft)

ρ_s = apparent solid density, lb dry solid/cu ft.

Z = length of drier, ft

Although the influence of the character of the solids can be considerable,[42] Friedman and Marshall[11] found that the holdup of a large number of solids under a variety of typical operating conditions could be expressed simply as

$$\phi_D = \phi_{D0} \pm KG \tag{12.35}$$

where ϕ_{D0} = holdup with no gas flow

$\pm KG$ = correction for influence of gas rate, G lb/(hr)(sq ft)

The + sign is used for countercurrent flow of gas and solid, the − sign for parallel flow. Holdup for conditions of no gas flow depends to some extent upon flight design and the nature of the solid, but, under typical conditions and for ϕ_{D0} not exceeding 0.08, their data may be described by

$$\phi_{D0} = \frac{0.0037 L_s}{\rho_s s n^{0.9} d} \tag{12.36}$$

where s = slope of drier, ft/ft

n = rotational speed, rpm

d = drier diameter, ft

The constant K is dependent upon the properties of the solid, and for rough estimates it may be taken as

$$K = \frac{0.0000933}{\rho_s d_p^{1/2}} \tag{12.37}$$

where d_p is the average particle diameter, ft. Holdups in the range 0.05 to 0.15 appear to be best. Higher holdup results in increased kiln action, with consequent poor exposure of the solid to the gas, and an increase in power required for operating the drier.

These empirical relationships are applicable only under conditions of reasonable gas rates which do not cause excessive dusting or blowing of the solid particles from the drier. It is ordinarily desirable to keep dust down to 2 to 5 percent of the feed material as a maximum, and the corresponding permissible gas rates depend greatly upon the nature of the solid. From 200 to 10,000 lb gas/ (hr)(sq ft) is used, depending upon the solid; for most 35-mesh solids (d_p approximately 0.00137 ft), 1,000 lb/(hr)(sq ft) is amply safe.[11] Dusting is less severe for countercurrent than for parallel flow, since then the damp feed acts to some extent as a dust collector, and it is also influenced by design of feed chutes and end breechings. In any case, it is best to depend upon actual tests for final design and to use the equations for initial estimate only.

Driers are most readily built with length/diameter ratios $Z/d = 4$ to 10. For most purposes, the flights extend from the wall of the drier a distance of 8 to 12 percent of the diameter, and their number range from $2d$ to $3d$. They should be able to lift the entire solids holdup, thus minimizing kiln action, which leads to low retention time. Rates of rotation are such as to provide peripheral speeds of 40 to 100 ft/min, and the slopes are usually in the range 0 to 0.08 ft/ft.[11] Negative slopes are sometimes necessary in the case of parallel-flow driers.

Through-circulation rotary driers

Driers of the type indicated in Fig. 12.23 combine the features of the through-circulation and rotary driers. The direct drier shown, the Roto-Louvre,[9] consists of a slowly revolving tapered drum fitted with louvers to support the drying solid and to permit entrance of the hot gas beneath the solid. The hot gas is admitted only to those

Longitudinal section

Product

Transverse section at discharge end

Fig. 12.23 *Continuous through-circulation rotary drier (Roto-Louvre).* (*Link-Belt Co.*)

louvers which are underneath the bed of solid.   There is substantially no showering of the solid through the gas stream, and consequently a minimum of dusting results. The device is satisfactory for both low- and high-temperature drying of the same materials ordinarily treated in a rotary drier.

Drum driers

Fluid and semifluid materials such as solutions, slurries, pastes, and sludges may be dried on an indirect drier, of which Fig. 12.24, a dip-feed drum drier, gives an example. A slowly revolving internally steam-heated metal drum continuously dips into a trough containing the substance to be dried, and a thin film of the substance is retained on the drum surface.   The thickness of the film is regulated by a spreader knife, as shown, and as the drum revolves, moisture is evaporated into the surrounding air by heat transferred through the metal of the drum.   The dried material is then continuously scraped from the drum surface by a knife.   For such a drier, heat transfer rather than diffusion is the controlling factor.   The liquid or solution is first heated to its boiling point; moisture is then evolved by boiling at constant temperature if a solute precipitates from a solution at constant concentration, or at increasing temperatures if the concentration change is gradual; and finally the dried solid is heated to approach the temperature of the drum surface.   In the case of slurries or pastes of insoluble solids, the temperature remains essentially constant at the solvent boiling point as long as the solid is completely wet and increases only during the last stages of drying.   The vapors are frequently collected by a ventilated hood built directly over the drier.

The ability of various slurries, solutions, and pastes to adhere to a heated drum varies considerably, and diverse methods of feeding the drum are resorted to accordingly.   Slurries of solids dispersed in liquids are frequently fed to the bottom of the drum on an inclined pan, and the excess nonadherent material is recycled to the feed reservoir.   Vegetable glues, and the like, may be pumped against the bottom surface of the drum.   The dip-feed arrangement shown in Fig. 12.24 is useful for heavy sludges, while, for materials which stick to the drum only with difficulty, the feed may be spattered on by a rapidly revolving roll.   Double-drum driers, consisting of two drums placed close together and revolving in opposite directions, may be fed from above by admitting the feed into the depression between the drums.   The entire drum drier may, on occasion, be placed inside a large evacuated chamber for low-temperature evaporation of the moisture.

Cylinder driers are drum driers used for material in continuous sheet form, such as paper and cloth.   The wet solid is fed continuously over the revolving drum, or a series of such drums, each internally heated by steam or other heating fluid.

Spray driers

Solutions, slurries, and pastes may be dried by spraying them as fine droplets into a stream of hot gas in a spray drier.[3,20]   One such device is shown in Fig. 12.25.   The liquid to be dried is atomized and introduced into the large drying chamber, where the droplets are dispersed into a stream of heated air.   The particles of liquid evaporate

Fig. 12.24 *Dip-feed single-drum drier. (Blaw-Knox Co.)*

Fig. 12.25 *Spray drier.* (*Nichols Engineering and Research Corp.*)

rapidly and dry before they can be carried to the sides of the chamber, and the bulk of the dried powder which results falls to the conical bottom of the chamber to be removed by a stream of air to the dust collector. The principal portion of the exit gas is also led to a dust collector, as shown, before being discharged. Installations may be very large, as much as 40 ft in diameter and 100 ft high. Arrangements and detailed designs vary considerably, depending upon the manufacturer. Spray driers are used for a wide variety of products, including such diverse materials as organic and inorganic chemicals, pharmaceuticals, food products such as milk, eggs, and soluble coffee, as well as soap and detergent products.

In order to obtain rapid drying, atomization of the feed must provide small particles of high surface/weight ratio, whose diameter is usually in the range 10 to 60 μ. For this purpose, spray nozzles or rapidly rotating disks may be used. Spray nozzles are of two major types: pressure nozzles, in which the liquid is pumped at high pressure and with a rapid circular motion through a small orifice, and two-fluid nozzles, in which a gas such as air or steam at relatively low pressures is used to tear the liquid into droplets. Nozzles are relatively inflexible in their operating characteristics and do not permit even moderate variation in liquid-flow rates without large changes in droplet size. They are also subject to rapid erosion and wear. Rotating disks are therefore favored in the chemical industry. These may be plane, vaned, or cup-shaped, up to 12 to 14 in. in diameter, and may rotate at speeds in the range 3,000 to 12,000 rpm. The liquid or slurry is fed onto the disk near the center and is centrifugally accelerated to the periphery, from which it is thrown in an umbrella-shaped spray. Appreciable variation in liquid properties and feed rates may be satisfactorily handled, and even thick slurries or pastes may be atomized without clogging the device provided they can be pumped to the disk.

The drying gas, either flue gas or air, may enter at the highest practical temperature, 175 to 1400°F, limited only by the heat sensitivity of the product. Since the contact time for product and gas is so short, relatively high temperatures are feasible. The short time of drying requires effective gas-spray mixing, and attempts to improve upon this account in part for the large number of designs of spray chambers. Cool air is sometimes admitted at the drying-chamber walls, in order to prevent sticking of the product to the sides. The effluent gas may convey all the dried product out of the drier, or else only the fines, but in either case the gas must be passed through some type of dust collector such as cyclones or bag filters, and these are sometimes followed by wet scrubbers for the last traces of dust. Recirculation of hot gas to the drier for purposes of heat economy is not practical, since the dust-recovery operation cannot usually be accomplished without appreciable heat loss.

The drops of liquid reach their terminal velocity in the gas stream quickly, within inches of the atomizing device. Evaporation takes place from the surface of the drops, and in the case of many products solid material may accumulate as an impervious shell at the surface. Since heat is nevertheless rapidly being transmitted to the particles from the hot gas, the entrapped liquid portion of the drop vaporizes and expands the still-plastic wall of the drop to 3 to 10 times the original size, eventually exploding a small blowhole in the wall and escaping, to leave a hollow, dried shell of solid as the product. In other cases, the central liquid core diffuses through the shell to the outside, and the reduced internal pressure causes an implosion. In any event, the dried product is frequently in the form of small hollow beads of low bulk density.[8] Some control over the bulk density is usually possible through control of the particle size during atomization or through the temperature of the drying gas (increased gas temperature causes decreased product bulk density by more extensive expansion of the drop contents). For high-density products, the dried beads may be crushed.

Spray drying offers the advantage of extremely rapid drying for heat-sensitive products, a product particle size and density which are controllable within limits, and relatively low operating costs, especially in the case of large-capacity driers. It is rapidly becoming more popular. Although a beginning has been made in the rational design of such driers, incomplete knowledge concerning drop size, drop trajectories, relative velocity of gas and drop, and rates of drying make it necessary to rely largely on experimental tests for spray-drying designs.

Fluidized and spouted beds

Granular solids, fluidized (see Chap. 11) by a drying medium such as hot air, may be dried, and cooled in a similar fluidized bed.[35] Coarse solids, too large for ready fluidization, may be dealt with in a *spouted bed*.[19,22] Here the fluid is introduced centrally into the cone-shaped bottom of the container for the solids instead of uniformly over the cross section; it flows upward through the center of the bed in a column, causing a fountainlike spout of solids at the top. The solids circulate downward around the fluid column. Such a bed has found particular use in the drying of wheat, peas, flax, and the like.[33]

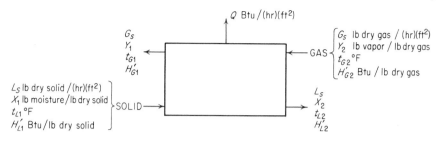

Fig. 12.26 *Material and enthalpy balances, continuous driers.*

Miscellaneous types

Pulverized and granular solids may be dried by suspending and conveying them in a stream of hot gas through a large pipe to a cyclone dust collector, in a system known as flash drying.[1]   Finely divided solids may be dried as they are moved through a screw conveyor, heated by condensing steam or other medium in a jacket surrounding the conveyor.   In such a drier, air need not necessarily be used, and the evaporated moisture may be led directly to a condenser for recovery, particularly if it is non-aqueous.   Continuous drying of pastes, slurries, and solutions on a belt, under vacuum, has also been done.[10]

Material and enthalpy balances

A general flow diagram for a continuous drier, arranged for countercurrent flow, is shown in Fig. 12.26.   Solid enters at the rate L_S lb dry solid/(hr)(sq ft),† is dried from X_1 to X_2 lb moisture/lb dry solid, and undergoes a temperature change t_{L1} to t_{L2}. The gas flows at the rate G_S lb dry gas/(hr)(sq ft) and undergoes a humidity change Y_2 to Y_1 lb moisture/lb dry gas and a temperature change t_{G2} to t_{G1}.   A moisture balance is then

$$L_S X_1 + G_S Y_2 = L_S X_2 + G_S Y_1 \tag{12.38}$$

or

$$L_S(X_1 - X_2) = G_S(Y_1 - Y_2) \tag{12.39}$$

The enthalpy of the wet solid is given by Eq. (11.23),

$$H_L' = C_L(t_L - t_0) + X C_A(t_L - t_0) + \Delta H_A \tag{11.23}$$

where H_L' = enthalpy of wet solid at t_L, referred to solid and liquid at reference
temp t_0, Btu/lb dry solid
C_L = heat capacity of dry solid, Btu/(lb)(°F)
C_A = heat capacity of moisture, as a liquid, Btu/(lb)(°F)
ΔH_A = integral heat of wetting (or of adsorption, hydration, or soln) referred
to pure liquid and solid, at t_0, Btu/lb dry solid

---

† For purposes of material and enthalpy balances alone, rates of flow of gas and solid may equally well be expressed as lb/hr.

Bound moisture will generally exhibit a heat of wetting (see Chap. 11), although data are largely lacking.   The enthalpy of the gas, H'_G Btu/lb dry gas, is given by Eq. (7.13).   If the net heat lost from the drier is Q Btu/hr, the enthalpy balance becomes

$$L_S H'_{L1} + G_S H'_{G2} = L_S H'_{L2} + G_S H'_{G1} + Q \qquad (12.40)$$

For adiabatic operation, $Q = 0$, and if heat is added within the drier to an extent greater than the heat losses, Q is negative.   If the solid is carried on trucks or other support, the sensible heat of the support should also be included in the balance. Obvious changes in the equations may be made for parallel-flow driers.

Illustration 12.7.   An uninsulated, hot-air countercurrent rotary drier of the type shown in Fig. 12.21 is to be used to dry ammonium sulfate from 3.5 to 0.2% moisture.   The drier is 4 ft in diameter, 22 ft long.   Atmospheric air at 75°F, 50% humidity, will be heated by passage over steam coils to 190°F before it enters the drier, and it is desired that it discharge at 90°F.   The solid will enter at 75°F, and it is expected to be discharged at 140°F.   One ton of product per hour will be delivered.
Estimate the air and the heat requirements for the drier.
Solution.   Define rates of flow in terms of lb/hr. $X_2 = 0.2/(100 - 0.2) = 0.0020$; $X_1 = 3.5/(100 - 3.5) = 0.0363$ lb water/lb dry solid. $L_S = 2,000(1 - 0.002) = 1,996$ lb dry solid/hr. The rate of drying is $1,996(0.0363 - 0.0020) = 68.5$ lb water evapd/hr.
At 75°F, 50% humidity, the absolute humidity of the available air is 0.0095 lb water/lb dry air, and this equals Y_2.   Since $t_{G2} = 190°F$, and with $t_0 = 32°F$, the enthalpy of the air entering the drier is (Table 7.1)

$$H'_{G2} = [0.24 + 0.45(0.0095)](190 - 32) + 1,075.8(0.0095) = 48.8 \text{ Btu/lb dry air}$$

For the exit air, $t_{G1} = 90°F$.

$$H'_{G1} = (0.24 + 0.45 Y_1)(90 - 32) + 1,075.8 Y_1 = 13.93 + 1,101.3 Y_1$$

The heat capacity of dry ammonium sulfate is $C_L = 0.36$ and that of water 1.0 Btu/(lb)(°F). ΔH_A will be assumed to be negligible for lack of better information.   Taking $t_0 = 32°F$ so that enthalpies of gas and solid are consistent, and since $t_{L1} = 75°F$, $t_{L2} = 140°F$, the solid enthalpies, Btu/lb dry solid, are [Eq. (11.23)]

$$H'_{L2} = 0.36(140 - 32) + 0.002(1)(140 - 32) = 39.07$$
$$H'_{L1} = 0.36(75 - 32) + 0.0363(1)(75 - 32) = 17.06$$

The estimated combined natural convection and radiation-heat-transfer coefficient from the drier to the surroundings[23] is 2.0 Btu/(hr)(sq ft)(°F).   Taking the mean Δt between drier and surroundings as $[(190 - 75) + (90 - 75)]/2 = 65°F$ and the exposed area as $\pi(4)(22) = 277$ sq ft, the estimated heat loss is

$$Q = 2.0(277)(65) = 36,000 \text{ Btu/hr}$$

Moisture balance [Eq. (12.39)],

$$1,996(0.0363 - 0.0020) = G_S(Y_1 - 0.0095)$$

Enthalpy balance [Eq. (12.40)],

$$1,996(17.06) + G_S(48.8) = 1,996(39.07) + G_S(13.93 + 1,101.3 Y_1) + 36,000$$

Solving simultaneously,

$$G_S = 6,450 \text{ lb dry air/hr} \qquad Y_1 = 0.0203 \text{ lb moisture/lb dry air}$$

The enthalpy of the fresh air (Fig. 7.5) is 21.5 Btu/lb dry air, and hence the heat load for the heater is 6,450(48.8 − 21.5) = 176,000 Btu/hr.   If 10 psig steam is used, whose latent heat is 952.1 Btu/lb, the steam required is 176,000/952.1 = 185 lb steam/hr, or 185/68.5 = 2.7 lb steam/lb water evapd.

Rate of drying for continuous direct-heat driers

Direct-heat driers are best placed in two categories, according to whether high or low temperatures prevail.   For operation at temperatures above the boiling point of the moisture to be evaporated, the humidity of the gas has only a minor influence on the rate of drying, and it is easiest to work directly with the rate of heat transfer.   At temperatures below the boiling point, mass-transfer driving forces are conveniently established.   In any case, it must be emphasized that our imperfect knowledge of the complex drying mechanisms makes experimental testing of the drying necessary. Calculations are useful only for the roughest estimate.

Drying at high temperatures. In a typical situation, three separate zones are distinguished in such driers, recognizable by the variation in temperatures of the gas and solid in the various parts of the drier.[11]   Refer to Fig. 12.27, where typical temperatures are shown schematically by the solid lines for a countercurrent drier.   In zone I, the preheat zone, the solid is heated by the gas until the rate of heat transfer to the solid is balanced by the heat requirements for evaporation of moisture.   Little actual drying will usually occur here.   In zone II, the equilibrium temperature of the solid remains substantially constant while surface and unbound moisture are evaporated.   At point *B*, the critical moisture of the solid is reached, and, in zone III, unsaturated surface drying and evaporation of bound moisture occur.   Assuming that the heat-transfer coefficients remain essentially constant, the decreased rate of evaporation in zone III results in increased solid temperature, and the discharge temperature of the solid approaches the inlet temperature of the gas.

Zone II represents the major portion for many driers, and it is of interest to consider the temperature-humidity relationship of the gas as it passes through this

Fig. 12.27 *Temperature gradients in a continuous countercurrent drier.*

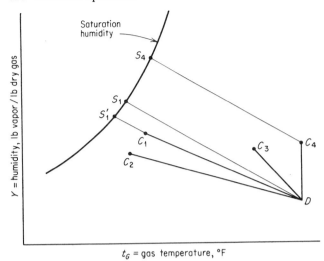

Fig. 12.28 *Temperature-humidity relations in continuous driers.*

section. On the psychrometric chart (Fig. 12.28), point D represents the gas conditions at the corresponding point D of Fig. 12.27. If drying is adiabatic, i.e., without addition to, or loss of heat from, the drier, the adiabatic-saturation line DC_1 will represent the variation of humidity and temperature of the gas as it passes through this section of the drier, and the conditions of the gas leaving this zone (point C, Fig. 12.27) are shown at C_1 on Fig. 12.28. The surface temperature of the solid, which can be estimated by the methods described earlier in the case of batch drying, will vary from that at S_1 (corresponding to point B of Fig. 12.27) to S_1' (corresponding to point A). If radiation and conduction through the solid may be neglected, these are the wet-bulb temperatures corresponding to D and C_1, respectively. For the system air–water, whose wet-bulb and adiabatic-saturation temperatures are the same, these will be both given by an extension of the adiabatic-saturation line DC_1 to the saturation-humidity curve. Heat losses may cause the gas to follow some such path as DC_2. On the other hand, if heat is added to the gas in this section, the path will be represented by a line such as DC_3 and, if the gas is kept at constant temperature, by line DC_4. In the case of the last, the surface temperature of the solid will vary from that at S_1 to that at S_4. For any specific drier, the temperatures and humidities may be computed by means of the moisture and enthalpy balances [Eqs. (12.39) and (12.40)] by application of these to each section separately.

Considering only heat transfer from the gas, and neglecting any indirect heat transfer between the solid and the drier itself, the loss in heat from the gas q_G may be equated to that which is transferred to the solid q and the losses Q. For a differential length of the drier, dZ, this becomes[11]

$$dq_G = dq + dQ \qquad (12.41)$$

Rearranging,

$$dq = dq_G - dQ = U \, dS(t_G - t_L) = Ua(t_G - t_L) \, dZ \qquad (12.42)$$

where U = overall heat-transfer coefficient between gas and solid
$t_G - t_L$ = temperature difference for heat transfer
$\quad S$ = interfacial surface/sq ft drier cross section
$\quad a$ = interfacial surface/cu ft drier volume
Then

$$dq = G_S C_S \, dt'_G = Ua(t_G - t_L) \, dZ \tag{12.43}$$

where dt'_G is the temperature drop experienced by the gas as a result of transfer of heat to the solid only, exclusive of losses, and C_S is the humid heat.

$$dN_{tOG} = \frac{dt'_G}{t_G - t_L} = \frac{Ua \, dZ}{G_S C_S} \tag{12.44}$$

and if the heat-transfer coefficient is constant,

$$N_{tOG} = \frac{\Delta t'_G}{\Delta t_m} = \frac{Z}{H_{tOG}} \tag{12.45}$$

$$H_{tOG} = \frac{G_S C_S}{U_a} \tag{12.46}$$

where N_{tOG} = number of heat-transfer units
H_{tOG} = length of heat-transfer unit
$\Delta t'_G$ = change in gas temperature owing to *heat transfer to solid only*
Δt_m = appropriate average temperature difference between gas and solid
If the temperature profiles in the drier may be idealized as straight lines, such as the broken lines of Fig. 12.27, then *for each zone taken separately* Δt_m is the logarithmic average of the terminal temperature differences and N_{tOG} the corresponding number of transfer units for each zone.   In the case of zone III, this simplification will be satisfactory for the evaporation of unsaturated surface moisture, but not for bound moisture, or where internal diffusion of moisture controls the rate of drying.

Tunnel Driers. In drying solids by cross circulation of air over the surface, as in the case of materials on trays or solids in sheet form, the surface temperature in zone II may be estimated through Eq. (12.18).   Unless all surfaces are exposed to heat transfer by radiation, this feature of the heat transfer is better ignored, and U in Eq. (12.46) may be taken as $h_c + U_k$.   This value will also serve in zone I, and in zone III only for cases of unsaturated surface drying.   The quantity a may be computed from the method of loading the drier.

Rotary Driers. The surface of the solid exposed to drying gas cannot be conveniently measured, so the group Ua must be considered together.   In countercurrent driers, Ua is influenced by changes in holdup due to changes in gas flow and solid feed rate, but effects of changes in slope or rate of rotation of the drier are small.[11,36]

The effect of gas mass velocity is uncertain.[24] In the absence of experimental data the group $Uad/G^{0.16}$ may be taken as about 10 for diameters in the range 1 to 2 ft, and about 20 for diameters of from 3 to 10 ft,[25] with the understanding that the character of the solids, since they may offer some of the heat-transfer resistance included in U, may also influence the size of the group.[34] For economical designs, the exit temperatures of the gas and solid should be chosen so as to provide for 1.5 to 2.5 transfer units in the drier.

Illustration 12.8. A preliminary estimate of the size of a countercurrent direct-heat rotary drier for drying an ore flotation concentrate is to be made. The solid is to be delivered from a continuous filter and introduced into the drier at 8% moisture, 80°F, and is to be discharged from the drier at 300°F, 0.5% moisture. There will be 5,000 lb/hr of dried product. The drying gas is a flue gas analyzing 2.5% CO_2, 14.7% O_2, 76.0% N_2, and 6.8% H_2O by volume. It will enter the drier at 900°F. Heat losses will be estimated at 15% of the heat in the entering gas. The ore concentrate is ground to 200 μ average particle diameter and has a bulk density of 81 lb dry solid/cu ft and a heat capacity 0.2 Btu/(lb)(°F) (dry). The gas rate ought not to exceed about 500 lb/(hr)(sq ft) to avoid excessive dusting.

Solution. $X_1 = 8/(100 - 8) = 0.0870$; $X_2 = 0.5/(100 - 0.5) = 0.00503$ lb water/lb dry solid. Define L_S and G_S as lb dry material/(hr)(sq ft). $L_S = 5,000(1 - 0.005) = 4,975$ lb dry solid/hr. Water to be evaporated $= 4,975(0.0870 - 0.00503) = 407$ lb/hr.
Basis: 1 mole gas in. Dry gas $= 1 - 0.068 = 0.932$ mole.

	Moles	lb	Av ht capacity, Btu/(lb mole)(°F), 900–32°F
CO_2	0.025	1.10	10.9
O_2	0.147	4.72	7.15
N_2	0.760	21.3	7.15
Total dry wt		27.1	

Av mol wt dry gas $= 27.1/0.932 = 29.1$ lb/lb mole, nearly the same as air.

$$Y_2 = \frac{0.068(18.02)}{0.932(29.1)} = 0.0452 \text{ lb water/lb dry gas} \qquad t_{G2} = 900°F$$

$$\text{Av ht capacity of dry gas} = \frac{0.025(10.9) + (0.147 + 0.760)(7.15)}{0.932(29.1)}$$

$$= 0.25 \text{ Btu/(lb)(°F)}$$

The exit-gas temperature will be tentatively taken as $t_{G1} = 250°F$. This is subject to revision after the number of transfer units is computed. In a manner similar to that above, the average heat capacity of the dry gas, 250 to 32°F, is 0.24 Btu/lb dry gas.

$$\text{Base temperature} = t_0 = 32°F$$

Eq. (7.13):

$$H'_{G2} = [0.25 + 0.47(0.0452)](900 - 32) + 1,075.2(0.0452) = 283.5 \text{ Btu/lb dry gas}$$
$$H'_{G1} = (0.24 + 0.45 Y_1)(250 - 32) + 1,075.2 Y_1 = 52.5 + 1,173 Y_1$$

Take $\Delta H_A = 0$. Eq. (11.23):

$$H'_{L1} = 0.2(80 - 32) + 0.0870(1)(80 - 32) = 13.78 \text{ Btu/lb dry solid}$$
$$H'_{L2} = 0.2(300 - 32) + 0.00503(1)(300 - 32) = 53.6 \text{ Btu/lb dry solid}$$
$$Q = \text{ht loss} = 0.15(283.5)G_S = 42.5G_S \quad \text{Btu/hr}$$

Eq. (12.39): $\qquad\qquad\qquad 407 = G_S(Y_1 - 0.0452)$

Eq. (12.40): $\quad 4{,}975(13.78) + G_S(283.5) = 4{,}975(53.6) + G_S(52.5 + 1{,}173\,Y_1) + 42.5G_S$

Solving simultaneously,

$$G_S = 5{,}170 \text{ lb dry gas/hr} \qquad Y_1 = 0.1238 \text{ lb water/lb dry gas}$$
$$H'_{G1} = 197.6 \text{ Btu/lb dry gas} \qquad Q = 220{,}000 \text{ Btu/hr}$$

Assuming that the psychrometric ratio of the gas is the same as that of air, its wet-bulb temperature is found to be [Eq. (7.26)] about 153°F. The surface of the drying solid particles is subject to radiation from the hot walls of the drier, and the surface of the solid in zone II is then estimated to be 160°F. (*Note:* This should be recalculated after the temperature at point D, Fig. 12.27, is known, but in this case any change will have no influence on the overall results.)

For lack of information on the critical moisture content of the solid, which is probably quite low for the conditions found in such a drier, it will be assumed that all moisture is evaporated in zone II at 160°F. Zone I will be taken as a preheat zone for warming the wet solids to 160°F, without drying. Enthalpy of the solid at 160°F, $X = 0.0870$ (point A, Fig. 12.27) $= 0.2(160 - 32) + 0.0870(1)(160 - 32) = 36.5$ Btu/lb dry solid. Similarly, enthalpy of the solid at 160°F, $X = 0.00503$ (point B, Fig. 12.27) $= 25.6$ Btu/lb dry solid.

Assuming heat losses in the three zones are proportional to the number of transfer units in each zone and to the average temperature difference between the gas and the surrounding air (80°F), the heat losses are apportioned (by a trial-and-error calculation) as 14% in zone I, 65% in zone II, 21% in zone III.

Calculations for zone III. Humid ht of entering gas $= 0.25 + 0.47(0.0452) = 0.272$ Btu/(lb dry gas)(°F). A heat balance,

$$5{,}170(0.272)(900 - t_{GD}) = 4{,}975(53.6 - 25.6) + 0.21(220{,}000)$$
$$t_{GD} = \text{gas temp at } D \text{ (Fig. 12.27)} = 768°F$$

The change in gas temperature, exclusive of that due to losses, is

$$\Delta t'_G = \frac{4{,}975(53.6 - 25.6)}{5{,}170(0.272)} = 99°F$$

Av temp difference between gas and solid $=$ av of $768 - 160 = 608°F$ and $900 - 300 = 600°F = 604°F = \Delta t_m$.

$$N_{tOG} = \frac{\Delta t'_G}{\Delta t_m} = \frac{99}{604} = 0.16$$

Calculations for zone I. Humid ht of exit gas $= 0.24 + 0.45(0.1238) = 0.294$ Btu/(lb dry gas) (°F). A heat balance,

$$5{,}170(0.294)(t_{GC} - 250) = 4{,}975(36.5 - 13.78) + 0.14(220{,}000)$$

$t_{GC} = \text{gas temp at } C \text{ (Fig. 12.27)} = 345°F \qquad \Delta t'_G = \dfrac{4{,}975(36.5 - 13.78)}{5{,}170(0.294)} = 74°F$

$\Delta t_m = $ av of $345 - 160 = 185°F$ and $250 - 80 = 170°F = 178°F$

$$N_{tOG} = \frac{\Delta t'_G}{\Delta t_m} = \frac{74}{178} = 0.42$$

Calculations for zone II

$$\text{Av humid ht of gas} = \frac{0.272 + 0.294}{2} = 0.28$$

$$\text{True change in gas temp} = 768 - 345 = 423°\text{F}$$

$$\text{Change in temp due to ht loss} = \frac{0.65(220,000)}{5,170(0.28)} = 99°\text{F}$$

$$\Delta t_G' \text{ due to ht transfer to solid} = 423 - 99 = 324°\text{F}$$

$$\Delta t_m = \frac{(768 - 160) - (345 - 160)}{\ln\left[(768 - 160)/(345 - 160)\right]} = 360°\text{F}$$

$$N_{toG} = \frac{\Delta t_G'}{\Delta t_m} = \frac{324}{360} = 0.90 \qquad \text{Total } N_{toG} = 0.16 + 0.42 + 0.90 = 1.48$$

Size of drier. Standard diameters available are 3, 4, 4.5, and 5 ft and larger. The cross-sectional area of the 4-ft diameter drier is $\pi(4^2)/4 = 12.58$ sq ft. Expressing the rates of flow as lb dry material/(hr)(sq ft), $G_s = 5,170/12.58 = 411$, $L_s = 4,975/12.58 = 396$ lb/(hr)(sq ft). This is the only size suitable in view of the permissible gas rate.

Av $G = G_s(1 + Y_{av}) = 411[1 + (0.0452 + 0.1238)/2] = 466$ lb/(hr)(sq ft). For lack of more specific information take $Ua = 20G^{0.16}/d = 20(446)^{0.16}/4 = 13.2$ Btu/(hr)(cu ft)(°F). $H_{toG} = G_s C_s/Ua = 411(0.28)/13.2 = 8.8$ ft.

$$Z = N_{toG}H_{toG} = 1.48(8.8) = 13.0$$

The nearest standard length is 16 ft.

Take the peripheral speed as 65 ft/min, whence the rate of revolution $= n = 65/4\pi = 5.2$ or 5 rpm.

$$d_p = (200\ \mu)(3.28)(10^{-6}) = 0.00065 \text{ ft} \qquad \rho_S = 81 \text{ lb/cu ft}$$

Eq. (12.37):
$$K = \frac{0.0000933}{81(0.00065)^{\frac{1}{2}}} = 0.000045$$

Take the hold-up $\phi_D = 0.05$, and $KG = 0.000045(446) = 0.02$.

Eq. (12.35):
$$\phi_{D0} = \phi_D - KG = 0.05 - 0.02 = 0.03$$

Eq. (12.36):
$$s = \frac{0.0037 L_S}{\phi_{D0}\rho_S n^{0.9}d} = \frac{0.0037(396)}{0.03(81)(5)^{0.9}(4)} = 0.0356 \text{ ft/ft, the drier slope}$$

Drying at low temperatures. Continuous driers operating at low temperatures may be divided into zones in the same manner as high-temperature driers. Since the surface moisture will evaporate at a comparatively low temperature in zone II, the preheat zone may generally be ignored and only zones II and III need be considered. Refer to Fig. 12.29, which shows an arrangement for countercurrent flow. In zone II, unbound and surface moisture is evaporated as discussed previously, and the moisture content of the solid falls to the critical value X_c. The rate of drying in this zone would be constant if it were not for the varying conditions of the gas. In zone III, unsaturated-surface drying and evaporation of bound moisture occur, and the gas humidity rises from its initial value Y_2 to Y_c. The latter may be calculated by applying the material-balance relation (12.39) to either zone separately. The

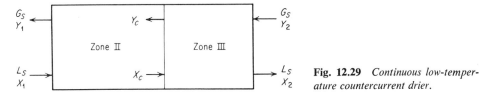

Fig. 12.29 *Continuous low-temper-ature countercurrent drier.*

retention time may be calculated by integration of Eq. (12.3),

$$\theta = \theta_{II} + \theta_{III} = \frac{L_S}{A}\left(\int_{X_c}^{X_1}\frac{dX}{N} + \int_{X_2}^{X_c}\frac{dX}{N}\right)$$ (12.47)

where A/L_S is the specific exposed drying surface, sq ft/lb dry solid.

Zone II, $X > X_c$. The rate N is given by Eq. (12.17), which, when substituted in the first part of Eq. (12.47), provides

$$\theta_{II} = \frac{L_S}{A}\frac{1}{k_Y}\int_{X_c}^{X_1}\frac{dX}{Y_s - Y}$$ (12.48)

Since $G_S\,dY = L_S\,dX$, Eq. (12.48) becomes

$$\theta_{II} = \frac{G_S}{L_S}\frac{L_S}{A}\frac{1}{k_Y}\int_{Y_c}^{Y_1}\frac{dY}{Y_s - Y}$$ (12.49)

Integration of Eq. (12.49) must take into account the variation of Y_s, the humidity of the gas at the solid surface, with Y. If the gas temperature, for example, is held constant in this zone by application of heat, the path of the gas resembles line DC_4 on Fig. 12.28. If furthermore, radiation and conduction effects can be neglected, Y_s for any value of Y on line DC_4 is the saturated humidity at the corresponding wet-bulb temperature. Equation (12.49) may then be integrated graphically.

For the case where Y_s is constant, as for adiabatic drying of water into air, Eq. (12.49) becomes

$$\theta_{II} = \frac{G_S}{L_S}\frac{L_S}{A}\frac{1}{k_Y}\ln\frac{Y_s - Y_c}{Y_s - Y_1}$$ (12.50)

Zone III, $X < X_c$. Some simplification is necessary for mathematical treatment. For the case where unsaturated-surface drying occurs and the drying rate is dependent strictly upon the conditions prevailing at any instant, independent of the immediate past history of the drying, Eqs. (12.8) and (12.17) apply. These provide

$$N = \frac{N_c(X - X^*)}{X_c - X^*} = \frac{k_Y(Y_s - Y)(X - X^*)}{X_c - X}$$ (12.51)

When this is substituted in the second part of Eq. (12.47), there results

$$\theta_{III} = \frac{L_S}{A}\frac{X_c - X^*}{k_Y}\int_{X_2}^{X_c}\frac{dX}{(Y_s - Y)(X - X^*)}$$ (12.52)

This may be evaluated graphically after determining the relationship between X, X^*, Y_s, and Y. For this purpose, the material balance may be written as

$$Y = Y_2 + (X - X_2)\frac{L_S}{G_S} \tag{12.53}$$

The surface humidity Y_s is found in the manner previously described, and X^* is given by the equilibrium-moisture curve for the appropriate Y.

For the special case where the bound moisture is negligible ($X^* = 0$) and Y_s is constant (adiabatic drying), substitution of Eq. (12.53) and its differential $G_S\,dY = L_S\,dX$ in Eq. (12.52) provides

$$\theta_{III} = \frac{G_S}{L_S}\frac{L_S}{A}\frac{X_c}{k_Y}\int_{Y_2}^{Y_c}\frac{dY}{(Y_s - Y)[(Y - Y_2)G_S/L_S + X_2]} \tag{12.54}$$

$$\theta_{III} = \frac{G_S}{L_S}\frac{L_S}{A}\frac{X_c}{k_Y}\frac{1}{(Y_s - Y_2)G_S/L_S + X_2}\ln\frac{X_c(Y_s - Y_2)}{X_2(Y_s - Y_c)} \tag{12.55}$$

These methods must not be applied to solids whose internal resistance to movement of moisture is large, where internal diffusion controls the rate of drying, and where casehardening occurs. In these cases, the instantaneous rate of drying under variable conditions is not merely a function of the prevailing conditions but depends upon the immediate past drying history as well. For such solids, the time for drying is best determined experimentally in a carefully planned test which simulates the countercurrent action of the continuous drier.[5]

In applying Eqs. (12.47) to (12.55), it is clear that, should drying take place only above, or only below, the critical moisture content, appropriate changes in the limits of moisture content and gas humidities must be made. In the case of parallel-flow driers, where gas enters at humidity Y_1 and leaves at Y_2, while solid enters at moisture content X_1 and leaves at X_2, Eqs. (12.50) and (12.55) become

$$\theta_{II} = \frac{G_S}{L_S}\frac{L_S}{A}\frac{1}{k_Y}\int_{Y_1}^{Y_c}\frac{dY}{Y_s - Y} = \frac{G_S}{L_S}\frac{L_S}{A}\frac{1}{k_Y}\ln\frac{Y_s - Y_1}{Y_s - Y_c} \tag{12.56}$$

$$\theta_{III} = \frac{L_S}{A}\frac{X_c - X^*}{k_Y}\int_{X_2}^{X_c}\frac{dX}{(Y_s - Y)(X - X^*)}$$

$$= \frac{G_S}{L_S}\frac{L_S}{A}\frac{X_c}{k_Y}\frac{1}{(Y_s - Y_c)G_S/L_S - X_2}\ln\frac{X_c(Y_s - Y_2)}{X_2(Y_s - Y_c)} \tag{12.57}$$

Illustration 12.9. Wet rayon skeins, after centrifuging, are to be air-dried from 46 to 8.5% water content in a continuous countercurrent tunnel drier. The skeins are hung on poles which travel through the drier. The air is to enter at 180°F, humidity 0.03 lb water/lb dry air, and is to be discharged at a humidity 0.08. The air temperature is to be kept constant at 180°F by heating coils within the drier. The air rate is to be 1,000 lb/(hr)(sq ft).

The critical moisture content of rayon skeins is 50%, and its percent equilibrium moisture at 180°F can be taken as one-fourth of the percent relative humidity of the air. The rate of drying is then [Simons, Koffolt, and Withrow, *Trans. AIChE*, **39**, 133 (1943)]

$$\frac{-dX}{d\theta} = 0.003G^{1.47}(X - X^*)(Y_W - Y)$$

where Y_W is the saturation humidity of the air at the wet-bulb temperature corresponding to Y.

Determine the time the rayon should remain in the drier.

Solution. $X_1 = 0.46/(1 - 0.46) = 0.852$; $X_2 = 0.085/(1 - 0.085) = 0.093$ lb water/lb dry solid. $Y_1 = 0.08$; $Y_2 = 0.03$ lb water/lb dry air. A water balance [Eq. (12.39)],

$$\frac{L_S}{G_S} = \frac{0.08 - 0.03}{0.852 - 0.093} = 0.0660 \text{ lb dry solid/lb dry air}$$

Since the initial moisture content of the rayon is less than the critical, drying takes place entirely within zone III. The form of the rate equation is the same as that of Eq. (12.22), where $k_Y A / L_S(X_c - X^*) = 0.003G^{1.47}$. Rearranging the rate equation,

$$\theta_{III} = \int_0^\theta d\theta = \frac{1}{0.003G^{1.47}} \int_{X_2}^{X_1} \frac{dX}{(X - X^*)(Y_W - Y)}$$

which is in the form of Eq. (12.52). On substituting $G = 1,000$, this becomes

$$\theta_{III} = 0.013 \int_{0.093}^{0.852} \frac{dX}{(X - X^*)(Y_W - Y)} \tag{12.58}$$

Consider that part of the drier where the moisture content of the rayon is $X = 0.4$.

Eq. (12.53): $\qquad Y = 0.03 + (0.4 - 0.093)0.066 = 0.0503$ lb water/lb dry gas

At $180°F$, $Y = 0.0503$, the wet-bulb temperature is $114°F$, and the corresponding saturation humidity $Y_W = 0.068$ (Fig. 7.5).

Eq. (7.8): $\qquad\qquad\qquad 0.0503 = \frac{p}{14.7 - p} \frac{18}{29}$

$$p = \text{partial pressure of water} = 1.10 \text{ psi}$$

The vapor pressure of water at $180°F = P = 7.51$ psi, and the relative humidity of the air = $(1.10/7.51)100 = 14.63\%$. The equilibrium moisture is $14.6/4 = 3.66\%$, and $X^* = 3.66/(100 - 3.66) = 0.038$ lb water/lb dry solid. Therefore

$$\frac{1}{(X - X^*)(Y_W - Y)} = \frac{1}{(0.4 - 0.038)(0.068 - 0.0503)} = 156$$

In a similar fashion, other values of this quantity are calculated for other values of X, as follows:

X	Y	Y_W	Percent relative humidity	X^*	$\dfrac{1}{(X - X^*)(Y_W - Y)}$
0.852	0.080	0.0950	22.4	0.0594	84
0.80	0.0767	0.0920	21.5	0.0568	88
0.60	0.0635	0.0790	18.17	0.0488	117
0.40	0.0503	0.0680	14.63	0.0380	156
0.20	0.0371	0.0550	11.05	0.0284	325
0.093	0.030	0.0490	9.04	0.0231	755

The integral of Eq. (12.58) is evaluated graphically by determining the area under a curve of the last column of the table plotted as ordinate against the first column as abscissa (not shown). The area = 151.6, whence, by Eq. (12.58),

$$\theta_{III} = 0.013(151.6) = 1.97 \text{ or } 2 \text{ hr} \quad \textbf{Ans.}$$

NOTATIONS FOR CHAPTER 12

a = interfacial surface of solid, sq ft/cu ft

A = drying surface, for cross-circulation drying, sq ft

= cross-sectional area of bed perpendicular to the direction of gas flow, for through-circulation drying, sq ft

A_m = a /erage cross-sectional area of a drying solid, sq ft

A_u = nondrying external surface, sq ft

b = a constant

C_A = heat capacity of liquid moisture, Btu/(lb)(°F)

C_L = heat capacity of dry solid, Btu/(lb)(°F)

C_p = heat capacity at constant pressure, Btu/(lb)(°F)

C_S = humid heat of a moist gas, Btu/(lb dry gas)(°F)

d = differential operator

= diameter of drier, ft

d_p = diameter of a particle, ft

= diameter of a sphere of same surface as particle, ft

D = diffusivity, sq ft/hr

e = 2.7183

f = function

G = mass velocity of gas, lb total gas/(hr)(sq ft)

G_S = mass velocity of dry gas, lb dry gas/(hr)(sq ft)

h_c = heat-transfer coefficient, for convection, Btu/(hr)(sq ft)(°F)

h_R = heat-transfer coefficient, for radiation, Btu/(hr)(sq ft)(°F)

ΔH_A = integral heat of wetting, Btu/lb dry solid

H_G' = enthalpy of a moist gas, Btu/lb dry gas

H_L' = enthalpy of a wet solid, Btu/lb dry solid

H_{tOG} = length of an overall gas transfer unit, ft

j_D = as defined by Eq. (12.19)

j_H = as defined by Eq. (12.19)

k_M = thermal conductivity of tray material, (Btu)(ft)/(hr)(sq ft)(°F)

k_S = thermal conductivity of the drying solid, (Btu)(ft)/(hr)(sq ft)(°F)

k_Y = gas-film mass-transfer coefficient, lb evaporated/(hr)(sq ft)(ΔY)

K = as defined by Eq. (12.37)

L_S = weight of dry solid in a batch, for batch drying, lb

= rate of flow of solid, for continuous drying, lb dry solid/(hr)(sq ft)

m = a constant

n = rate of revolution, rpm

N = rate of drying, lb moisture evaporated/(hr)(sq ft solid surface)

N_c = constant rate of drying, lb/(hr)(sq ft)

N_{tG} = number of gas transfer units, dimensionless

N_{tOG} = number of overall gas transfer units, dimensionless

p = partial pressure, atm (unless otherwise specified)

P = vapor pressure, atm (unless otherwise specified)

Pr = Prandtl number = $C_p \mu / k$, dimensionless

q = heat received at the drying surface, batch drying, Btu/(hr)(sq ft solid surface)

= heat received by the solid, continuous drying, Btu/(hr)(sq ft drier cross section)

q_c = heat transferred by convection, Btu/(hr)(sq ft solid surface)

q_G = heat transferred from the gas, Btu/(hr)(sq ft drier cross section)

q_k = heat transferred by conduction, Btu/(hr)(sq ft solid surface)

q_R = heat transferred by radiation, Btu/(hr)(sq ft solid surface)

Q = net heat loss, Btu/(hr)(sq ft drier cross section)

Re_x = Reynolds number $= xG/\mu$, dimensionless

s = slope of a drier, ft/ft

S = interfacial surface, sq ft/sq ft cross section

Sc = Schmidt number $= \mu/\rho D$, dimensionless

t_G = gas temperature, °F

t_L = solid temperature, °F

t_R = temperature of radiator, °F

t_s = temperature of surface, °F

t_0 = reference temperature, °F

T = absolute temperature, °R

U = overall heat-transfer coefficient, Btu/(hr)(sq ft)(°F)

x = length of drying surface in direction of gas flow, ft

X = moisture content of a solid, lb moisture/lb dry solid

X_c = critical moisture content, lb moisture/lb dry solid

X^* = equilibrium moisture content, lb moisture/lb dry solid

Y = humidity of a gas, lb moisture/lb dry gas

z_M = thickness of tray material, ft

z_S = thickness of drying solid, ft

Z = length of drier, ft

α = a constant

Δ = difference

ε = emissivity of drying surface, dimensionless

θ = time, hr

λ_s = latent heat of vaporization at t_s, Btu/lb

μ = viscosity, lb/(ft)(hr)

π = 3.1416

ρ_G = gas density, lb/cu ft

ρ_S = apparent solid density, lb dry solid/cu ft

ϕ_D = holdup of solid in a continuous drier, cu ft solid/cu ft drier

ϕ_{D0} = holdup of solid at no gas flow, cu ft solid/cu ft drier

Subscripts:

as = adiabatic-saturation conditions

c = critical

max = maximum

m = average

s = surface

W = wet-bulb conditions

I, II, III = pertaining to zones I, II, and III in a continuous drier

REFERENCES

1. Aldrich, R. S.: *Chem. Eng. Progr.*, **58**(6), 62 (1962).
2. Allerton, J., L. E. Brownell, and D. L. Katz: *Chem. Eng. Progr.*, **45**, 619 (1949).

3.   Belcher, D. W., D. A. Smith, and E. M. Cook: *Chem. Eng.*, **70,** Sept. 30, 83; Oct. 14, 201 (1963).

4.   Brier, J. C., and A. S. Foust: *Trans. AIChE*, **35,** 797 (1939).

5.   Broughton, D. B., and H. S. Mickley: *Chem. Eng. Progr.*, **49,** 319 (1953).

6.   Chu, J. C., S. Finelt, W. Hoerner, and M. Lin: *Ind. Eng. Chem.*, **51,** 275 (1959).

7.   Comings, E. W., and T. K. Sherwood: *Ind. Eng. Chem.*, **26,** 1096 (1934).

8.   Crosby, E. J., and W. R. Marshall, Jr.: *Chem. Eng. Progr.*, **54**(7), 56 (1958).

9.   Erisman, J. L.: *Ind. Eng. Chem.*, **30,** 996 (1938).

10.   Fixari, F., W. Conley, and G. K. Viall: *Chem. Eng. Progr.*, **53**(3), 110 (1957).

11.   Friedman, S. J., and W. R. Marshall, Jr.: *Chem. Eng. Progr.*, **45,** 482, 573 (1949).

12.   Gilliland, E. R., and T. K. Sherwood: *Ind. Eng. Chem.*, **25,** 1134 (1933).

13.   Harper, J. C., and A. L. Tappel: "Advances in Food Research," vol. 7, p. 171, Academic Press Inc., New York, 1957.

14.   Hougen, O. A., and H. J. McCauley: *Trans. AIChE*, **36,** 183 (1940).

15.   Hurxtal, A. O.: *Ind. Eng. Chem.*, **30,** 1004 (1938).

16.   Lane, A. M., and S. Stern: *Mech. Eng.*, **78,** 423 (1956).

17.   Lapple, W. C., W. E. Clark, and E. C. Dybdal: *Chem. Eng.*, **62**(11), 117 (1955).

18.   Loesecke, H. W. von: "Drying and Dehydration of Foods," 2d ed., Reinhold Publishing Corporation, New York, 1955.

19.   Malɘk, M. A., L. A. Madonna, and B. C. Y. Lu: *Ind. Eng. Chem. Process Design Develop.*, **2,** 31 (1963); *Can. J. Chem. Eng.*, **42,** 14 (1964).

20.   Marshall, W. R., Jr.: "Atomization and Spray Drying," *Chem. Eng. Progr. Monograph Ser.*, **50**(2) (1954).

21.   Marshall, W. R., Jr., and O. A. Hougen: *Trans. AIChE*, **38,** 91 (1942).

22.   Mathur, K. B., and P. E. Gishler: *AIChE J.*, **1,** 157 (1955).

23.   McAdams, W. H.: "Heat Transmission," 3d ed., McGraw-Hill Book Company, New York, 1954.

24.   McCormick, P. Y.: *Chem. Eng. Progr.*, **58**(6), 57 (1962).

25.   McCormick, P. Y.: sec. 20, "The Chemical Engineers' Handbook," 4th ed., McGraw-Hill Book Company, New York, 1963.

26.   McCready, D. W., and W. L. McCabe: *Trans. AIChE*, **29,** 131 (1933).

27.   Miskell, F., and W. R. Marshall, Jr.: *Chem. Eng. Progr.*, **52**(1), 35-J (1956).

28.   Molstad, M. C., P. Farevaag, and J. A. Farrell: *Ind. Eng. Chem.*, **30,** 1131 (1938).

29.   Newitt, D. M., et al.: *Trans. Inst. Chem. Engrs.* (*London*), **27,** 1 (1949); **30,** 28 (1952); **33,** 52, 64 (1955).

30.   Nissan, A. H., W. A. Kaye, and J. R. Bell: *AIChE J.*, **5,** 103, 344 (1959).

31.   Pasquill, F.: *Proc. Roy. Soc.*, **A182,** 75 (1944).

32.   Pearse, J. G., T. R. Oliver, and D. M. Newitt: *Trans. Inst. Chem. Engrs.* (*London*), **27,** 1, 9 (1949).

33.   Peterson, W. S.: *Can. J. Chem. Eng.*, **40,** 226 (1962).

34.   Porter, S. J.: *Trans. Inst. Chem. Engrs.* (*London*), **41,** 272 (1963).

35.   Quinn, M. F.: *Ind. Eng. Chem.*, **55**(7), 18 (1963).

36.   Saeman, W. C.: *Chem. Eng. Progr.*, **58**(6), 49 (1962).

37.   Saeman, W. C., and T. R. Mitchell: *Chem. Eng. Progr.*, **50,** 467 (1954).

38.   Shepherd, C. B., C. Haddock, and R. C. Brewer: *Ind. Eng. Chem.*, **30,** 389 (1938).

39.   Sherwood, T. K.: *Ind. Eng. Chem.*, **21,** 12, 976 (1929); **22,** 132 (1930); **24,** 307 (1932).

40.   Sherwood, T. K.: *Trans. AIChE*, **27,** 190 (1931).

41.   Sherwood, T. K., and E. W. Comings: *Ind. Eng. Chem.*, **25,** 311 (1933).

42.   Spraul, J. R.: *Ind. Eng. Chem.*, **47,** 368 (1955).

43.   Uhl, V. C., and W. L. Root: *Chem. Eng. Progr.*, **58**(6), 37 (1962).

44.   Victor, V. P.: *Chem. Met. Eng.*, **52**(7), 105 (1945).

45.   Wheat, J. A., and MacLeod, D. A.: *Can. J. Chem. Eng.*, **37,** 47 (1959).

46.   Whitwell, J. C., and R. K. Toner: *Textile Res. J.*, **17,** 99 (1947).

PROBLEMS

12.1. A plant wishes to dry a certain type of fiberboard in sheets 4 by 6 ft by ½ in. To determine the drying characteristics, a 1- by 1-ft sample of the board, with the edges sealed so that drying took place from the two large faces only, was suspended from a balance in a laboratory cabinet drier and exposed to a current of hot, dry air. The initial moisture content was 75%. The sheet lost weight at the constant rate of 0.8 lb/hr until the moisture content fell to 60%, whereupon the drying rate fell. Measurements of the rate of drying were discontinued, but after a long period of exposure to this air it was established that the equilibrium moisture content was 10%. The dry weight of the sample was 2 lb. All moisture contents are on the wet basis.

Determine the time for drying the large sheets from 75 to 20% moisture under the same drying conditions.

12.2. A sample of a porous, manufactured sheet material of mineral origin was dried from both sides by cross circulation of air in a laboratory drier. The sample was 1 ft square, ¼ in. thick, and the edges were sealed. The air velocity over the surface was 10 ft/sec, its dry-bulb temperature was 125°F, and its wet-bulb temperature 70°F. There were no radiation effects. The solid lost moisture at a constant rate of 0.6 lb water/hr until the critical moisture content, 15% (wet basis), was reached. In the falling-rate period, the rate of evaporation fell linearly with moisture content until the sample was dry. The equilibrium moisture was negligible. The dry weight of the sheet was 4.0 lb.

Estimate the time for drying sheets of this material 2 by 4 ft by ½ in. thick from both sides, from 25 to 2% moisture (wet basis), using air of dry-bulb temperature 150°F, but of the same absolute humidity, at a linear velocity over the sheet of 15 ft/sec. Assume no change in the critical moisture with the changed drying conditions. **Ans.:** 3.95 hr.

12.3. Estimate the rate of drying during the constant-rate period for the conditions existing as the air enters the trays of the drier of Illustration 12.2. The solid being dried is a granular material of thermal conductivity when wet = 1 (Btu)(ft)/(hr)(sq ft)(°F), and it completely fills the trays. The metal of the trays is stainless steel, 16 BWG (0.065 in. thick). Include in the calculations an estimate of the radiation effect from the undersurface of each tray upon the drying surface.

12.4. A laboratory drying test was made on a 1-sq-ft sample of a fibrous boardlike material. The sample was suspended from a balance, its edges were sealed, and drying took place from the two large faces. The air had a dry-bulb temperature of 150°F, wet-bulb temperature 84°F, and its velocity was 5 ft/sec past the sample. The following are the weights recorded at various times during the test:

Time, hr	Wt., lb	Time, hr	Wt., lb	Time, hr	Wt., lb	Time, hr	Wt., lb
0	10.625	2.6	9.570	6.0	8.670	14	8.420
0.1	10.597	3.0	9.412	6.5	8.610	16	8.420
0.2	10.548	3.4	9.273	7.0	8.565		
0.4	10.470	3.8	9.150	7.5	8.535		
0.8	10.305	4.2	9.045	8.0	8.507		
1.0	10.225	4.6	8.944	9.0	8.469		
1.4	10.063	5.0	8.852	10.0	8.448		
1.8	9.900	5.4	8.772	11	8.432		
2.2	9.735	5.8	8.700	12	8.423		

The sample was then dried in an oven at 220°F, and the dry weight was 8.301 lb.

a. Plot the rate-of-drying curve.

b. Estimate the time required for drying the same sheets from 20 to 2% moisture (wet basis) using air of the same temperature and humidity, but with a 50% greater air velocity. Assume the critical moisture remains unchanged. **Ans.:** 7.25 hr.

12.5. A pigment material which has been removed wet from a filter press is to be dried by extruding it into small cylinders and subjecting these to through-circulation drying. The extrusions are ¼ in. in diameter, 2 in. long, and are to be placed on screens to a depth of 2.5 in. The surface of the particles is estimated to be 90 sq ft/cu ft of bed and the apparent density 65 lb dry solid/cu ft. Air at a mass velocity 700 lb dry air/(hr)(sq ft) will flow through the bed, entering at 250°F, humidity 0.05 lb water/lb dry air.

a. Estimate the constant rate of drying to be expected. (*Note:* For long cylinders it is best to take the equivalent diameter as the actual cylinder diameter.) **Ans.:** 21.7 lb/(hr)(sq ft).

b. Estimate the constant rate of drying to be expected if the filter cake were to be dried on trays by cross circulation of the air over the surface at the same mass velocity, temperature, and humidity. Neglect radiation and heat conduction through the solid. **Ans.:** 0.247 lb/(hr)(sq ft).

12.6. A louver-type continuous rotary drier (Fig. 12.23) was used to dry wood chips from 40 to 15% moisture [Horgan, *Trans. Inst. Chem. Engrs.,* **6**, 131 (1928)]. The wood entered at 33°F, while the dried product was discharged at 100°F at the rate of 3,162 lb/hr. The drying medium was the gas resulting from the combustion of fuel, but for purposes of the present calculation it may be assumed to have the characteristics of air. It entered the drier at 715°F, with a humidity of 0.038 lb water vapor/lb dry gas, at the rate of 275 lb/min (wet). The gas was discharged at 175°F. The heat capacity of the dry wood may be taken as 0.42 Btu/(lb)(°F), and the heat of wetting may be ignored. Estimate the heat losses, Btu/hr.

12.7. A direct-heat parallel-flow rotary drier, 8-ft diameter, 60 ft long, was used to dry chopped alfalfa [see Gutzeit and Spraul, *Chem. Eng. Progr.,* **49**, 380 (1953)]. Over a 5-hr test period, the drier delivered an average of 2,220 lb/hr of dried product at 11% moisture and 145°F, when fed with alfalfa containing 79% moisture at 80°F. The drying medium was the combustion products resulting from the burning of 13,074 cu ft/hr (80°F, 4 oz gauge pressure) of natural gas (85% methane, 10% ethane, 5% nitrogen by volume) with air at 80°F, 50% humidity. The gas analyzed 2.9% CO_2, 15.8% O_2, 81.3% N_2 by volume on a dry basis; it entered the drier at 1500°F and left at 195°F. The heat capacity of dry alfalfa is estimated to be 0.37 Btu/(lb)(°F), and the heat of wetting may be neglected. Compute the volumetric rate of gas flow through the exhaust fan, cu ft/min, and the heat losses, Btu/hr.

12.8. A direct-heat countercurrent rotary hot-air drier is to be chosen for drying an insoluble crystalline organic solid. The solid will enter at 70°F, containing 20% water. It will be dried by air entering at 310°F, 0.01 lb water/lb dry air. The solid is expected to leave at 250°F, with a moisture content 0.3%. One thousand pounds per hour of dried product will be delivered. The specific heat of the dry solid is 0.2 Btu/(lb)(°F), and its average particle size is 0.5 mm. The superficial air velocity should not exceed 5 ft/sec in any part of the drier. The drier will be insulated, and heat losses may be neglected for present purposes. Choose a drier from among the following standard sizes, and specify the amount of air which should be used: 36 in. by 10 ft, 36 in. by 20 ft, 48 in. by 25 ft, 54 in. by 30 ft, 60 in. by 35 ft. **Ans.:** 48 in. by 25 ft.

12.9. A manufactured material in the form of sheets 2 by 4 ft by ¼ in. is to be continuously dried in an adiabatic countercurrent hot-air tunnel drier at the rate of 100 sheets per hour. The sheets will be supported on a special conveyor carrying the material in tiers 30 sheets high, and they will be dried from both sides. The dry weight of each sheet is 25 lb, and the moisture content will be reduced from 50 to 5% water by air entering at 250°F, humidity 0.01 lb water/lb dry air. Forty pounds dry air will be passed through the drier per pound dry solid.

In a small-scale experiment, when dried with air at constant drying conditions, dry-bulb temperature 200°F, wet-bulb temperature 120°F, and at the same velocity to be used in the large drier, the constant drying rate was 0.25 lb water evaporated/(hr)(sq ft) and the critical moisture content 30%. The equilibrium moisture content was negligible.

a. Calculate the value of k_Y from the data of the small-scale experiment. **Ans.**: 12.5.

b. For the large drier, calculate the humidity of the air leaving, and at the point where the solid reaches the critical moisture content.

c. Estimate the time of drying in the large drier. **Ans.**: 7.3 hr.

d. How many sheets of material will be in the drier at all times?

12.10. A continuous countercurrent hot-air tunnel drier is to be designed to dry a filter-press cake of coarse crystals of an inorganic material, insoluble in water. The filter-press cake will be placed on trays 3 by 3 ft by 1 in., 20 trays to a truck, with 2 in. between trays. The tunnel drier will have a cross section 6 ft high by 40 in. wide. The trays have a reinforced screen bottom, so that drying takes place from both top and bottom of each tray. Production is such as to permit introducing one truckload per hour. Each tray contains 65 lb dry solid, which will enter the drier at 75°F, 50% moisture, and will be dried to negligible moisture content. The critical moisture content is 15%, and the equilibrium moisture is negligible. The trucks are steel, each weighing about 300 lb. The air is to enter at 300°F, humidity 0.03 lb water/lb dry air, and the discharged solid is expected to leave at 275°F. The air is to be blown over the trays so that the average velocity at the air entrance is to be 15 ft/sec over the trays. The specific heat of the dry solid is 0.3 Btu/(lb)(°F). The drier is to be well insulated.

a. Calculate the length of the drier required. **Ans.**: 40 ft.

b. The entering air is to be prepared by recycling a portion of the discharged air with atmospheric air (75°F, humidity = 0.01 lb water/lb dry air) and heating the mixture to 300°F. Calculate the percentage of discharge air to be recycled and the heat required. Calculate the heat also as Btu/lb water evaporated. **Ans.**: 38.3%; 1530 Btu/lb water.

CHAPTER THIRTEEN
LEACHING

Leaching is the preferential solution of one or more constituents of a solid mixture by contact with a liquid solvent. This unit operation, one of the oldest in the chemical industries, has been given many names, depending to some extent upon the technique used for carrying it out. *Leaching* and *lixiviation* both originally referred to percolation of the liquid through a fixed bed of the solid, but the former term at least is now used to describe the operation generally, by whatever means it may be done. The term *extraction* is also widely used to describe this operation in particular, although it is applied to all the separation operations as well, whether mass-transfer or mechanical methods are involved. *Decoction* refers specifically to the use of the solvent at its boiling temperature. When the soluble material is largely on the surface of an insoluble solid and is merely washed off by the solvent, the operation is sometimes called *elutriation*, or *elution*. This chapter will also consider these washing operations, since they are frequently intimately associated with leaching.

The metallurgical industries are perhaps the largest users of the leaching operation. Most useful minerals occur in mixtures with large proportions of undesirable constituents, and leaching of the valuable material is a separation method which is frequently applied. For example, copper minerals are preferentially dissolved from certain of their ores by leaching with sulfuric acid or ammoniacal solutions, and gold is separated from its ores with the aid of sodium cyanide solutions. Leaching similarly plays an important part in the metallurgical processing of aluminum, cobalt, manganese, nickel, and zinc. Many naturally occurring organic products are separated from their original structure by leaching. For example, sugar is leached from sugar beets with hot water, vegetable oils are recovered from seeds such as soybeans and cottonseed by leaching with organic solvents, tannin is dissolved out of various tree barks by leaching with water, and many pharmaceutical products are similarly recovered from plant roots and leaves. Tea and coffee are prepared both domestically and industrially by leaching operations. In addition, chemical precipitates are frequently washed of their adhering mother liquors by techniques and in equipment quite similar to those used in true leaching operations, as in the washing of caustic soda liquor from precipitated calcium carbonate following the reaction between soda ash and lime.

Preparation of the solid

The success of a leaching and the technique to be used will very frequently depend upon any prior treatment which may be given the solid.

In some instances, small particles of the soluble material are completely surrounded by a matrix of insoluble matter. The solvent must then diffuse into the mass, and the resulting solution must diffuse out, before a separation can result. This is the situation in the case of many metallurgical materials. Crushing and grinding of such solids will greatly accelerate the leaching action, since then the soluble portions are made more accessible to the solvent. A certain copper ore, for example, can be leached effectively by sulfuric acid solutions within 4 to 8 hr if ground to pass through a 60-mesh screen, in 5 days if crushed to $\frac{1}{4}$-in. granules, and only in 4 to 6 years if 6-in. lumps are used.[29] Since grinding is expensive, the quality of the ore will have much to do with the choice of size to be leached. In the case of certain gold ores, on the other hand, the tiny metallic particles are scattered throughout a matrix of quartzite which is so impervious to the leaching solvent that it is essential to grind the rock to pass through a 100-mesh screen if leaching is to occur at all. When the soluble substance is more or less uniformly distributed throughout the solid or even in solid solution, the leaching action may provide channels for the passage of fresh solvent and fine grinding may not be necessary. Collapse of the insoluble skeleton which remains after solute removal may then present problems, however.

Vegetable and animal bodies are cellular in structure, and the natural products to be leached from these materials are usually found inside the cells. If the cell walls remain intact upon exposure to a suitable solvent, then the leaching action involves osmotic passage of the solute through the cell walls. This may be a slow process. It is, however, impractical and sometimes undesirable to grind the material sufficiently small to release the contents of individual cells. Thus, sugar beets are cut into thin, wedge-shaped slices called "cossettes" before leaching in order to reduce the time required for the solvent water to reach the individual plant cells. The cells are deliberately left intact, however, so that the sugar will pass through the semipermeable cell walls while the undesirable colloidal and albuminous materials largely remain behind. In the case of many pharmaceutical products recovered from plant roots, stems, and leaves, the plant material is frequently dried before treatment, and this does much toward rupturing the cell walls and releasing the solute for direct action by the solvent. Vegetable seeds and beans, such as soybeans, are usually rolled or flaked to give particles in the size range 0.005 to 0.02 in. The cells are, of course, smaller than this, but they are largely ruptured by the flaking process, and the oils are then more readily contacted by the solvent.

When the solute is adsorbed upon the surface of solid particles or merely dissolved in adhering solution, no grinding or crushing is necessary, and the particles may be washed directly.

Temperature of leaching

It is usually desirable to leach at as high a temperature as possible. Higher tempera- tures result in higher solubility of the solute in the solvent, and consequently higher ultimate concentrations in the leach liquor are possible. The viscosity of the liquid is lower and the diffusivities larger at higher temperatures, and this leads to increased rates of leaching. In the case of some natural products such as sugar beets, however, temperatures which are too high may lead to leaching of excessive amounts of un- desirable solutes or chemical deterioration of the solid.

Methods of operation and equipment

Leaching operations are carried out under batch and semibatch (unsteady-state) as well as under completely continuous (steady-state) conditions. In each category, both stagewise and continuous-contact types of equipment are to be found. Two major handling techniques are used: spraying or trickling the liquid over the solid, and immersing the solid completely in the liquid. The choice of equipment to be used in any case depends greatly upon the physical form of the solids and the difficulties and cost of handling them. This has led in many instances to the use of very special- ized types of equipment in certain industries.

I. UNSTEADY-STATE OPERATION

The unsteady-state operations include those where the solids and liquids are contacted in purely batchwise fashion and also those where a batch of the solid is contacted with a continually flowing stream of the liquid (semibatch method). Coarse solid particles are usually treated in fixed beds by percolation methods, whereas finely divided solids, which may more readily be kept in suspension, may be dispersed throughout the liquid with the help of some sort of agitator.

In-place leaching

This refers to the percolation leaching of minerals in place at the mine, by circulation of the solvent over and through the ore body. It has been applied to the leaching of low-grade copper ores containing less than 0.5 percent copper, whose value was too low to warrant the expense of mining.[30] It is also regularly used in the removal of salt from deposits below the earth's surface by solution of the salt in water which is pumped down to the deposits.

Heap leaching

Low-grade ores whose mineral values do not warrant the expense of crushing or grinding may be leached in the form of run-of-mine lumps built into huge piles upon impervious ground. The leach liquor is then pumped over the ore and collected as it drains from the heap. Copper has been leached from pyritic ores in this manner, in heaps containing as much as 25,000,000 tons of ore, using over 5,000,000 gal of leach liquor per day. It may require up to 7 or more years to reduce the copper content of such heaps from 2 to 0.3 percent.

Percolation tanks

Solids of intermediate size may be conveniently leached by percolation methods in open tanks. The construction of these tanks varies greatly, depending upon the nature of the solid and liquid to be handled and the size of the operation, but they are relatively inexpensive. Small tanks are frequently made of wood, provided that this material is not chemically attacked by the leach liquid. The solid particles to be leached rest upon a false bottom, which in the simplest construction consists of a grating of wooden strips arranged parallel to each other and sufficiently close to support the solid. These in turn may rest upon similar strips arranged at right angles, 6 in. or more apart, so that the leach liquor may flow to a collection pipe leading from the bottom of the tank. For supporting fairly fine particles, the wood grating may be further covered by a coconut matting and a tightly stretched canvas filter cloth, held in place by calking a rope into a groove around the periphery of the false bottom. Small tanks may also be made entirely of metal, with perforated false bottoms upon which a filter cloth is placed, as in the leaching of pharmaceutical products from plants. Very large percolation tanks (150 by 110 by 18 ft deep) for the leaching of copper ores have been made of reinforced concrete and lined with lead or bituminous mastic. Small tanks may be provided with side doors near the bottom for sluicing away the leached solid, while very large tanks are usually emptied by excavating from the top. Tanks should be filled with solid of as uniform a particle size as practical, since then the percentage of voids will be largest and the pressure drop required for flow of the leaching liquid least. This also leads to uniformity of the extent of leaching individual solid particles and less difficulty with channeling of the liquid through a limited number of passageways through the solid bed.

The operation of such a tank may follow any of several procedures. After the tank is filled with solid, a batch of solvent sufficient completely to immerse the solid may be pumped into the tank and the entire mass may be allowed to steep or soak for a prescribed period of time. During this period the batch of liquid may or may not be circulated over the solid by pumping. The liquid may then be drained from the solid by withdrawing it through the false bottom of the tank. This entire operation then represents a single stage. Repetition of this process will eventually dissolve all the solute. The only solute then retained is that dissolved in the solution wetting the drained solid.   This may be washed out by filling the tank with fresh solvent and repeating the operation as many times as necessary.   An alternative method is continuously to admit liquid into the tank and continuously to withdraw the resulting solution, with or without recirculation of a portion of the total flow.   Such an operation may be equivalent to many stages.   Since the solution which results is usually more dense than the solvent, convective mixing is reduced by percolation in the downward direction.   Upward flow is sometimes used, nevertheless, in order to avoid clogging of the bed or the filter with fines, but this may result in excessive entrainment of the fines in the overflow liquid.   Still a further modification, less frequently used, is to spray the liquid continuously over the top and allow it to trickle downward through the solid without fully immersing the solid at any time.

Retention of liquid after drainage

Imagine a bed of granular solids whose void space is completely filled with liquid.   When the liquid is allowed to drain under the influence of gravity, with admission of air to the voids from the top of the bed, the rate of liquid flow is at first very rapid.   The rate gradually falls, and after a relatively long period of time no additional drainage occurs.   The bed still contains liquid, however.   The fraction of the void volume still occupied by liquid is termed the *residual saturation* S.   Figure 13.1 shows the variation of S with height of the bed.[6]   In the upper part of the bed the value of S is constant at S_0, and this represents the liquid which remains in the crevasses and small angles between the particles as fillets, held in place by surface tension.   In the lower part of the bed, the liquid is held up in the voids, filling them completely ($S = 1.0$) by capillary action.   The drain height Z_D is defined as the height where the value of S is the average in the range S_0 to unity, as shown in the figure.   The average value of S for the entire bed will be the area between the ordinate axis and the curve of the figure, divided by the bed height Z,

$$S_{\text{av}} = \frac{(Z - Z_D)S_0}{Z} + \frac{Z_D}{Z} \tag{13.1}$$

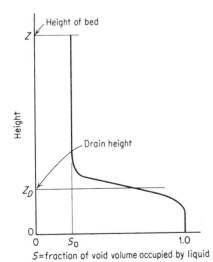

S = fraction of void volume occupied by liquid   **Fig. 13.1**   *Drainage of packed beds.*[6]

A large number of measurements of Z_D under a wide variety of conditions showed that, approximately,[6]

$$Z_D = \frac{0.275}{(K/g)^{0.5}(\rho_L/\sigma)} \tag{13.2}$$

where K is the "permeability" of the bed, ρ_L the liquid density, and σ the surface tension of the liquid. The value of S_0 was found to depend upon the group $K\rho_L/g\sigma$, called the *capillary number*, as follows:

$$S_0 = \begin{cases} 0.075 & \dfrac{K\rho_L}{g\sigma} < 0.02 \tag{13.3} \\[2ex] \dfrac{0.0018}{K\rho_L/g\sigma} & \dfrac{K\rho_L}{g\sigma} \geq 0.02 \tag{13.4} \end{cases}$$

In these expressions it is assumed that drainage has occurred under the action of the force of gravity only and that the contact angle between liquid and solid surfaces is 180°.

The permeability K is the proportionality constant in the flow equation for laminar flow through the bed,

$$G = \frac{K\rho_L \, \Delta P}{\mu_L Z} \tag{13.5}$$

where ΔP is the drop in pressure across the bed and G is the mass velocity of flow based on the entire cross section of the bed. Equation (6.36) describes the flow through beds of granular solids, and for laminar flow only the first term of the right-hand side of this expression is used. If $\Delta P/Z$ from this equation is substituted in Eq. (13.5), with Re replaced by $d_p G/\mu_L$, simplification leads to

$$K = \frac{d_p^2 \epsilon^3 g_c}{150(1 - \epsilon)^2} \tag{13.6}$$

where d_p is the diameter of a sphere of the same surface/volume ratio as the particles of the bed and ϵ is the fractional-void volume. For fibrous material and others whose value of d_p may be difficult to estimate, K may be obtained from Eq. (13.5) after experimental measurement of the pressure drop for laminar flow through the bed.

Illustration 13.1. The sugar remaining in a bed of bone char used for decolorization is leached by flooding the bed with water, following which the bed is drained of the resulting sugar solution. The bed is 10 ft deep, the temperature is 150°F, and the sugar solution which drains has a density 71 lb/cu ft and a surface tension 66 dynes/cm. The bulk density of the char is 60 lb/cu ft and the individual particle density 110 lb/cu ft. The particles have a specific external surface 80 sq ft/lb.

Estimate the weight of solution still retained by the bed after dripping of the solution has stopped. Express this also as lb solution/lb dry bone char.

Solution. The fractional void volume $= \epsilon = 1 - $ (bulk density/particle density) $= 1 - \frac{60}{110} = 0.455$ cu ft voids/cu ft bed. The particle surface $= a_p = (80 \text{ sq ft/lb})60 = 4,800$ sq ft/ cu ft bed.

Eq. (6.37):
$$d_p = \frac{6(1 - \epsilon)}{a_p} = \frac{6(1 - 0.455)}{4,800} = 0.000569 \text{ ft}$$

Eq. (13.6):
$$K = \frac{(0.000569)^2(0.455)^3(4.17)(10^8)}{150(1 - 0.455)^2} = 0.285 \text{ cu ft/hr}^2$$

$$\sigma = (66 \text{ dynes/cm})(6.89)(10^{-5}) = 455(10^{-5}) \text{ lb/ft}$$

$$\frac{K\rho_L}{g\sigma} = \frac{0.285(71)}{4.17(10^8)(455)(10^{-5})} = 10.67(10^{-6})$$

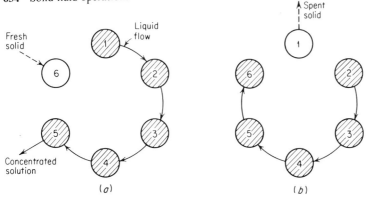

Fig. 13.2   *Countercurrent multiple contact, Shanks system.*

Eq. (13.3): $S_0 = 0.075$

Eq. (13.2): $Z_D = \dfrac{0.275}{[0.285/4.17(10^8)]^{0.5}[71/455(10^{-5})]} = 0.675$ ft

$$Z = 10 \text{ ft}$$

Eq. (13.1): $S_{av} = \dfrac{(10 - 0.675)(0.075)}{10} + \dfrac{0.675}{10} = 0.1375$

$$\dfrac{\text{Vol of liquid retained}}{\text{Vol of bed}} = 0.1375\epsilon = 0.1375(0.455) = 0.0625 \text{ cu ft/cu ft}$$

$$\text{Wt of liquid in bed} = 0.0625 \dfrac{\pi(3)^2(10)}{4} \, 71 = 313 \text{ lb}$$

$$\dfrac{\text{Wt of liquid}}{\text{Wt of dry solid}} = \dfrac{0.0625(71)}{1(60)} = 0.073 \text{ lb/lb}$$

Countercurrent multiple contact; the Shanks system

Leaching and washing of the leached solute from the percolation tanks by the cross-current methods described above will inevitably result in weak solutions of the solute. The strongest solution will result if a countercurrent scheme is used, wherein the final withdrawn solution is taken from contact with the freshest solid and the fresh solvent is added to solid from which most of the solute has already been leached or washed. In order to avoid moving the solids physically from tank to tank in such a process, the arrangement of Fig. 13.2, shown schematically for a system of six tanks, is used.   This *Shanks system,*† as it is called, is operated in the following manner:

    † Named after James Shanks, who first introduced the system in 1841 into England for the leaching of soda ash from the "black ash" of the Le Blanc process.   It was, however, apparently a German development.

1. Assume at the time of inspecting the system at Fig. 13.2*a* that it has been in operation for some time.   Tank 6 is empty, tanks 1 to 5 are filled with solid, tank 5 most recently and tank 1 for the longest time.   Tanks 1 to 5 are also filled with leach liquid, and the most concentrated is in tank 5 since it is in contact with the freshest solid.   Fresh solvent has just been added to tank 1.

2. Withdraw the concentrated solution from tank 5, transfer the liquid from tank 4 to tank 5, from 3 to 4, from 2 to 3, and from 1 to 2.   Add fresh solid to tank 6.

3. Refer to Fig. 13.2*b*.   Discard the spent solid from tank 1.   Transfer the liquid from tank 5 to tank 6, from 4 to 5, from 3 to 4, and from 2 to 3.   Add fresh solvent to tank 2.   The circumstances are now the same as they were at the start in Fig. 13.2*a*, except that the tank numbers are each advanced by one.

4. Continue the operation in the same manner as before.

The scheme is identical with the batch simulation of a multistage countercurrent operation shown in Fig. 10.58.   After several cycles have been run through in this manner, the concentrations of solution and in the solid in each tank approach very closely the values obtaining in a truly continuous countercurrent multistage leaching. The system can, of course, be operated with any number of tanks, and anywhere from 6 to 16 are common.   They need not be arranged in a circle but are better placed in a row, called an "extraction battery," so that additional tanks may be conveniently added to the system if desired.   The tanks may be placed at progressively decreasing levels, so that liquid may flow from one to the other by gravity with a minimum of pumping.

Such leaching tanks and arrangements are used extensively in the metallurgical industries, for recovery of tannins from tree barks and woods, for leaching sodium nitrate from Chilean nitrate-bearing rock (*caliche*), and in many other processes.

Percolation in closed vessels

When the pressure drop for flow of liquid is too high for gravity flow, closed vessels must be used, and the liquid is pumped through the bed of solid.   Such vessels are sometimes called "diffusers."   Closed tanks are also necessary to prevent evaporation losses when the solvent is very volatile or when temperatures above the normal boiling point of the solvent are desired.   For example, some tannins are leached with water at 250°F, 50-psi pressure, in closed percolation tanks.

Designs vary considerably, depending upon the application.   In the case of leaching of sugar from sugar-beet slices, or cossettes, a diffuser of the type shown in Fig. 13.3 is used.   These are arranged in a battery containing up to 16 vessels, and the beets are leached with hot water in the countercurrent fashion of the Shanks system. Heaters are placed between the diffusers to maintain a solution temperature of 160 to 170°F.   In this manner 95 to 98 percent of the sugar, in beets containing initially about 18 percent, may be leached to form a solution of 12 percent concentration. Countercurrent, continuous equipment is also used in the sugarbeet industry.[13]

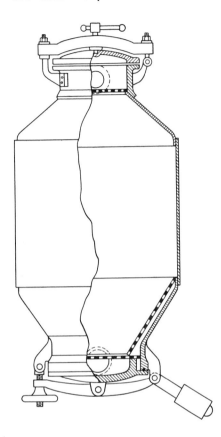

Fig. 13.3 *Sugarbeet diffuser.*[7] *(Courtesy of the Institution of Chemical Engineers.)*

Filter-press leaching

Finely divided solids, too fine for treatment by percolation in relatively deep percolation tanks, may be filtered and leached in the filter press by pumping the solvent through the press cake. This is, of course, common practice in the washing of mother liquor from precipitates which have been filtered.

Agitated vessels

Channeling of the solvent in percolation or filter-press leaching of fixed beds, with its consequent slow and incomplete leaching, may be avoided by stirring the liquid and solid in leaching vessels. For coarse solids, many types of stirred or agitated vessels have been devised.[24] In such cases, closed cylindrical vessels are arranged vertically (Fig. 13.4a) and are fitted with power-driven paddles or stirrers on vertical shafts, as well as false bottoms for drainage of the leach solution at the end of the operation. In others, the vessels are horizontal, as in Fig. 13.4b, with the stirrer arranged on a horizontal shaft. In some cases, a horizontal drum is the extraction vessel, and the solid and liquid are tumbled about inside by rotation of the drum on rollers, as in Fig. 13.4c. These devices are operated in batchwise fashion and provide a single leaching stage.   They may be used singly but very frequently also are used in batteries arranged for countercurrent leaching.   They have been used extensively in the older European and South American installations for leaching of vegetable oils from seeds, but relatively little in the United States.

Finely divided solids may be suspended in leaching solvents by agitation, and for batch operation a variety of agitated vessels are used.   The simplest is the Pachuca tank (Fig. 13.5), which is employed extensively in the metallurgical industries.   These tanks may be constructed of wood, metal, or concrete and may be lined with inert metal such as lead, depending upon the nature of the leaching liquid.   Agitation is accomplished by an air lift: the bubbles of air rising through the central tube cause the upward flow of liquid and suspended solid in the tube and consequently vertical circulation of the tank contents.[17]   The standard mechanical agitators, with turbine-type impellers, for example, may also be used to keep the finely divided solids suspended in the liquid.   After the leaching has been accomplished, the agitation is stopped, the solid is allowed to settle in the same or a separate vessel, and the clear, supernatant liquid may be decanted by siphoning over the top of the tank or by withdrawal through discharge pipes placed at an appropriate level in the side of the tank. If the solids are finely divided and settle to a compressible sludge, the amount of solution retained in the settled solids will be considerable.   Agitation and settling with several batches of wash solvent may then be necessary to recover the last traces of solute, and this may be done in a countercurrent fashion.   Alternatively, the solid may be filtered and washed in the filter.

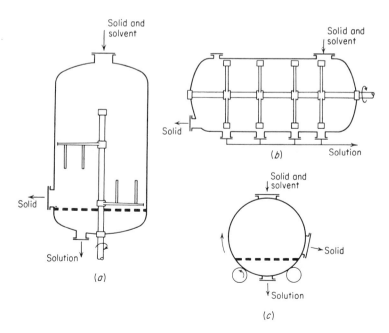

Fig. 13.4 *Agitated batch leaching vessels.*

Batch settling

The settling characteristics of a slurry consisting of a finely divided solid, of uniform density and reasonably uniform particle size, which is dispersed in a liquid are easily followed by observing a sample of the slurry when allowed to stand undisturbed in a vertical cylinder of transparent glass. If the slurry is initially very dilute, the particles will be observed to settle down through the liquid individually, each at a rate dependent upon the particle size, the relative density of solid and liquid, and the viscosity of the liquid, eventually to collect in a pile at the bottom. Ultimately the liquid becomes clear, but at no time until the end is there a sharp line of demarcation between clear liquid and the settling slurry. For more concentrated slurries, of the sort usually encountered in leaching and washing operations, the behavior is different, however. It will usually be observed that the particles settle more slowly owing to mutual interference (hindered settling). Furthermore, except

Section *A-A*

Fig. 13.5   *Pachuca tank.*[18]

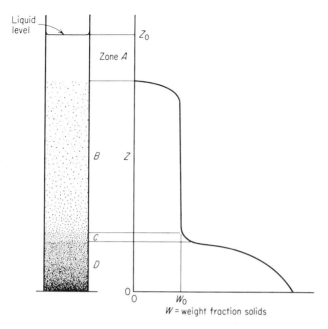

Liquid
level

Z_0

Zone A

B Z

C

D

0

0   W_0

W = weight fraction solids

Fig. 13.6 *Batch settling.*

for a few particles of relatively large size which may be present, there is little classification according to size, and the particles largely settle together.   As a result there is usually a reasonably sharp line of demarcation between the clear, supernatant liquor in the upper part of the cylinder and the settling mass of solids in the lower part.

Consider the cylinder of Fig. 13.6, initially filled to a height Z_0 with a slurry of uniform concentration w_0 weight fraction solids, in which some settling has already taken place.   At the time of observation, there is a zone A of clear liquid at the top.   Directly beneath this is zone B, throughout which the solids concentration is reasonably uniform at the initial value w_0, as shown by the accompanying graph.[4]   In zone D at the bottom, usually called the "compression zone," the particles accumulating from above have come to rest upon each other, and, owing to their weight, liquid is squeezed out from between the particles.   For compressible sludges, this results in increasing solids concentration with depth in this zone, as shown by the curve.   Zone C is a transition zone between B and D, and it may not always be clearly defined.   As settling continues beyond the time corresponding to that in the figure, the line of demarcation between zones A and B falls and the height of zone D rises, until eventually zone B disappears and only a compression zone containing all the solids remains.   This then slowly subsides to some ultimate height.

The rate of settling is usually followed by plotting the height of the line of demarcation between zones A and B against time, as shown by the solid curve of Fig. 13.7.   The broken curve represents the position of the upper level of zone D.   The top of zone B settles at constant rate (curve of Z vs. time straight) from the beginning until zone B has nearly disappeared and all the solids are in the compression zone.   The rate of settling of the compression zone to its ultimate height Z_∞ is then relatively slow and is not constant.   In a few cases, two constant-rate settling periods may be observed, with substantially no compression period.   The appearance of the curves depends not only upon the type of slurry (nature and particle size of the solid, and nature of the liquid) but also upon the initial height and concentration of the slurry, as well as the extent of flocculation and whether or not any stirring is done during settling.

Flocculation. If the finely divided solid particles are all similarly electrically charged, they repel each other and remain dispersed.   If the charge is neutralized by addition, for example, of an electrolyte (flocculating agent) to the mixture, the particles may form aggregates, or flocs.   Since the

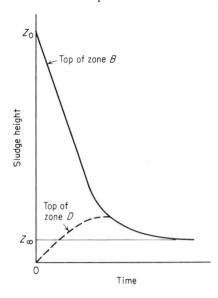

Fig. 13.7 *Rate of settling.*

flocs are of larger size, they settle more rapidly.   The slurries and suspensions encountered in chemical operations are usually flocculated.

Stirring. Very slow stirring, so slow that eddy currents are not formed within the liquid, changes the character of the settling profoundly.   The floc structure is altered so that the solids concentration in zone B is no longer uniform at the initial value[5] and zone D may not be clearly defined. The ultimate height of the settled slurry may be only a fraction of that obtained without stirring[14]

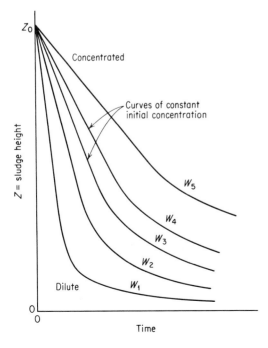

Fig. 13.8 *Batch settling of slurries. Effect of slurry concentration.*

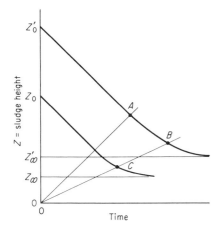

Fig. 13.9 *Batch settling of slurries at different initial heights.*

owing to breakdown of bridged floc structures in the compression zone, and the ultimate concentration of solids in the settled mass is corresponding greater. Generally, however, the zones of constant- and falling-rate settling are still observed, although the rates will be different from those obtained without stirring.[31]

Concentration. The rate of settling decreases with increased initial concentration of the solids owing to the increase of the effective density and viscosity of the medium through which the particles settle. Figure 13.8 illustrates the effect usually to be expected when slurries of increasing concentration of the same substance are settled in columns of the same height. Various attempts have been made to predict the effect of concentration on the settling rate, from knowledge of the curves at one or more concentrations. This has been successful only for slurries which are not compressible.[27]

Height. Refer to Fig. 13.9, which shows settling curves for the same slurry begun at different initial heights. The initial constant settling rate is independent of height, and provided some critical minimum value of Z_0 is exceeded, the ultimate value of Z_∞/Z_0 will apparently also be constant. The constant-settling-rate lines both terminate on a line OA radiating from the origin, and in general any line[31] radiating from the origin such as OB will be cut so that line OC/line $OB = Z_0/Z_0'$. It follows that the time for a slurry to settle to a fixed fractional height Z/Z_0 is proportional to the initial height Z_0. In this way it is possible reasonably well to predict the settling curves for deep tanks from results obtained in small laboratory cylinders. In making such laboratory tests, however, it is important[14] to use cylinders at least 3 ft tall and at least 2 in. in diameter and to maintain all other conditions in the laboratory test identical with those expected to prevail on the large scale.

Percolation vs. agitation

If a solid in the form of large lumps is to be leached, a decision must frequently be made whether to crush it to coarse lumps and leach by percolation or whether to fine-grind it and leach by agitation and settling. No general answer can be given to this problem owing to the diverse leaching characteristics of the various solids and the values of the solute, but among the considerations are the following: Fine grinding is more costly but provides more rapid and possibly more thorough leaching. It suffers the disadvantages that the weight of liquid associated with the settled solid may be as great as the weight of the solid, or more, so that considerable solvent is used in washing the leached solute free of solute and the resulting solution is dilute. Coarsely ground particles, on the other hand, leach more slowly and possibly less thoroughly but on draining may retain relatively little solution, require less washing, and thus provide a more concentrated final solution.

II. STEADY-STATE (CONTINUOUS) OPERATION

Equipment for continuous steady-state operations may be broadly classified into two major categories, according to whether it operates in stagewise or in continuous-contact fashion. Stagewise equipment may sometimes be assembled in multiple units so as to produce multistage effects, whereas continuous-contact equipment may provide the equivalent of many stages in a single device.

Leaching during grinding

As has been pointed out earlier, many solids require grinding in order to make the soluble portions accessible to the leaching solvents, and if continuous wet grinding is practiced, some of the leaching may be accomplished at this time. As much as 50 to 75 percent of the soluble gold may be dissolved by grinding the ore in the presence of cyanide solution, for example. Similarly, castor seeds are ground in an attrition mill with solvent for the castor oil. The liquid and solid flow through a grinding mill in parallel and consequently tend to come to a concentration equilibrium. Such operations are therefore single-stage leachings and are usually supplemented by additional agitation or washing operations, as described later.

Agitated vessels

Finely ground solids which can be readily suspended in liquids by agitation may be continuously leached in any of the many types of agitated tanks or vessels. These must be arranged for continuous flow of liquid and solid into and out of the tank and must be carefully designed so that no accumulation of solid occurs. Owing to the thorough mixing ordinarily obtained these devices are single-stage in their action, the liquid and solid tending to come to equilibrium within the vessel.

Mechanically agitated vessels may be used, for which the turbine-type agitator is probably most generally suitable. Pachuca tanks are frequently used in the metallurgical industries. The Dorr agitator (Fig. 13.10) utilizes both the air-lift principle and mechanical raking of the solids and is extensively used in both the metallurgical and the chemical industry for continuous leaching and washing of finely divided solids. The central hollow shaft of the agitator acts as an air lift and at the same time revolves slowly. The arms attached to the bottom of the shaft rake the settled solids toward the center of the tank bottom, where they are lifted by the air lift through the shaft to the revolving launders attached to the top. The launders then distribute the elevated mixture of liquid and solid over the entire cross section of the tank. The rake arms may be lifted to free them of solids which may settle during a shutdown, and they are also provided with auxiliary air lines to assist in freeing them from settled solid. For unevenly sized solids, operation of the agitator may be so adjusted that coarse particles, which may require longer leaching time, remain in the tank for longer periods of time

Fig. 13.10 *Dorr agitator.*
(*The Dorr Co.*)

than the finer.   These agitators are regularly built in sizes ranging from 5 to 40 ft in diameter.

The average holding time in an agitated vessel may be calculated by dividing the vessel contents by the rate of flow into the vessel.   This may be done separately for solid and liquid, and the holding time for each will be different if the ratio of the amounts of one to the other in the vessel is different from that in the feed.   The average holding time of the solid must be sufficient to provide the leaching action

PLAN

SECTION ELEVATION

Fig. 13.11 *Dorr thickener.* (*The Dorr Co.*)

required.   Individual solid particles, of course, may short-circuit the tank, by which is meant that they may pass through in times much shorter than the calculated average, and this will lead to low stage efficiency.   Short circuiting may be eliminated by passing the solid-liquid mixture through a series of smaller agitated vessels, one after the other, the sum of whose average holding time is the necessary leach time.   This may be readily accomplished with gravity flow of the slurry by placing the individual tanks in the series at progressively lower levels.   Three vessels in series are usually sufficient to reduce short circuiting to a negligible amount.   It should be noted that, since liquid and solid pass through these vessels in parallel flow, the entire series is still equivalent to only a single stage.

The effluent from continuous agitators may be sent to a filter for separating liquid from solid, upon which the solid may be washed free of dissolved solids, or to a series of thickeners for countercurrent washing.

Thickeners

Thickeners are mechanical devices designed especially for continuously increasing the ratio of solid to liquid in a dilute suspension of finely sized particles by settling and decanting, producing a clear liquid and a thickened sludge as two separate products. Thickeners may be used prior to any ordinary filter in order to reduce filtering costs. Owing to the fact that both effluents are pumpable and consequently readily transported, however, thickeners are frequently used to wash leached solids and chemical precipitates free of adhering solution in a continuous multistage countercurrent arrangement, and it is in this application that they are of interest here.

A typical single-compartment thickener of the Dorr Company's design is shown in Fig. 13.11.   The thin slurry of liquid and suspended solids enters a large settling tank through a feed well at the top center, in such a manner as to avoid mixing of the slurry with the clear liquid at the top of the tank.   The solids settle from the liquid which fills the tank, and the settled sludge is gently directed toward the discharge cone at the bottom by four sets of plow blades or rakes.   These revolve slowly so as not to disturb the settled solid unduly.   The sludge is pumped from the discharge cone by means of a diaphragm pump.   The clear, supernatant liquid overflows into a launder built about the upper periphery of the tank.   Thickeners are built in sizes ranging from 6 to 325 ft in diameter, for handling granular as well as flocculent solids, and of varying detail design depending upon the size and service.   In order to reduce the ground-area requirements, several thickeners operating in parallel, and superimposed as in Fig. 13.12, may be used.   Such a device delivers a single sludge product.

The liquid content of the sludge is greatly dependent upon the nature of the solids and liquid and upon the time allowed for settling but in typical cases might be in the range 15 to 75 percent liquid.   The less liquid retained, the more efficient will be the leaching or washing process which is being carried on.

Continuous countercurrent decantation

Leaching equipment such as agitators or grinding mills may discharge their effluent into a cascade of thickeners for continuous countercurrent washing of the finely divided solids free of adhering solute.   The same type of cascade may also be used to wash the solids formed during chemical reactions, as in the manufacture of phosphoric acid, by treatment of phosphate rock with sulfuric acid, or of blanc fixe, by reaction of sulfuric acid and barium sulfide, or of lithopone.

A simple arrangement is shown in Fig. 13.13*a*.   The solids to be leached (or the reagents for a reaction), together with solution from the second thickener, are introduced into the leaching agitators at the left, and the strong solution thus produced is decanted from the solids by the first thickener.   The agitators together with the first thickener then constitute a single stage.   The sludge is passed through the cascade to be washed by the solvent in true countercurrent fashion, and the washed solids are discharged at the right.   There may, of course, be more or fewer than the four stages shown, and the agitators may be replaced by any continuous-leaching device, such as a grinding mill.   Many variations in the flow sheet are regularly made.   For example, the sludge from each stage may be "repulped," or vigorously beaten with the solvent, between stages in order to improve the washing efficiency.   Figure 13.13*b* shows an arrangement whereby the underflow from the first thickener is agitated with overflow from the third, for the purpose of bringing about the additional leaching possible with dilute solution.   The sludge from the final stage may be filtered, as shown, when the solid is valuable and is to be delivered reasonably dry or when the solute is valuable and solution adhering to the washed solids must be reduced to a minimum.   For successful operation of these plants, very carefully controlled rates of

Fig. 13.12   *Dorr balanced-tray thickener.*   (*The Dorr Co.*)

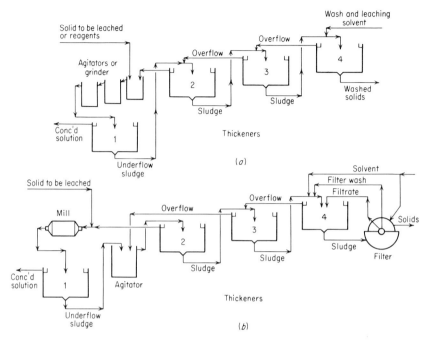

Fig. 13.13   *Continuous countercurrent decantation.* (a) *Simple flow sheet;* (b) *with inter-mediate agitation and filtration of washed solids.*

flow of both sludges and solution are necessary so as not to disturb the steady-state conditions prevailing.

For small decantation plants, where ground area may be limited, it is possible to obtain a countercurrent cascade of thickeners built in superimposed fashion into a single shell.

Continuous settling

The concentrations existing at the various levels of a continuous thickener under steady-state operation differ considerably from those found in batch settling.   The solid curve of Fig. 13.14 shows typical concentrations during normal operation,[5] and four clearly defined zones are found in the thickener corresponding to the various sections of the curve.   The feed slurry is diluted as it issues from the feed well of the thickener, and the bulk of the liquid passes upward to overflow into the launder about the thickener periphery.   The solid concentration in the top zone is negligible if the overflow is clear.   The solids and the remainder of the feed liquid move downward through the lower three zones and leave in the thickened underflow.   The solids concentration in the settling zone is much lower than that in the feed, owing to the dilution, but rises rapidly in the compression zone immediately below.   In the bottom zone, the action of the rake disturbs arched structures which the settling solids may form, the weight of the solids presses out the liquid, and the concentration rises to the value in the underflow.   If the feed rate to the thickener is increased, the concentration of solids in the settling zone rises and reaches a constant maximum value not related to the feed concentration when the settling capacity of this zone is exceeded.   The excess solids, which cannot

Fig. 13.14   *Continuous thickener characteristics.[5]   (Courtesy of Industrial and Engineering Chemistry.)*

settle, overflow with the liquid, as indicated by the broken curve of concentrations in Fig. 13.14 for this condition.

The concentration of solids in the underflow sludge for a given rate and concentration of feed may be increased by reducing the rate of withdrawal of sludge.   This increases the depth of the compression zone and increases the detention time of the solids within the thickener, although it is important not to raise the level of the compression zone to such an extent that solids appear in the overflow liquid.

The capacity of continuous thickeners, or their cross-sectional area required for a given solids throughput, can be roughly estimated from batch-settling tests.[8,27]   *Initial* settling velocities u for slurries of the solid at various initial uniform concentrations c are determined from the slopes of curves such as those of Fig. 13.8, covering the entire range of solids concentration to be dealt with (it is best to determine these curves for slurries made by suspending a given weight of solids in varying amounts of liquid by adding and subtracting liquid).   The flux of solids during settling, $G_s = cu$, is then plotted against c to produce a curve such as that of Fig. 13.15.   The tangent of smallest negative slope is then drawn to the curve from point ($G_s = 0$, $c = c_U$), where c_U is the desired underflow concentration, to intersect the ordinate at G_{SL}, the limiting solids flux.   The minimum required

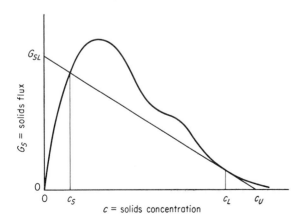

Fig. 13. 5   *Determination of thickener area from flux curve.*

thickener cross section for handling W lb/hr of solids is then

$$A = \frac{W}{G_{sL}} \tag{13.7}$$

Concentration c_L is that at the point of compression and c_s that in the settling zone.

Hydrocyclones

Hydrocyclones, similar to those used for size classification of solids (Fig. 13.16) may also be used as liquid-solid separators in place of thickeners in countercurrent washing of solids in a slurry.

Continuous leaching of coarse solids

Many ingenious devices have been used for moving the solids continuously through a leaching device so that countercurrent action may be obtained. With the exception of the classifiers, which are used principally in the metallurgical industries, these machines were principally developed for the special solids-handling problems arising in the leaching of sugar beets.and of vegetable seeds such as cottonseed, soybeans, and the like. Donald[7] has described many of the early devices used for sugar beets. Only the more important of the currently used machines can be described here.

Classifiers

Coarse solids may be leached, or more usually washed free of adhering solution or solute, in some types of machinery ordinarily used in the metallurgical industries

Fig. 13.16 *Hydrocyclone.*

Fig. 13.17   *Single Dorr classifier for washing coarse solids.*   (*The Dorr Co.*)

for classification according to particle size.   One such device is shown in Fig. 13.17. The solids are introduced into a tank, which is made with a sloping bottom and which is partly filled with the solvent.   The rakes, which are given a reciprocating and circular lifting motion by the driving mechanism, rake the solids upward along the bottom of the tank and out of the liquid.   In the upper part of the tank the solids are drained and discharged.   The liquid overflows at the deep end of the tank.   The solute concentration in the liquid is reasonably uniform throughout the tank owing to the agitation by the rakes, so that the apparatus produces a single-stage action.   Several classifiers may be placed in a cascade for continuous multistage countercurrent action, however, in which case they may be operated by a single drive mechanism.

Leaching of vegetable seeds

Cottonseeds, soybeans, linseeds (flaxseeds), peanuts, rice bran, castor beans, and many other similar products are regularly leached, or *extracted*, with organic solvents for removing the vegetable oils which they contain.   The seeds must usually be specially prepared for most advantageous leaching, and this may involve dehulling, precooking, adjustment of the moisture (water) content, and rolling or flaking. Sometimes a portion of the oil is first removed mechanically by expelling or expression. Leaching solvents are usually petroleum naphthas, for most oils a fraction corresponding closely to hexane; chlorinated hydrocarbons leave too toxic a residue for the leached meal to be used as an animal feed.   The oil-solvent solution, which usually contains a small amount of finely divided, suspended solids, is called "miscella" and the leached solids "marc." The various leaching devices are usually called "extractors" in this industry.

The *Rotocel*[1,19] is essentially a modification of the Shanks system wherein the leaching tanks are continuously moved, in that way permitting continuous introduction and discharge of the solids. Figure 13.18 is a schematic representation of the device, simplified to show the working principle. A circular rotor, containing 18 cells, each fitted with a hinged screen bottom for supporting the solids, slowly revolves above a stationary compartmented tank. As the rotor revolves, each cell passes in turn under a special device for feeding the prepared seeds and then under a series of sprays by which each is periodically drenched with solvent for leaching. After nearly one revolution, the leached contents of each cell are automatically dumped into one of the lower stationary compartments, from which they are continuously conveyed away. The solvent from each spray percolates downward through the solid and the supporting screen into the appropriate compartment of the lower tank, from which it is continuously pumped to the next spray. The leaching is countercurrent, and the strongest solution is taken from the freshest seeds. A number of ingenious mechanical devices are necessary for maintaining smooth operation, and the entire machine is enclosed in a vaportight housing to prevent escape of solvent vapors.

The *Kennedy* extractor,[26] a modern arrangement of which is indicated schematically in Fig. 13.19, is another stagewise device which has been in use since 1927, originally for leaching tannins from tanbark. It is now used for oilseed and other chemical leaching operations. The solids are leached in a series of tubs and are pushed from one to the next in the cascade by paddles, while the solvent flows in

Fig. 13.18 *Schematic arrangement of the Rotocel.*

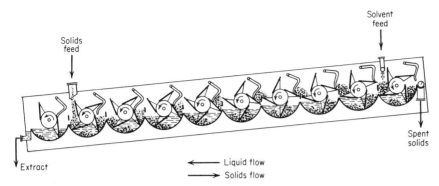

Fig. 13.19 *Kennedy extractor.* (*The Vulcan Copper and Supply Co.*)

Fig. 13.20 *Bollman extractor.*

Fig. 13.21   *Continuous horizontal extractor (schematic).*

countercurrent.   Perforations in the paddles permit drainage of the solids between stages, and the solids are scraped from each paddle as shown.   As many tubs may be placed in a cascade as are required.

The *Bollman* extractor[26] (Fig. 13.20) is one of several basket-type machines. Solids are conveyed in perforated baskets attached to a chain conveyor, down on the right and up on the left in the figure.   As they descend, they are leached in parallel flow by a dilute solvent-oil solution ("half miscella") pumped from the bottom of the vessel and sprayed over the baskets at the top.   The liquid percolates through the solids from basket to basket, collects at the bottom as the final strong solution of the oil ("full miscella"), and is removed.   On the ascent, the solids are leached counter-currently by a spray of fresh solvent to provide the half miscella.   A short drainage time is provided before the baskets are dumped at the top.   There are many variants of this device, the horizontal arrangement of Fig. 13.21, for example.   In still another variation[23] the baskets remain stationary while the filling, leaching, and dumping equipment revolves.

Continuous tilting-pan filters and horizontal filters[9] are also commonly used. Figure 13.22 shows a typical flow-sheet arrangement for a horizontal filter.   The filter, in the form of a circular wheel, is divided into a number of sectors and revolves in the horizontal plane.   Prepared seeds are slurried with solvent which has already been used for leaching, and the slurry sent to the filter.   The first filtrate is passed again through the filter cake to remove finely divided solids (polishing) prior to being discharged as miscella.   The principle is much the same as that of the Rotocel.   Horizontal moving screen-type belts[28] are also used for conveying the solids during leaching.

The recovery of solvent from both the miscella and the leached seeds or beans is an

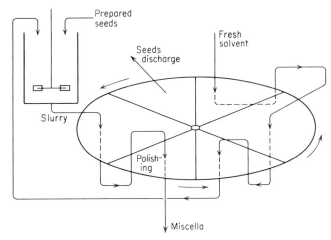

Fresh
solvent

Prepared
seeds

Seeds
discharge

Slurry

Polish-
ing

Miscella

Fig. 13.22   *Flow sheet for hor-
izontal-filter leaching.*

essential part of the vegetable-oil leaching process.   In a typical arrangement, the
filtered miscella is passed to an evaporator for removal of solvent, sometimes followed
by final stripping in a tray column, to produce the solvent-free oil.   The wet seeds are
steamed to remove residual solvent and air-cooled.   Vented gas from condensers may
be sent to an absorber to be scrubbed with petroleum white oil, and the resulting
solvent–white oil solution stripped to recover any solvent.

METHODS OF CALCULATION

It is important to be able to make an estimate of the extent of leaching which may be
obtained for a given procedure, i.e., to calculate the amount of soluble substance
leached from a solid, knowing the initial solute content of the solid, the number and
amount of washings with leaching solvent, the concentration of solute in the leaching
solvent, if any, and the method, whether batch or continuous countercurrent.   Alternatively, it may be necessary to compute the number of washings, or number of
stages, required to reduce the solute content of the solid to some specified value,
knowing the amount and solute concentration of the leaching solvent.

Stage efficiency

Consider a simple batch leaching operation, where the solid is leached with more than
enough solvent to dissolve all the soluble solute and where there is no preferential
adsorption of either solvent or solute by the solid.   If adequate time of contact of
solid and solvent is permitted, all the solute will be dissolved, and the mixture is then
a slurry of insoluble solid immersed in a solution of solute in the solvent.   The
insoluble phases are then separated physically by settling, filtration, or drainage, and
the entire operation constitutes one stage.   If the mechanical separation of liquid
and solid were perfect, there would be no solute associated with the solid leaving the

operation and complete separation of solute and insoluble solid would be accomplished with a single stage. This would be an ideal stage, of 100 percent stage efficiency. In practice, stage efficiencies are usually much less than this: (1) the solute may be incompletely dissolved because of inadequate contact time; (2) most certainly it will be impractical to make the liquid-solid mechanical separation perfect, and the solids leaving the stage will always retain some liquid and its associated dissolved solute. In cases where solute is adsorbed by the solid, even though equilibrium between the liquid and solid phases is obtained, imperfect settling or draining will result in lowered stage efficiency.

Practical equilibrium

In the general case, it will be easiest to make calculations graphically, as in other mass-transfer operations, and this will require graphical representation of equilibrium conditions. It is simplest to use practical equilibrium conditions which take stage efficiencies into account directly, either entirely or in part, much as was done in the case of gas absorption and distillation. In the simplest cases, we must deal with three-component systems containing pure solvent (A), insoluble carrier solid (B), and soluble solute (C). Computations and graphical representation can be made on triangular coordinates for any ternary system of this sort, and the details of this have been worked out.[10,25] Owing to frequent crowding of the construction into one corner of such a diagram, it is preferable to use a rectangular-coordinate system patterned after that used for fractional adsorption.

The concentration of insoluble solid B in any mixture or slurry will be expressed as N lb B/lb ($A + C$), whether the solid is wet with liquid solution or not. Solute C compositions will be expressed as weight fractions on a B-free basis: x = wt fraction C in the effluent solution from a stage (B-free basis), and y = wt fraction C in the solid or slurry (B-free basis). The value of y must include all solute C associated with the mixture, including that dissolved in adhering solution as well as undissolved or adsorbed solute. If the solid is dry, as it may be before leaching operations begin, N is the ratio of weights of insoluble to soluble substance, and $y = 1.0$. For pure solvent A, $N = 0$, $x = 0$.

The coordinate system then appears as in Fig. 13.23. Consider first a simple case of a mixture of insoluble solid from which all the solute has been leached, suspended in a solution of the solute in a solvent, as represented by point M_1 on the figure. The concentration of the clear solution is x, and the insoluble solid/solution ratio is N_{M1}. Let the insoluble solid be nonadsorbent. If this mixture is allowed to settle, as in a batch-settling tank, the clear liquid which may be drawn off will be represented by point R_1 and the remaining sludge will consist of the insoluble solid suspended in a small amount of the solution. The composition of the solution in the sludge will be the same as that of the clear liquid withdrawn, so that $y^* = x$. The concentration of solid B in the sludge N_{E1} will depend upon the length of time θ_1 which was allowed for settling, so that point E_1 then represents the slurry. Line E_1R_1 is a vertical tie line joining the points representing the two effluent streams, clear liquid and slurry. If the circumstances described were maintained in an actual leaching, points E_1 and R_1

x, y^* = weight fraction C, B- free basis   **Fig. 13.23** *Concentrations in leaching and washing.*

can be taken as the practical conditions of equilibrium for that leaching. Clearly if less time was allowed for settling, say θ_1', the sludge would be less concentrated in insoluble solids and might be represented by point E_1'. There will be some maximum value of N for the sludge, corresponding to its ultimate settled height, in accordance with the description of batch settling given earlier, but usually in practice insufficient time is allowed for this to be attained. Since the concentration of insoluble solid in a sludge settled for a fixed time depends upon the initial concentration in the slurry, a mixture M_2 settled for time θ_1 might result in a sludge corresponding to point E_2. If the solid does not settle to give an absolutely clear solution, if too much solution is withdrawn from the settled sludge so that a small amount of solid is carried with it, or if solid B dissolves to a small extent in the solution, the withdrawn solution would be represented by some point such as R_2, somewhat above the lower axis of the graph. Similar interpretations may be made for compositions obtained when wet solids are filtered or drained of solution rather than settled, or when continuously thickened.

The settling or thickening characteristics of a slurry depend, as shown earlier, upon the viscosity and relative density of the liquid in which the solid is suspended. Since these in turn depend upon the solution composition, it is possible to obtain experimental data showing the variation of compositions of thickened solids with composition of solution and to plot these on the diagram as practical equilibrium conditions. It is evident, however, that in every case they must be obtained under conditions of time, temperature, and concentrations identical with those pertaining in the plant or process for which the calculations are being made. In the case of drained beds of impervious solids, the equilibrium corresponding to the residual saturation after long-time drainage may be estimated by the methods of Illustration 13.1. Data for short-time drainage must be obtained experimentally.

In washing operations where the solute is already dissolved, uniform concentration throughout all the solution is rapidly attained, and reduced stage efficiency is most likely to be entirely the result of incomplete drainage or settling. In leaching an undissolved solute interspersed throughout the solid, on the other hand, lowered stage efficiency may be the result of inadequate time of contact as well as incomplete mechanical separation of liquid and solid.   In this case it is possible (but not necessary) to distinguish experimentally between the two effects by making measurements of the amount and composition of liquid retained on the solid after short and after long contact time and to use the latter to establish the equilibrium conditions.

Let us now examine a few of the types of equilibrium curves which may be encountered.   Figure 13.24a represents data which might be obtained for cases where solute C is infinitely soluble in solvent A, so that x and y may have values over the entire range from 0 to 1.0.   This would occur in the case of the system soybean oil (C)–soybean meal (B)–hexane (A), where the oil and hexane are infinitely soluble. The curve DFE represents the separated solid under conditions actually to be expected in practice, as discussed above.   Curve GHJ, the composition of the withdrawn solution, lies above the $N = 0$ axis, and in this case, therefore, either solid B is partly soluble in the solvent or an incompletely settled liquid has been withdrawn.   The tie lines such as line FH are not vertical, and this will result (1) if insufficient time of contact with leaching solvent to dissolve all solute is permitted, (2) if preferential adsorption of the solute occurs, or (3) if the solute is soluble in the solid B and distributes unequally between liquid and solid phases at equilibrium.   The data may be projected upon a plot of x vs. y, as in the manner of adsorption or liquid-extraction equilibria.

Figure 13.24b represents a case where no adsorption of solute occurs, so that withdrawn solution and solution associated with the solid have the same composition,

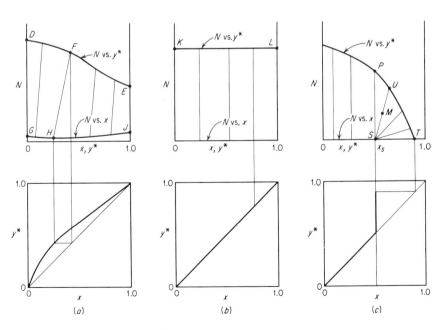

Fig. 13.24 *Typical equilibrium diagrams.*

and the tie lines are vertical. This results in an xy curve in the lower figure identical with the 45° line, and a distribution coefficient m, defined as y^*/x, equals unity. Line KL is horizontal, indicating that the solids are settled or drained to the same extent at all solute concentrations. It is possible to regulate the operation of continuous thickeners so that this will occur, and the conditions are known as "constant under-flow." The solution in this case contains no substance B, either dissolved or sus-pended. Figure 13.24c represents a case where solute C has a limited solubility x_S in solvent A. No clear solution stronger than x_S can be obtained, so that the tie lines joining slurry and saturated solution must converge, as shown. In this case any mixture M to the right of line PS will settle to give a clear saturated solution S and a slurry U whose composition depends on the position of M. Point T represents the composition of pure solid solute after drainage or settling of saturated solution. Since the tie lines to the left of PS are shown vertical, no adsorption occurs, and overflow liquids are clear. It will be appreciated that combinations of these various charac-teristics may appear in a diagram of an actual case.

Single-stage leaching

Consider the single real leaching or washing stage of Fig. 13.25. The circle represents the entire operation, including mixing of solid and leaching solvent and mechanical separation of the resulting insoluble phases by whatever means may be used. Weights of the various streams are expressed as pounds for a batch operation or as lb/hr [or lb/(hr)(sq ft)] for continuous flow. Since for most purposes the solid B is insoluble in the solvent and a clear liquid leach solution is obtained, the B discharged in the leached solids will be taken as the same as that in the solids to be leached. By defini-tion of N,

$$B = N_F F = E_1 N_1 \qquad (13.8)$$

A solute (C) balance,

$$F y_F + R_0 x_0 = E_1 y_1 + R_1 x_1 \qquad (13.9)$$

A solvent (A) balance,

$$F(1 - y_F) + R_0(1 - x_0) = E_1(1 - y_1) + R_1(1 - x_1) \qquad (13.10)$$

and a "solution" (solute + solvent) balance,

$$F + R_0 = E_1 + R_1 = M_1 \qquad (13.11)$$

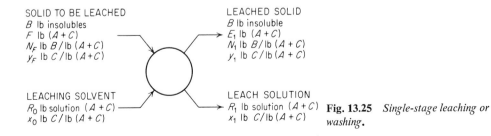

SOLID TO BE LEACHED
B lb insolubles
F lb $(A + C)$
N_F lb B/lb $(A + C)$
y_F lb C/lb $(A + C)$

LEACHED SOLID
B lb insoluble
E_1 lb $(A + C)$
N_1 lb B/lb $(A + C)$
y_1 lb C/lb $(A + C)$

LEACHING SOLVENT
R_0 lb solution $(A + C)$
x_0 lb C/lb $(A + C)$

LEACH SOLUTION
R_1 lb solution $(A + C)$
x_1 lb C/lb $(A + C)$

Fig. 13.25 *Single-stage leaching or washing.*

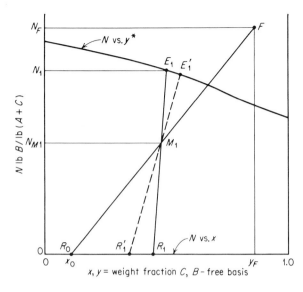

Fig. 13.26 *Single-stage leaching or washing.*

Mixing the solids to be leached and leaching solvent produces a mixture of B-free weight M_1 lb such that

$$N_{M1} = \frac{B}{F + R_0} = \frac{B}{M_1} \tag{13.12}$$

$$y_{M1} = \frac{y_F F + R_0 x_0}{F + R_0} \tag{13.13}$$

These relations may be shown on the coordinate system of Fig. 13.26. Point F represents the solids to be leached and R_0 the leaching solvent. Point M_1, representing the overall mixture, must fall on the straight line joining R_0 and F, in accordance with the characteristics of these diagrams described in Chap. 9. Points E_1 and R_1, representing the effluent streams, are located at opposite ends of the tie line through M_1, and their compositions may be read from the diagram. Equation (13.8) permits calculation of the weight of E_1 and Eq. (13.11) that of R_1. Modification to allow for the presence of B in the liquid withdrawn, necessitating an equilibrium diagram of the type shown in Fig. 13.24a, is readily made by analogy with the corresponding problem in liquid extraction.

If the equilibrium data of Fig. 13.26 were obtained experimentally after long contact time of solid and liquid and therefore represent inefficiency of mechanical separation of liquid and solid only, then in a real stage there may be an additional inefficiency owing to short time of contact. The effluent streams may then be represented by points E_1' and R_1' on the figure, and a stage efficiency $(y_F - y_1')/(y_F - y_1)$ may be ascribed to this. In case the equilibrium curve was obtained under conditions of contact time corresponding to the actual leaching, the tie line $E_1 R_1$ will give directly the effluent composition.

Multistage crosscurrent leaching

By contacting the leached solids with a fresh batch of leaching solvent, additional solute may be dissolved or washed away from the insoluble material. The calculations for additional stages are merely repetitions of the procedure for a single stage, with the leached solids from any stage becoming the feed solids to the next. Equations (13.8) to (13.13) apply, with only obvious changes in the subscripts to indicate the additional stages. When the number of stages for reducing the solute content of a solute to some specified value must be determined, it must be recalled that we are dealing with real stages, owing to the use of "practical" equilibrium data, and that therefore the number found must be integral. This may require adjustment by trial of either the amount of solute to be leached or the amount and apportioning of solvent to the stages.

Illustration 13.2. Caustic soda is being made by treatment of slaked lime, $Ca(OH)_2$, with a solution of sodium carbonate. The resulting slurry consists of particles of calcium carbonate, $CaCO_3$, suspended in a 10% solution of sodium hydroxide, NaOH, 0.125 lb suspended solid/lb solution. This is settled, the clear sodium hydroxide solution withdrawn and replaced by an equal weight of water, and the mixture thoroughly agitated. After repetition of this procedure (a total of two fresh-water washes), what fraction of the original NaOH in the slurry remains unrecovered and therefore lost in the sludge? The settling characteristics of the slurry, determined under conditions representing the practice to be followed in the process [Armstrong and Kammermeyer, *Ind. Eng. Chem.*, **34**, 1228 (1942)], show adsorption of the solute on the solid.

x = wt fraction NaOH in clear soln	N = lb $CaCO_3$/lb soln in settled sludge	y^* = wt fraction NaOH in soln of the settled sludge
0.0900	0.495	0.0917
0.0700	0.525	0.0762
0.0473	0.568	0.0608
0.0330	0.600	0.0452
0.0208	0.620	0.0295
0.01187	0.650	0.0204
0.00710	0.659	0.01435
0.00450	0.666	0.01015

Solution. The equilibrium data are plotted in Fig. 13.27. *Basis:* 1 lb solution in the original mixture, containing 0.1 lb NaOH (C) and 0.9 lb H_2O (A). $B = 0.125$ lb $CaCO_3$.

The original mixture corresponds to M_1 with $N_{M1} = 0.125$ lb $CaCO_3$/lb soln, $y_{M1} = 0.10$ lb NaOH/lb soln. M_1 is plotted on the figure, and the tie line through this point is drawn. At point E_1 representing the settled sludge, $N_1 = 0.47$, $y_1 = 0.100$.

Eq. (13.8):
$$E_1 = \frac{B}{N_1} = \frac{0.125}{0.47} = 0.266 \text{ lb soln in sludge}$$

$$1 - 0.266 = 0.734 \text{ lb clear soln withdrawn}$$

Stage 2. $R_0 = 0.734$ lb water added, $x_0 = 0$ lb NaOH/lb soln. Eq. (13.11) adapted to this stage:

$$M_2 = E_1 + R_0 = E_2 + R_2$$

$$M_2 = 0.266 + 0.734 = 1.0 \text{ lb liquid}$$

Fig. 13.27   *Solution to Illustration* 13.2.

Eq. (13.12): $$N_{M2} = \frac{B}{E_1 + R_0} = \frac{B}{M_2} = \frac{0.125}{1.0} = 0.125$$

M_2 is located on line R_0E_1 at this value of N, and the tie line through M_2 is drawn.   At E_2, $N_2 =$ 0.62, $y_2 = 0.035$.

Eq. (13.8): $$E_2 = \frac{B}{N_2} = \frac{0.125}{0.62} = 0.202 \text{ lb}$$

$$1 - 0.202 = 0.789 \text{ lb soln withdrawn}$$

Stage 3. $R_0 = 0.798$ lb water added, $x_0 = 0$.

Eq. (13.11): $$M_3 = E_2 + R_0 = 0.202 + 0.798 = 1.0$$

$$N_{M3} = \frac{B}{M_3} = \frac{0.125}{1} = 0.125$$

Tie line E_3R_3 is located through M_3 as in the case of stage 2, and, at E_3, $N_3 = 0.662$, $y_3 = 0.012$. By Eq. (13.8), $E_3 = B/N_3 = 0.125/0.662 = 0.189$ lb soln in final sludge. $E_3y_3 = 0.189(0.012) = 0.00227$ lb NaOH in sludge, or $(0.00227/0.1)100 = 2.27\%$ of original.

The process permits an appreciable loss and produces three solutions, two of which (R_2 and R_3) are quite dilute.   It should be compared with the countercurrent washing operation of Illustration 13.3.

Multistage countercurrent leaching

A general flow sheet for either leaching or washing is shown in Fig. 13.28.   Operation must necessarily be continuous for steady-state conditions to prevail, although leaching according to the Shanks system will approach the steady state after a large number

SOLIDS TO BE
LEACHED

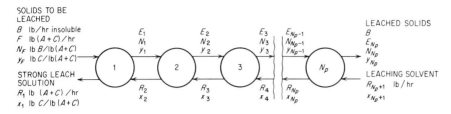

Fig. 13.28 *Multistage countercurrent leaching or washing.*

of cycles have been worked through. In the flow sheet shown, it is assumed that solid B is insoluble and is not lost in the clear solution, but the procedure outlined below is readily modified to take care of cases where this may not be true.†

A solvent balance for the entire plant is

$$F + R_{Np+1} = R_1 + E_{Np} = M \tag{13.14}$$

and a "solution" $(A + C)$ balance,

$$Fy_F + R_{Np+1}x_{Np+1} = R_1x_1 + E_{Np}y_{Np} = My_M \tag{13.15}$$

M represents the hypothetical B-free mixture obtained by mixing solids to be leached and leaching solvent. Refer to Fig. 13.29, the operating diagram for the plant. The coordinates of point M are

$$N_M = \frac{B}{F + R_{Np+1}} \tag{13.16}$$

$$y_M = \frac{Fy_F + R_{Np+1}x_{Np+1}}{F + R_{Np+1}} \tag{13.17}$$

Points E_{Np} and R_1, representing the effluents from the cascade, must lie on a line passing through M, and E_{Np} will be on the "practical" equilibrium curve. Equation (13.14) may be rearranged to read

$$F - R_1 = E_{Np} - R_{Np+1} = \Delta_R \tag{13.18}$$

Similarly, a solution balance about any number of stages, such as the first three, may be arranged in this form,

$$F - R_1 = E_3 - R_4 = \Delta_R \tag{13.19}$$

Δ_R represents the constant difference in flow $E - R$ (usually a negative quantity) between each stage. On Fig. 13.29, it can be represented by the intersection of lines FR_1 and $E_{Np}R_{Np+1}$ extended, in accordance with the characteristics of these coordinates. Since the effluents from each stage are joined by the practical tie line for the

† See Illustration 13.4, for example.

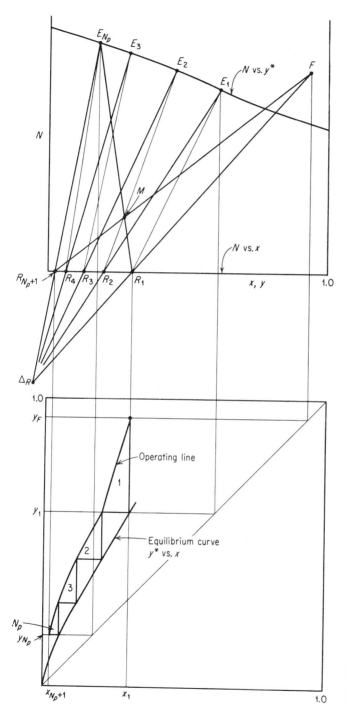

Fig. 13.29 *Multistage countercurrent leaching or washing.*

particular conditions which prevail, E_1 is found at the end of the tie line through R_1. A line from E_1 to Δ_R provides R_2, and so forth.   Alternatively the stage constructions may be made on the x, y coordinates in the lower part of the figure after first locating the operating line.   This may be done by drawing random lines from point Δ_R and projecting their intersections with the equilibrium diagram to the lower curve in the usual manner.   The usual staircase construction then establishes the number of stages.   The stages are real rather than ideal, the practical equilibrium data having already taken into account the stage efficiency, and hence there must be an integral number.   Especially when the number of stages required is the unknown quantity, some trial-and-error adjustment of the concentrations of the effluents or amount of solvent will be required to obtain an integral number.

If the equilibrium curve of Fig. 13.29 represents inefficiency of mechanical separation of liquid and solid only, and not that resulting from short contact time of solvent and solid, the effect of the latter, if known, may be taken care of by drawing a new equilibrium curve on the x, y coordinates. This should be located between the equilibrium curve shown and the operating line, at a fractional distance from the operating line corresponding to the stage efficiency due to the short contact time, in the manner used earlier in gas absorption and distillation.

In the special case where "constant underflow," or constant value of N for all sludges, pertains, the operating line on the xy diagram is straight and of constant slope R/E.   If in addition the practical equilibrium curve on this plot is straight, so that $m = y*/x = $ const, then Eqs. (5.54) and (5.55) apply.   Adapting the former to the present situation,

$$\frac{y_F - y_{Np}}{y_F - mx_{Np+1}} = \frac{(R/mE)^{Np+1} - R/mE}{(R/mE)^{Np+1} - 1} \tag{13.20}$$

Figure 5.16 may be used to solve this rapidly, using $(y_{Np} - mx_{Np+1})/(y_F - mx_{Np+1})$ as ordinate, R/mE as parameter.   If in addition the tie lines of the equilibrium diagram are vertical, $m = 1.0$.   The form of the equation shown is that which is applicable when the value of F for the feed solids is the same as E, so that R/E is constant for all stages, including the first.   It frequently may happen, especially in the case where dry solids comprise the feed, that the ratio R_1/E_1 for stage 1 will be different from that pertaining to the rest of the cascade.   In this case Eq. (13.20) or Fig. 5.16 should be applied to that part of the cascade excluding the first stage, by substitution of y_1 for y_F and N_p for $N_p + 1$.   In general, the equation or chart may be applied to any part of the cascade where operating line and equilibrium line are both straight, and this may be particularly useful for cases where the solute concentration in the leached solution is very small.   Just as in the case of liquid extraction and gas absorption, there is an economic optimum combination of treating solvent/solids ratio, number of stages, and extent of leaching.[3]

Illustration 13.3. Sodium hydroxide, NaOH, is to be made at the rate of 400 lb/hr (dry weight) by reaction of soda ash, Na_2CO_3, with slaked lime, $Ca(OH)_2$, using a flow sheet of the type shown in Fig. 13.13a.   The reagents will be used in stoichiometric proportions, and for simplicity it will be assumed that reaction is complete. Pure water is to be used to wash the calcium carbonate, $CaCO_3$, precipitate, and it is desired to produce as overflow from the first thickener a solution containing 10% NaOH. It will be assumed that the settling data of Illustration 13.2 apply.

a. If three thickeners are used, determine the amount of wash water required and the percentage of the hydroxide lost in the discharged sludge.

b. How many thickeners would be required to reduce the loss to at least 0.1% of that made?

Solution. a. Mol wt of $CaCO_3$ (B) = 100, of NaOH (C) = 40. NaOH produced = 400 lb/hr or $^{400}/_{40}$ = 10 lb moles/hr. $CaCO_3$ produced = $^{10}/_2$ = 5.0 lb moles/hr or 5.0(100) = 500 lb/hr = B. The water required is that leaving in the strong solution plus that in the final sludge. The amount in the final sludge, according to the settling data, depends upon the NaOH concentration in the final sludge, which is not known. After a trial calculation, it is assumed that the solution in the final sludge will contain 0.01 wt fraction NaOH (y_3 = 0.01), and the settling data indicate N_3 = 0.666 lb $CaCO_3$/lb soln in the final sludge.

$$E = \frac{B}{N_3} = \frac{500}{0.666} = 750 \text{ lb/hr soln lost}$$

$$\text{NaOH lost} = E_3 y_3 = 750(0.01) = 7.50 \text{ lb/hr}$$

$$\text{Water in sludge} = 750 - 7.5 = 742.5 \text{ lb/hr}$$

$$\text{NaOH in overflow} = 400 - 7.5 = 392.5 \text{ lb/hr}$$

$$x_1 = 0.1 \text{ wt fraction NaOH in overflow}$$

$$R_1 = \frac{392.5}{0.1} = 3{,}925 \text{ lb overflow or strong soln/hr}$$

$$\text{Water in } R_1 = 3{,}925 - 392.5 = 3{,}532.5 \text{ lb/hr}$$

$$\text{Fresh water required} = R_{Np+1} = 3{,}532.5 + 742.5 = 4{,}275 \text{ lb/hr}$$

For purposes of calculation, it may be imagined that the agitators are not present in the flow sheet and that the first thickener is fed with a dry mixture of the reaction products, $CaCO_3$ and NaOH, together with overflow from the second thickener.

$$F = 400 \text{ lb NaOH/hr} \qquad N_F = \frac{B}{F} = \frac{500}{400} = 1.25 \text{ lb } CaCO_3/\text{lb NaOH}$$

$$y_F = 1.0 \text{ wt fraction NaOH in the dry solid, } CaCO_3\text{-free basis}$$

Plot points R_1, E_3, R_{Np+1}, and F on Fig. 13.30, and locate the difference point Δ_R at the intersection of lines FR_1 and $E_3 R_{Np+1}$ extended. The coordinates of point Δ_R are $N_{\Delta R} = -0.1419$, $y_{\Delta R} = -0.00213$. (These may be determined analytically, if desired, by simultaneous solution of the equations representing the intersecting lines.) Further computations must be done on an enlarged section of the equilibrium diagram (Fig. 13.31). Point Δ_R is plotted and the stages stepped off in the usual manner. The construction may be projected on to the xy diagram as shown, if desired. Three stages produce a value $y_3 = 0.01$, so that the assumed value of y_3 is correct. The NaOH lost in the sludge = (7.5/400)100 = 1.87% of that made.

b. $\qquad\qquad\qquad$ NaOH lost = 0.001(400) = 0.4 lb/hr

$$\text{Lb } CaCO_3/\text{lb NaOH in final sludge} = \frac{500}{0.4} = 1{,}250 = \frac{N_{Np}}{y_{Np}}$$

In order to determine the liquid content of the final sludge, convert the equilibrium data for dilute

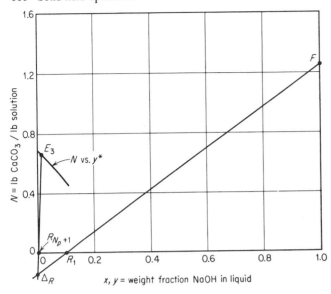

Fig. 13.30 *Solution to Il-lustration 13.3.*

mixtures into the following form:

N	0.659	0.666	0.677	0.679	0.680
y^*	0.01435	0.01015	0.002†	0.001†	0.0005†
N/y^*	45.6	65.6	338	679	1,360

† Estimated values.

By interpolation for $N/y^* = 1{,}250$, $N_{Np} = 0.680$ lb $CaCO_3$/lb soln, and $y_{Np} = 0.680/1{,}250 = 0.000544$ wt fraction NaOH in the liquid of the final sludge.

$$E_{Np} = \frac{B}{N_{Np}} = \frac{500}{0.680} = 735 \text{ lb/hr}$$

Water in $E_{Np} = 735 - 0.4 = 734.6$ lb/hr
NaOH in overflow $= 400 - 0.4 = 399.6$ lb/hr

$$R_1 = \frac{399.6}{0.1} = 3{,}996 \text{ lb/hr}$$

Water in $R_1 = 3{,}996 - 399.6 = 3{,}596$ lb/hr
Fresh water $= R_{Np+1} = 3{,}596 + 734.6 = 4{,}331$ lb/hr

On the operating diagram (Fig. 13.32) point Δ_R is located in the same way as before, and the stages are constructed in the usual fashion. It becomes impractical to continue graphical construction beyond the fourth stage unless considerable magnification of the chart is made, but computations beyond this point may be made with the help of Fig. 5.16. Beyond the fourth stage, the ratio of overflow to liquid in the sludge becomes substantially constant and equal to $R_{Np+1}/E_{Np} = 4{,}331/735 = 5.90 = R/E$. This is the initial slope of the operating line on the lower part of Fig. 13.32. The slope of the equilibrium curve at these low concentrations is also substantially constant,

$m = y^*/x = 0.01015/0.00450 = 2.26$, and $R/mE = 5.90/2.26 = 2.61$. $x_{Np+1} = 0$, and $y_4 = 0.007$. Therefore $(y_{Np} - mx_{Np+1})/(y_4 - mx_{Np+1}) = 0.000544/0.007 = 0.0777$. From Fig. 5.16, an additional 2.3 stages beyond the 4 computed graphically are required.

An additional two stages (six thickeners) would make $y_{Np}/y_4 = 0.099$, or $y_{Np} = 0.099(0.007) = 0.000693$, corresponding to 0.51 lb NaOH lost/hr, while an additional three stages (seven thickeners) would make $y_{Np} = 0.0365(0.007) = 0.000255$, corresponding to 0.187 lb NaOH lost/hr.

It must be emphasized that the cost of these numbers of thickeners probably could not be justified when balanced against the value of the lost NaOH. The very low NaOH loss was specified in order to demonstrate the computation methods.

Fig. 13.31 *Solution to Illustration* 13.3.

Fig. 13.32 *Solution to Illustration* 13.3.

Illustration 13.4. Flaked soybeans are to be leached with hexane to remove the soybean oil. A 12-in.-thick layer of the flakes (0.009 in. flake thickness) will be fed onto a slowly moving, perforated endless belt which passes under a series of continuously operating sprays.[28] As the solid passes under each spray, it is showered with liquid which percolates through the bed, collects in a trough below the belt, and is recycled by a pump to the spray. The spacing of the sprays is such that the solid is permitted to drain 6 min before it reaches the next spray. The solvent also passes from trough to trough in a direction countercurrent to that of the moving belt, so that a truly continuous countercurrent stagewise operation is maintained with each spraying and draining constituting one stage. Experiments[28] show that the flakes retain solution after 6 min drain time to an extent depending upon the oil content of the solution, as follows:

Wt % oil in soln	0	20	30
Lb soln retained/lb insoluble solid	0.58	0.66	0.70

It will be assumed that the retained solution contains the only oil in the drained flakes.

The soybean flakes enter containing 20% oil and are to be leached to 0.5% oil (on a solvent-free basis). The net forward flow of solvent is to be 1.0 lb hexane introduced as fresh solvent per pound flakes, and the fresh solvent is free of oil. The solvent draining from the flakes is generally free of solid except in the first stage: the rich miscella contains 10% of the insoluble solid in the feed as a suspended solid, which falls through the perforations of the belt during loading. How many stages are required?

Solution. The tie lines are vertical, $x = y^*$. Rearrange the drainage data as follows:

Percent oil in soln $= 100y^*$	$\dfrac{\text{Lb soln retained}}{\text{Lb insoluble solid}} = \dfrac{1}{N}$	N	$\dfrac{\text{Lb oil}}{\text{Lb insoluble solid}} = \dfrac{y^*}{N}$
0	0.58	1.725	0
20	0.66	1.515	0.132
30	0.70	1.429	0.210

Basis: 1 lb flakes introduced.

Soybean feed. $B = 0.8$ lb insoluble; $F = 0.2$ lb oil; $N_F = 0.8/0.2 = 4.0$ lb insoluble solid/lb oil; $y_F = 1.0$ wt fraction oil, solid-free basis.

Solvent. $R_{Np+1} = 1.0$ lb hexane; $x_{Np+1} = 0$ wt fraction oil.

Leached solids. Lb oil/lb insoluble solid $= 0.005/0.995 = 0.00503$. By interpolation in the equilibrium data, $N_{Np} = 1.718$ lb solid/lb soln.

$$\text{Insoluble solid lost to miscella} = 0.8(0.1) = 0.08 \text{ lb}$$

$$\text{Insoluble solid in leached solids} = 0.8(0.9) = 0.72 \text{ lb}$$

$$E_{Np} = \frac{0.72}{1.718} = 0.420 \text{ lb soln retained}$$

$$\text{Lb oil retained} = 0.00503(0.72) = 0.00362 \text{ lb}$$

$$\text{Lb hexane retained} = 0.420 - 0.00362 = 0.416 \text{ lb}$$

$$y_{Np} = \frac{0.00362}{0.420} = 0.0086 \text{ wt fraction oil in retained liquid}$$

Miscella. Hexane $= 1 - 0.416 = 0.584$ lb; oil $= 0.2 - 0.00362 = 0.196$ lb. $R_1 = 0.584 + 0.196 = 0.780$ lb clear miscella; $x_1 = 0.196/0.780 = 0.252$ wt fraction oil in liquid. $N_{R1} = 0.08/0.780 = 0.1027$ lb insoluble solid/lb soln.

The operating diagram is shown in Fig. 13.33. Point R_1 represents the cloudy miscella and is therefore displaced from the axis of the graph at N_{R1}. Point Δ_R is located as usual and the stages determined with the $N = 0$ axis for all stages but the first. Between four and five stages are necessary. Adjustment of the amount of solvent or the amount of unextracted oil, by trial, will provide an integral number.

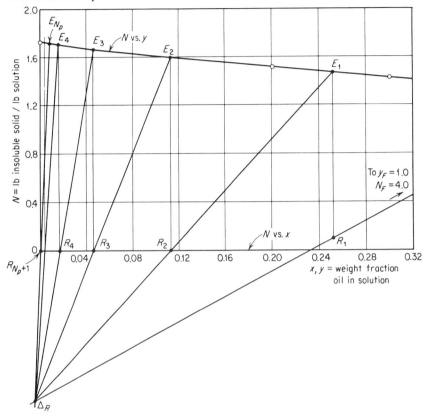

Fig. 13.33 *Solution to Illustration* 13.4.

Rate of Leaching

The many diverse phenomena encountered in the practice of leaching make it impossible to apply a single theory to explain the leaching action. As has been shown, leaching may involve simple washing of the solution from the surface of a solid, or dissolving of a solute from a matrix of insoluble matter, osmosis, and possibly other mechanisms. Our knowledge of these is very limited. The washing of a solution from the surface of impervious solid particles may be expected to be very rapid, requiring only the blending of solution and solvent, and stage efficiencies are then quite likely to be governed entirely by the completeness of the mechanical separation of liquid from solid.

Leaching of a solute from the internal parts of a solid, on the other hand, will be relatively slow. Solids made up of a skeletal structure of insoluble substance, with the pores impregnated with the solute, can be described in terms of a pore-shape factor, as outlined in Chap. 4. The factor is a function of the solid, independent of the nature of the solute and solvent, and is a measure of the complexity of the path through which the solute diffuses. In the case of natural products such as plant materials, the complexity of the structure may make application of these methods difficult. In the case of sugar-beet cossettes,[32] for example, about one-fifth of the cells are ruptured in producing the cossettes, and leaching of sugar from these cells is probably a simple washing process. The remaining cells lose sugar by a diffusion process, and the combination of events produces curves on coordinates such as Fig. 4.2, which deviate considerably from those developed from simple diffusion with constant effective diffusivity or pore-shape factor. Many mechanisms have been considered in an attempt to explain such observations.[2] In another example, wood will show different rates of leaching of an impregnating solute depending upon whether diffusion is in a direction parallel to or across the grain of the wood.[20] If solutes must pass through cell walls by dialysis, it may not be possible to apply the concepts at all. The rates of diffusion of soybean oil from soybean flakes, which do not permit simple interpretation, have been attributed to the presence of several types of structures in the matrix[16] as well as to the presence of a slowly dissolving constituent in the oil.[11,15] Whole seeds cannot be leached; rolling and flaking evidently crushes cell walls and opens up passageways for penetration of the solvent by capillary action.[21,22] The fact that rate of leaching increases with increased surface tension of the solvent-oil solutions and the fact that even for flaked seeds there is a residue of unextractable oil which increases with flake thickness support this view. That the leached oil is composed of several different substances is evident from the different properties of oil obtained after short and long leaching times. A method of dealing with such differently leached substances has been suggested,[12] but these examples serve at least to indicate the complexity of many practical leaching processes. Very little study has been given most of them.

When solids such as those described above are immersed in leaching solvents, it is reasonable to suppose that the resistance to mass transfer within the solid itself is likely to be the controlling resistance and that of the liquid surrounding the solid to be quite minor.[32] In such cases increasing the rate of movement of liquid past the solid surface will not appreciably influence the rate of leaching.

NOTATION FOR CHAPTER 13

a = a constant
a_p = surface of particles, sq ft/cu ft of packed space
A = pure leaching solvent
= thickener cross section, Eq. (13.7), sq. ft
b = a constant
B = insoluble carrier solid, lb (in a batch operation) or lb/hr or lb/(hr)(sq ft)(in a continuous operation)
c = solids concentration in a slurry, lb/cu ft
c_U = underflow solids concentration, lb/cu ft
C = soluble solute
d_p = diameter of a sphere of same surface/volume ratio as a particle, ft
E = solvent and solute associated with the leached solids, lb (in a batch operation) or lb/hr or lb/(hr)(sq ft)(in a continuous operation)

F = solute and solvent in solids to be leached, lb (in a batch operation) or lb/hr or lb/(hr)(sq ft)(in a continuous operation)

g = acceleration due to gravity, ft/hr²

g_c = conversion factor, 4.17(10⁸) lb mass (ft)/(lb force)(hr)²

G = mass velocity, lb/(hr)(sq ft)

G_S = flux of settling solids, lb/(hr)(sq ft)

G_{SL} = limiting solids flux, lb/(hr)(sq ft)

K = permeability, cu ft/hr²

m = slope of equilibrium curve, $dy*/dx$, dimensionless

M = solvent and solute content of a slurry or mixture, lb (in a batch operation) or lb/hr or lb/(hr)(sq ft)(in a continuous operation)

N = ratio of weight of insoluble solid to weight of solute and solvent, lb B/lb $(A + C)$

N_p = number of stages, dimensionless

ΔP = pressure drop, lb/sq ft

R = solvent and solute in a leaching solution, lb (in a batch operation) or lb/hr or lb/(hr)(sq ft)(in a continuous operation)

S = residual saturation of a bed of solids, fraction of void volume occupied by liquid, dimensionless

S_0 = residual saturation in the upper part of a packed bed, dimensionless

S_{av} = average residual saturation, dimensionless

u = initial setting rate, ft/hr

w = concentration of insoluble solids in a slurry, weight fraction

W = rate of solids flow, lb/hr

x = concentration of solute in solution, weight fraction, B-free basis

y = concentration of solute in a mixture, weight fraction, B-free basis

$y*$ = value of y at equilibrium

Z = height of a percolation bed or of a settling solid, ft

Z_D = drain height, ft

Z_0 = initial height of a slurry, ft

Z_∞ = ultimate height of settled solids, ft

ϵ = fractional void volume of a packed bed, dimensionless

θ = time, hr

μ_L = liquid viscosity, lb mass/(ft)(hr)

ρ_L = liquid density, lb mass/cu ft

σ = surface tension, lb force/ft = (dynes/cm)(6.89)(10⁻⁵)

Subscripts:

F = feed; solids to be leached

S = saturated

1, 2, etc. = stage 1, stage 2, etc.

REFERENCES

1. Anderson, E. T., and K. McCubbin: *J. Am. Oil Chemists' Soc.*, **31**, 475 (1954).

2. Bruniche-Olsen, H.: "Solid-Liquid Extraction," NYT Nordisk Forlag Arnold Busch Copenhagen, 1962.

3. Colman, J. E.: *Chem. Eng.*, **70**, Mar. 4, 93 (1963).

4. Comings, E. W.: *Ind. Eng. Chem.*, **32**, 663 (1940).

5. Comings, E. W., C. E. Pruiss, and C. De Bord: *Ind. Eng. Chem.*, **46**, 1164 (1954).

6. Dombrowski, H. S., and L. E. Brownell: *Ind. Eng. Chem.*, **46**, 1267 (1954).

7. Donald, M. B.: *Trans. Inst. Chem. Engrs.* (*London*), **15**, 77 (1937).

8. Fitch, B.: *Ind. Eng. Chem.*, **58**(10), 18 (1966).

9. Gastrock, E. A., et al.: *Ind. Eng. Chem.*, **49**, 921, 930 (1957); *J. Am. Oil Chemists' Soc.*, **32**, 160 (1955).

10. George, W. J.: *Chem. Eng.*, **66**, Feb. 9, 111 (1959).

11. Goss, W. H.: *Oil and Soap*, **23**, 348 (1946).

12. Hassett, N. J.: *Brit. Chem. Eng.*, **3**, 66, 182 (1958).

13. Havighorst, C. R.: *Chem. Eng.*, **71**, Mar. 30, 72 (1964).

14. Kammermeyer, K.: *Ind. Eng. Chem.*, **33**, 1484 (1941).

15. Karnofsky, G.: *J. Am. Oil Chemists' Soc.*, **26**, 564 (1949).

16. King, C. O., D. L. Katz, and J. C. Brier: *Trans. AIChE*, **40**, 533 (1944).

17. Lamont, A. G. W.: *Can. J. Chem. Eng.*, **36**, 153 (1958).

18. Liddell, D. M.: "Handbook of Non-ferrous Metallurgy," 2d ed., McGraw-Hill Book Company, New York, 1945.

19. McCubbins, K., and G. J. Ritz: *Chem. Ind. (London)*, **66**, 354 (1950).

20. Osburn, J. Q., and D. L. Katz: *Trans. AIChE*, **40**, 511 (1944).

21. Othmer, D. F., and J. C. Agarwal: *Chem. Eng. Progr.*, **51**, 372 (1955).

22. Othmer, D. F., and W. A. Jaatinen: *Ind. Eng. Chem.*, **51**, 543 (1959).

23. Price, F. C.: *Chem. Eng.*, **67**, July 25, 84 (1960).

24. Rushton, J. H., and L. H. Maloney: *J. Metals*, **6**, *AIME Trans.*, **200**, 1199 (1954).

25. Sattler-Dornbacher, E.: *Chem.-Ing.-Tech.*, **30**, 14 (1958).

26. Scofield, E. P.: *Chem. Eng.*, **58**(1), 127 (1951).

27. Shannon, P. T., E. M. Tory, et al.: *Ind. Eng. Chem.*, **57**(2), 18 (1965); *Ind. Eng. Chem. Fundamentals*, **2**, 203 (1963); **3**, 184, 250 (1964); **4**, 195, 367 (1965).

28. Smith, C. T.: *J. Am. Oil Chemists' Soc.*, **28**, 274 (1951).

29. Van Arsdale, G. D.: "Hydrometallurgy of Base Metals," McGraw-Hill Book Company, New York, 1953.

30. Weed, R. C.: *Mining Eng.*, **8**, 721 (1956).

31. Work, L. T., and A. S. Kohler: *Ind. Eng. Chem.*, **32**, 1329 (1940).

32. Yang, H. H., and J. C. Brier: *AIChE J.*, **4**, 453 (1958).

PROBLEMS

13.1. A 3-ft-diameter tank fitted with a false bottom and canvas filter is partly filled with 2,000 lb (dry weight) of sea sand wet with seawater. The sand is allowed to drain until it stops dripping, whereupon 1,500 lb fresh water is added and recirculated to reach a uniform salt concentration. The sand is again allowed to drain until dripping stops and is then removed from the tank and dried. Estimate the salt content of the dried sand.

The sand particles have an average particle size $d_p = 0.0013$ ft, a particle density 166 lb/cu ft, and a bulk density 93 lb (dry weight)/cu ft. Seawater contains 3.5% salt; its density is 63.6 lb/cu ft and surface tension 73.6 dynes/cm. The surface tension of water is 72.8 dynes/cm.

13.2. Derive expressions for the coordinates of point $\Delta_R(y_{\Delta R}, N_{\Delta R})$ (Fig. 13.29), and check the results by determining the numerical values in the case of Illustration 13.3a.

13.3. In order to eliminate the solids in the final miscella of Illustration 13.4, it is decided to pass liquid from stage 3 to stage 1, where the liquid will contact fresh solids. The drained liquid from stage 1, containing the suspended solids, will then be passed to stage 2, where it is filtered by passage of the liquid through the bed of solids in this stage. The final miscella is then withdrawn as a clear solution from stage 2. How many stages will then be required for the same solvent/seeds ratio and the same oil concentration in the discharged solids? **Ans.:** 6.

13.4. A mineral containing 20% elemental sulfur is to be leached with hot gas oil, in which the sulfur is soluble to the extent of 10% by weight. The solvent will be repeatedly pumped over the batch of ground mineral, using 1.5 lb fresh solvent/lb mineral. After no further solution of sulfur is obtained, the liquid will be drained and replaced with a fresh batch of 1.5 lb oil/lb original mineral, and the operation repeated. On drainage, the solid materials retain the solution to the extent of one-tenth the weight of undissolved solid (sulfur and gangue). No preferential adsorption takes place.

   a. Calculate the equilibrium data, and plot them in the usual manner.

   b. Determine the amount of sulfur unextracted and the sulfur concentration of the composited leach liquors.

   c. Repeat *b* for the case where a two-stage Shanks system is used, with 3 lb fresh solvent/lb unleached solid. Assume steady state has been reached.

   13.5. Aluminum sulfate, $Al_2(SO_4)_3$, is to be produced by action of sulfuric acid, H_2SO_4, on bauxite in a series of agitators, with a cascade of continuous thickeners to wash the insoluble mud free of aluminum sulfate.

$$Al_2O_3 + 3H_2SO_4 \rightarrow Al_2(SO_4)_3 + 3H_2O$$

The flow sheet is similar to that of Fig. 13.13*a*. The reaction agitators are fed with (1) 25 tons bauxite/day, containing 50% Al_2O_3 and the rest insoluble; (2) the theoretical quantity of aqueous acid containing 60% H_2SO_4; and (3) the overflow from the second thickener. Assume the reaction is complete. The strong product solution is to contain 22% $Al_2(SO_4)_3$, and no more than 2% of the $Al_2(SO_4)_3$ produced is to be lost in the washed mud. The last thickener is to be fed with pure wash water. The underflow from each thickener will contain 4 lb liquid/lb insoluble solid, and the concentration of solubles in the liquid of the underflow for each thickener may be assumed to be the same as that in the overflow. Calculate the number of thickeners required and the amount of wash water required per day. **Ans.:** 3 thickeners.

   (*Note:* In solving this problem, be certain to account for the water in the acid as well as that produced by the reaction. Adapt Fig. 5.16 to all but the first thickener in the cascade.)

   13.6. Barium, occurring naturally as the sulfate, $BaSO_4$, is put in water-soluble form by heating with coal, thus reducing the sulfate to the sulfide, BaS. The resulting reaction mixture, barium "black ash" containing 65% soluble BaS, is to be leached with water. One hundred tons black ash per day is fed to a tube mill, together with the overflow from the second of a cascade of thickeners, and the effluent from the mill is fed to the first thickener. All the barium is dissolved in the mill. The strong solution overflowing from the first thickener is to contain 20% BaS by weight. The thickeners will each deliver a sludge containing 1.5 lb liquid/lb insoluble solid. The solution in the overflow and that in the sludge leaving any thickener may be assumed to have the same BaS concentration. It is desired to keep the BaS lost with the final sludge to at most 2 lb/day.

   a. How many thickeners are required? [Adapt Eq. (5.55) to all except the first thickener.] **Ans.:** 6.

   b. It is decided to pass the final leached sludge to a continuous filter, as in Fig. 13.13*b*, where the liquid content of the filtered solids will be reduced to 15% by weight. The filtrate will be returned to the last thickener, but the filter cake will not be washed. How many thickeners will then be required? **Ans.:** 5.

   13.7. In the manufacture of potassium nitrate, KNO_3, potassium chloride, KCl is added to a hot, concentrated aqueous solution of sodium nitrate, $NaNO_3$,

$$KCl + NaNO_3 \rightleftharpoons KNO_3 + NaCl$$

Owing to its relatively low solubility, part of the sodium chloride, $NaCl$, precipitates and is filtered off. A little water is added to the filtrate to prevent further precipitation of $NaCl$, the mixture is cooled to 20°C, and pure KNO_3 crystallizes. The resulting slurry contains, per 100 lb precipitated KNO_3, 239 lb of a solution analyzing 21.3% KNO_3, 21.6% $NaCl$, and 57.1% water. The slurry is fed to the first of a cascade of four continuous classifiers, where each 100 lb of crystals is countercurrently washed with 75 lb of a saturated solution of KNO_3, containing 24.0% KNO_3, in order to free them of $NaCl$. The wet crystals leaving each classifier retain 25% liquid, and the liquid overflows are clear. The washed crystals discharged from the fourth classifier, containing 25% liquid, are sent to a continuous drier. All liquid except that discharged with the washed crystals leaves in the overflow from the first classifier. Equilibrium between solid and liquid is attained in each classifier, and the clear overflows have the same composition as the liquid retained by the crystals. The solubility of KNO_3 in NaCl solutions (KNO_3 is the equilibrium solid phase) at the prevailing temperature is given by the following table:

% NaCl	0	6.9	12.6	17.8	21.6
% KNO_3	24.0	23.3	22.6	22.0	21.3

a. Plot the equilibrium data [N = lb KNO_3/lb (NaCl + H_2O) for both clear overflow and wet crystals; x and y = lb NaCl/lb (NaCl + H_2O)].

b. Calculate the percent NaCl content which may be expected on the dried KNO_3 product. Ans.: 0.306%.

PART FIVE
THE LESS
CONVENTIONAL
OPERATIONS

CHAPTER FOURTEEN
THE LESS
CONVENTIONAL
OPERATIONS

The operations considered in this chapter involve, with a few exceptions, solid-fluid contact of various kinds. While some have been applied industrially, they are not commonly used and in most cases their technology is relatively undeveloped. Only a brief, qualitative discussion will be given, to indicate their field of usefulness and some of the problems they entail.

FRACTIONAL CRYSTALLIZATION

The common crystallization process is a solute-recovery operation rather than a fractionation, such as the crystallization of a nonvolatile solid from a solution with a volatile solvent. If it is done by progressively cooling the saturated solution, mass transfer from the bulk solution to the crystal surface and transfer of sensible heat and heat of solution in one fashion or another are involved. In most cases, solute and solvent are insoluble in the solid state, and this gives rise to an equilibrium diagram of the sort shown in Fig. 14.1.

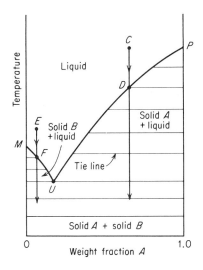

Fig. 14.1 *Binary liquid-solid equilibria, components insoluble in the solid state.*

In Fig. 14.1, M is the melting point of component B, P that of A.   Curves MFU and PDU are the solubilities of these components in the liquid solution.   A liquid solution C, if cooled, first precipitates pure A at the temperature corresponding to D, and as the temperature is further lowered, additional A crystallizes while the liquid remaining moves along the curve DU toward U.   At temperature t_U, the liquid remaining has the eutectic composition at U, and further cooling results in complete solidification of a "eutectic mixture" of A and B, a mass of insoluble crystals which ordinarily cannot be mechanically separated.   If the solution is initially at E, the phenomena are much the same except that crystallization begins at F, with pure B solidifying until the liquid remaining reaches the eutectic composition.   The diagram is analogous to that for vapor-liquid equilibrium between two components which are completely insoluble in the liquid state.

While in principle a pure component may be recovered up to the point where the eutectic composition is reached, there are practical difficulties.   The crystals may mechanically occlude portions of the solution, thus rendering them impure; and complete mechanical separation of crystals from adhering mother liquor is difficult without washing them with some of the pure solvent, which entails some redissolving of the crystals.   In any case, the yield of the pure component first precipitated in such a process cannot be larger than that which produces the eutectic composition in the solution remaining.   This difficulty is frequently circumvented by boiling or evaporating off the volatile, low-melting component (in Fig. 14.1, component B might be volatile water and A a nonvolatile salt, for example), and if evaporation is carried to dryness, the yield of nonvolatile component can be complete.   This is a well-established procedure, the technology of which is highly developed.   The rate of crystallization and the phenomenon of nucleation, or initial precipitation of solid, is not fully understood, and will not be considered here.   A good review is available.[16]

When, however, the components of a binary mixture have a very low relative

Fig. 14.2 *Continuous, countercurrent crystallizer.*

volatility, boiling or vaporization will not serve. If crystallization is to be used, the problem is then one of making suitably pure crystals by lowering the temperature only. While batch crystallization and washing of the solid has been the general practice in such cases, a recently developed technique uses a continuous, countercurrent operation which conceivably has other applications as well. In the process of separating *p*-xylene from the meta and ortho isomers (boiling point range of the pure components = 11°F), the device of Fig. 14.2 is used.[26,29] A feed containing 65 percent *p*-xylene is cooled in a scraper-chiller to a mass consisting of a thick slurry of impure *p*-xylene crystals. The slurry enters the continuous crystallizer, where mother liquor is withdrawn from the side through a suitable filter, and the crystals proceed toward the product outlet. Near the outlet the pure crystals are melted, part of the resulting liquid is withdrawn as product, and part is returned as reflux to wash the crystals countercurrently free of the undesired meta and ortho isomers, which leave with the mother liquor. Movement of the liquid and compaction of the crystals to form a suitable moving bed is accomplished by the pulse pump (see page 430). The device thus accomplishes the purification (product is 98+ percent pure *p*-xylene) and by withdrawing the product as a liquid eliminates the problem of mechanical separation of the crystals.

When the components of the binary mixture are soluble in the solid state (solid-liquid equilibrium diagram resembles the vapor-liquid diagram of Fig. 9.2), or when it is desired to circumvent the yield limit imposed by the eutectic mixture, the following fractionation techniques are possibilities, although they have had as yet only limited application. Rapid extension of their use is anticipated as their technology is developed.

Direct fractional crystallization

When the components of a binary mixture are soluble in the solid state, at least over a range of compositions if not entirely, as well as in the liquid state, separation can be made by a direct countercurrent fractional crystallization. The binary pairs gold-silver and cyclohexane-methylcyclopentane[11] are representative of this type. One can envisage devices of the sort shown in Fig. 14.2 operated in the manner of Fig. 14.3*a*, although at present no industrial applications are known. Matz[28] has pointed out the applicability of enthalpy-concentration diagrams of the sort shown in Fig. 14.3*b* to such operations, and the computations for stages would be made in precisely the same manner as shown in Chap. 9 for fractional distillation. Figure 14.3*b* is representative of the case where the components are completely miscible in both liquid and solid phases. If partial miscibility occurs in the solid, the equilibria are analogous to those for vapor mixtures which condense to form partly soluble liquids.

Zone refining is a batch fractional crystallization which is capable of ultra-purification.[4,22,32] The principle is simple: a zone of liquid is repeatedly passed through a solid ingot of the substance to be purified. This is accomplished by repeatedly moving a high-temperature zone along the ingot which melts the solid, the liquid freezing behind the zone as it moves. Impurities which are more soluble in the liquid phase than in the solid (the usual case) move with the zone and are swept along with the liquid to accumulate at one end of the ingot; impurities which are more soluble in the solid move opposite to the zone, but this is a relatively rare occurrence.

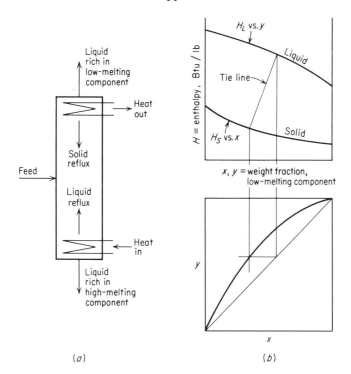

Fig. 14.3 *Direct fractional crystallization.*

Multipassage of the liquid zone then concentrates the impurities at one end of the ingot. The length of the molten zone may approximate one-tenth that of the ingot, and the rate of travel ⅛ to 1.5 in./hr.   The operation is most economically applied to remove trace impurities.   Industrial applications have largely been confined to purification of semiconductors such as silicon and germanium (six passes of a molten zone have reduced the impurities in germanium to 1 part in 10^{10}), but there is no limitation: organic chemicals, pharmaceuticals, even water, have been purified in this manner.   Any of a variety of heating arrangements are possible: heating with a moving flame; induction heating, particularly for metals and semiconductors; or even electric-resistance heating by a number of stationary coils surrounding the ingot which are activated in turn along the ingot.   The operation described above is *zone melting*, but it is equally possible to purify by *zone freezing*, whereby a solid zone is passed through a column of liquid.   Continuous techniques have not yet been developed for either.

Extractive fractional crystallization

Here a solvent which will dissolve both solid components to be separated is used. The solvent may enhance the selectivity (ratio of solutes in liquid/ratio of solutes in solid), or it may be used when melting cannot be done.   An excellent example is the

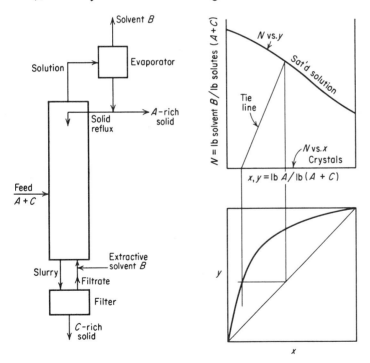

Fig. 14.4   *Continuous, countercurrent, extractive fractional crystallization of a binary solid, A and C, with A more soluble.*

separation of barium and lead nitrates, which form a continuous series of solid solutions, using water as the extractive solvent.[28] A continuous, countercurrent separation might then follow the scheme of Fig. 14.4a. The contacting device might be the sort shown in Fig. 14.2, the classifier type of Fig. 13.17, teeter beds (see Chap. 11), a cascade of stages made up of agitator vessels and filters, or the like. Matz[28] made such a continuous separation in a small, column-type device (using only the section below the feed of Fig. 14.4a), producing $Ba(NO_3)_2$ of 89.8 percent purity from a 50 percent mixture with $Pb(NO_3)_2$, with a remarkably small height equivalent to a theoretical stage. The minimum reflux ratio and number of stages at a suitable operating reflux ratio may be computed on a diagram similar to that used in liquid extraction and leaching (Fig. 14.4b).[28] The application of such a diagram to the similar process of washing crystals free of contaminating mother liquor is given in Prob. 13.7. Batch simulation of continuous, countercurrent separations of this sort have been known for many years, e.g., the separation of rare-earth-metal salts (now replaced by ion-exchange methods), but it is believed that the truly continuous operation has not yet been used commercially.

Adductive fractional crystallization

Here an added substance is used which enters the solid phase. There are four major types:[10]

1. *Solid solutions.* Although there are no presently known fractionation processes of this type, a possibility is suggested by Findlay,[10] namely, separation of solutions of hexane and methylcyclopentane by countercurrent contact with solid cyclohexane, which preferentially forms solid solutions with methylcyclopentane. A complete fractionation process, with feed introduced centrally into a cascade of stages and use of reflux, would be required.

2. *Addition compounds of fixed composition.* Again there is no industrial example, but several have been suggested. For example, carbon tetrachloride forms the compound $CCl_4 \cdot p\text{-}C_6H_4(CH_3)_2$ with *p*-xylene but forms no such compound with the meta or ortho isomers.[9] Selectivity in this case is excellent for separating the para isomer, and the equivalent of an absorption or extraction section of a complete countercurrent cascade of stages would be all that is necessary. The limitation on yield imposed by eutectic compositions in the mixture to be separated would disappear. Separation of the solid product would involve melting and distillation.

3. *Clathrates.*[18] Here a molecule of twisted or crooked shape, which can crystallize in the form of a cage, is used to entrap a compound in the crystal lattice preferentially, based on shape. As an example which is used industrially we can cite the separation of *p*-xylene from a mixture of *m*- and *p*-xylenes, using nickel thiocyanate with γ-picoline.[33] The complex including the metal, the nitrogen base, and the negative radical entraps the para isomer preferentially. The dry, solid complex may be agitated or ground with the feed to be separated (diluted if necessary with a suitable solvent to form a workable slurry); alternatively a solvent for the complex may be used, and when mixed with the feed to be separated, cooling produces crystals which selectively remove one solute from solution. Another proposed process is the recovery of water from brines by clathration with hydrocarbon gases such as propane.[21] Ordinarily a cascade of stages is required, to free the crystals of adhering or entrapped solution. Recovery procedures involve destruction of the clathrate crystal by melting or by vaporization since the clathrate may exhibit a solute vapor pressure.

4. *Adducts.*[12] These involve crystals whose tunnellike or channellike passageways hold one shape of molecule but exclude another. For example, urea in the presence of hydrocarbons crystallizes in a structure which can enclose straight-chain hydrocarbons but which accepts only with difficulty highly branched hydrocarbons. The adduct behaves much like a solid solution, or homogeneous crystal of variable composition. Frequently an "activator," or polar organic solvent in the case of urea, is also needed. An industrial example is the adductive dewaxing of oils with urea in the presence of methylene chloride for producing oils of very low pour point.[19] A fractionation is required for complete solute separation, and the adducts are destroyed by melting to release the solute.

In all these operations, the computations of stages, flow ratios, and the like can be made on phase diagrams plotted with pounds added substance/pounds total solute as ordinate vs. weight fraction of one solute, additive-free basis, as abscissa, with the principles developed in earlier chapters.

SUBLIMATION

Sublimation, a solid-vapor operation, is essentially distillation of a solid. It is ordinarily done batchwise. In cases where only one component of a solid mixture is volatile, we have the analog of evaporation of a liquid solution of a nonvolatile solid, and freeze drying (see Chap. 12) is a particular example. If both components of a binary solid are volatile, fractional sublimation, done batchwise by a simulation of a multistage countercurrent technique, could eventually produce a separation. Extractive sublimation uses a noncondensing gas to carry the vapors.

One of the principal difficulties in many cases is the inability to apply the required heat rapidly without melting the solid (see page 580) or raising the temperature of the solid to the extent that it is damaged. Another is the problem of condensing the vapor. Cold condenser surfaces rapidly accumulate a thick coating of solid, through which heat is very poorly transmitted. In some cases the condenser can be cleared by periodic heating to melt the accumulated solid; where this is impractical the solid can be knocked off with hammers. An alternative is to mix the vapors with a cold, inert, noncondensable gas, which causes precipitation of solid in the vapor-gas mixture as snow. The residual gas will, however, be saturated with the vapor, and when it is cooled for reuse, the vapor condenses as solid upon the cooling surface. The advantage is that less solid is condensed on the cooling surface than by direct condensation of all the vapor. Perhaps the most promising development is the possibility of contacting the vapors with solid sublimate in a fluidized bed[6,27] cooled by internal cooling coils or by a cooling jacket about the bed wall. Evidently the abrasive action of the solids keeps the cooling surface reasonably clear.

FOAM SEPARATIONS

If the solute of a liquid solution is surface-active, it collects at the solution surface when the liquid is exposed to a gas, and there then exists a concentration difference of the solute between the bulk solution and the surface layer.   This is accompanied by a lowering of the surface tension of the solvent when the solute is dissolved.   If the surface layer is then collected, a certain amount of separation of solute will have been achieved.   Foaming the solution by bubbling or sparging a gas into it, followed by collection of the foam and mechanical separation of the liquid and gas of the foam provides a means of accomplishing this.[35]   The phenomenon is not one of interphase, i.e., liquid-to-gas, mass transfer, but rather an *intraphase* transfer of solute from the bulk liquid to the surface.   The method is particularly effective at low concentrations.

Great interest has developed in this technique for the removal of detergents (which are surface-active) from sewage effluents.[5,15]   Solutes which are not surface-active, such as metal ions, can sometimes be complexed with other material to become so and are then amenable to foam collection.[36]   Figure 14.5 shows a schematic arrangement for solute collection.   The foam-drainage section serves to remove the great part of the liquid from the foam but not the surface layer, thus concentrating the collected solute.   For successful operation, the foam must be reasonably stable, which requires that the surface film have a high viscosity, and also be readily destructible at the top of the column.   Foam breaking may be accomplished by heating; by

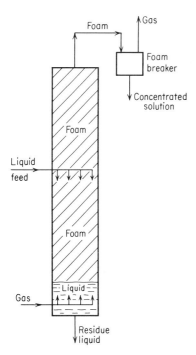

Fig. 14.5 *Solute collection by foaming.*

rupture of the liquid surface mechanically by a sonic whistle or through reduction of the gas pressure, as when the foam flows through an orifice; or by centrifuging.[17] Refluxing part of the liquid reclaimed from the broken foam to the column is possible; this would be important if two solutes of different tendency to collect at the surface were to be separated by *foam fractionation*.

MEMBRANE SEPARATIONS

Separations may be produced by transfer of material between fluids separated by a permeable membrane. For effective separation, of course, the membrane must be differently permeable to the substances to be separated. There are various methods whereby this is accomplished.[13,23,34,41] In some cases the membrane acts somewhat like a mechanical filter, much as a filter paper separates a two-phase solid-liquid mixture, but in the operations considered here the filtration is on a molecular scale. In some cases the components of the solution to be separated diffuse through the passageways of the membrane at different rates by any of a variety of mechanisms (see Chap. 4). In others the membrane may selectively dissolve a component which can then diffuse through.

Separations of both liquid and gas solutions are possible. The principal difficulty in most cases is that the rate of passage through the membrane is small and becomes smaller the more selective the membrane.

Dialysis

Dialysis is the separation of solutes of different molecular size in a liquid solution by use of a suitable membrane. In practice the membrane separates the solution from a quantity of solvent, whereupon solvent and solute of small molecular size pass through relatively easily while passage of large molecules is more difficult. Practical industrial applications include the separation of sodium hydroxide (small molecules or ions) from hemicellulose (large molecules) in the solutions of the viscose-rayon process using cellophane membranes,[42] separation of sulfuric acid from nickel and copper sulfates in aqueous solutions[41] and from steel-pickling liquors with vinyl-polymer membranes. In the field of medicine, cellulose membranes are used to dialyze human blood free of poisonous substances in the artificial kidney.

It is possible to make membranes which are highly selective. For example, early scientific work in this area used membranes of gelatinous copper ferrocyanide precipitated within a porous porcelain support. Such a membrane will permit passage of water but will prevent passage of ordinary solutes such as sugar or glycerin and even ionic particles such as those of salt solutions. If a solution is separated from pure solvent by such a membrane, solvent passes through the membrane in the direction solvent to solution, in the direction of concentration drop, and dilutes the solution. This is known as *osmosis*. For most practical dialyses such selectivity is not ordinarily required, and the pores of the membrane used in the viscose-rayon process are of the order of 10^{-6} cm in diameter (crystalline solutes have molecular diameters of the order of 10^{-8} cm, and will pass through, along with the solvent).

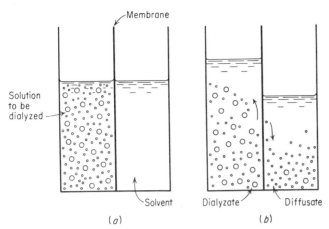

Fig. 14.6 *Batch dialysis.*

Consider the schematic representation of a batch dialysis in Fig. 14.6.   The solution to be dialyzed contains large and small solute molecules, represented schematically as shown at *a*, and it is separated initially from a batch of pure solvent by a suitable membrane.   The solvent immediately begins to move through the membrane and into the solution by osmosis, and since it ordinarily has a lower specific gravity, a convection current of rising solvent develops on the left of the membrane as at *b* in the figure.   If the liquids are not agitated, the solvent spreads out in a layer over the top of the solution and will mix with the solution only very slowly.   The solute particles also diffuse through the membrane into the solvent, the smaller ones rapidly but the larger only very slowly.   Since the solution formed on the right side of the membrane will generally be more dense than the solvent, it will tend to stratify at the bottom of the vessel, as shown.   Owing to the osmotic flow of solvent, the volume of the *dialyzate*, or dialyzed solution, will increase at the expense of the *diffusate*.   If the membrane is permeable to both solutes, the solution on either side will eventually come to the same concentrations, and an equilibrium will be established.   Because the larger molecules dialyze only very slowly, however, it is possible to make a separation by periodically replacing the diffusate with fresh solvent before equilibrium is established.   The concentration of the dialyzate may be kept relatively high, and the rate of dialysis maintained at a reasonable level, by careful withdrawal of the layer of solvent at the top.

Alternatively, a continuous rather than a batch operation may be carried out in the countercurrent manner shown schematically in Fig. 14.7.   The solutions flow in such a direction as to take advantage of the tendency toward stratification: the liquid to be dialyzed is introduced at the bottom and withdrawn at the top, while the diffusate flows downward.   The membrane is arranged vertically for this reason also.

Typical of the commercial devices is the filter-press type of Fig. 14.8, which uses the principles developed in Fig. 14.7 directly.   The membranes are placed between metal frames arranged in a manner reminiscent of the ordinary filter press.   A mechanical membrane support built into the frames, not shown in the sketch, may also be used.   Holes in the frames and the membranes form continuous conduits for the liquids when the entire assemblage is pressed tightly together.   Feed solution to be dialyzed is distributed to alternate frames and flows upward past the membranes, and the dialyzate discharges through a channel at the top.   Solvent, in a similar manner, enters the remaining frames and flows downward, and the diffusate leaves through a channel at the bottom.   The liquids flow under the force of gravity, as shown schematically in Fig. 14.7, and are not pumped through the dialyzer.   In the larger units particularly, where many frames may be used, there may be several channels in the frames for introducing feed and solvent, each leading to separate groups of frames.   In this way, more equitable distribution of the flow is obtained.

Reverse osmosis (ultrafiltration)

This operation, not yet commercialized, has possible application in the desalting of brackish water and seawater,[24] for which pilot-plant studies have been made.   The principle is simple: a highly selective membrane is used between pure water and brine. Only the water may pass through, and normally will do so in the direction water to brine (osmosis).   This diffusive flow of solvent can be prevented by a pressure difference in the direction brine to water equal to the equilibrium osmotic pressure (in the case of seawater about 350 psi).   By superimposing a still larger pressure difference, the water flow is reversed to the direction brine to water, and the brine is separated. The expected advantage is the low energy cost for the separation, since latent heat of

Fig. 14.7   *Continuous, counter-current dialysis.*

Fig. 14.8 *Filter-press-type dialyzer, Brosites Machine Co.* [*U.S. Patent* 2,399,471 (1946).]

neither vaporization nor freezing is involved. The membranes used are usually of either cellulose acetate, especially cast from solution, or other polymeric materials. Among the difficulties are the required membrane strength, membrane life, and the fact that water transfer causes the concentration of salt to increase at the surface of the brine side of the membrane (a sort of polarization effect), thus increasing the osmotic pressure which must be overcome.[38]

Electrodialysis[43]

When electrolytic crystalline substances are to be separated from colloids in solution by dialysis methods, the rate of removal of the ions can be considerably increased by imposing an electromotive force across the membrane, as in Fig. 14.9. Here the solution to be dialyzed is placed in the central compartment, separated from the anode and cathode compartments by the semipermeable membrane. The ions then move

Fig. 14.9   *Electrodialysis.*

through the membrane toward the electrodes much more rapidly than in ordinary dialysis.   In practice two difficulties arise.   The first is due to the electroosmotic transfer of water through the membranes, usually from the anode to the cathode compartments, which not only dilutes the dialyzate but also carries the ions back into the central compartment.   The second is due to the tendency of the membranes to assume an electric charge on each face, positive on that side facing the cathode, negative on the side facing the anode.   The inner face of the membrane nearest the cathode then tends to accumulate hydroxyl ions, which give an alkaline reaction, while the inner face of the membrane nearest the anode tends to give an acid reaction. This may bring about undesirable effects such as coagulation or precipitation of many colloids.   Electrodialysis is nevertheless used extensively in biological-solution separations.

If the membrane nearest the cathode is permeable only to cations but impermeable to anions, and if the other membrane is permeable to anions but not to cations, it is possible to remove the ions from an electrolytic solution efficiently, since the backward flow of ions then ceases.   Membranes are available, made from ion-exchange resins, which are nearly perfectly semipermeable.[13]   Thus, a cation-exchange resin membrane exchanges cations and is permeable to these but will offer considerable resistance to the passage of anions.   Similarly, an anion-exchange resin membrane is preferentially permeable to anions.   Full-scale industrial processes of demineralization by this operation include treatment of brackish water[37] and removal of salts from whey; many others have been proposed.   Equipment is usually arranged with the membranes alternating in stacks of a variety of designs.[8,25,31]

Pervaporation

In this case the membrane is placed between a liquid solution of volatile components to be separated and a vapor phase.   Owing to the different rates of permeation of the liquid components through the membrane, the vapor issuing from the downstream face of the membrane is of different composition from the liquid.   A permanent gas may also be used to carry the vapor away.   The enrichment produced is different from that in ordinary distillation, and solutions which are usually azeotropic are effectively separable.[3,20]   Other separations difficult by distillation, such as that of the xylene isomers, have also been made.[30]   No industrial applications are known.

Gas permeation

Selective permeation through membranes can also be used for separating gas mixtures. In the case of the helium-hydrocarbon mixtures of natural gas, for example, silica or glass is permeable only to the helium, and this could be the basis of separation of helium from the mixture, although the rate is very slow.   Membranes of fluoro-carbons are very selective in this system, although not as completely so as silica, and permit much higher rates.[39]   The process is not yet in commercial use.

Gaseous diffusion

We have seen [Eq. (4.19)] that if a pure gas flows through a diaphragm or barrier containing small holes (whose diameter is of the order of one-tenth the mean free path of the molecules) under conditions of small pressure drop, the rate of flow is inversely proportional to the square root of the molecular weight of the gas and to the drop in pressure across the barrier.   If the gas is a binary mixture of components of different molecular weight, the relative rates of flow of the components through the barrier will be different, and a separation becomes possible.

Since the diffused gas may still not be enriched appreciably in comparison with the feed by one such passage, it may be sent to another barrier or stage; additional stages may then be used for still further enrichment, thus leading to a cascade of stages, as in Fig. 14.10.   Similarly the undiffused gas from any stage may be recycled to the preceding stage for further treatment, and the cascade develops the usual "enriching" and "stripping" sections on either side of the point of introducing the feed.   Since the quantity of gas passing forward toward either product becomes less with each stage, the size of the stage may be progressively reduced in passing from the feed to the products.   Alternatively, instead of very large stages near the center of the cascade, a large number of small units may be operated in parallel, as shown in the figure.   Since, however, all the units operating in parallel bring about identical composition changes, together they affect the enrichment of only one stage, so that the arrangement of Fig. 14.10 is considered as containing only five stages.   It is further characteristic of the gas-diffusion cascade that the gas must be compressed between stages, and the heat developed by the compression must be removed by a cooler, as shown in the figure.

The work of compression, the size and expense of constructing and operating the cascade, and the engineering problems associated with making adequate barriers make gas diffusion useful as a separation method only in cases where other, more conventional methods are unusually difficult or impossible.   This may be the case especially in the separation of isotopes of the elements.   The conventional operations described in the earlier chapters of this book depend essentially on differences in the chemical properties of compounds which lead to their unequal distribution between immiscible phases.   Two compounds which differ only because an element in one is replaced by

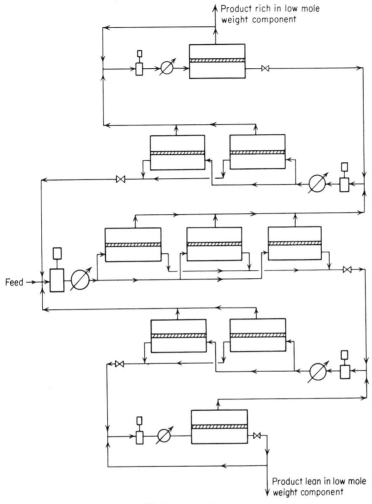

Product rich in low mole weight component

Feed →

Product lean in low mole weight component

Fig. 14.10   *A five-stage gas-diffusion cascade.*

its isotope in the other will frequently show such small differences in their distribution that the conventional methods become impractical.

Such is the case for separation of the isotopes of uranium, U^{235} and U^{238}, and the gas-diffusion plants for separating the gaseous uranium hexafluorides are examples of the large-scale application of this operation.   The compounds $U^{235}F_6$ and $U^{238}F_6$ have molecular weights 349 and 352, respectively, so that the differential enrichment per stage is very small.   For a feed made from natural uranium and containing 0.71 percent $U^{235}F_6$ to be separated into products containing 99 and 0.1 percent $U^{235}F_6$, roughly 4,000 stages are used.   For each mole of $U^{235}F_6$-rich product withdrawn, some 70,000,000 moles of gas are recycled between the stages, which requires enormous power for pumps and prodigious amounts of cooling water.   The requirements for the porous barrier are equally extraordinary: it must contain tremendous numbers of holes of diameters measured in hundredths of microns, be able to withstand a difference in pressure on either side of roughly 1 atm, be chemically indifferent to the gas, and be capable of mass production in quantities that are most conveniently measured in acres.

THERMAL DIFFUSION

If two reservoirs containing a gas mixture are connected by a tube and maintained at different temperatures, it is found that the heavier molecules concentrate in the cooler reservoir, while the lighter molecules concentrate in the warmer.[14]   If the molecules are of equal masses, those of smaller diameter tend to concentrate in the region of higher temperature.   This movement under an imposed temperature gradient is known as thermal diffusion, and the effect can be multiplied by using the apparatus first described by Clusius and Dickel,[7] shown schematically in Fig. 14.11.   Natural convection currents develop in the annular space as shown, owing to the change in gas density with temperature, and these, combined with the tendency to separate by thermal diffusion in the horizontal direction, provide an arrangement which may be equivalent to many stages.   In a well-designed column, the height of a transfer unit may be only a few centimeters.   Even so, a cascade of columns in the general arrangement of Fig. 14.10 would be required for large degrees of separation.   The cold wall of the column would ordinarily be kept at the lowest possible temperature provided by the available cooling water, and a hot-wall temperature of 600 to 900°F would be preferred.[2]   The heat requirements are very large, and the process can be considered practically applicable only to very difficult isotope separations.   For example, commercial-scale separation of the very rare He^3 from He^4 is carried out to provide He^3 for scientific work.

The thermal-diffusion phenomenon is also known to occur in liquid solutions, where it is sometimes called the *Soret effect*.

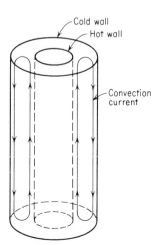

Cold wall
Hot wall
Convection current

Fig. 14.11   *Thermal-diffusion column.*[2]   (*Courtesy of The American Institute of Chemical Engineers.*)

REFERENCES

1. Anon.: *Chem. Eng.*, **71**, Aug. 17, 72 (1964).
2. Benedict, M.: *Chem. Eng. Progr.*, **43**, 41 (1947).
3. Binning, R. C., R. J. Lee, J. Jennings, and E. C. Martin: *Ind. Eng. Chem.*, **53**, 45 (1961).
4. Brooks, M. S., and K. Kennedy: "Ultrapurification of Semiconductor Materials," The Macmillan Company, New York, 1962.
5. Brunner, C. A., and D. G. Stephan: *Ind. Eng. Chem.*, **57**(5), 40 (1965).
6. Ciborowski, J., and S. Wronski: *Chem. Eng. Sci.*, **17**, 481 (1962); *Intern. Chem. Eng.*, **2**, 105 (1962).
7. Clusius, K., and G. Dickel: *Z. Physik. Chem.*, **B44**, 397 (1939).
8. Cohan, H. J.: *Chem. Eng. Progr.*, **57**(2), 72 (1961).
9. Egan, C. J., and R. V. Luthy: *Ind. Eng. Chem.*, **47**, 250 (1955).
10. Findlay, R. A.: in H. M. Schoen (ed.), "New Chemical Engineering Separation Techniques," p. 257, Interscience Publishers, Inc., New York, 1962.
11. Findlay, R. D., and D. L. McKay: *Chem. Eng. Progr. Symp. Ser.*, **55**(25), 163 (1959).
12. Findlay, R. A., and J. A. Weedman: "Separation and Purification by Crystallization," *Advan. Petrol. Chem. Refining*, **1**, 118 (1958).
13. Friedlander, H. Z., and R. N. Rickles: *Chem. Eng.*, **73**, Feb. 28, 111; Mar. 28, 121; Apr. 25, 163; May 23, 153; June 6, 145; June 20, 217 (1966).
14. Grew, K. E., and T. L. Ibbs: "Thermal Diffusion in Gases," Cambridge University Press, London, 1952.
15. Grieves, R. B., C. J. Crandall, and R. K. Wood: *Intern. J. Air Water Pollution*, **8**, 501 (1964).
16. Grove, C. S., R. V. Jelinek, and H. M. Schoen: in T. B. Drew, J. W. Hoopes, Jr., and T. Vermeulen (eds.), "Advances in Chemical Engineering," vol. 3, p. 1, Academic Press Inc., New York, 1962.
17. Haas, P. A., and H. F. Johnson: *AIChE J.*, **11**, 319 (1965).
18. Hagan, M.: "Clathrate Inclusion Compounds," Reinhold Publishing Corporation, New York, 1962.
19. Hoppe, A., and H. Franz: *Petrol. Refiner*, **36**(5), 221 (1957).
20. Kammermeyer, K., and D. H. Hagerbaumer: *AIChE J.*, **1**, 215 (1955).
21. Knox, W. G., M. Hess, G. E. Jones, and H. B. Smith: *Chem. Eng. Progr.*, **57**(2), 66 (1961).
22. Lawson, W. D., and S. Nielsen: in H. M. Schoen (ed.), "New Chemical Engineering Separation Techniques," p. 183, Interscience Publishers, Inc., New York, 1962.
23. Li, N. N., R. B. Long, and E. J. Henley: *Ind. Eng. Chem.*, **57**(3), 18 (1965).
24. Loeb, S., and S. Sourirajan: *UCLA Rept.*, **60–60** (1960); **61–42** (1961).
25. Mason, E. A., and T. A. Kirkham: *Chem. Eng. Progr. Symp. Ser.*, **55**(24), 173 (1959).
26. Marwil, S. J., and S. J. Kolner: *Chem. Eng. Progr.*, **59**(2), 60 (1963).
27. Matz, G.: *Chem.-Ing.-Tech.*, **20**, 319 (1950).
28. Matz, G.: *Wärme*, **68**, 33 (1961); **69**, 127 (1963); Symposium on Zone Melting and Column Crystallization, Karlsruhe, June, 1963, p. 345.
29. McKay, D. L., et al.: *Chem. Eng. Progr.*, **61**(11), 99 (1965); *Ind. Eng. Chem.*, **52**, 197 (1960).
30. Michaels, A. S., R. F. Baddour, H. J. Bixler, and C. Y. Choo: *Ind. Eng. Chem. Process Design Develop.*, **1**, 14 (1962).
31. Mintz, M. S.: *Ind. Eng. Chem.*, **55**(6), 18 (1963).
32. Pfann, W. G.: "Zone Melting," John Wiley & Sons, Inc., New York, 1956.
33. Radzitzky, P. de, and J. Hanotier: *Ind. Eng. Chem. Process Design Develop.*, **1**, 10 (1962).
34. Rickles, R. N.: *Ind. Eng. Chem.*, **58**(6), 19 (1966).
35. Rubin, E., and E. L. Gaden, Jr.: in H. M. Schoen (ed.), "New Chemical Engineering Separation Techniques," p. 319, Interscience Publishers, Inc., New York, 1962.
36. Schnepf, R. W., E. L. Gaden, Jr., E. Y. Microcznik, and E. Schonfeld: *Chem. Eng. Progr.*, **55**(5), 42 (1959).

37. Shaffer, L. H., and M. S. Mintz: in K. S. Spiegler (ed.), "Principles of Desalination," Academic Press Inc., New York, 1966.

38. Sherwood, T. K., P. L. T. Brian, and R. E. Fischer: *Ind. Eng. Chem. Fundamentals,* **4,** 113 (1965).

39. Stern, S. A., T. F. Sinclair, P. J. Garies, N. P. Vahldieck, and P. H. Mohr: *Ind. Eng. Chem.,* **57**(2), 49 (1965).

40. Turwiner, S. B.: "Diffusional Membrane Technology," Reinhold Publishing Corporation, New York, 1962.

41. Turwiner, S. B., and J. R. Smith: "Extractive Metallurgy of Copper and Cobalt," Interscience Publishers, Inc., New York, 1961.

42. Volrath, H. B.: *Chem. Met. Eng.,* **43,** 303 (1936).

43. Wilson, J. R.: "Demineralization by Electrodialysis," Butterworth Scientific Publications, London, 1960.

INDEX

INDEX